PHYSIOLOGY OF MOLLUSCA

Volume I

PHYSIOLOGY OF MOLLUSCA

A Treatise in Two Volumes

Contributors to Volume I

E. J. Denton

V. Fretter

A. Graham

G. Hoyle

W. Russell Hunter

J. E. Morton

G. E. Newell

J. A. C. Nicol

Gareth Owen

C. P. Raven

James D. Robertson

P. R. Walne

Karl M. Wilbur

C. M. Yonge

PHYSIOLOGY
OF MOLLUSCA

Edited by

KARL M. WILBUR

DEPARTMENT OF ZOOLOGY
DUKE UNIVERSITY
DURHAM, NORTH CAROLINA

C. M. YONGE

DEPARTMENT OF ZOOLOGY
UNIVERSITY OF GLASGOW
GLASGOW, SCOTLAND

VOLUME 1

1964

ACADEMIC PRESS—New York and London

ACADEMIC PRESS INC.
111 Fifth Avenue, New York, New York 10003

United Kingdom Edition published by
ACADEMIC PRESS INC. (LONDON) LTD.
Berkeley Square House, London W.1

LIBRARY OF CONGRESS CATALOG CARD NUMBER: 63–16979

PRINTED IN THE UNITED STATES OF AMERICA

Contributors

Numbers in parentheses indicate the pages on which the authors' contributions begin.

E. J. DENTON, Marine Biological Laboratory, Plymouth, England (425)

V. FRETTER, Department of Zoology, University of Reading, Reading, England (127)

A. GRAHAM, Department of Zoology, University of Reading, Reading, England (127)

G. HOYLE, Department of Biology, University of Oregon, Eugene, Oregon (313)

W. RUSSELL HUNTER,* Department of Zoology, University of Glasgow, Glasgow, Scotland (83)

J. E. MORTON, Department of Zoology, University of Auckland, Auckland, New Zealand (1, 383)

G. E. NEWELL, Department of Zoology, Queen Mary College, University of London, London, England (59)

J. A. C. NICOL, Marine Biological Laboratory, Plymouth, England (353)

GARETH OWEN, Department of Zoology, University of Glasgow, Glasgow, Scotland (211)

C. P. RAVEN, Zoological Laboratory, University of Utrecht, Janskerkhof, The Netherlands (165)

JAMES D. ROBERTSON, Department of Zoology, University of Glasgow, Glasgow, Scotland (283)

P. R. WALNE, Fisheries Experiment Station, Conway, North Wales (197)

KARL M. WILBUR, Department of Zoology, Duke University, Durham, North Carolina (211, 243)

C. M. YONGE, Department of Zoology, University of Glasgow, Glasgow, Scotland (1)

---

* PRESENT ADDRESS: Department of Zoology, Syracuse University, Syracuse, New York.

Preface

Winterstein's monumental "Handbuch der vergleichenden Physiologie" published as a series of volumes between 1910 and 1925 reviewed the main features of the physiology of molluscs. Since that period there has been no comprehensive treatment of molluscan physiology. Of recent years, the areas of investigation have extended in many directions; the literature is voluminous and, forming an added difficulty, extremely scattered. In the present volume, and in a second which will follow, an attempt is made to give a full and critical survey of this literature. Physiology has been interpreted very broadly in these volumes. In addition to the subdivisions usually found in physiological treatises, chapters are included dealing with the physiological aspects of development (although not with classic embryology), also with ecology in the sea, in fresh waters, and on land, and with behavior and learning in those most highly evolved molluscs, the Cephalopoda. In recognition of the fact that physiology must be firmly based on structure and systematics, a lengthy introductory chapter is provided, based largely on the results of research on functional morphology.

We have felt it necessary to forego the pleasure of the historical approach. The lineages of physiological ideas have, in consequence, usually not been traced. Rather, emphasis has been placed on developments and experimentation of recent years. So as to discover which periods have provided the greater number of contributions to the present volume, we have been interested in making a frequency plot of the distribution of the 1434 references since 1900. There are two peaks: one in the later 1930's when the post First World War interest in comparative physiology had reached a climax, the other in the mid-1950's when the effect of resumption of disinterested scientific investigation following the Second World War had presumably had its effect. Of the reported studies, 54% are more recent than 1950.

The Mollusca constitute a phylum of unusual interest. Built on a relatively simple (although possibly secondarily simplified) ground plan, they display a range of adaptive radiation unparalleled outside the Arthropoda and the Chordata. They possess a remarkable degree of plasticity; in no other phylum are there so many instances of convergence. The success of the Mollusca has been due to the efficiency of their various, and often characteristic, organ systems and it is with this success that these volumes are primarily concerned. So great are the structural and functional divergences within the phylum that workers on the Gastropoda, on the Bivalvia, and on the smaller molluscan classes may not be conversant with the investigations of those who study the more highly organized Cephalopoda, and the converse may also be true. We would hope that in the present volumes all groups of malacologists would find common meeting grounds.

As Editors, we hope that this volume will be of service to many: to the comparative physiologist who seeks similarities and differences in function, to the cellular biologist who finds particularly suitable material in the nerves, muscles, and other tissues of the Mollusca, to the ecologist for whom physiology is increasingly important, and to the many who are interested in the Mollusca for systematic or economic reasons or just because they are fascinated by these remarkable animals. To others—advanced undergraduates, graduate students, established investigators in various disciplines—we would wish to introduce molluscan physiology as a stimulating field of study with a wealth of experimental material especially suitable for experimentation on a variety of physiological parameters.

We both owe a deep debt of gratitude to our collaborators and first of all to our authors who with understanding and patience have kept their chapters current during the inevitably slow development of this first volume. One of us (K.M.W.) wishes to record his gratitude to Dr. Elizabeth A. McMahan for her indefatigable editorial services, to Mrs. Dorothy S. Fry and Mrs. Ann M. Ellington for their services with manuscripts and bibliographies; and also to the Office of Naval Research and the National Institutes of Health for financial support of experimental studies and the preparation of manuscripts. The other (C.M.Y.) has to record his indebtedness to his research assistant, Miss J. I. Campbell, for help with figures and especially with the systematic index and to his secretary, Miss M. McDill, for continued help in the preparation of manuscripts and with endless correspondence. We also acknowledge a most pleasant collaboration with Academic Press.

K.M.W.
C.M.Y.

January, 1964

CONTENTS

Classification and Structure of the Mollusca

J. E. MORTON AND C. M. YONGE

Physiological Aspects of the Ecology of Intertidal Molluscs

G. E. NEWELL

Physiological Aspects of Ecology in Nonmarine Molluscs

W. RUSSELL HUNTER

Reproduction

V. FRETTER AND A. GRAHAM

Development

C. P. RAVEN

The Culture of Marine Bivalve Larvae

P. R. WALNE

Growth

KARL M. WILBUR AND GARETH OWEN

Shell Formation and Regeneration

KARL M. WILBUR

Osmotic and Ionic Regulation

JAMES D. ROBERTSON

Muscle and Neuromuscular Physiology

G. HOYLE

Special Effectors: Luminous Organs, Chromatophores, Pigments, and Poison Glands

J. A. C. NICOL

Locomotion

J. E. Morton

The Buoyancy of Marine Molluscs

E. J. Denton

Contents of Volume II

xiii

CHAPTER 1

Classification and Structure of the Mollusca

J. E. Morton
DEPARTMENT OF ZOOLOGY, UNIVERSITY OF AUCKLAND, AUCKLAND, NEW ZEALAND

C. M. Yonge
DEPARTMENT OF ZOOLOGY, UNIVERSITY OF GLASGOW, GLASGOW, SCOTLAND

Part 1. Classification

I. Class Monoplacophora

Typified living by *Neopilina* (order Tryblidiacea). Almost bilaterally symmetrical molluscs, with a ventral foot, and median posterior anus. The mantle completely covered by a single-piece oval shell, and the mantle cavity is a shallow space containing five pairs of uniseriate branched branchiae. Dorsolateral and ventral coelomic cavities are relatively well developed. The auricles are in two pairs, the gonads two-paired, discharging through two of the six pairs of renal organs. The nervous system is primitive with longitudinal pallial and pedal cords.

II. Class Amphineura

Elongated, bilaterally symmetrical molluscs with mouth and anus terminal. Mantle very extensive covering the dorsal surface and sides. Heart dorsal and posterior with ventricle and lateral auricles. Nervous system with longitudinal (ganglionic) pallial and pedal cords with cross anastomoses.

A. Subclass Polyplacophora

Flattened littoral or sublittoral Amphineura with a broad ventral foot; the mantle bearing eight transverse shell plates, bordered by a spiculose or scaly girdle. Ctenidia multiplied into numerous pairs, adjacent ones functionally associated so dividing each pallial groove into anterior and outer inhalant, and posterior and inner exhalant, cavities. Characteristically intertidal.

B. Subclass Aplacophora

Aberrant worm-like elongated Amphineura with the mantle completely investing the body, save for a longitudinal ventral groove (in Neomeniomorpha) containing a linear vestige of the foot. The mantle is studded with numerous calcified spicules. Living in deeper water, feeding upon deposits in ooze (Chaetodermomorpha) or on corals and hydroids (Neomeniomorpha).

III. Class Gastropoda

Asymmetrical Mollusca with a well-developed head and, at least primitively, a broad flattened foot. The shell is in one piece, coiled in a helical spiral, at least in the young stages. The visceropallium has undergone torsion of 180°; because of its asymmetrical coiling (distinct from torsion) the palliopericardial complex is usually reduced and one-sided.

A. Subclass Prosobranchia

Generally aquatic gastropods with the visceral mass retaining pronounced torsion and the visceral loop crossed into a figure of eight. The head carries a single pair of tentacles with eyes at the base. The spiral shell is closed by an operculum. The mantle cavity contains primitively two ctenidia but usually there is reduction to one (posttorsional left). The heart is posterior to this. The solitary gonad opens on the right, either through the right kidney (where the left one is suppressed) or through the renal duct (where the left kidney is retained and functional). In the latter case the genital ducts become elaborate. Usually a free-swimming veliger larva.

1. Order Archaeogastropoda

Prosobranchs often with indications or more of original bilateral symmetry, most primitively with two ctenidia but even where reduced to one, always bipectinate (aspidobranch). The Patellacea (limpets) with one ctenidium (Acmaeidae), with secondary gills in the pallial grooves (Patellidae), or without gills (Lepetidae). Heart with two auricles (diotocardiate), right renal organ always a functional kidney but also conveying genital products, fertilization being external. Nervous system little concentrated.

1a. Order Neritacea

Distinct from Archaeogastropoda owing to enlargement of left renal organ which becomes the functional kidney; right organ lost apart from the duct which becomes incorporated in the genital tract (i.e., as in Mesogastropoda). In consequence males possess a cephalic penis and females a glandular genital tract, hence internal fertilization and egg capsules. In further consequence, unlike Archaeogastropoda, have extensively invaded fresh water and land.

2. Order Mesogastropoda
   Organs of right side of palliopericardial complex lost. Ctenidium monopectinate (pectinibranch), osphradium well-developed, sometimes pectinate. Nervous system more concentrated. Left kidney alone functional,
   genital products conveyed via former right kidney duct with pallial
   glandular extensions producing egg capsules or jelly mass. Cephalic penis
   and internal fertilization. Usually a free-swimming veliger. Shell sometimes siphonate, carnivorous habit with eversible proboscis in some.

3. Order Neogastropoda
   Most advanced Prosobranchia, with highly concentrated nervous system,
   a siphonate shell, and eversible proboscis. Carnivorous habits, feeding on
   living or dead animals. Free-swimming veliger usually suppressed, with
   embryos as a rule intracapsular, sometimes practicing embryonic can-
   nibalism. Osphradium large, bipectinate.

B. Subclass Opisthobranchia
   Marine hermaphrodite Gastropoda; shell reduced, becoming internal and
   finally disappearing with an accompanying tendency to detorsion, the mantle
   cavity moving back along the right side and widely opening before final
   loss; also uncrossing and shortening of the visceral loop. Gill probably never
   a ctenidium. Calcareous spicules often developed in notum of naked forms.
   With loss of torsion and of asymmetrical shell, eventual return to bilateral
   external symmetry, with great adaptive range of form and color, feeding,
   and locomotion. Usually with a (reduced) free-swimming veliger.

   1. Order Cephalaspidea (Bullomorpha)
      Shell moderately large and pallial cavity well-developed, with a single
      plicate gill. Head forming a large shield for burrowing. Parapodia prom-
      inent and sometimes fin-like.

   2. Order Anaspidea (Aplysiomorpha)
      Shell reduced and internal, mantle cavity a small recess on right side. No
      head shield; animals crawling or swimming by enlarged parapodia.

   3. Order Thecosomata
      Planktonic pteropods with parapodial fins, with a spirally coiled shell, or
      a modified nonspiral "pseudoconch." Pallial cavity well-developed.

   4. Order Gymnosomata
      Naked planktonic pteropods with small ventral parapodial fins. No shell
      or mantle cavity, externally symmetrical, and fast-swimming.

   5. Order Notaspidea (Pleurobranchomorpha)
      Shell reduced and internal, no mantle cavity, but a naked gill overhung
      by the mantle on the right side. Becoming flattened, slug-like, and ex-
      ternally almost symmetrical.

   6. Order Acochlidiacea
      Tiny interstitial sand-dwelling opisthobranchs, visceral mass marked off
      as a long hump from the foot, without dorsal appendages, though with
      spicules.

   7. Order Sacoglossa
      Herbivorous suctorial opisthobranchs with characteristically modified rad-
      ula and buccal mass. Running from primitive shelled and spirally coiled
      forms to slug-like "nudibranchs."

   8. Order Acoela (Nudibranchia)
      Naked, externally almost symmetrical slugs, no mantle cavity or external
      shell. Dorsal integument with outgrowths such as cerata, or with pinnate
      retractile gills encircling a median anus.

C. Subclass Pulmonata

Hermaphrodite Gastropoda, with no ctenidium, with mantle cavity vascularized as a lung. A small contractile pallial aperture. Detorsion seldom complete, but nervous system concentrated to lose all trace of chiastoneury. Shell and visceral mass primitively spiral but may assume slug-like form.

1. Order Basommatophora

Head with a single pair of noninvaginable tentacles with eyes at base; most species aquatic, primitively or by reversion, and may acquire secondary gills.

2. Order Stylommatophora

Two pairs of invaginable tentacles, eyes on summit of hinder pair. Terrestrial snails, giving rise by loss of spiral shell to slugs.

IV. Class Scaphopoda

Marine and bilaterally symmetrical molluscs, mantle and shell elongated, uniting ventrally to form a tapered tube open at either end. Foot cylindrical and pointed. No ctenidium. Head without eyes but carrying paired clusters of food-catching captacula. Sexes separate without special genital ducts. Fertilization external.

V. Class Bivalvia

Bilaterally symmetrical Mollusca with rudimentary head, without radula. Ciliary feeders using labial palps and greatly enlarged ctenidia. Two mantle lobes enclosing laterally compressed body and secreting single shell consisting of two calcified valves and a dorsal ligament which, usually together with teeth formed from the valves, constitutes the hinge. Compressed foot adapted for burrowing, without plantar surface. Fertilization external; usually long larval life.

A. Subclass Protobranchia

Ctenidia with flat, nonreflected filaments, hypobranchial glands retained. Foot opening out to expose flattened ventral surface and with numerous retractors. Apart from Solemyidae, feeding primarily by means of extensile "proboscides" from enlarged labial palps. With primitive but also some very specialized characters.

B. Subclass Lamellibranchia

Ctenidia much larger relative to palps and forming feeding organs; filaments greatly elongated and reflected, forming two-sided lamellae the arms being usually united by lamellar junctions. Adjacent filaments attached by ciliary junctions (filibranch condition) or united by tissue (eulamellibranch condition).

1. Order Taxodonta

Gill filaments free and without interlamellar junctions. Mantle lobes free throughout, anterior and posterior adductors subequal. Hinge with numerous similar teeth.

2. Order Anisomyaria

Gills usually filibranch with vascular interlamellar junctions. Byssal fixation leading to diminution of anterior adductor, giving rise eventually to monomyarian condition with radical rearrangement of symmetry leading sometimes to cementation (e.g., Ostraeidae), sometimes to freedom (e.g., many Pectinidae). Apart from separation of exhalant aperture, mantle open; foot small (sometimes absent) and usually without siphons.

3. Order Heterodonta

Gills eulamellibranch and shell less modified than in Anisomyaria, with adductors similar. Hinge dentition is of the "heterodont" type. Mantle edges usually united at one or more points ventrally, and often produced

posteriorly into siphons. Shallow or deep-burrowing, or occasionally sur-
face-living.

4. Order Schizodonta
Gills eulamellibranch but probably an artificial group, associating, by
virtue of their similar "schizodont" hinge, marine Trigoniacea and fresh-
water Unionacea.

5. Order Adapedonta
Eulamellibranch gills, and the mantle margins completely closed ventrally
save for pedal gape. Siphons long and united; the gills may extend into
them. The ligament is weak or wanting and the shell gaping. Deep and
permanent burrowing, often penetrating hard substrata.

6. Order Anomalodesmata
Eulamellibranch gills, the mantle edges extensively fused. Hinge teeth
lacking. Foot small, external gill plate directed dorsally, Hermaphrodite,
with separately opening ovary and testis.

C. Subclass Septibranchia
Adductors equal; mantle edges not extensively fused. Gills transformed into
a muscular septum pumping water through the mantle cavity. Macrophagous,
feeding, often at considerable depth, upon animal remains.

VI. Class Cephalopoda
Bilaterally symmetrical Mollusca with circle of tentacles round the head. Circulation in the mantle cavity reversed with epipodium modified to form a pallial
funnel through which passes the concentrated exhalant current which serves for
jet propulsion. Nervous system greatly concentrated and highly organized
sense organs. Of higher metabolism than other Mollusca.

A. Subclass Nautiloidea
Extinct save for genus *Nautilus*, but formerly very numerous. An external,
many-chambered siphunculate shell, coiled or straight. Head with numerous
tentaculate appendages, retractile, and lacking suckers. Funnel of two separate folds. Ctenidia and renal organs increase to two pairs. Eyes open without
cornea or lens.

B. Subclass Ammonoidea
A vast extinct group, in general comparable with and radiating parallel to
the Nautiloidea. Of the structure of the animal, little can be reliably known.

C. Subclass Coleoidea
In living forms the mantle is naked and forms a sac covering the viscera and
containing a more or less rudimentary shell. The head has always eight
sucker-bearing arms, and there may be in addition a pair of longer and retractile tentaculate arms between the third and fourth short pairs. Funnel
always a closed tube. Ctenidia and renal organs a single pair. Eye with a
crystalline lens and closed or open cornea. Ink sac present.

1. Order Decapoda
Tentacular retractile arms in addition to eight normal arms which are
shorter than the body. Suckers pedunculate with horny rings. Internal
shell relatively well-developed. Squids and cuttlefish. Teuthoidea, Sepioidea.

2. Order Octopoda
Eight uniform arms longer than the body, with nonpedunculate suckers.
The mantle encloses the viscera in a rounded muscular sac, and the internal
shell is lacking, although the female *Argonauta* has an external "shell"
secreted by the dorsal arms. Polypoidea, Cirroteuthoidea.

3. Order Vampyromorpha
"Vampire squids," now separated from Octopoda by differences in the

arm pattern; eight long arms united by a swimming web and two small, retractile, tendril-like arms.

Part 2. Basic Anatomy

I. PRIMITIVE MOLLUSCA

The first molluscs were probably flat-bodied animals crawling on a flat sole. Judging from the basic shape and locomotion of the most primitive existing forms, affinities, although distant, were closest to the Turbellaria. Despite *Neopilina*, there would seem to be no advantages and formidable obstacles to linking the molluscs with any worm visibly metamerically segmented. Certainly, if *Neopilina* displays primitive structure, then a major secondary simplification must have preceded the evolution of the other molluscan classes. The early anteroposterior axis was in line with the foot and there was complete bilateral symmetry with mouth anterior and anus posterior. The head carried sensory tentacles and perhaps eyes. The snout was carried close to the ground, particulate matter being scraped by a protrusible radula. Initially, both feeding and locomotion were probably muscular activities with other functions performed by cilia and mucus secretion.

Early in the molluscan evolution a second, dorsoventral, growth axis appeared. The viscera became concentrated within a dome-shaped protuberance carried on the muscular foot. This *visceropallium*, which constitutes the second recognizable element of molluscan design, was covered by a secreting epithelium, the *pallium* or *mantle*, which extended peripherally to overlap the foot. This secreted the protective shell, initially probably noncalcareous, and both mantle and shell grew radially by marginal increment. Many complexities of molluscan form can best be understood by reference to the interacting symmetries of the head-foot (bilateral) and of the visceropallium (radial or biradial).

Series of shell muscles (Fig. 1), inserted some distance from the margin of the shell and radiating into the substance of the foot, attached the visceropallium to the head-foot and enabled the shell to be drawn down against the substratum.

As recently stressed by Fretter and Graham (1962) in their "British Prosobranch Molluscs" (a book of great importance), the original molluscan *pallial cavity* not improbably consisted of a groove between mantle skirt and foot into which kidneys and anus opened and which housed paired series of gills (possibly prectenidia). But further molluscan evolution followed its great posterior enlargement with formation of a combined respiratory and cloacal chamber into which an enlarged foot could be withdrawn.

The respiratory organs now undoubtedly consisted of a single pair of *ctenidia* (Fig. 2C), each being made up of a central axis bearing on each side alternating rows of elongated triangular *filaments*. Within the axis ran an upper afferent, and a lower efferent blood vessel, the ctenidium being

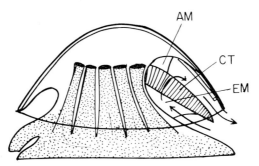

Fig. 1. Primitive Mollusc. Basic plan from which all existing classes (other than Monoplacophora) can be derived. Ventral head and foot with anteroposterior axis and shell muscles penetrating dorsally shown stippled; dorsal visceropallium with radial (or biradial) symmetry; posterior mantle cavity with single pair of ctenidia (*CT*) attached by long efferent (*EM*) and short afferent (*AM*) membrane, arrows showing direction of respiratory current.

attached to the floor of the cavity by a long efferent membrane (*EM*) (also possibly to the roof by a short afferent membrane (*AM*)). Between each ctenidium and the rectum lay a thick, ciliated, mucus-producing *hypobranchial gland* (Fig. 2A, c., *HYP*). This, together with the frontal and abfrontal cilia running along the margins of the filaments, constituted the sanitation mechanism of the mantle cavity, carrying finely particulate waste toward the median dorsal line for rejection. Powerful water currents were drawn ventrally and laterally into the mantle cavity by the beating of lateral cilia on the opposed faces of the filaments. Passing between the filaments the currents converged into a median dorsal exhalant current. The sediment content and possibly the chemical composition of the entering current was sampled by a small sensory *osphradium* (Fig. 5, *OS*) lying at the base of each ctenidium in the path of the inhalant current (Yonge, 1947).

Primitively the heart probably comprised a median ventricle (Fig. 2A, *V*), partly surrounding the rectum, in the posterior dorsal mid-line, with a pair of auricles (*AUR*) receiving blood from the efferent vessels of the respective ctenidia. The early coelom possibly consisted of little more than the *pericardium* (*PC*) and contained a watery filtrate from the blood system. Into the pericardium opened the probably paired gonads (*G*) (it is uncertain whether the sexes were primitively separate or united) forming a forward extension lined by germinal epithelium. A

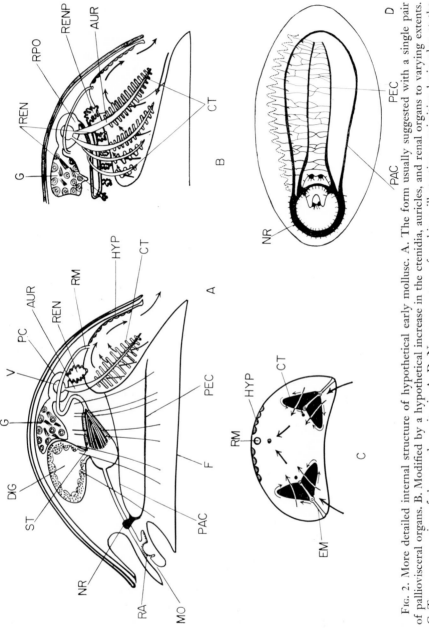

Fig. 2. More detailed internal structure of hypothetical early mollusc. A. The form usually suggested with a single pair of pallovisceral organs. B. Modified by a hypothetical increase in the ctenidia, auricles, and renal organs to varying extents. C. Transverse section of the mantle cavity in A. D. Nervous system of a chiton illustrating a primitive basic plan at the early molluscan level. *AUR*, auricle; *DIG*, digestive diverticulum; *F*, foot; *G*, gonad; *HYP*, hypobranchial gland; *MO*, mouth; *NR*, neural ganglion; *PAC*, pallial cord; *PEC*, pedal cord; *PC*, pericardium; *RA*, radula; *REN*, renal sac; *RENP*, posterior renal sac; *RPO*, renopericardial opening; RM, rectum; *ST*, stomach; *V*, ventricle. Other lettering as before.

pair of *coelomoducts* or *renal organs* (*REN*) opened internally into the pericardium by *renopericardial ducts* and externally into the exhalant region of the mantle cavity, nitrogenous excrement and genital products being discharged. Fertilization was inevitably external. Extended larval life began with formation of a trochophore like that of an annelid which, with development of the characteristic molluscan velum, became a veliger.

The rest of the body cavity was hemocoelic and blood-filled, formed by the enlargement of the venous spaces of the body by the process Ray Lankester has called *phleboedesis*. An arterial system with anterior and visceral aortas led from the ventricle. With few capillary channels the returning blood ultimately found its way into the extensive hemocoelic spaces.

A muscular buccal bulb contained a cartilage-supported *odontophore* or "tongue." Spread on the surface of the odontophore was a chitinous membrane, with very numerous file-like teeth, the *radula* (Fig. 2A, *RA*). Food was carried backward from the buccal mass into a narrower esophagus in a series of small boluses, united into a more or less coherent mucous rope which entered the stomach. Even primitively this chamber must have been elaborate. Toward the intestine a firmly compacted fecal rod, the *protostyle*, rotated by strong cilia, pulled in the food strings like rope round a capstan. The rotating string was swept repeatedly over the ciliated stomach wall and particles shed or detached were graded for size and heaviness by an extensive *ciliary sorting area*. Small, usually nutritive particles eventually entered one of a pair of spacious ducts leading into the ramifying mass of *digestive diverticula* (*DIG*). Here they were probably digested intracellularly. Coarser particles were added to the protostyle or by-passed it to enter the intestine where mucus-bound fecal pellets were molded by cilia and feeble peristalsis.

The nervous system of the first mollusc was probably almost as simple as that of a flatworm. The *central nerve ring* (Fig. 2A,D, *NR*) formed a loop around the anterior esophagus. Dorsally it consisted of a cerebral band, diffusely studded with neurones, centrally of two commissures, a labial band in front and a pedal commissure linking the anterior ends of the pedal cords. From the nerve ring, two pairs of longitudinal cords, also diffusely nerve-celled, extended posteriorly. The more dorsal and lateral *pleurovisceral cords* (Fig. 2A,D, *PAC*) united beneath the posterior end of the gut, ran near the junction of the pallial skirt and innervated the pallial organs and visceral mass. The ventral *pedal nerve cords* (*PEC*), with ladder-like cross-connections ran close together along the pedal floor of the hemocoele.

This common structural plan is recognizably present in the whole subsequent evolution of the molluscs, a unified phylum with unparalleled adaptive diversity. Words with a different evolutionary context well apply to molluscs: there is a basic theme "suivi avec tenacité mais varié avec richesse" (J. F. Correa da Serra, botanist, 1806). In this chapter is presented sufficient of the essential anatomy of each class to reveal the possibilities of variant molluscan design, particularly as it affects the basic relations between the parts of the body and the changing patterns of symmetry. Detailed anatomy, particularly of the digestive, nervous, and circulatory systems, for fuller functional treatment must be deferred to the appropriate special chapters.

Mosaic evolution is a commonplace in the Mollusca as elsewhere; primitive in many features as the classes Amphineura and Monoplacophora undoubtedly are, we have felt it better to consider the progressive evolution of the large class Gastropoda from primitive ancestors before dealing with the associated archaisms and specializations present in those small "primitive" classes.

II. GASTROPODA

A. Torsion

In the early gastropods the head-foot and the visceropallium played a balanced role, neither predominating. They constituted real structural entities, the first primarily muscular in its workings, the second ciliary and mucous. The head-foot was concerned with the external relations, moving upon and feeding from the substrate, the visceropallium with the domestic activities of digestion, circulation, reproduction, and excretion. The anterior mantle cavity became established as in some respects the antechamber to the world outside, and the focal point of many functions.

The head-foot and visceropallium are in gastropods interconnected only by a narrow neck behind the head, through which pass esophagus, rectum, anterior aorta, visceral loop, and the attaching muscle of the shell. Taking the head-foot as fixed, the visceropallium undergoes separate evolution involving reorientation of its parts. An early and fundamental event in gastropod ontogeny (the event in phylogeny which brought the Gastropoda into being) is that of torsion, whereby the visceropallium rotates through 180° upon the head-foot. The site of torsion is the narrow neck behind the head-foot. An asymmetrical development of the right and left muscles attaching the shell to the head-foot in the early veliger brings about a change in orientation: the parts of the mantle cavity and pericardial complex lying ventrally and posteriorly move up the right side to lie dorsally and to face forward. Points lying dorsally move down the left side to become ventral (see Fig. 3). The left gill, hypobranchial gland, osphradium, auricle, and renal organ become those of the right, and conversely the right-hand members move to the left. The left and right

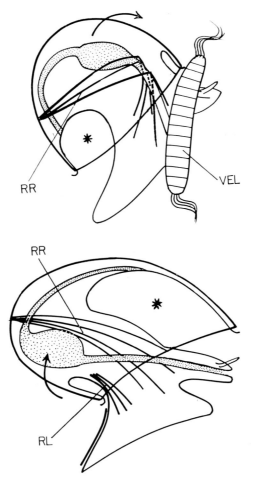

FIG. 3. Gastropoda. The process of torsion in a prosobranch veliger, showing the position of the asymmetrically developed shell muscle (see Crofts, 1955). Asterisk indicates position of the mantle cavity. *RL*, left retractor muscles; *RR*, right retractor muscles; *VEL*, velum.

parietal ganglia likewise exchange positions. In gastropod veligers such as *Acmaea* and *Trochus* up to 90° torsion may take place by rapid asymmetrical muscle contraction in the course of a few hours [Fig. 3 shows the shell muscles as determined by Crofts (1955)]; the remainder of the change through 180° is completed by slower larval growth.

Torsion alters the position and aspect of the pallial cavity which originally faced ventrally and backward and now moves upward to face anteriorly. After torsion in the veliger, retraction of the animal into the protective mantle cavity and shell will allow the sensitive and vulnerable

head and velum to be accommodated first, with the entry afterward of
the tougher foot. The later acquired operculum seals the opening. This,
as Garstang first perceived, is of high adaptive advantage to the larva as
a protection from such predators as medusae, chaetognaths, and planktonic crustaceans (most probably by allowing them to survive passage
through the gut of these animals).

The final effects of torsion on the adult snail are profound. Indeed, to
one of us (J.E.M.) no theory of torsion can be wholly satisfactory that
postulates transplantation of the mantle cavity as a larval mutation with
any but advantageous consequences to the subsequent adult. But to the
other (C.M.Y.) it seems impossible to conceive of the initial selective
value of this mutation except in terms of immediate advantage to the
larva, i.e., regardless of effects on the adult, although clearly with consequences which were not positively harmful. But the problems of sanitation, met initially by the posttorsional appearance of a mantle slit shown
in Fig. 4 (later sometimes an aperture or apertures) were not satisfactorily solved until a left-right circulation was achieved. Certainly the
initial disadvantages due to torsion become changed to advantages owing
to the plasticity of the essentially simple molluscan ground plan and the
ability now acquired of drawing in water from ahead with the sensory
benefits this confers.

These advantages, on which we are completely agreed, include achieve-
ment of a new stability in the siting of the bulky visceral mass ventrally
and nearer the substratum. This is the only feasible position as the hump
enlarges (but justifying torsion only *after* the event) while the anterior
mantle cavity, no longer encumbered by overhanging visceral coils, assumes a commanding role in the subsequent functional advance of the
Gastropoda. Certainly in the Mesogastropoda and Neogastropoda, where
it has lost the disadvantages first of paired gills and then of the left filaments on the single, now pectinibranch, ctenidium (Fig. 6I), the mantle
cavity becomes a mechanism of beautiful efficiency.

This forward-facing cavity makes continuous exchange of water in
front of the advancing animal. Increasingly this cavity assumes additional sensory and exploratory functions. The distinctive pallial sense
organs, the osphradia, which presumably before torsion were tactile
organs concerned with estimating the amount of entering sediment and
which appear to retain this function in Archaeogastropoda and also at
least in sessile Mesogastropoda, tend to increase in complexity with the
evolution of carnivorous and prey-stalking habits, notable in the Neogastropoda. With the location of the inhalant opening at the advancing
end of the animal, then its forward extension at the tip of a mobile siphon,
the sensory functions of the mantle cavity become associated with those

of the head. Movement can then be delicately adjusted in response to information from in front of the animal.

B. Spiral Coiling and Pallial Asymmetry

The changes produced by torsion are diagnostic of early gastropods. Almost equally fundamental is the coiling of the visceropallium and shell cone, the dorsoventral axis describing a helicoid spiral. The head-foot withdraws into the shell and so becomes subordinate to the visceropallium in the total symmetry of the animal, though never—in itself—losing its

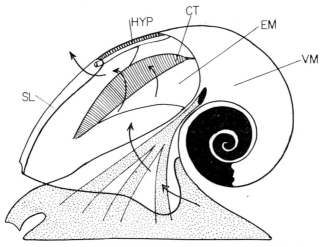

FIG. 4. Posttorsional organization of an early gastropod, based schematically on *Bellerophon. SL,* mantle (and shell) slit; *VM,* visceral mass. Other lettering as before.

essentially bilateral anteroposterior symmetry. Visceral coiling is totally distinct from torsion. Some gastropods with torsion do not show it. It probably preceded torsion and certainly occurred without it in fossil Monoplacophora, and even in the early larva of *Neopilina.* It achieves an economy in the disposition of the increasingly bulky visceral sac, antero-posterior elongation being restricted by the forward site of the anus, and upward dorsal growth being mechanically unfeasible. The earliest gastro-pods, the Amphigastropoda, as represented typically by the Bellero-phontacea, had a short compact planospire (Fig. 4) with perfect bilateral symmetry (Fig. 5A) but this had disadvantages due to its tendency to bilateral restriction of the mantle cavity, and reduction of the available diameter of the visceral spire at higher levels of the coil (Fig. 4). The most primitive living Archaeogastropoda—the Pleurotomariidae (Fig. 6D)—have already adopted the more convenient design of skewed helical or turbinate coil with the tip displaced to the right.

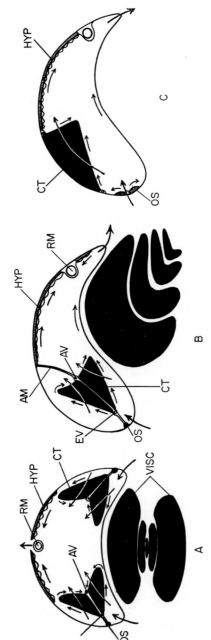

Fig. 5. Transverse section through the prosobranch mantle cavity with relative position of the visceral coil shown in black in A and B. A. Assumed condition of bilaterally symmetrical amphigastropod, e.g., *Bellerophon*. B. A trochid archaeogastropod with a single (left) bipectinate (aspidobranch) ctenidium. C. A neogastropod, *Buccinum*, with a single (left) monopectinate (pectinibranch) ctenidium. *OS*, osphradium. *VISC*, coils of visceral mass. Other lettering as before.

Further bilateral asymmetry between the right and left halves of the pallial cavity follows. With a skewed helical spire displaced to the right (Fig. 5B), the second whorl will tend to bulge against and occlude the right side of the pallial cavity. Although in the earliest Archaeogastropoda with a right skewed spiral both sides of the pallial complex are represented [Pleurotomariidae (Fig. 6D), Scissurellidae, Haliotidae (Fig. 6E)], yet the right pallial organs (including the right auricle) are reduced and doomed to disappearance. With them goes the shell slit (present in the Pleurotomariidae, absent in the Trochacea). The now restricted inhalant current, created by the solitary aspidobranch ctenidium (Fig. 5B), enters on the left side and, carrying fecal, renal, and reproductive products, leaves on the right (see arrows in Fig. 5B). The problem of sanitation posed by torsion is now solved. Final simplification with completed efficiency is attained by loss of the left filaments and fusion of the ctenidial axis to the left pallial wall, producing the pectinibranch ctenidium of the higher Prosobranchia (Fig. 5C).

The double pallial and pericardial complex is thus lost. The bilateral symmetry of the Fissurellidae (Fig. 6F) with an upwardly directed exhalant aperture in the middle line represents reversion to a basic bilaterality by Gastropoda that [unlike the Patellacea (Fig. 6G)] never fully lost their right pallial organs. Thus gastropod history (after probably initial coiling in a plane spiral) has involved first torsion, then helical coiling, and finally left-handedness.

In all Gastropoda the gonad is represented by the left member of the original pretorsional pair (Fig. 6A) and always opens by way of the right renal duct (Fig. 6B). In the Archaeogastropoda, where the renal organs are asymmetrical with the left one often small and the right one always large, this involves passage of the gametes through a functional kidney, entering directly or via the renopericardial duct. Elaboration of a penis or of a glandular oviduct is impossible and fertilization is inevitably external with consequent ecological limitations.

In the higher Prosobranchia—and also the Neritacea which are here removed from their usual inclusion within the Archaeogastropoda—the left renal organ alone persists and is the functional kidney (Fig. 6I$_1$). A vestige of the right organ survives to form the proximal part of the genital duct, now emancipated from dependence on a functional kidney. Elaboration of glandular genital ducts is now possible. Sperm is conveyed from the original aperture by a ciliated pallial furrow running forward along the right side to a muscular cephalic penis. Eggs are carried along a glandular pallial furrow, the female aperture moving forward within the pallial cavity. This new pallial duct secretes in succession an albuminous nutritive layer, an egg capsule, and sometimes a jelly mass. These are added after fertilization by sperm stored following copulation in a re-

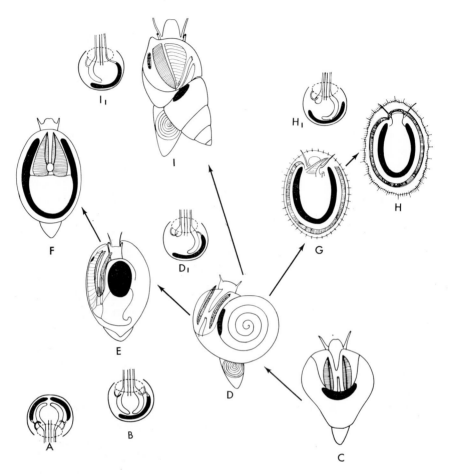

Fig. 6. Evolution of the mantle cavity and asymmetry of the pallial and visceral organs in the Prosobranchia. The smaller diagrams represent the relationships of the pericardium (broken line), gonads (black), gonoduct and renal organs (white). Opening of anus between renal openings. Larger diagrams with shell muscles in black. A. Primitive molluscan condition, mantle cavity posterior, paired gonads (opening via renal organs). B. Primitive gastropod condition with mantle cavity anterior, solitary right (posttorsional) gonad but renal organs of same size. C. Primitive externally bilateral gastropod such as *Bellerophon*. D. Most primitive existing archaeogastropod, *Pleurotomaria*. D_1. Renoreproductive arrangements in Archaeogastropoda. E. More modified zygobranchous gastropod, *Haliotis*. F. Secondarily symmetrical *Fissurella* (ctenidia of same size, unlike D and E). G. Later evolved limpet, *Lottia*, coming from trochid, i.e., with one (left) ctenidium and also ring of pallial gills. H. More modified *Patella* with only pallial gills. H_1. Renal and reproductive arrangements in *Patella*. I. Neogastropod, *Buccinum*, with pectinibranch ctenidium (osphradium and hypobranchial gland, respectively, on left and right). I_1. Showing separation of renal system (left) and the reproductive system (right) in Mesogastropoda and Neogastropoda.

ceptaculum seminis. The duct early becomes a closed tube; in the male, part of the sperm-conducting tract closes to form a prostate. With possession of the means of internal fertilization and better provision for nutrition and protection of the developing eggs, wider possibilities of evolutionary radiation appear. Already in the Neritacea there is a radiation of freshwater and terrestrial offshoots which rivals the later evolution of the Pulmonata.

C. Prosobranch Radiation

Alone among the large molluscan classes, the Gastropoda were initially so unspecialized as to be able to produce any of the modifications of structure and habit of which the phylum is capable. Ecologically and structurally they are among the widest ranging classes in the animal kingdom. Some of the fundamental modifications of outward symmetry and of the interrelations of head-foot and visceropallium that have contributed to the diversity of gastropods may here be examined. The main axes of symmetry appearing at the outset are indicated in Fig. 7. The laws of growth of the gastropod shell were illuminated by D'Arcy Thompson in his classic "On Growth and Form" (1942) and represent the achieved possibilities of evolution in the visceropallium which produces the shell.

From the bellerophontids onward (Fig. 7B) the anteroposterior axis, if by this is meant the line between mouth and anus, has been modified by the involvement of the gut in torsion. Yet the head-foot still has an important bilaterality and its axis (Fig. 7, *ap*) may now be taken as a line running back from the mouth along the median line of the sole. The most useful descriptive axis of the visceropallium was originally the *dorsoventral or median axis* (*dv*) running from the apex of the cone to the mid-point of the sole. This is now involved in coiling and is a plane or a skewed helix. A new straight line may now replace it in orientation, the *axis of volution* (*av*), or the axis about which the generating figure of the growing shell revolves; this will run from the shell apex to the mid-point of the umbilicus or the base of the columella. The generating figure (D'Arcy Thompson) hardly ever forms a perfect circle and the diameter running, for example, through the pallial slit in a torqued gastropod like *Bellerophon* may be regarded as a subsidiary axis. The loss of pallial bilaterality raises into prominence what may be conveniently designated the *normal axis* (*na*), running from the apex through those points of successive generating figures that are most remote from the dorsoventral axis (*dv*). As shown in Figure 7B, it coincides with the most spacious extent of the mantle cavity.

In the Trochidae (see Fig. 5B, based on *Calliostoma*) there are two changes from *Bellerophon*. First, the angle of retardation in coiling, infinite in a plane spiral, becomes smaller—about 35°—so that the spire is skewed or turbinate (Fig. 7C). Second, the axis of volution has shifted in both planes that determine it in space, moving backward at a known angle ("regulatory detorsion") and at the same time being markedly inclined upward out of the horizontal plane. In more advanced and faster moving

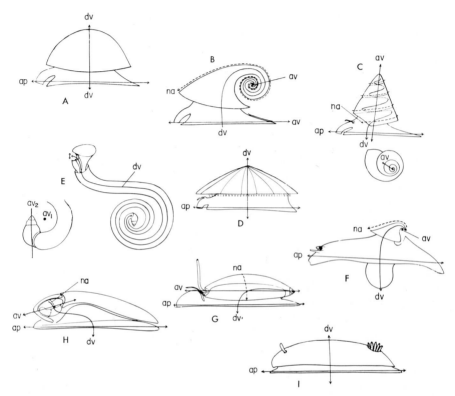

Fig. 7. The axes of symmetry in the evolution of the Gastropoda. A. Primitive mollusc. B. Early planospiral gastropod (cf. *Bellerophon*). C. Trochacea. D. Patellacea. E. Vermetidae (showing change in plane of axis of volution with transition from embryonic (av_1) to adult spire (av_2). F. *Carinaria* (Heteropod). G. *Oliva* (Neogastropod). H. *Philine* ("tectibranch"). I. Dorid ("nudibranch"). *ap*, anteroposterior axis; *dv*, dorsoventral axis; *av*, axis of volution; *na*, normal axis.

prosobranchs the axis of volution may point horizontally backward to lie parallel with the axis of the elongated foot. Either, as in the Turritellidae and the Terebridae, the spire relapses into a trailing position which is the only mechanically feasible posture for an attenuate spire with a small angle of retardation, or else, as in the sand-burrowing Olividae and Volutidae (Fig. 7G), the head-foot comes to exert a new influence on the symmetry of the visceropallium. The sides of the foot may embrace the shell in the form of parapodia, so securing conformity of the entire body to an outward bilaterality. The inhalant siphon carries a median "movable nostril" ahead of the point of advance, and the visceropallium is carried upon the narrow rectangular foot. The angle of retardation again increases, though approaching infinity only in the involute shell of some opisthobranchs.

A coiled turbinate shell sealed by an operculum is posturally unstable in disturbed water: hence many gastropods maintain a permanent contact with the substratum, the foot serving as an adhesive disc. An operculum is unnecessary, since the simple, wide-mouthed shell with reduced spire forms a protective cap fitting closely against the substratum. The limpet form is one of the commonest gastropod themes, having convergently appeared in many families of prosobranchs, opisthobranchs and pulmonates. The radial symmetry of the visceropallium is now given fuller expression with reduction in the extent and speed of forward movement. Full radial symmetry is never attained—although the Patellacea (Fig. 7D) come nearest with the foot an oval or rounded disc, cephalic eyes, and tentacles reduced and with tactile tentacles around the mantle margin. Initially there is a single, laterally disposed aspidobranch ctenidium (Acmaeidae). Pallial gills associated with the pallial blood vessel are then added (*Lottia*) (Fig. 6G) to become the sole means of respiration in the Patellidae (Fig. 6H), although both are lost in the deeper water Lepetidae. With the loss of the ctenidium in the last two families, most of the characteristics of the forward-facing mantle cavity disappear.

Permanent attachment is acquired in the Hipponicidae (Yonge, 1953b) by a fused calcareous plate secreted beneath the foot, or more frequently (as in the Vermetidae and Siliquariidae) by the embedding or cementing of the shell tube covering the loosely or irregularly coiled visceropallium (Morton, 1955a). Here the foot is withdrawn into the shell, with its metapodial surface (with or without an operculum) acting as a stopper. The sole is reduced, with its anteroposterior axis greatly reduced and the elongated visceropallium now dominant (Fig. 7E). The mantle cavity and contained ctenidium may be greatly enlarged for ciliary feeding.

An essentially opposite symmetry is found in the pelagic Heteropoda. In the shelled Atlantidae the axis of volution is again transverse and horizontal, with the compressed shell held upright to form a vertical cutwater keel. In the Carinariidae (Fig. 7F), the visceropallium is subordinated to a small appendage with a cap-like shell, held downward in swimming. The whole body is reorganized on anteroposterior lines with the foot reduced to a narrow vertical fin. We may regard the bilaterally symmetrical body with its trunk-like proboscis as an enlarged head and the tail as the backward extension of that part of the foot not involved in the fin. In Pterotracheidae the shell is lost and the visceropallium is entirely absorbed as a fusiform nucleus within the contours of the elongate body.

D. Opisthobranchia

Opisthobranch evolution has led to development of a smooth, slug-like body; the anteroposterior symmetry of the head-foot early takes full command (Fig. 7H,I). Few opisthobranchs can retreat fully into a spiral shell and even in these, e.g., *Actaeon* and *Ringicula*, a process of detorsion has begun, followed by reduction in size and prominence of the viscero-pallium, as shown diagrammatically in Fig. 8A. In *Akera* (Fig. 8B), the

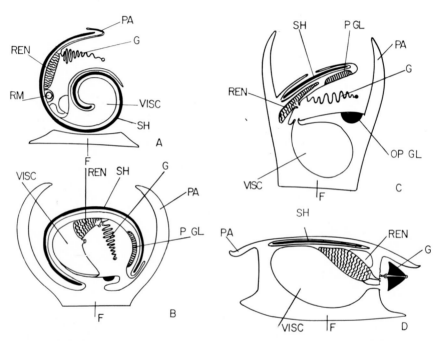

Fig. 8. Transverse sections through the pallial region and adjacent structures in four "tectibranch" opisthobranchs, showing the reduction and rearrangements of the pallial cavity and its contained organs. A. *Actaeon;* B. *Akera;* C. *Aplysia;* D. *Pleuro-branchus.* G, gill; *OP GL,* opaline gland; *PA,* pallial margin; *PGL,* pallial gland; *SH,* shell. Other lettering as before.

pallial aperture is already remote from the anterior end, moving back along the right side: the plicate secondary gill now lies behind the auricle. Respiratory currents are now created by the powerful ciliary tracts of a pallial cecum. The axis of volution runs anteroposteriorly; the normal axis is in the transverse plane. In almost all bullomorph opisthobranchs the shell is smooth and thin, the spire sunken or involute, becoming semi-internal by the overgrowth of thin extensions of the mantle skirt. The sides of the foot generally become prolonged upward in fleshy parapodia, eventually concealing the shell and mantle, and subordinating the visceropallial element to the increasing bilaterality manifested by the enlarging foot. Especially in *Philine* and *Scaphander* and other burrowers, the head enlarges to occupy more than half the total body length as a broad cephalic shield, displacing the visceropallium backward.

With the protective shell reduced and the function of chemoreception transferred to the rhinophoral grooves upon the head, the mantle cavity, no longer large enough for the retreat of the head-foot, loses its commanding role. Its anterior-facing position is lost in the continuing process of detorsion. This change is less rapid than was the original torsion: it is achieved by slower postlarval growth (T. E. Thompson, 1958, 1962), reversing the torsion still displayed in the opisthobranch veliger. The figure-of-eight disposition of the visceral loop becomes uncrossed and the parietal ganglia return to their original sides. But the right half of the pallial complex has already been lost and before it can retain its original posterior position, the cavity is itself abolished. *Aplysia* (Fig. 8C) shows a stage where the visceropallium plays no further part in external symmetry and the pallial cavity is a narrow triangular cleft, almost filled by the gill, and overarched by the vestigial shell plate concealed in the pallial integument and covered by the parapodia. In the slug-like pleurobranchoids (Notaspidea) (Fig. 8D) the secondary plicate gill on the right side briefly outlasts the vanished pallial cavity, with the renal, anal, and common genital openings situated nearby. As in *Aplysia*, a small osphradium persists together with the derivative of the hypobranchial gland in the purple gland or Blochmann's gland.

The "Nudibranchia" or true sea slugs become almost fully bilateral, the visceral mass having been resorbed within the flattened slug-like contour (Fig. 7I). In the Aeolidiacea and the Dendronotacea the anus remains on the right, but in the Doridacea it moves to a posterior site in the dorsal mid-line, surrounded by a circlet of pinnately branched, sometimes invaginable gills. Their homology with the plicate pleurobranchoid gill remains uncertain. The renal and genital openings remain on the right side, relics of a past external asymmetry. Among the first doridomorphs, the mantle remains as a tough, protective dorsal notum projecting skirt-like at the sides and, though naked, often incorporating calcareous or siliceous spicules. It no longer lodges a shell although in *Bathydoris*, among early dorids, a shallow subintegumentary cavity persists as if recently vacated by a shell plate. The whole body, released from its shell cover, is more mobile and plastic, and the notum shows a lavish development of color and delicate excrescences. Many of its processes are sensitively tactile; in Dendronotacea with no circumanal gills they may be respiratory, drawn out into long dendritic appendages or expanded leaf-like structures. In the Polyceratidae, among higher dorids, the skirt of the notum has retreated, to be replaced by slender horn-like tentacles. The notal coloring of opisthobranchs may either form a protective camouflage or be brilliantly aposematic (warning coloration) when the epithelium develops acid-secreting repugnatorial glands apparently widespread among naked gastropods. Among several groups, e.g., Aeolidiacea, Dotonidae, and the higher Sacoglossa, external expression of the visceral mass is reasserted in special club-like appendages or *cerata* containing outgrowths of the digestive gland. In the aeolids these are terminally perforate and contain a cnidus sac containing nematocysts from coelenterate prey. In Sacoglossa they are contractile and respiratory, and coloring from the algal pigments is visible through their walls to give a protective resemblance to the food plant.

This changing organization of the opisthobranch body forms a recurrent theme taking its separate course through the eight orders of the subclass. There is no natural division into "Tectibranchia" and "Nudibranchia": the tectibranch form is shared by early members in several independent lines, and the nudibranch condition, including final development of cerata, can be attained by different groups with different histories. With some oversimplification we may permissibly depict five stages in the evolutionary "program" of the Opisthobranchia:

1. With animal still displaying torsion and with visceral connectives still crossed (chiastoneury), with spacious pallial cavity and gill, and fully spiral shell; sometimes with an operculum.

2. With parapodia enlarging and mantle beginning to enclose the fragile shell with reduced or involute spire; pallial cavity reduced and to the right, the spiral visceropallium already dominated by the bilateral head-foot.

3. With complete enclosure of visceral mass and vestigial shell plate within a slug-like contour, mantle cavity still a small recess on the right, or the mantle skirt projecting over fully exposed gill.

4. With a shell-less, externally symmetrical form; mantle cavity lost and with sensory, respiratory, and protective functions devolving upon the naked upper surface.

5. With external prominence of the visceral mass reasserted by the extension of the digestive gland into club-like cerata.

Imposed upon this main plan and cropping up adventitiously through each opisthobranch line we find the habit of temporary or permanent swimming, either by parapodia or by the action of the whole body; in pelagic pteropods, swimming and equilibrating adaptations take command of the whole structural plan. Swimming is dealt with in detail in Chapter 12.

E. *Pulmonata*

The large subclass of Pulmonata, whether living on land or as any of the numerous genera which have returned to fresh water or colonized the shore, is a structurally more conservative group. Evolutionary advances have consisted primarily of physiological innovations necessary to overcome problems of terrestrial life, especially desiccation. Many of their adaptations concern habit; there is much less reform of body structure than in opisthobranchs. [Comparisons of the primitive features of Prosobranchia, Pulmonata, and Opisthobranchia are made by Morton (1955b,c).] Nearly every pulmonate shows traces of torsion (passed through in abbreviated form during embryonic growth) in the anterior and forward-facing pallial cavity.

This cavity is fully closed, except at the rhythmically opening aperture of the *pneumostome* at the right side, by a thin septum running between the mantle skirt and the wall of the body. The relations of the pallial cavity are comparable with those of prosobranchs without a ctenidium or hypobranchial gland. Even in many which have returned to aquatic life a vascular anastomosis of the roof provides a lung for atmospheric respiration. Some aquatic pulmonates may fill this lung secondarily with water, as in the Siphonariidae with their pallial gills, and in some more thoroughly aquatic Lymnaeidae. Aquatic respiration is generally effected by the development of elaborately folded, neomorphic, extrapallial branchiae as in Physidae and Planorbidae. In the Ancylidae of faster running waters and in the Otinidae, living upon wave-exposed shores, the diminished pallial cavity is functionally insignificant. The osphradium is important in those aquatic Basommatophora where it has migrated outside the mantle cavity. With the closure of this cavity the anus and the renal duct (tubular and forward-prolonged) open externally near the pneumostome. The common genital duct originally opened close to these, but now usually lies on the right side of the head, with the glandular (pallial-derived) genital ducts sinking in to become hemocoelic and losing their connection with the body wall.

Torsion is not reversed in pulmonates, although much of the evidence for it, especially in the disposition of the visceral nerve loop, is suppressed by the shortening of the commissures and the drawing-up of the ganglia within the concentrated nerve ring.

The shells of land snails vary in form from the turbinate (helicid) to discoidal (zonitid) or elongate (pupid or clausiliid) shapes. Usually they have a well-marked relation to resting posture and mode of progression. Anteroposterior bilateral symmetry is regained in the pulmonate groups that have adopted the slug form. The pallium becomes reduced to a small shield or saddle-like anterodorsal area, applied to the elongated muscular body, and perforated on the right side by the pneumostome. The shell may be a vestigial cap or plate with a reduced spiral, or more often be enclosed in the pallial tissues in the form of a horny plate or discrete granules of calcium carbonate. The viscera that formed the shelled bulge of the visceropallium are transferred to lie within the muscular walls of the elongated bilateral body derived from the head-foot.

The limpet form has been adopted by many aquatic pulmonates with the same partial approach to radial symmetry shown by archaeogastropod and mesogastropod limpets. Siphonariidae, Gadiniidae, and Otinidae are marine limpets; freshwater limpets comprise the Ancylidae, Latiidae, and even *Lanx* and *Patelloplanorbis*, specialized members of the Lymnaeidae and Planorbidae.

III. AMPHINEURA AND MONOPLACOPHORA

A. *Amphineura: Polyplacophora*

The primitive nervous system alone stamps the Amphineura and Mono-placophora as the most archaic existing molluscs but they have such ad-mixture of specialized features that their consideration has been post-poned till after that of the early gastropods. The Amphineura are most familiarly represented by the chitons (Fig. 9) which retain bilateral sym-metry and anteroposterior orientation, being flat and limpet-like with the body closely applied to the substratum. Intimate marginal contact is main-

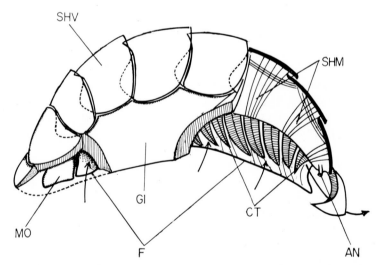

Fɪɢ. 9. Amphineura. Diagram of the essential structural features of a chiton (cf. Fig. 1). *AN*, anus; *GI*, girdle; *SHM*, shell muscles; *SHV*, shell valves. Other letter-ing as before.

tained by a flexible, scaly, or thick, fleshy, encircling girdle (*Gl*). The shell is divided into eight arched transverse plates (*SHV*) articulated so as to permit attachment to irregular substrata and allow the animal to roll up protectively when detached. With this habit comes reduction of the cephalic sense organs and extension of the originally posterior mantle cavity into shallow grooves along either side between foot and girdle. The head and mouth lie in front of the flat sole, and the anus behind it. An inhalant pallial opening can be created at any point on either side by the local lifting of the girdle; the exhalant current passes out behind with the feces and the renal and reproductive products (Fig. 10A). The gills (Fig. 10A–C) are a series of ctenidia multiplied along either side—17 in number in the common British *Lepidochitona cinereus*—all save the last curving inward (Fig. 10C) toward the side of the foot. There are fewer pairs (about 7) in the more primitive Lepidopleuridae. Each gill is homologous with a separate gastropod ctenidium; they interlock by cilia along either side (Fig. 10B) to form a functionally continuous curtain (Yonge, 1939). The filaments are greatly shortened, but have a compensating wide zone of lateral cilia. As indicated by the arrows in Fig. 10E, the pallial inhalant chamber lies outside the ctenidial curtain, the exhalant chamber within, bounded by the sides of the foot. The two renal pores lie immediately in front of the last gills, these postrenal gills making contact with the girdle fold to close the pallial groove behind. Sexes are separate and the gametes are released from a pair of reproductive pores (*Go*) between the second and third gills from behind.

Chitons have pallial mucous glands, a glandular tract on the outer side of the roof of the exhalant chamber being the probable homolog of the hypobranchial gland. Most Chitonidae possess simple osphradia, situated on the roof of the pallial groove in a strip running from the anus to the postrenal gill, and lying immediately over the pallial nerve cord. They are thus sited as in bivalves in the exhalant and not—as in gastropods—in the inhalant chamber. Anterior olfactory organs in *Lepidochitona* take the form of longitudinal strips of sensory epithelium along the roof of the pallial grooves in front of the gill series. These are pedally innervated and possibly perform additional osphradial functions.

The redeployment of the external sense organs is a specialized feature of the chitons. The head bears neither eyes nor tentacles, merely a set of gustatory organs in the buccal cavity. Pallial chemoreception is subserved by the special pallial sense organs. Densely penetrating the shell valves in many genera, especially toward the anterior end, is a series of light-sensitive and tactile organs, the micraesthetes and megalaesthetes (Fig. 10E, *AE*), the latter equipped with elementary retina, lens, and cornea. Such receptors are sensitive to stimuli of light, pressure, and gentler tactile

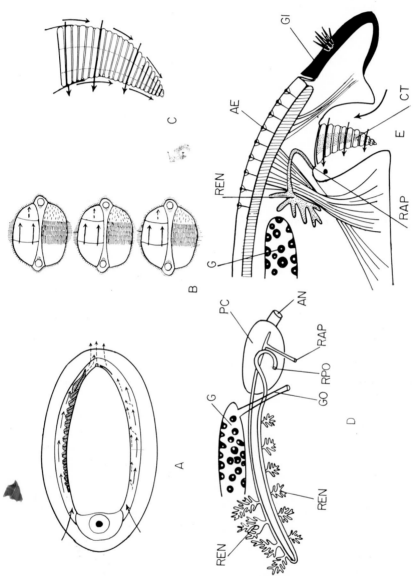

Fɪɢ. 10. A. Ventral surface of *Lepidochitona cinereus*, showing the disposition and currents of the ctenidia. B. Three adjacent ctenidia of a chiton shown in diagrammatic section to illustrate the structure, ciliation, and currents of the filaments. C. A single ctenidium with its currents, viewed posteriorly. D. The renopericardial organs of a chiton represented schematically. E. Schematic transverse section of the right half of the mantle cavity and associated structures in a chiton. *AE*, shell aesthetes; *GO*, gonoduct; *RAP*, renal aperture. Other lettering as before.

contact, and provide a sensory basis for the well-developed behavioral responses of light avoidance and thigmotaxis.

The genitopericardial organs (Fig. 10D) in the chitons are symmetrically paired, though departing somewhat from the primitive state, the gonads now possessing separate external openings. The two symmetrical renal organs are essentially double-bent tubes, with their two openings posterior, a proximal renopericardial communication (*RPO*) and a distal renal pore (*RAP*). Both limbs of the tube are elaborated at intervals by clusters of arborescent side branches (*REN*) that ramify extensively among the viscera.

B. *Amphineura: Aplacophora*

This division of the Amphineura, very distinct embryologically (Thompson, 1960), contains two small groups of shell-less, worm-like animals living in shallow offshore or deep oozy bottoms. The Neomeniomorpha crawl and feed upon the tissues of corals, alcyonarians, and hydroids; the Chaetodermomorpha are said to take Protozoa and other deposit-inhabiting microbenthos. In both groups the body is completely hidden by the mantle containing numerous calcified spicules embedded in a thick cuticle. The Neomeniomorpha retain a longitudinal ventral groove, which—with the longitudinal ridge running along it—represents the last remains of the foot. A large anteroventral mucous gland discharges its secretion into the anterior part of this furrow. The mantle cavity is represented only by the deep posterior depression, into which open the anus and the renal apertures. This cloacal space contains a circlet of epithelial folds of greater or less complexity through which the blood circulates for respiratory interchange. Circulation is very simple; there are no true blood vessels but a ventral sinus between the foot and the gut and a tubular dorsal sinus forming at its posterior end a contractile heart. The pericardial complex keeps its archaic molluscan condition. A pair of renal organs or coelomoducts open from the dorsal pericardium, below the anus, by a common median aperture. As in Polyplacophora, the renal organs are directed forward and then sharply reflected back as double tubes, but are simple without branching tufts. A pair of hermaphrodite tubular gonads open separately into the pericardium and the gametes pass through the renal ducts which are also gonoducts. These are very glandular, especially in their conjoined terminal part where they secrete material for an egg shell. They also bear cecal outgrowths on their proximal parts functioning as vesiculae seminales.

In the Chaetodermomorpha there is no longitudinal pedal groove. The posterior mantle cavity or "cloaca" is bell-shaped and contractile, being equipped with a pair of bipectinate gills which certainly resemble ctenidia. The sexes are separate and there is a single dorsal gonad communicating by a median aperture with the pericardium. The gametes are conveyed to the exterior by the renal tubes.

The nervous system in Aplacophora corresponds in general to that of the chitons, revealing the very archaic condition hidden in part by the specialized features of these molluscs. There are two pairs of longitudinal cords, the pallial and the pedal, proceeding backward from a simply organized nerve ring, and communicating by pedal and pedopallial cross connections.

C. Monoplacophora

The discovery by the Danish Galathea Expedition in 1952, in a depth of 3570 meters off the Pacific coast of Costa Rica, of *Neopilina galatheae* (Fig. 11A–C), a living representative of the Monoplacophora hitherto regarded as extinct, has renewed interest in the origins of the Mollusca. The morphology of this form, beautifully worked out by Lemche and Wingstrand (1959), displays many archaic features, bearing closest comparison with conditions in the chitons. The shell is a depressed limpet-like cap, subcircular, and 35 mm long; its apex may bear a spirally coiled embryonic shell (Fig. 11A, inset) revealing the tendency to visceral spirality so persistent in many molluscan groups, and so seldom found elsewhere. There is no trace of torsion; the animal is bilaterally symmetrical with the mouth in front of and the anus behind the flattened, rather thinly muscular disc of the foot. Of the internal anatomy several features are highly archaic: the nervous system (Fig. 11C), with its ladder-like ventral arrangement and weakly developed cerebral ganglia, is clearly amphineuran. The gut has a long, coiled radular sac, a simple stomach with a crystalline-style sac, and a much coiled intestine, characters typical of an unspecialized herbivore or deposit feeder. The radula, especially in its comb-like fourth lateral teeth, has strong chitonid resemblances. The coelomic spaces are rather more extensive than in any later molluscs except cephalopods. They apparently comprise paired dorsal pericardial sacs posteriorly and a dorsal body coelom, also paired in origin, lying more anteriorly, without apparent pericardial communication. The dorsal coelom, although sterile in *Neopilina*, corresponds to the gonadial sacs in chitons; the gonads consist of paired ventral coelomic sacs unrepresented in chitons. Wide perivisceral hemocoelic spaces exist more ventrally.

The head of *Neopilina* bears structures absent in chitons. The preoral cephalic tentacles (T) are small papillae, while at the sides of the mouth lie lateral flaps (VE), homologized by Lemche and Wingstrand with the velum of molluscan larvae and the outer labial palps of bivalves. Behind the mouth lie a pair of much branched postoral tentacular tufts (PT), possibly associated with feeding, although their action in life is still un-

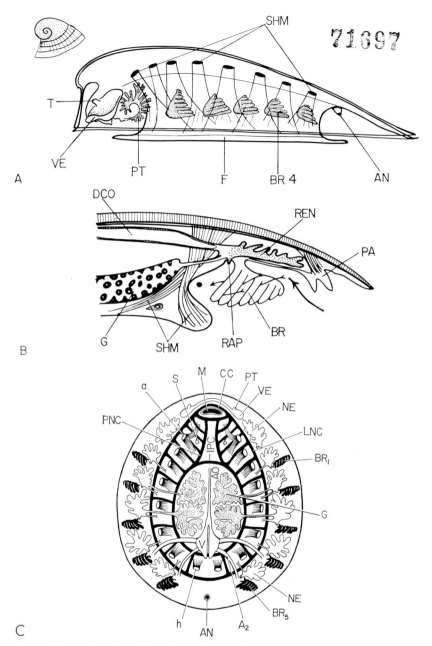

Fig. 11. Monoplacophora. *Neopilina galatheae*, figures adapted from those of Lemche and Wingstrand (1959). A. Schematic lateral view. (Inset) Spirally coiled embryonic shell. B. Schematic transverse section of the right half of the pallial cavity. C. Diagrammatic view of the whole animal. *a–h*, foot retractor muscles (shell muscles); A_2, second auricle of heart; *AO*, aorta; *BR*, branchiae; *CC*, cerebral commissure; *DCO*, dorsal coelom; *IPC*, interpedal commissure; *LNC*, lateral nerve cord; *NE*, "nephridia"; *PNC*, pedal nerve cord; *PT*, postoral tentacle; *S*, statocysts; *SHM*, shell muscles; *T*, preoral tentacle; *VE*, velum. Other lettering as before.

known. They have been equated with scaphopod captacula and cephalopod head tentacles, although such suggestions can only be provisional.

The palliopericardial complex provides strikingly interesting features,
on the basis of which a general segmental metamerism has been attributed
to *Neopilina* and, by extrapolation, to early molluscs as a whole. First, the
shallow lateral grooves of the mantle cavity contain no fewer than 5 pairs
of gills (*BR*), each a central axis with alternating unequal rows of
lamellae. In their microanatomy and histology these gills are very unlike
the model of a primitive molluscan ctenidium—one from which those of
the Gastropoda, Polyplacophora, Bivalvia, and Cephalopoda can all most
certainly be derived. Nevertheless Lemche and Wingstrand endeavor to
find a general resemblance between them and chitonid ctenidia. But their
drawing of the latter, shown as separated from one another and bending
back instead of inward, is incorrect and reveals failure to realize that
these ctenidia work as a unit which the widely separated gills of *Neopilina* could not do. Although on the basis of topography and especially
of vascular relations it is difficult to deny some structural homology, yet
the differences in fine anatomy and mode of action make it very difficult
to regard these structures as anything more than derivatives from
prectenidial structures. The pericardium contains a median ventricle with
2 pairs of auricles (Fig. 11C, A_2). The coelomoducts or renal organs lie
in 6 pairs, each much branched and lobulated. Gametes are discharged by
the 2 pairs of gonads (*G*) through the third and fourth coelomoducts,
which are found densely filled with eggs or sperm.

Further paired repetition is shown by the 8 pairs of shell muscles
(Fig. 11C, *a–h*) inserted in an oval zone on the interior of the shell and
striking down into the foot. Judging from the shell scars in many extinct
Monoplacophora, not visibly represented in *Neopilina*, the number of
paired shell muscles differed rather widely from group to group.

These features may be interpreted in two ways: as primitive metameric
characters betraying a segmental origin of the molluscs, perhaps near the
annelids, with which they share a trochophore larva, or as multiplications
of a kind found in various archaic molluscs (see Amphineura and *Nautilus*). These express an early tendency toward repetition to varying extents of special organs in no way necessarily of the essence of the primitive mollusc. In chitons, for example, shell valves, shell muscles, and
ctenidia are each multiplied, though in different numbers; but no metameric interpretation had ever been advanced on the support of chitonid
evidence alone. Similarly the palliopericardial organs of *Nautilus* increase
to 2 pairs, a matter—it has been thought—of functional rather than
historic significance (Yonge, 1947).

Although chitonid renal organs are never multiplied it is impossible
not to be struck by the lobulated appearance of the paired, forward,

elongated coelomoducts of a chiton, and by the possible derivation of the neopilinid condition by acquisition of separate openings of discrete groups of renal lobules (see Fig. 2B).

If *Neopilina* is indeed to be credited with metamerism, it is a metamerism totally unrepresented ectodermally, unmarked by an external intersegmental furrowing of the body wall, and with only slight involvement of the nervous system. Moreover, it is a very irregular metamerism as between different organ systems, and one in which it would be difficult to recognize—as with metameric Annulata and Chordata—the basic constitution of any typical segment. Embryology must be the next step in the elucidation of these and other aspects of *Neopilina;* but whatever results this brings, Lemche's discovery will remain one of surpassing interest. To place it in any commanding position as a general basal mollusc is certainly premature, especially if we are to take from it, as urged by Lemche and Wingstrand, any implications of general segmental origins for the Mollusca. If it does represent initial molluscan structure then this must have undergone great *secondary simplification* before giving rise to the remaining molluscan classes. Undoubtedly a, possibly *the,* major reason for the success of the phylum resides in a fundamental simplicity of structure which, the discovery of *Neopilina* reveals, may well have been secondary.

To what extent, however, may our idea of the basically primitive mollusc maintained in this chapter need revision in the light of *Neopilina?* First, many of its attributes, such as the structure of the gut and the nervous system, the archaically wider extent of the coelom, the gonopericardial interrelationships, and the general form of the body have been admirably upheld. So far *Neopilina* runs true to morphologic expectation. A posteriorly placed pallial cavity with two ctenidia, receiving water laterally and expelling it in the mid-line, has been in the past a cardinal criterion of the early mollusc: certainly it represents a condition from which that in all other existing molluscs can be derived. Ctenidial multiplication in the chitons might appear to indicate direct relationship to conditions in *Neopilina* (as Lemche and Wingstrand think) but the weight of evidence, in our opinion, is against this. Earlier ideas about the initial fixity to one pair of the number of gills and other pallioperi-cardial structure may need revision as far as the earliest Mollusca are concerned, but *Neopilina* (and other possibly undiscovered living mono-placophorans) may represent the only descendants of these earliest molluscs, later ones having sprung from secondarily simplified ancestors.

A leading structural element in the first Metazoa that could be considered molluscs must have been the dorsal palliovisceral eminence tending toward a radial symmetry in defiance of the anteroposteriality of a worm-like body, henceforward surviving only in the head-foot. A calcified one-piece shell, an increasing visceral hump and a spacious mantle cavity, and a molluscan pedal locomotor wave are innovations difficult to imagine in any worm-like animal visibly metameric; and with the first appearance of the elongated, segmented, and parapodiate facies, annelid evolution must have already been switched in a direction irrevocably nonmolluscan.

IV. SCAPHOPODA

The Scaphopoda or elephant's tusk shells (Fig. 12) are the smallest molluscan class, of very uniform though specialized habits and somewhat simplified structure. Extreme elongation has taken place in the dorso-ventral axis, the visceropallium being a slightly curved narrowly tapering cone, circular in transverse section. The mantle skirt (*PA*) closes to form a sphincter-like aperture, through which the structures of the head-foot can be withdrawn or freely protruded. Pallial water currents, in-halant created by cilia and exhalant by muscular contraction, pass through a foramen opening at the narrow extremity of the shell, the pallial space extending freely along the curved (posterior) side from one end of the shell to the other. There is no gill: respiratory interchange largely pro-ceeds through transverse ciliated folds lining portions of the mantle wall (*RESP*). There is neither heart nor well-differentiated blood vessels; the rhythmic protrusion and retraction of the foot apparently serving to circulate hemocoelic blood. The unpaired, distally placed gonad (*G*) opens by its duct through the right renal organ (*REN*). The renal organs are paired and symmetrical, with no renopericardial duct.

The head has become raised from the substratum and withdrawn within the shell as in the Bivalvia, but particles of food consisting mostly of small, testaceous Foraminifera are conveyed to the mouth by means of numerous finely produced retractile filaments known as *captacula* (*CAP*), originating in clusters at the base of the head and freely extend-ing in the surrounding substratum. They are expanded terminally into spoon-like enlargements, each bearing a shallow depression perhaps form-ing a prehensile disc (Morton, 1959). The foot (*F*) is an elongate, tapered muscular column, employed in burrowing essentially in the man-ner of a bivalve (see Chapter 12). Its principal retractor muscles (*SHM*) are the paired longitudinal muscle bands running far backward to be inserted on the distal wall of the shell tube.

V. BIVALVIA

A. Early History

The distinctive feature of the Bivalvia is the subdivision of the shell which consists of *two valves* calcified from lateral centers with, mid-

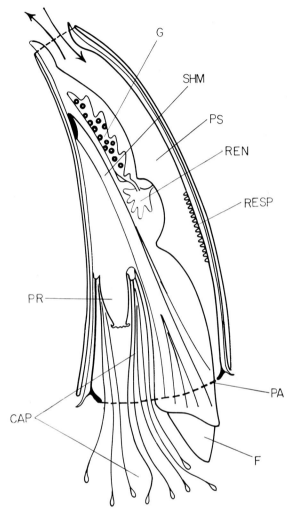

Fig. 12. Scaphopoda. Diagram of the essential features of *Dentalium* (cf. Fig. 1). *CAP*, captacula; *PS*, pallial space; *RESP*, ciliated, respiratory area; *PR*, proboscis. Other lettering as before.

dorsally, a connecting *ligament* of uncalcified conchiolin. The mantle, which secretes all regions of the shell, envelops the whole body. In the forerunners of the bivalves the body must have been limpet-like with the mantle and *uncalcified* shell exerting full dominance over the head-foot. Bivalves are sedentary ciliary feeders with ciliary and mucous systems predominant. The muscle attachments of shell and mantle are shown in Fig. 13. The shell muscles, probably originally numerous and regularly spaced, pass into the foot. The mantle is connected with the shell submarginally by *pallial muscles* (*PM*) not present in gastropods. Marginally the mantle carries three folds (Fig. 18A, *O,M,I*), an outer or secretory fold, a middle and usually sensory fold, and an inner, muscular fold (known as the velum or pallial curtain in *Pecten, Ostrea*, and

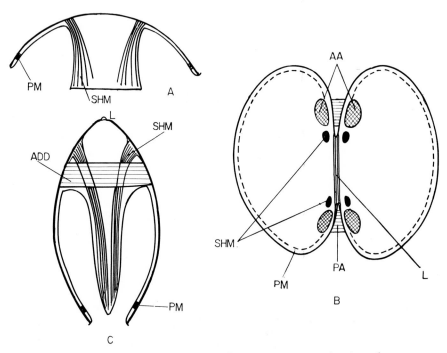

Fig. 13. Evolution of the Bivalvia. A. Before lateral compression but after appearance of the pallial muscles. B. After compression, shell (valves and ligament) viewed from above showing cross fusion of pallial muscles at either end of mid-dorsal ligament forming adductors (*AA, PA*). C. After compression, diagrammatic transverse section cutting through an adductor (*ADD*) but also ligament (*L*). *PM*, pallial muscle. (After Yonge, 1953a.) Other lettering as before.

other genera where it is highly developed). The inner surface of the outer fold secretes the outermost layer of the shell, the noncalcareous periostracum which originates in a groove at its base and initially covers the entire surface of the shell; the outer surface of this fold secretes the outer calcareous, or ligament, layer. The inner calcareous layer of the valves is secreted by the general surface of the mantle, the inner ligament layer by the mid-dorsal mantle isthmus. Fusion of the mantle margins, which has a profound effect on evolution of form and habit within the Bivalvia, proceeds, both in ontogeny and phylogeny, by union first of the inner, then of the middle folds, and finally of the inner surfaces of the outer folds (see Fig. 18A). Attachment is initially by cilia then by cuticular fusion followed by tissue union.

The derivation of the bivalve requires lateral compression of the body (visceral mass and foot) between the two lobes of what may be termed the mantle/shell. This involves an inward pushing or embayment of the mantle tent anteriorly and posteriorly which is restricted mid-dorsally to the narrow and progressively shortening mantle isthmus. The isthmus secretes the inner layer of the ligament (Fig. 13, L) already noted as being formed in the same manner as the inner surface of the rest of the shell. The primary ligament of inner and outer layers may be secondarily extended by a fusion layer formed by union of the outer surface of the outer mantle folds within the embayments (Fig. 18C).

With compression and embayment of the mantle/shell, the standard arrangement of bivalve muscles comes about. The shell muscles (SHM), ultimately restricted to anterior and posterior pairs although initially more numerous, become the pedal protractors and retractors. They correspond to the columellar muscles of Gastropoda. The anterior and posterior adductors (Fig. 13B, AA, PA) are peculiar to the Bivalvia, arising by local cross fusion and hypertrophy of the pallial muscles where these come in contact in the mantle embayments. Their contraction closes the shell and isolates the animal from the external environment. The two may be the same size (isomyarian) or the anterior one may be reduced (heteromyarian) or lost (monomyarian). They come into being *pari passu* with the elastic ligament, the effect of which they antagonize by their resistance to tension in the more external, and to compression in the more internal, ligament layers.

The mantle margin now provides the principal sensory contacts with the environment, assuming some of the attributes of the head largely lacking in bivalves, although vestiges of cephalic eyes sometimes persist. The middle and primarily sensory fold of the mantle margin is often produced into tactile, even eye-bearing, tentacles, especially around the inhalant region. The inner muscular fold controls the flow of water into and out of the mantle cavity; this is a matter of major importance owing to the great size of the ctenidia and so of the water current produced primarily for feeding.

B. Nuculoid Protobranchia

This introduction brings us to what represents, on balance, the most primitive living bivalve, the protobranch *Nucula* (Fig. 14). The shell possesses a somewhat specialized ligament and has numerous interlocking hinge teeth (i.e., taxodont dentition which is probably primitive) that stabilize the valves against fore-and-aft displacement upon each other.

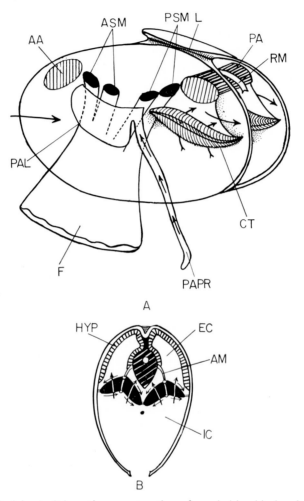

Fig. 14. Bivalvia. A. Schematic reconstruction of a primitive bivalve, largely based on structure of a nuculoid protobranch (cf. Fig. 1). B. Transverse section of *Nucula* through region of the ctenidia. *AA*, anterior adductor; *ASM*, anterior shell muscles; *EC, IC*, exhalant and inhalant chambers; *L*, ligament; *PA*, posterior adductor; *PAL*, palp lamella; *PAPR*, palp proboscis; *PSM*, posterior shell muscles. Other lettering as before.

The adductors are equal (isomyarian) and there are *two* pairs each of retractor and protractor pedal muscles, i.e., four pairs of shell muscles (Fig. 14A, *ASM, PSM*). The mantle cavity is more spacious than in any gastropod but the paired ctenidia retain their primitive posterior molluscan position. The filaments, much less numerous than in higher bivalves and not reflected, are horizontally disposed (see Fig. 14B). With the exception of the presence of laterofrontal "straining" cilia and of ciliary connections between filaments and between filaments and mantle, the ctenidia resemble those of the primitive zygobranch Gastropoda. The mesial filaments of either gill interlock loosely by cilia at their tips and the lateral filaments similarly connect with the mantle wall, separating an exhalant chamber above from an inhalant chamber below (Fig. 14B, *EC*, *IC*). In the exhalant chamber lie large hypobranchial glands (*HYP*), associated with continued passage of particles between the ctenidial filaments. A simple osphradial patch lies at the base of each gill, within the exhalant chamber. The palliopericardial organs are still referable to the primitive molluscan organization, being paired throughout. Each renal organ is a simple cylindrical sac, folded on itself and in *Nucula* entirely glandular, opening by a renal pore into the exhalant chamber. The two limbs are in secondary communication near the renal pore where the renopericardial duct opens. Genital products in each sex are passed direct into the renal tube near the renopericardial duct. The later bivalves acquire short separate gonadial ducts (see Fig. 15B). As in all bivalves, fertilization is external, although in a few later forms this occurs within the mantle cavity of the female, followed by pallial incubation of the enlarged eggs.

The inhalant current is drawn in *anteriorly* (Fig. 14A), primitive bivalve character, the lateral cilia driving the currents upward between the gill filaments into the dorsal exhalant chamber. Although enlarged, the ctenidia of *Nucula* remain primarily respiratory but the originally purely cleansing frontal and abfrontal cilia do now pass some material toward the *palp lamellae* (Fig. 14A, *PAL*). These, with their appendages (*PAPR*), represent a new set of organs. The enclosure of the head by the mantle/shell in the Bivalvia involves the loss of its feeding (as well as of its sensory) functions, which are taken over by extensions of the lips in early cooperation with the enlarged ctenidia.

The palps in *Nucula* consist of a pair of large triangular folds extending back from either side of the mouth. They are richly ciliated and both in the Nuculidae and Nuculanidae (but not in the remaining protobranch family Solemyidae nor in any later bivalves) the outer palp lamellae are prolonged into *palp proboscides* (*PAPR*), with an intervening palp pouch. Each proboscis gropes in the substratum into which the animals superficially burrow and organic debris is passed along a ciliated groove on the inner surface and so comes between the lamellae (*PAL*). Their inner faces bear a series of ridges and folds with a complex series of ciliary tracts, the whole effectively forming a sorting and rejection system of crucial importance in all bivalves. The activity of the proboscides or of some labial appendage (such as apparently occurs in *Neopilina*) appears as a necessary accompaniment of the raising of the mouth from the substratum with eventual loss of the radula (not in *Neopilina*)

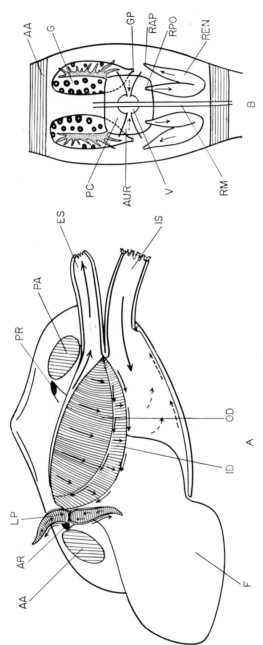

Fig. 15. A. Main anatomical features, with ciliary currents, of a representative eulamellibranch bivalve, *Amphidesma*, viewed from left side. B. Diagram showing arrangement of the pericardial complex in a typical eulamellibranch. *AR*, anterior pedal retractor (shell muscle); *ES*, exhalant siphon; *ID*, inner demibranch; *IS*, inhalant siphon; *LP*, labial palp; *OD*, outer demibranch; *PR*, posterior pedal retractor. Other lettering as before.

and also the initially small ctenidia. The function of food collection is soon passed on to the ctenidia (even in the protobranch *Solemya*) which extend forward almost to the mouth. Their filaments elongate and (apart from *Solemya*) are variously reflected and united, first by cilia and then by tissue, with oralward currents usually along the axis and in marginal grooves. With much specialization of cilia and of ciliary currents there is finally formed the compact lamella of the higher bivalves. Muscle plays an important part with cilia and mucus in ctenidial activity, which involves much sorting of material, largely on the basis of size. The process is completed by the palps which retain this function, although varying greatly in size in accordance with the need for their services.

In relation to the environment the dominant organ of the original head-foot is the muscular and extensile foot which in *Nucula* is somewhat compressed but opens out laterally, the better to grip the soft substratum, when fully extended. The foot is responsible for the vigorous forward movement of many bivalves (see Chapter 12). At its posterior end the foot may house a byssiferous gland [possibly always present in post-larval life for attachment during metamorphosis (Yonge, 1962b)] secreting thin or stronger protein threads for temporary or permanent attachment. In the Mytilidae, and particularly in the permanently attached Anomiidae, the pedal retractors are specialized as byssal retractors (in the latter effectively as adductors). But the majority of bivalves move about freely and burrow or bore with great efficiency. The Bivalvia have become the most widely radiating and most successful of the ciliary-feeding invertebrates. They have not suffered the loss of mobility which has been the fate of many groups of ciliary feeders. They have compensated for the loss of the head even when this has been followed by loss of bilateral symmetry, as in the scallops (see Section V,C).

C. Form and Symmetry

The external form of a bivalve is the product of the mantle/shell, each valve growing by marginal increment, the body retaining the antero-posterior growth axis. It follows that while different shells may be compared by suitable distortion of radial coordinates, the contained bodies are comparable only by the use of rectangular coordinates.[1] Owen (1953a) has analyzed the components in the growth of the mantle/shell. There is a (1) *radial* component radiating out from the umbones, (2) a *transverse* component at right angles to this, and (3) a *tangential* component, not always present and most fully expressed in the Chamacea and in *Glossus* acting in the plane of the generating curve and directed anteriorly. Where bilateral asymmetry occurs this is associated with the *transverse* component (one valve may be flat, the other internally very concave),

[1] See note on p. 58.

occasionally (as in the Anomiidae) the *radial* component, but never the *tangential* component (see also Chapter 7).

With the loss of the head, the most convenient *anteroposterior axis* (Fig. 16A, *a*) in a bivalve is represented by a line running from the mouth through the middle of the posterior adductor (near the anus). The dorsoventral *median axis* (*m*) of primitive molluscs and of gastropods persists as a line running from the mid-dorsal point to the ventral mid-point of the foot. For the mantle/shell two *lines* may be recognized, the *hinge line* (*h*) (the axis of motion of the valves, primitively parallel to the anteroposterior axis and at right angles to the median axis), and the *demarcation line* (*d*). The latter represents the projection onto the sagittal plane of a line starting at the umbo and following the region of greatest inflation of the valve (due to the transverse component) and separating *anterior* and *posterior territories* (Yonge, 1955). These by no means inevitably agree with the anterior and posterior portions (not necessarily "halves") of the enclosed body. They do so in the simple case of *Glycymeris* (Fig. 16A) where the zone of greatest marginal increment coincides with the point where the demarcation line meets the shell margin. Where there is a tangential component, the demarcation line is curved to a greater or lesser extent anteriorly (i.e., the spiral of growth becomes helicoidal instead of being in the one plane).

Changes in the shape of bivalves are due to changes in the growth gradients around the generating curve of the mantle margin. In this way an equilateral shell such as *Glycymeris* may be changed into an elongated "razor shell" such as *Ensis* where the *posterior territory* (where growth gradients are great) is many times larger than the *anterior territory* (they are separated by line *d* in Fig. 16C). The proportions of the enclosed body remain unaltered; their *disposition* changes and this, together with the altered external form, makes possible change in habit and so in habitat. Thus, the Solenacea become capable of rapid vertical movement in unstable substrata. Such alterations in the growth gradients of the mantle/shell have been a major cause of evolutionary change within the Bivalvia.

Where the body is more or less permanently fixed (thinking in terms of phylogeny) by a massive byssus then its proportions may alter and always by an increase in the posterior at the expense of the anterior portion. This necessarily involves the form of the mantle/shell leading from the initial isomyarian to a heteromyarian (e.g., *Mytilus*, Fig. 16B) and finally to a monomyarian condition (*Pinctada*, *Pecten*, Fig. 16,D,E). Wherever heteromyarianism occurs, e.g., Mytilacea, Pinnidae, Dreissenacea, *Sphenia* (Myacea), *Entodesma* (Pandoracea), etc., it can be directly associated with byssal attachment. The major advantage is increase in the inhalant opening which is raised higher above the attaching surface.

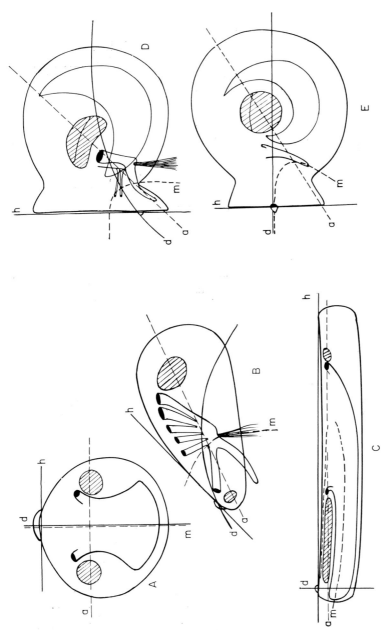

FIG. 16. Relation between body and mantle/shell in the Bivalvia as indicated by the anteroposterior (a) and median (m) axes of body and the hinge (b) and demarcation (d) lines of the mantle/shell. A. Glycymeris (isomyarian). B. Mytilus (heteromyarian). C. Ensis (elongated posteriorly). D. Pinctada (monomyarian, byssal attached). E. Pectinidae (monomyarian, cemented or free).

Monomyarianism has arisen in relation to byssal attachment in the Pteriacea, Pectinacea, Anomiacea, and Ostreacea (all Anisomyaria) and in the Tridacnidae (Cardiacea). Apart from the Limidae (Pectinacea) and the Tridacnidae it is associated with change from a vertical to a horizontal disposition. This involves much bilateral asymmetry with reorganization of both body and mantle/shell around the enlarged posterior adductor, the visceral ganglia becoming the major nerve centers. There are contrary tendencies toward (1) more permanent fixation either by means of the byssus emerging through a major embayment on the under (right) valve in the Anomiacea or by cementation (i.e., attachment by way of the mantle/shell) either by the right (e.g., *Spondylus*) or left (Ostreacea) valve; or (2) complete freedom as in the majority of scallops (Pectinidae), with powers of jet propulsion representing modification of the mechanism for cleansing the mantle cavity. Swimming also occurs, although with the body disposed vertically, in some Limidae (e.g., *Lima hians*). (See also Chapter 12.)

In the Etheriidae (Unionacea) alone is attachment associated with, and not the predisposing cause of, monomyarianism. In this family cementation, with consequent great bilateral asymmetry, can take place indifferently by either valve (Yonge, 1962a).

D. Ctenidia

The bivalve ctenidium has been used extensively in classification. The simple protobranch filament—found only in the Nuculacea (Fig. 17A)—probably extended horizontally and then became U-shaped, as indicated in Fig. 17B. This seems the most probable origin of the *filibranch* ctenidia present in *Glycymeris, Mytilus, Pecten*, etc. (Fig. 17C). Each filament is elongate and bent, the whole series forming a V-shaped demibranch, the entire ctenidium of each side making a W. A food-collecting groove extends along the axis between the demibranchs. As in *Nucula*, adjacent filaments are connected by cilia but, except in the Taxodonta, the two limbs of each bent filament are united by vascular interfilamentar junctions. In the more closely knit *eulamellibranch* ctenidia (Fig. 17D), adjacent filaments are intimately united by vascular and skeletal junctions each demibranch being thus converted into a coherent double lattice. The abfrontal cilia, having lost their function, here disappear. The laterofrontals, which first appear in the Protobranchia, are compound cilia forming largely inert, straining platelets intercepting particles between the lateral and frontal cilia. There is much variation in the manner in which food particles are conveyed to the mouth and also in the manner in which the inhalant chamber is cleansed of the mucus-laden excess of particles, or pseudofeces, which continually accumulates. After collection by ciliary currents mid-ventrally or posteroventrally, this material is

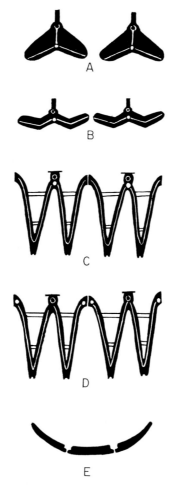

FIG. 17. Diagrams illustrating the evolution of the ctenidium within the Bivalvia. A. Nuculidae (protobranch condition). B. Possible hypothetical intermediate condition leading to C. Filibranch condition with interlamellar (not interfilamentary) tissue junctions. D. Eulamellibranch condition with interfilamentary tissue junctions and also with efferent blood vessel split and moved to outer margins of demibranchs. E. Pumping ctenidial septum of septibranch *Cuspidaria* (see Yonge, 1947).

periodically ejected by sudden contractions of the "quick" component of the adductor or adductors. The evolution of the mantle cavity as a site of ciliary collection and sorting involving an accompanying elaboration of a cleansing system is well described in the classic papers of Atkins (1936–1943).

The most extreme modification of the ctenidia in the Bivalvia appears in the small group of the Septibranchia. Coming largely from deep water, they are the only bivalve carnivores. By hypertrophy of their contained muscle, the ctenidia are converted into a horizontally slung muscular septum (Fig. 17E) which continues the division of the mantle cavity into inhalant and exhalant chambers. The septum is perforated by ciliated pores or larger sieve-like areas and can be raised and lowered, acting as a pump driving water intermittently from ventral to dorsal chamber and at the same time drawing in the probably always dead animals on which these bivalves feed and which are pushed into the mouth by the muscular palps. It is noteworthy that pumping ctenidia, of even greater elaboration because formed of modified filaments united by extensive ciliary junctions, occur in the protobranch Nuculanidae; but there feeding is by way of the palp proboscides.

E. Evolutionary Trends

The evolutionary trends so obvious in the Gastropoda and so striking in the Cephalopoda are not so obvious in the Bivalvia. Some trends are apparent, especially in the degree of fusion of the mantle margins which involves the mode of formation of the siphons (Fig. 18B) and also secondary extension of the ligament (Fig. 18C) (Yonge, 1957) and in the elaboration of the ctenidia. Yet in the main we seem to be viewing the effects of radiating evolution with many examples of convergence. Repeatedly, for instance, has the capacity for deep burrowing and for boring into rock been independently evolved. The independent appearance of heteromyarianism (always associated with byssal attachment) has already been noted, and also of monomyarianism. Cementation by one valve, i.e., attachment by way of the mantle/shell, has come about a number of times in the Anisomyaria (and at various stages in the life history) and also in the Chamacea, the Etheriidae (Unionacea), and the Myochamidae (Pandoracea). Study of the bivalve stomach (Purchon, 1960) provides further evidence of radiating evolution. There is, in the strong opinion of one of us (C.M.Y.) no evidence whatever to support suggestions, originating with Douvillé (1912), of the existence of "normal," "sessile," and "deep-burrowing" lineages.

Certainly from a very early period, evolution would appear to have proceeded independently within the Protobranchia. Here it has diverged widely as between the Nuculidae and the Nuculanidae (both feeding largely by means of palp proboscides but with the latter possessing highly specialized "pumping" ctenidia and a posterior inhalant current), on the one hand, and the Solemyidae with enlarged ctenidia and extremely reduced palps, on the other. But all are burrowers.

The Taxodonta (Arcacea) and superfamilies comprising the Anisomyaria possess in common a usually massive byssus and filibranch ctenidia; there is also little fusion of the mantle margins. The Ostreacea, where the byssal apparatus disappears after providing for postlarval cementation and where the ctenidia are eulamellibranch, stand a little apart. But in form, as in all other Anisomyaria, they show clear evidence of byssal attachment in their evolutionary history. Apart from the burrowing Arcacea and the secondarily adapted Pinnidae, all of these animals, by virtue of byssal attachment or of secondary cementation or of freedom, are members of the epifauna. It is suggested that the retention of the byssus into adult life (as distinct from its presence as an organ for temporary attachment in the postlarva) is *not* primitive in the Bivalvia (Yonge, 1962b).

Within the remaining eulamellibranch bivalves, the major changes have been concerned with greater fusion of mantle margins, both in area and in the degree of actual union. This also affects both the siphons and the ligament (Fig. 18). The superficial burrowing of the Protobranchia and nonattached Arcacea is retained in many groups, such as the Astartacea, Unionacea, Cyprinacea, Isocardiacea, Cardiacea, and most Veneracea, all with no more than very short siphons although with varyingly modified ligaments. Adaptations for deep burrowing, involving extension of the fused siphons and suitable modification of shell and foot, have been independently achieved in the Mactracea, Myacea, Saxicavacea, and Adesmacea. Modification, primarily of the shell and foot with little elongation of the siphons, has fitted the Solenacea for rapid vertical movement in relatively unstable substrata. All of these bivalves are suspension feeders, but deep burrowing has no less successfully been achieved by the deposit-feeding Tellinacea in which the siphons, composed exclusively of the inner, muscular fold of the mantle margin, are separate with the longer inhalant one groping widely over the surface. Ctenidia and palps are enlarged and the stomach is gizzard-like; the great size of the foot involves so large a pedal gape that the region of mantle union at the base of the siphons has to be braced by the cruciform muscle characteristic of this large and important group.

Boring into rock has been independently achieved in some anisomyarian Mytilacea (*Botula* and *Lithophaga*), some Cardiacea (*Tridacna* spp.), some Veneracea (*Petricola*), and some Myacea (*Platyodon*); all Gastrochaenacea and Adesmacea (apart from the few burrowing into clay) are borers, the latter also in wood (Teredinidae, Xylophaginidae) (see Chapter 12). Two groups possess, by reacquisition, an anterior inhalant current, namely, the Erycinacea which are often attached by a fine byssus superficially to other animals on which they are commensal, and the Lucinacea which burrow to medium depths. The Dreissenacea are attached by byssus, the Chamacea by cementation. The Pandoracea are a group of very mixed habits although all have a highly characteristic ligament. Along with the Clavagellacea, which extend the shell to form an enclosing tube, and the carnivorous Septibranchia (or

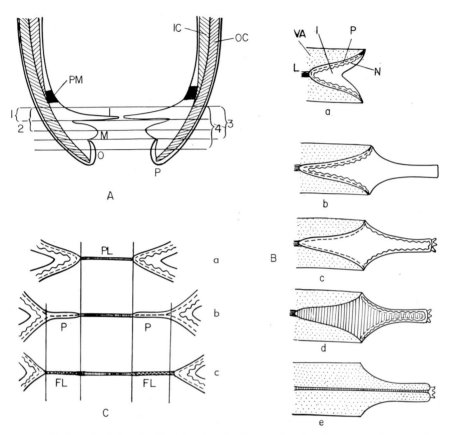

Fig. 18. Mantle fusion in Bivalvia. A. Mantle margins showing inner (*I*), middle (*M*), and outer (*O*) folds with periostracum (*P*) and outer calcareous layer of valves (*OC*) formed by inner and outer surfaces, respectively, of outer fold. Inner calcareous layer (*IC*) formed by mantle surface usually within line of pallial attachment (*PM*). Fusion of mantle margins in stages: (*1*) inner folds only, (*2*) inner folds with inner surface of middle, (*3*) inner and middle folds, (*4*) inner surface of outer folds also (see Yonge, 1957). B. Formation of siphons with varying degrees of mantle fusion (Yonge, 1957); *I*, inner fold; *N* (wavy line) middle fold; *P* (broken line) periostracal groove at base of outer fold; *L*, ligament; *VA*, valve. (*a*) Posterior embayment without formation of siphons; (*b*) siphons formed from inner mantle folds only (e.g., Tellinacea); (*c*) siphons from inner folds with inner surface of outer mantle folds (e.g., Cardiacea); (*d*) siphons from inner and middle folds with inner surface of outer mantle folds, i.e., secreting periostracum (e.g., Myacea); (*e*) all folds extending posteriorly forming calcareous tube enclosing siphons (e.g., *Cuspidaria*). C. (*a*) Primary ligament (*PL*) formed from inner and outer ligament layers with superficial periostracum (this the primitive condition); (*b*) secondary ligament by possible extension at both ends by fusion of the periostracal secreting surfaces (*P*), i.e., of inner surfaces of outer folds; (*c*) secondary ligament by possible extension by fusion of outer surfaces of outer folds so forming fusion layer (*FL*) (e.g., Pectinidae).

Poromyacea), with the ctenidium modified to form a septum, they help to complete a picture of great adaptive radiation with repeated instances of convergence.

VI. CEPHALOPODA[2]

A. *Early Evolution*

The cephalopods stand apart from other molluscs in their larger size, higher metabolism, and faster tempo of life. They receive wider ranging and more precise sensory information, and show much greater motor precision. Cerebral development and learning are well developed in some modern forms. Although highly specialized they conform to the basic molluscan plan, but we have no detailed information from fossils as to their links with other molluscs. The head-foot and the visceropallium are well represented although the mantle cavity, while retaining (indeed, developing) its respiratory function, has also become a means of jet propulsion. The gut has also partly relinquished dependence on ciliary mechanisms. All modern cephalopods except *Nautilus* show various degrees of reduction of the shell.

The foot is highly modified and evidence from development and innervation indicates that it is probably represented in part by the funnel. The mouth has moved ventrally and become surrounded by a circlet of tentacular arms, possibly of cephalic rather than pedal origin (in other words, Cephalopoda may be a misnomer). The original anteroposterior axis has been greatly shortened and lies almost at right angles to the new anteroposterior axis; the new axis largely coincides with the dorsoventral axis of the visceropallium, which represents the dominant growth gradient. This was early shown by the increase in height of the visceropallial sac and the elongation of the cap-like external shell. Cephalopods are disposed with the posterior surface undermost and the combined anterior and ventral surface foremost.

In all early cephalopods the shell became partitioned into gas-filled chambers by successive concave septa, the animal occupying only the last and widest body chamber. These gas-filled camerae (Fig. 19, *CA*) must early have lightened the body, permitting larger size and making possible, as the funnel developed, the use of short but effective spurts off the substratum. The calcareous siphuncular tube (*SI*) running as a closed passage through the shell camerae appears initially to have been fairly wide, holding part of the visceral mass surrounded by an outer gas-filled investment. With the narrowing of the siphuncular tube (as can be traced in nautiloid phylogeny) it retained only a narrow vascular appendage of the visceral hump. The shell camerae have been thought to hold a static

[2] This section was prepared with assistance from Anna M. Bidder and K. A. Joysey.

gas mixture, and to provide a closed buoyancy system. Recent findings by Denton and others (see Chapter 13) have shown osmotic and hydrostatic control of the fluid and gas content of the camerae of the cuttlefish. Observations by Bidder (1962) on living *Nautilus* revealed small

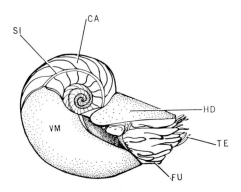

Fig. 19. Cephalopoda. *Nautilus*, from right side with shell shown in section (after Thiele, 1935). *CA*, camerae; *FU*, funnel; *HD*, hood; *SI*, siphuncle; *TE*, tentacles; *VM*, visceral mass.

changes in buoyancy and the presence of both liquid and gas in the camerae, thus suggesting an active control comparable to that found in *Sepia*. By inference, these observations must raise the possibility of similar mechanisms being present in extinct shelled cephalopods. But even without active buoyancy control, the camerae must have provided an effective flotation device, and jet locomotion was probably soon achieved. [In the Ordovician *Orthonybyoceras* we can see in the rocks the traces made by an orthoconic nautiloid propelled by funnel jets and can find evidence of its proficiency at steering by side deflections of the funnel (Flower, 1955).]

B. Nautiloids and Ammonoids

The first nautiloids had short cap-like external shells with a slight endogastric coil but other forms appeared early in the history of the group, some with straight shells, and some coiled with the gradient of incremental growth greatest posteriorly, producing an exogastric shell as in *Nautilus*. Bilateral symmetry is disturbed by skewed coiling only in a few later forms, and the mantle cavity is never displaced by torsion. The coiling of the camerate gas-filled shell has evolved on lines very different from the heavy viscera-filled gastropod coil.

A wide range of shell form is found among Palaeozoic nautiloids, and it is presumed that each represents a definite relationship between the buoyant properties of the shell and the postural requirements of the animal. In a tightly coiled shell like that of *Nautilus* (Fig. 19), the relationship between the center of gravity and the center of buoyancy determines that the body chamber lies almost horizontally below the gas-filled chambers, but in some of the more loosely coiled cyrtocones the aperture probably faced obliquely downward. Several groups of Palaeozoic nautiloids independently developed long straight shells, and it appears that in some of these the apical end was counterbalanced by siphuncular or cameral deposits which enabled those animals to adopt a horizontal posture. Perhaps the most remarkable shell form is that of *Ascoceras*, in which the orthoconic juvenile stage was shed from the inflated flask-like adult shell. Within this shell the septa curved obliquely forward and so the gas-filled camerae lay in a saddle-like bulge above the horizontal body chamber.

Many different groups of nautiloids and ammonoids have abandoned the coiled shape and fast swimming existence to return to a neobenthonic habit at the bottom, or to take on a life of passive floating. In many of the short, vertically floating brevicones of Ordovician nautiloids (*Mandaloceras, Trimeroceras*) the apertural margins became so inflected as to allow only restricted openings for funnel, eyes, tentacles, and mouth, a facies from which one might suspect a microphagous plankton-feeding mode of life. Some genera of Mesozoic ammonoids, such as *Macroscaphites* and *Hamites*, abandoned the coiling of the younger shell to give a long, straight, or ultimately recurved terminal chamber. Such forms may have swum slowly or remained hung suspended with the mouth raised just above the bottom in a highly advantageous posture for leisured foraging, but planktonic feeding seems more likely for the recurved forms in which the aperture faced upward. Certain ammonoids (such as *Turrilites*) and nautiloids (*Trochoceras*) developed a skewed spiral with a coiled turbinate shell from which must be inferred a reversion to a crawling benthonic habit.

With the pallial cavity still enclosed within the terminal chamber of an external shell, none of the extinct ammonoids and nautiloids could have developed the efficient contractile mechanism of the pallial musculature seen in the modern naked cephalopods, where the water jet is expelled powerfully through the tubular funnel. If we may judge by modern *Nautilus*, jet expulsion must have been effected by the contraction of the funnel musculature itself, which here forms not a closed tube but an approximation of two fleshy lateral lobes in the central mid-line (Fig. 19, *FU*).

C. Modern Cephalopoda

The living Cephalopoda, with the exception of *Nautilus*, belong to the subclass Coleoidea (Fig. 20). In all of them the shell (*P*) is reduced and invested by the fleshy integument, being altogether lost in the living Oc-

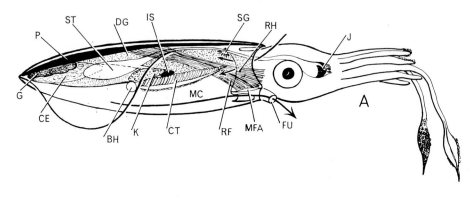

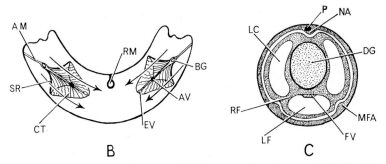

Fig. 20. Diagrams showing essential features of modern coleoid Cephalopoda. **A**, General structure in lateral view. **B**, Transverse section through mantle cavity in region of ctenidia. **C**, Transverse section through region of collar. *BG*, branchial gland; *BH*, branchial heart; *CE*, caecum; *DG*, digestive gland; *FV*, funnel valve; *IS*, ink sac; *J*, jaws; *K*, kidney; *LC*, lumen of collar; *LF*, lumen of funnel; *MC*, mantle cavity; *MFA*, mantle-funnel articulation; *NA*, nuchal articulation; *P*, pen; *RF*, *RH*, retractor muscles of funnel and head; *SG*, stellate ganglion; *SR*, secondary (afferent) skeletal rod. Other lettering as before. Arrows in **B**, **C** show direction of respiratory current.

topoda. The strong pallial musculature is now set free for the contractions that provide the jet mechanism, beautifully coordinated, especially in the fast-swimming squids, with a system of giant neurones (see Young, 1939) that secures both speed and synchronization of the passage of the nerve impulses in pallial contraction. Here, with the loss of the chambered shell, speed of movement can overcome gravity and the dominating evolutionary trends have been concerned less with buoyancy than with greater efficiency of pallial contraction, fast swimming, and the development of enhanced sensory and cerebral powers. A squid such as *Loligo* displays the greatest emancipation from benthic life and from the constraint of the external shell. Every line of the body is beautifully subservient to speed and maneuverability. *Loligo* is circular in cross section, pointed at the end remote from the head like a torpedo, where there are also a pair of triangular stabilizing fins that can be shut down in fast motion. The shell is fully internal, lying just beneath what has become the upper surface in swimming (the former anterior aspect). It is a light and chitinized "*pen*" (*P*), which points the body like a rigid arrow, and becomes expanded laterally into a flexible vane giving some support to the pallial musculature. No chambered portion survives or is even indicated in development. The cephalic end of the body, which in slower swimming with the funnel (*FU*) turned back may be directed foremost, is also streamlined with the eight short arms completing the smooth, wedge-shaped contour. The two longer, tentaculate arms are kept ensheathed, being extruded with a lightning movement, mediated by giant neurones, to take active prey. The tubular funnel is freely movable, the animal moving in the opposite direction to that in which water is expelled.

The modern sepioid shell or "cuttlebone" (Fig. 21C) is much more primitively complete than the reduced pen of the squids (Fig. 21E). It displays the persistent outer or uppermost side of the chambered shell of extinct forms, now broad and flat with the septa very numerous and closely crowded together. Its smooth inner surface represents the siphuncle so widely opened out that the lower wall of the chambered shell has vanished (see Chapter 13 for functions of this shell). The unique small *Spirula*, which swims or floats obliquely with the head downward, retains at the apical end a small completely enclosed ophiocone.

The pallial cavity in the Coleoidea contains two long ctenidia (Fig. 20, *CT*) attached along the *afferent* side. Their alternating rows of filaments are not ciliated but the respiratory surface is increased with both secondary and tertiary folds. Although the muscularly produced water flow passes from afferent to efferent side (Fig. 20B), the blood flow is through elaborate capillary networks within the folds. These ctenidia are well adapted for the high respiratory needs of an active cephalopod. The rapid exchange of pallial water, and the greater oxygen utilization in cephalopods, subserve these same needs. Water is taken in laterally by contraction of the radial fibers in the pallial wall. This reduces its thickness and so increases the capacity of the cavity. Water is expelled through the funnel in the mid-ventral line by contraction of the circular muscles of the mantle. The sides of the funnel are produced into a "collar" (Fig.

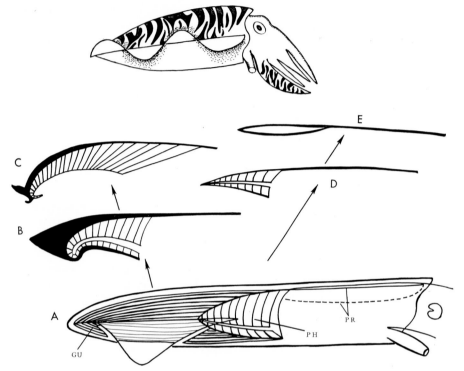

Fig. 21. The evolution and reduction of the shell in the Coleoidea. A. Belemnoid with primitively complete internal shell. B. Primitive sepioid *Belosepia*. C. *Sepia* (juvenile external appearance of animal shown above). D. *Conoteuthis*. E. *Loligo*. *GU*, guard; *PH*, phragmocone; *PR*, pro-ostracum.

20A, C) which forms a valve and so prevents exit of water laterally. An efficient "resisting apparatus," formed by cartilaginous prominences fitting into corresponding sockets (Fig. 20, *MFA*), locks the funnel and mantle together against the force of the contracting pallial muscles.

The composition and arrangement of the pallial organs show several differences from what we have seen in gastropods. First, hypobranchial glands and osphradia have been lost in coleoid cephalopods: cleansing of inborne sediment raises no problem in a pelagic animal, and the chemo-receptors are located elsewhere and are subordinate to the visual and tactile organs. In Gastropoda the skeletal rods and suspensory membrane of the gill filament lie on its efferent side. But the cephalopod filament is supported from the afferent side, and this margin develops secondary supporting rods (Fig. 20D, *SR*) acting as ties between the filament and its afferent membrane (Yonge, 1947). Unlike the flow in other molluscs, the main direction of the forcibly pumped water is from the afferent to the efferent side, the exhalant site being in the mid-line between the efferent margins of the two gills. An important accessory structure opening into the mantle cavity is the rectal ink sac (*IS*), present in virtually all Coleoidea and discharging a concealing or distracting cloud of melanoid secretion through the anal aperture, to be expelled through the funnel.

The cephalopod coelom is very much wider than in other molluscs, and the hemocoelic spaces are relatively less prominent. Large volumes of blood are not required for use as a hemoskeleton, but the perivisceral freedom for the digestive system and gonad, advantageous for active animals, is supplied to varying degrees by coelomic spaces. In the Decapoda there is a large body cavity partially divided by an imperfect septum into a small anterior pericardium and a large posterior

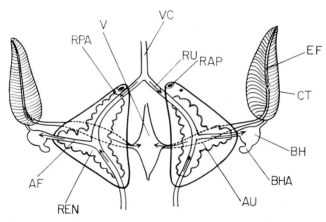

Fig. 22. Heart, ctenidia, and renal organs of a coleoid cephalopod. *AF*, afferent branchial vessel; *AU*, auricle; *BH*, branchial heart; *BHA*, branchial heart appendage; *CT*, ctenidium; *EF*, efferent branchial vessel; *RAP*, renal aperture; *REN*, spongy renal tissue; *RPA*, renopericardial aperture; *RU*, renal vein; *V*, ventricle; *VC*, vena cava.

gonocoele, which contains the gonad and stomach, and, in the Teuthoidea, the cecum of the gut. In the Sepioidea this organ lies in a dorsal renal sac which in this group connects the paired sacs of the kidney. In the Octopoda, the gonocoele contains the gonad only, there is no true pericardium, the heart apparently gaining freedom for its beat from its position just dorsal to the kidney sacs. The crop, stomach, and cecum are contained in venous sacs which are enlargements of the dorsal vein.

The renal organs (Fig. 22, *REN*) communicate near their external (pallial) orifices by renopericardial ducts (*RPA*) leading to the visceropericardial coelom. They form large inflated sacs with smooth outside walls and are traversed by the afferent branchial vessels (*AF*) arising from the bifurcation of the vena cava (*VC*). Their glandular excretory tissue forms a spongy mass of renal appendages surrounding these vessels, which are themselves peristaltic, forcing small amounts of fluid filtrate into the renal appendages through the small blood vessels entering these processes in a labyrinth from the veins. At the base of either gill the afferent vein is enlarged to a strongly contractile accessory branchial heart (*BH*), increasing both the speed and pressure of the outward branchial blood flow. A glandular appendage (*BHA*), of each branchial heart represents the pericardial excretory glands found in gastropods and bivalves, having a complex labyrinthine interior, opening into the small pocket of the pericardium in which lies the branchial heart.

[The following statements, up to Section D, are by Dr. Anna M. Bidder.] The Coleoidea are, on the whole, an oceanic group, pelagic or bathypelagic, and it is unfortunate, although understandable, that almost the whole of known cephalopod physiology is based on observations made on three or four exceptional families which have adopted a littoral or sublittoral habit or are restricted to the continental shelf.

There are five main divisions: the Teuthoidea, or squids; the Sepioidea or cuttlefish and sepiolas; the Polypoidea and Cirroteuthoidea, two very different octopod groups; and the Vampyromorpha represented by a single known bathypelagic genus, the little *Vampyroteuthis*.

The Teuthoidea can be traced back to early Mesozoic times; Naef (1923) shows them radiating from the main coleoid stock shortly after the comparable radiation of the Belemnites had begun. The squids are thus a very ancient group. The Sepioidea can be traced into the Jurassic, and later Tertiary forms suggest that the sepias and *Spirula* arose from separate ancestral strains; at what point they branched off is not known, but their origin is certainly independent of, and possibly later than, that of the Teuthoidea. Only one fossil octopod is known: *Palaeoctopus* from the Upper Cretaceous. It is neither a polypoid nor a cirroteuthoid, and suggests an octopod origin at least as early as the Lower Cretaceous. The main divisions of the modern coleoids are thus separated from one another by an ancient family history: a fact which must be borne in mind when considering their physiology comparatively.

The Teuthoidea are, except for the Loliginidae, oceanic and "open-eyed" (oegopsid); the covered eye of the Loliginidae may be regarded as an adaptation to the sediment-rich waters of the continental shelf. Oegopsid squids include the largest, as well as the smallest, known cephalopods. While the torpedo-like body is a current form, squids with blunter, wider bodies are known, and the position and shape of the fins, and the proportion of body to head and arms, vary greatly. The tentacular arms are not drawn back into pits, as in *Loligo* (or *Sepia*) but simply contracted or extended. In some forms they reach enormous length; in the giant *Architeuthis* the extended tentacles may be more than five times the mantle length, and more than ten times the mantle length in the much smaller *Chiroteuthis veranyi*.

Many squids possess light organs of great complexity and beauty. The ink sac is never large, and is probably used to form a "dummy" rather than a "smoke-screen." All are perpetual, although not all equally rapid swimmers, but they include the fastest marine invertebrates known.

The Sepioidea fall into three clear-cut groups; the Sepiidae, or true cuttlefish, with broadly oval bodies, reaching a foot or more in length, and made rigid by the cuttlebone, and with narrow fringing fins, short heads, and arms. They are a bottom-living group and their restriction to the continental shelf is consistent with the work of Denton and Gilpin-Brown, showing that their buoyancy control is unlikely to work below about 240 meters (see Chapter 13). *Spirula*, on the other hand, is a purely pelagic oceanic form, descending to great depths, unique in its coiled internal shell (see p. 51). The sepiolids have either reduced or lost the shell and are characterized by their small size, short sac-like bodies, and large rounded fins; most are bottom-living, often burying themselves in the sand, but one subfamily, the Heteroteuthinae, is pelagic. The ink sac tends to be large, and "smoke-screens" as well as "dummies" are produced. While all are capable of active swimming, they do not show the lightning speed of the fastest squids. Light organs are found on *Spirula* and on some sepiolids.

The Octopodidae are the only bottom-living family of the Polypoidea. The common octopus gives a good idea of their general facies. Some of the Bathypolypodines are smaller, shorter armed, have lost the ink sac, and sometimes have gelatinous tissues. The best-known pelagic polypoids are the Argonautidae, characterized by marked sexual dimorphism: small males with complex, detachable hectocotylized arms. The female *Argonauta* secretes, by means of two membranes on the dorsal arm-pair, the thin "paper-nautilus" shell, in which she lives and incubates her eggs. *Argonauta*, although encountered in the open sea, can crawl about on the bottom inshore. The rest of the group is purely pelagic, and includes *Alloposus*, which can probably reach gigantic size (Joubin, 1920). The Argonautide are a short-bodied, long-armed group, and *Alloposus* has a deep web; it has a markedly gelatinous mantle (Joubin, 1895).

The remainder of the polypoid octopods known are small, delicate forms, some short-armed (Bolitaenids), sometimes deep-webbed and gelatinous (*Amphitretus*); none of the group is a truly rapid swimmer. The ink sac is rather small in these forms, its use unknown. Smoke-screen formation is recorded for *Octopus vulgaris*. Light organs are not recorded in the group.

The Cirroteuthoidea probably live near the bottom at great depths. They have short bodies, and deeply webbed arms, which carry two rows of cirri, one on each side of the suckers. They have fins, and a small skeletal support for the fin muscles. The coelom is even more reduced than in the Polypoidea, and the blood spaces surrounding the digestive organs are greatly reduced or absent. They are a soft-bodied gelatinous group, and jet propulsion is probably not important in their swimming, so that it is possible that perivisceral freedom is less required than in other forms. There is no ink sac, and light organs are not recorded.

Vampyroteuthis is a little, octopod-like, deep-webbed animal, with fins, light organs, and a pair of "tentacles" not homologous with those of the squids and cuttlefish. It has a pen of archaic type (Pickford, 1949).

It will be noted that gelatinous tissues have been several times mentioned: these appear independently in the Teuthoidea (large cranchids), Polypoidea and Cirroteuthoidea. Another recurrent feature is the reduction of the viscera, which is characteristic of the cranchid teuthoids, and the polypoid *Vitreledonella* and the Bolitaenidae, but is not recorded in the Sepioidea. Completely transparent tissue is not uncommon, and is known in the Loliginidae, small cranchids, and in *Vitreledonella*; it is associated with completely contracted chromatophores in the undisturbed animal.

D. *Living Nautilus*

The primitive surviving cephalopod *Nautilus* (Fig. 19) needs special mention, in respect both of its primitive and of its peculiar features. Its head-foot can be accommodated completely within the mantle cavity and has an appearance very unlike that of other modern cephalopods. The tentacular crown (*TE*) surrounding the mouth consists of two sets of lappets, inner and outer, carrying several concentric rows of small tentacles—about 90 in all—slender and annulated, without suckers but strongly adhesive, and retractable into basal sheaths. A fleshy hood (*HD*) lies over the head, covering completely the withdrawn animal. The funnel (*FU*) is formed of two separate halves, approximated in the mid-line. There is some evidence from fossil impressions that such a large tentacle number may not represent a primitive condition in nautiloids generally; undoubted archaic features must, however, include the condition of the eye with an ocular cavity open directly to the exterior and no lens, and the absence of integumentary chromatophores and rectal ink sac.

An outstanding feature of *Nautilus* is the duplication of the pallio-pericardial complex into two sets of paired organs. We have little means of knowing whether this was a primitively general feature or a secondary specialization peculiar to *Nautilus* and its relatives. There are four ctenidia, four auricles, and four renal organs, these lacking pericardial orifices since the pericardium communicates directly with the exterior. These duplications may represent adaptive compensation for the relative circulatory inefficiency of the nautiloid ctenidium with its lack of capillaries and branchial hearts. It seems most unwise to cite them as evidence of a general archaic metamerism either in cephalopods or in molluscs generally (see also discussion of *Neopilina*, pp. 28–32). As recently established (Bidder, 1962), circulation of water in the mantle cavity is due to changes in the internal volume of the funnel. When the two halves of this separate, water is drawn into the funnel from the surrounding mantle cavity; when they come together water is expelled through the tip and this involves its simultaneous replacement by water drawn into the cavity through the posterior angle of the shell.

REFERENCES

NOTE. This chapter is primarily concerned with the results of studies on functional morphology in the Mollusca with which the two authors have been particularly concerned. To a considerable extent this represents new, or modified, interpretation of well-known structures fully described in standard works. For this reason only a few references to literature are provided, but certain of these contain extensive literature lists; see especially Morton (1955b, 1958) and Yonge (1947, 1953a).

Atkins, D. (1936–1943). On the ciliary mechanisms and interrelationships of lamellibranchs. Parts I–VIII. *Quart. J. Microscop. Sci.* **79**, 181–308, 339–373, 375–421, 423–445; **80**, 321–329, 331–344, 345–436; **84**, 187–256.

Bidder, A. M. (1962). Use of the tentacles, swimming and buoyancy control in the pearly Nautilus. *Nature* **196**, 451–454.

Crofts, D. R. (1955). Muscle morphogenesis in primitive gastropods and its relation to torsion. *Proc. Zool. Soc. London* **125**, 711–750.

Douvillé, H. (1912). Classification des Lamellibranches. *Bull. soc. geol. France* **12**, No. 14, 419–467.

Flower, R. H. (1955). Trails and tentacular impressions of orthoconic cephalopods. *J. Paleontol.* **29**, 857–867.

Fretter, V., and Graham, A. (1962). "British Prosobranch Molluscs," 755 pp. Ray Society, London.

Joubin, L. (1895). Contribution à l'étude des Céphalopodes de l'Atlantique Nord. *Résult. Comp. Sci. Monaco*, fasc. IX, 63pp.

Joubin, L. (1920). Céphalopodes provenant des campagnes de la Princesse Alice (1898–1910). 3 ser. *Research Comp. Sci. Albert I Monaco* **54**, 1–95.

Lemche, H., and Wingstrand, K. G. (1959). The anatomy of *Neopilina galatheae* Lemche, 1957 (Mollusca Tryblidacea). *Galathea Rept.* **3**, 9–72.

Morton, J. E. (1955a). The evolution of Vermetid gastropods. *Pacific Sci.* **9**, 3–15 (and other papers on vermetids therein quoted).

Morton, J. E. (1955b). The functional morphology of the British Ellobiidae (Gastropoda Pulmonata) with special reference to the digestive and reproductive system. *Phil. Trans. Roy. Soc.* **B239**, 89–160.

Morton, J. E. (1955c). The evolution of the Ellobiidae with a discussion on the origin of the Pulmonata. *Proc. Zool. Soc. London* **125**, 127–168.

Morton, J. E. (1958). "Molluscs." Hutchinson, London.

Morton, J. E. (1959). The habits and feeding organs of *Dentalium entalis*. *J. Marine Biol. Assoc. U.K.* **38**, 225–238.

Naef, A. (1923). Die Cephalopoden. *Fauna u. Flora Neapel* **35**, 1–148.

Owen, G. (1953a). The shell in the Lamellibranchia. *Quart. J. Microscop. Sci.* **94**, 57–70.

Owen, G. (1953b). On the biology of *Glossus humanus* (L.) (*Isocardia cor* Lam.). *J. Marine Biol. Assoc. U.K.* **32**, 85–106.

Pickford, G. E. (1949). *Vampyroteuthis infernalis* chun au archaeidibranchiate Cephalopod. II. External anatomy. *Dana Rept. Copenhagen* **82**, 1–132.

Purchon, R. D. (1960). Phylogenetic classification of the Lamellibranchia with special reference to the Protobranchia. *Proc. Malacological Soc. London* **33**, 224–230.

Stasek, C. R. (1963a). Orientation and form in the bivalved Mollusca. *J. Morph.* **112**, 195–214.

Stasek, C. R. (1963b). Geometrical form and gnomonic growth in the bivalved Mollusca. *J. Morph.* **112**, 215–229.

Thiele, J. (1935). "Handbuch der systematischen Weichtierkunde," Bd. 2, pp. 779–1154, Fischer, Jena.

Thompson, D'Arcy W. (1942). "On Growth and Form," rev. ed. Cambridge Univ. Press, London and New York.

Thompson, T. E. (1958). The natural history, embryology, larval biology and post-larval development of *Adalaria proxima* (Alder and Hancock) (Gastropoda Opisthobranchia). *Phil. Trans. Roy. Soc.* **B242**, 1–58.

Thompson, T. E. (1960). The development of *Neomenia carinata* Tullberg (Mollusca Aplacophora). *Proc. Roy. Soc.* **B153**, 263–278.

Thompson, T. E. (1962). Studies on the ontogeny of *Tritonia hombergi* Cuvier (Gastropoda Opisthobranchia). *Phil. Trans. Roy. Soc.* **B245**, 171–218.

Yonge, C. M. (1939). On the mantle cavity and its contained organs in the Loricata (Placophora). *Quart. J. Microscop. Sci.* **81**, 367–390.

Yonge, C. M. (1947). The pallial organs in the aspidobranch Gastropoda and their evolution throughout the Mollusca. *Phil. Trans. Roy. Soc.* **B232**, 443–518.

Yonge, C. M. (1953a). The monomyarian condition in the Lamellibranchia. *Trans. Roy. Soc. Edinburgh* **62**, 443–478.

Yonge, C. M. (1953b). Observations on *Hipponix antiquatus* (Linnaeus). *Proc. Calif. Acad. Sci.* [4] **28**, 1–24.

Yonge, C. M. (1955). Adaptation to rock boring in *Botula* and *Lithophaga* (Lamellibranchia, Mytilidae) with a discussion on the evolution of this habit. *Quart. J. Microscop. Sci.* **96**, 383–410.

Yonge, C. M. (1957). Mantle fusion in the Lamellibranchia. *Pubbl. staz. zool. Napoli* **29**, 151–171.

Yonge, C. M. (1962a). On *Etheria elliptica* Lam. and the course of evolution, including assumption or monomyarianism, in the family Etheriidae (Bivalvia: Unionacea). *Phil. Trans. Roy. Soc.* **B244**, 423–458.

Yonge, C. M. (1962b). On the primitive significance of the byssus in the Bivalvia and its effects in evolution. *J. Marine Biol. Assoc. U.K.* **42**, 113–125.

Young, J. Z. (1939). Fused neurons and synaptic contacts in the giant nerve fibers of cephalopods. *Phil. Trans. Roy. Soc. London* **B229**, 465–503.

Note added in page proof (see p. 39): Recently Stasek (1963a, b) has shown that the criterion of the demarcation line applied by Owen (1953a, b) and Yonge (1955), namely that it is a projection onto the sagittal plane of a line following the regions of greatest inflation of the valves, does not always apply. Nevertheless, the division of the mantle/shell into anterior and posterior territories which do not correspond to the anterior and posterior regions of the enclosed body remains unaffected. By a series of elaborate diagrams he is able to make direct comparison between the form of both mantle/shell and body in different bivalves. This does not dispose of the fact that the two have different growth axes; it provides additional evidence that, inevitably, the one profoundly influences the other (Yonge, 1953a, 1955, 1962a).

CHAPTER 2

Physiological Aspects of the Ecology of Intertidal Molluscs

G. E. Newell

ZOOLOGY DEPARTMENT, QUEEN MARY COLLEGE,
UNIVERSITY OF LONDON, LONDON, ENGLAND

I. THE DISTRIBUTION OF MOLLUSCS ON THE SHORE

A. Exposure-Immersion Times

Descriptions of the zonation of plants and animals in the intertidal zone appeared as early as the 1820's; since then shores in most parts of the world have been studied from this point of view. The mass of descriptive information which has accumulated has been ably summarized on several occasions in the last ten years—notably by the Stephensons (1949), Yonge (1949), Womersley and Edmonds (1952), Chapman and Trevarthen (1953), Lewis (1955), Doty (1957), and Southward (1958). In all of these accounts prominent mention is made of the zonation of certain molluscs, notably, littorinids, limpets, and topshells (trochids). The consensus of opinion is that zonation can be correlated not only with position on the shore relative to tidal levels (although subject to much variation according to the precise geographical situation, amplitude of tidal oscillation, climate, degree of exposure to wave action, and other local effects) but is causally related to it.

In many instances a good correlation has been obtained for a variety of organisms between the observed zonation and exposure/immersion times so that "critical levels," beyond which a species can exist only with difficulty, can be determined with some precision (Colman, 1933; Delf, 1942; Doty, 1946; Doty and Archer, 1950; Beveridge and Chapman, 1950; Guiler, 1952; Carnahan, 1952; Knox, 1953; and R. G. Evans, 1947a,b, 1949, 1957). As explained by Doty (1957) such critical levels often coincide with sharp differences in exposure/immersion times and are due to irregularities in the rate of rise and fall of the tide at certain points in the cycle, sometimes resulting in the time of exposure or immersion differing by a factor of 2 or 3 from one level to the next. The experimental evidence supporting the essentially common-sense view that exposure/immersion times at least play an important part in determining zonation is, however, far less than could be desired and much of what there is relates to shore algae. This is nonetheless important to zoologists since the plants may greatly influence the distribution of the animals whose food they form and to whom they give shelter. For example, *Littorina obtusata* (= *littoralis*) is found only on fucoids to which the animals are chemotactically attracted (van Dongen, 1956) or, more rarely, on *Zostera;* high-level littorinids feed on encrusting algae but may move up to browse on the blue-green algae during rough weather (Dellow, 1950); *Patina pellucida* lives and feeds almost entirely on *Laminaria* (Graham and Fretter, 1947). Graham (1955) gives many other examples of the diets of various molluscs which may restrict them to particular situations (see also Pelseneer, 1935; Braams and Geelen, 1953; and Bakker, 1959).

Baker (1909, 1910) showed that the growth rates of various species of *Fucus* and of *Ascophyllum nodosum* were greatest with exposure/immersion times corresponding with those which they normally experience on the shore. A graded resistance to the effects of exposure to air has been reported for green, brown, and red algae, those occurring higher up the shore showing the greater tolerance (E. Fischer, 1929; Isaac, 1933, 1935; Biebl, 1952; Boney and Corner, 1959). These results may be partly explicable as direct or primary effects of the tidal oscillation but it must be borne in mind that many secondary or dependent effects, such as changes in the intensity and duration of light, in temperature, humidity, available oxygen, and (for animals) the time available for feeding and other activities vary with shore level. On particulate shores, the nature of deposits is also zoned (Newell, 1954). It is to these dependent properties that organisms may be responding when they adopt particular zones. Thus, Gail (1918, 1922) and several subsequent workers showed that light of a particular intensity is essential for maximum photosynthesis of shore algae. In a paper valuable not only for its results but for a summary of previous work, Boney and Corner (1962) showed that photosynthesis in red algae is sensitized by the red phycobilin pigments they contain. The red pigments probably are "an adaptation to the green light which prevails under the sea." These workers, as well as Jones (1959), showed also that the red pigment favors rapid growth in red algae, probably, as Boney and Corner suggest, by protecting young plants from growth-inhibiting effects of green light in the wave band 500–540 mμ. But information dealing with even the direct effects of coverage and exposure on animals is very meager and although the zonation of molluscs, particularly that of prosobranchs, has been well described, their reaction to immersion/exposure has been little studied. One early study was that made in 1910 by Colgan, who determined the survival times of some common shore molluscs in dry air, in fresh water, and in water of high salinity, such as might be expected to occur in tidal pools. He found not only that high level species show a greater tolerance than those living lower down the shore, but also that within a single species individuals collected from high levels were more resistant than those from lower levels. A similar result was obtained by Gowanloch (1926) and Gowanloch and Hayes (1926) working in the Bay of Fundy on littorinids. Henderson (1929) came to essentially the same conclusion for 18 species of bivalves. Broekhuysen (1940) showed that there is a good correlation between the zonal distribution and resistance to desiccation, high temperatures, and salinities above and below that of normal sea water in five out of six species of prosobranchs (*Littorina knaensis, Thais dubia, Oxystele variegata, O. tigrina, O. sinensis,* and *Cominella cincta*) living on the rocky shore at False Bay, South Africa. The exception, *O. tigrina*, is mainly an inhabitant of rocky pools. Only isolated and conflicting results can be traced on the effects of prolonged immersion on common shore molluscs. Oft-quoted is the claim by Herdman (1890) that *Littorina rudis* (= *saxatilis*) becomes moribund if kept below sea water for only 2 or 3 days, but my own observations show that this is not true. It can certainly withstand immersion for 30 days and probably much longer.

B. Temperature

1. EFFECTS OF HIGH TEMPERATURE

Evans (1948) determined the thermal death points of a series of British prosobranchs, warming them in water (1°C/5 min) and thus ruling out desiccation effects. This is a procedure followed by most earlier workers from Huntsman and Sparks (1924) onward with whose results Evans' can be directly compared. Evans also studied the effects of prolonged immersion at high temperatures. All the animals could temporarily tolerate temperatures well in excess of those experienced on the shore, and the possibility of heat death under natural conditions is remote. Possibly temperature alone is not important in determining the upper limits of zonation. Contrary to some other workers, Evans found no correlation between thermal resistance and zonational sequence nor any variation in tolerance between individuals of the same species taken from different levels on the shore. He points out, however, that the degree of exposure to temperature changes on a broken shore, such as that of Cardigan Bay, varies more with the precise situation in which each species tends to be restricted—gully, overhang, exposed upper surface, and so on —than with shore level. It is with conditions in these smaller habitats that the thermal resistance of different species may be linked.

The information on thermal death points of marine molluscs is summarized in tabular form by Gunter (1957) to whose paper reference should be made for a full discussion on temperature as an ecological factor in the sea. Occasionally intertidal communities are faced with exceptional climatic or tidal conditions and the unusual rigors which they then experience throw light on factors influencing distribution under more normal conditions. For example, Hodgkin (1959) reports the effects of exceptionally low tides on the reefs near Freemantle which were exposed to heat and drying during low tide on several successive days when only the extreme outer edges of the reef were periodically refreshed. The effect on animal and plant life "was catastrophic," many animals and plants being killed, although not all were uniformly affected. Such extreme conditions are reflected in an annual mortality of organisms near the top of their vertical range; during winter the "higher sea level, almost continuous wave action and lower temperatures allow plants and animals to establish themselves above the level at which they can survive in summer." This annual mortality is doubtless a potent factor in maintaining the characteristic shore zonation. It would be valuable to have more information on the thermal death points of representative marine animals, particularly if they were determined in the way described by Orr (1955) which takes into account time as well as temperature. Such results can be conveniently expressed as a graph of time against temperature. Recent work by Fraenkel (1960) gives the thermal death point for *Littorina littorea* for 1 hour exposure as 40–41°C.

Such results as those quoted above strongly suggest that, particularly on smooth rocky shores, the heat-light-desiccation complex, whose intensity will vary with times of exposure, directly or indirectly determines the upper limit of distribution of plants and animals, but that its effects can be masked or overridden by irregularities and other purely local features or by the adoption by the organisms of special habits and habitats. Thus, a great variety of animals do not merely crawl or cling on the rock faces but inhabit crevices, live under boulders, or actively bore into the rock itself and so escape the full rigors of desiccation and temperature changes or of dislodgment by wave action. Even so, it is an ecological rule for the British Isles that no species which can thrive below tidemarks can extend its range above mid-tide level (J. E. Smith, 1959). Nevertheless, all must in some measure be adapted to withstand desiccation, to breathe atmospheric oxygen, to maintain their position, or actively to regain it. In short, all are to some extent amphibious, for only the most tightly closing bivalve can completely isolate itself from aerial conditions.

2. EFFECTS OF LOW TEMPERATURE

Information can be found in only a few instances on the effects and physiological responses of very low temperatures on molluscs. It would appear obvious that in winter in many parts of the world the low temperatures prevailing on the shore must represent extreme conditions—so severe, in fact, that mass mortalities may result there and in the sublittoral (for summary see Brongersma-Sanders, 1957). Many animals, including molluscs, migrate downshore or into the sublittoral during the autumn, although migrations in the reverse direction have been reported for *Patella vulgata* (Lewis, 1954), presumably as a desiccation avoidance response in the summer, with a return to optimal levels in the winter. Some molluscs that remain intertidally (e.g., *Littorina littorea*) became inactive, ceasing to feed or move at about 8°C on the North Kent coast (Newell 1958a). As shown by Barry and Munday (1959), the glycogen content of the digestive gland of *Patella vulgata* decreases during the winter, a sign of decreased feeding activity.

Available information shows that some common shore molluscs can withstand extremely low temperatures. In this they contrast with animals from below tidemarks, none of which can tolerate temperatures below those experienced in nature and to which a limit is set by the freezing point of sea water (about $-2°C$). Resistance to freezing runs parallel with ability to withstand desiccation. *Mytilus edulis, Modiolus modiolus, Littorina littorea* and *L. rudis* (= *saxatilis*) can survive exposure to temperatures of $-15°C$ when over 60% of the body water may be frozen, and *L. littorea* recovers after freezing at $-22°$ when 76% of its body water is in the form of ice (Kanwisher, 1955), resulting in a severe (but reversible) distortion of the tissues and a drastic drop in respiratory rate (Kanwisher, 1959). *Mytilus edulis* revives after 6 to 8 months at $-20°C$ or below in solid ice at Labrador. Doubtless many other shore molluscs—limpets, topshells, and the like—are also very resistant to frost, and this property is essential for the permanent colonization of shores in cold climates. As A. U. Smith (1958) points out, "the usually accepted view that intracellular crystallization of ice is invariably fatal should be critically examined," and it is also true that the reasons why some animals are able to survive while others perish when subjected to extreme cold remain obscure.

II. THE ATTAINMENT AND MAINTENANCE OF POSITION ON THE SHORE BY MOLLUSCS

In addition to the factors, mainly physical ones, which have been considered in the previous section, the observed pattern of distribution of shore molluscs is due to a complex set of circumstances, among which are chance settlement over a wide area with subsequent death except in favorable situations; an active choice of substratum or microhabitat; migration to situations favoring survival; behavioral activities such as the "homing" of various gastropods as well as less well-defined kineses and taxes in response to environmental cues; and the maintenance of position by boring, burrowing, or adhesion. Although each of these topics is worthy of lengthy treatment, all that can be attempted here is a brief summary and mention of some of the more recent key references.

A. Larval Life

Many, but by no means all, shore molluscs have larvae which for a variable time sojourn in the plankton, the time depending largely on the amount of yolk in the egg. Those with large amounts of yolk (lecithotrophic larvae) have a brief or no planktonic life; those with a smaller amount of yolk (planktotrophic larvae) depend more on the plankton for food (see Thorson, 1946 and 1950, for full reviews). The planktonic phase is customarily regarded as a mechanism whereby the species is dispersed but this can hardly be the full story, as the following considerations will suggest. First, a planktonic larval phase is omitted from the life history of many of the most widely distributed shore molluscs. For example, *Littorina rudis* (= *saxatilis*) (viviparous) has a wider distribution than *L. littorea* (oviparous, with a lengthy planktotrophic larval life) and is the only winkle found on Rockall (a small islet over 200 miles west of the Hebrides, Scotland) and various other islands. Many prosobranchs lay large-yolked eggs enclosed in horny capsules (e.g., *Nucella, Urosalpinx, Buccinum*, etc.) from which hatch miniature adults. Many nudibranchs enclose their eggs in "jelly cocoons" and the planktonic phase is omitted, or curtailed, apparently without detracting from a wide distribution. Indeed, Thorson (1946) found that in Danish waters 8% of the tectibranchs, 34% of the prosobranchs, and 18% of the bivalves have nonplanktonic larvae. Much higher figures for nonpelagic development are quoted for Arctic, Antarctic, and deep-sea species (Thorson, 1950). It is a practically invariable rule that the numbers of eggs produced by shore molluscs (and indeed by other invertebrates) having planktotrophic larvae are large when compared with those having lecithotrophic larvae or with those which are viviparous or practice "brood protection" in various forms. Since over a period of years any population remains at least approximately constant in numbers, there must be a gigantic wastage of larvae which is greater in species with planktotrophic larvae than in those having greater provision for their young. Thorson gives good reasons for the belief that the main cause of wastage is predation in the plankton. Why then is this type of development adopted by so many benthonic species? The usual answer is that the pelagic larval phase is mainly of use in dispersing the species, thus preventing overcrowding. But the adults of many species with planktotrophic larvae are closely crowded—consider, for example, limpets or mussels—but their populations are obviously thriving. Perhaps the survival value of a pelagic larval phase is that it allows access to the rich food supplies of the plankton and, understandably, the food requirements are often different and greater, weight for weight, than those of the adults (Zeuthen, 1947; Thorson, 1950), (see also Chapter 6). Certain it is that the main spawning periods for most molluscs occur when the phyto- and nano-plankton are most abundant.

A review of the invertebrate animals as a whole reveals that a great variety, perhaps the majority, of those with pelagic larvae include features in their life-history which are unconnected with dispersion. These features include behavioral ones (Ewer, 1956), such as the ability of the larvae to delay metamorphosis until an acceptable substratum is reached (see Wilson, 1952, for an excellent summary of factors affecting settlement), sometimes followed by preferential settlement (gregariousness) in areas occupied by members of the same species (Cole and Knight-Jones, 1939; Knight-Jones, 1951, 1953a,b; Knight-Jones and Crisp, 1953), and, involving a period of "searching" for a suitable substratum, e.g. in *Hiatella* (Hunter, 1949) or *Adalaria* on the bryozoan, *Electra pilosa* and *Tritonia* on *Alcyonium* (Thompson, 1958, 1962). Juvenile bottom stages, scattered over wide areas, may later migrate and aggregate in the zone populated by the adults as, for example, do littorinids (Fraenkel, 1927; J. E. Smith and Newell, 1955). A remarkable example is given by Verwey (1952, 1954, 1957) who shows that the larvae of *Mytilus edulis*, when ready to metamorphose, require a high light intensity before they settle and so tend to settle in shallow waters. The juveniles have a preference for dark, thread-like material for their attachment but, after growing for some time, they detach themselves and are transported by currents to resettle in other places (de Blok and Geelen, 1958). This behavior may be repeated several times but eventually they "seek" a stable substratum rich in niches, such as are provided by banks of adult mussels, and there they remain.

B. *Behavior*

Recently it has been shown (Newell, 1960, 1962) that the adults of the small prosobranch *Peringia* (= *Hydrobia*) *ulvae,* occupy a mainly mid-tide level zone on mud flats at low tide, crawling and browsing on the surface. Then they burrow for a time and resurface just before the incoming tide reaches them. After that they float by means of a mucous raft, which also serves to entrap the plankton that is engulfed by means of the radula. The cycle of tidal activities is completed by the animals sinking to the bottom again when the receding tide reaches the zone occupied by the animals at low water. This is an example of an intertidal gastropod with an unusual range of movement, but most gastropods (and also some bivalves) retain their motility although some of them have remarkable powers of adhering to rocks. *Patella,* an extreme example, can resist dislodgment by a force equal to 15 kg (Pelseneer, 1935), or a straight pull equal to a force of 70 lb for a limpet having a base area of a little less than 1 sq in. (Sinel, 1906). Others, e.g., chitons, trochids, and littorinids, although able to cling to surfaces, avoid wave action or desiccation by seeking the less-exposed places, often congregating in crevices, or beneath stones or algae. Most of them crawl about and feed for part of the tidal cycle. If their movements were disorientated it is obvious that after a time the species would be randomly dispersed, but during these excursions some gastropods and bivalves are known to orientate to environmental cues, such as light and gravity, and kineses (Fraenkel and Gunn, 1940) in response to various stimuli have often been observed. F. Evans (1961) reports that on the Ghana coast *Littorina punctata* orientates not only to the sun and to gravity but also to the configuration of the shore line which implies that in this animal there is, even if somewhat limited, a degree of "form vision" recalling that postulated for *Talitrus saltator* by Williamson (1951). A feature common to the movements which have been studied from this point of view is that the sign of the response to a directional stimulus reverses after a time so that the animal retraces its path and arrives back at roughly the place from which it started (Fraenkel, 1927; F. G. C. Evans, 1951; Burdon-Jones and Charles, 1958; Newell, 1958a,b; Brafield and Newell, 1961). These orientated excursions reach their greatest precision in limpets of various kinds and it is generally believed that some kind of "memory" of the topography helps to ensure accurate return to their particular scar on the rock face (see Thorpe, 1956, for summary and references).

After arrival at their final station on the shore many species of molluscs adopt a sedentary mode of life and thereafter are suspension or deposit feeders. Among these must be counted all the deep burrowers into mud, sand, wood, or rocks; those bivalves which attach themselves by a permanent byssus made mainly of collagen (Rudall, 1955); and gastropods of such families as Vermetidae and Siliquariidae. For a review of molluscan borers see P. H. Fischer (1950) and Yonge (1951, 1955). The consensus of opinion (Hunter, 1949) is that boring into rocks can be accounted for largely by movements of the shell valves, although Yonge (1955) gives good evidence for the view that *Lithophaga* (but not the allied *Botula*) first softens calcareous rocks by a secretion of glands on the anterior edge of the mantle, while Carriker (1955) finds that the oyster drill, *Urosalpinx cinerea,* softens the shell of its prey by secretions of the glands in the accessory proboscis located in the foot. Similar glands have been described in other stenoglossans by Fretter (1941, 1946). The nature of these secretions is not well known. Yonge (1955), adhering to the views of earlier workers, postulates "an acid mucus," an idea which is certainly made more tenable by the discovery by Thompson (1960a,b) that several naked gastropods can secrete mixtures of hydrochloric and sulfuric acids sufficiently strong to lower the pH value to 2 or in one instance to 1. On the other hand, it is possible that chelating compounds, known to exist in bivalves (Simkiss, 1960), may be used by some species for the removal of calcium carbonate from rocks and shells. Obviously, the subject needs more investigation.

III. RESPIRATION AND EXCRETION OF SHORE MOLLUSCS

A. Respiration

Most shore-dwelling prosobranchs are to varying degrees adapted for aerial breathing. In many, the roof of the mantle cavity is thin, vascularized, and acts as an additional respiratory surface. This is particularly true for high level littorinids and shore pulmonates such as members of the Siphonariidae, Otinidae, and Amphibolidae. These have become readapted for aquatic breathing also by the development of a secondary gill. But all can breathe under water, a respiratory current being maintained mainly by ciliary tracts. Obviously, a delicate balance must be struck between the need to resist desiccation and the requirements of gaseous interchange. Thus practically all prosobranchs have retained the operculum on the hinder part of the foot which, when the body is withdrawn (as it usually is when the tide recedes), closes the shell aperture. When the tide withdraws, most shore "snails" close down partially or completely after taking in a bubble of air which is released, along with accumulated feces, as soon as the animals become active again on reimmersion. "Limpets," on the other hand, can clamp down firmly on the rocks (although under humid conditions they may become active when the tide is out), fitting snugly into scars made by the shell margins. Usually, however, they do not clamp down firmly and air can enter and leave

the mantle cavity. All but a few bivalves can close their cavities by contraction of the adductor muscles (whose special properties are discussed
in Chapter 10.

Many shore molluscs must rely partly or solely on cutaneous respiration and many small prosobranchs which inhabit intertidal pools have
no ctenidia and only small mantle cavities; e.g., members of the Omalo-
gyridae, Rissoellidae, and Pyramidellidae (Fretter, 1948). A full account
of the functional morphology of the pallial complex of prosobranchs is
given by Yonge (1947) and that of the siphonariids in later papers (1952,
1958). Even those shore molluscs (the vast majority) which retain
ctenidia would seem the more efficient if they did not rely entirely on
these organs as respiratory surfaces. Like other forms of gills, ctenidia
function efficiently only when a current of water is passing over them,
whereas the less specialized surfaces of the mantle and foot can, because
of their large area, at least in some pulmonates (Pelseneer, 1935), account
for over 50% of gaseous interchange—an interesting parallel with, for
example, the eel (Carter, 1957) which can live for long periods out of
water. Figures for the degree of cutaneous respiration in shore molluscs
are few but its importance can be inferred from the following considerations. (*1*) Some prosobranchs (for example Lepetidae) (Yonge, 1960),
some nudibranchs and some pulmonates (for example, many of the On-
chidiidae) have neither ctenidia, pallial gills, nor a lung. (2) In many
instances part or all of the blood supply from the general surface returns
to the auricle without passing through any special respiratory organ.
Some of the blood from the mantle of chitons goes direct to the auricle,
by-passing the gills, and the same is true for many prosobranchs (for
example, Littorinidae, Cyclostomidae, Vermetidae), for opisthobranchs
(Scaphandridae and doubtless many others), and even more conspicu-
ously in most bivalves (Pelseneer, 1935). (*3*) In a few instances experimental evidence is available which also indicates an important role for
cutaneous respiration. Thus it is known that the lung of some freshwater
and land pulmonates can be put out of action by filling it with paraffin
wax after which respiration is reduced but not abolished. Of the common shore gastropods only the littorinids, *L. neritoides* and *L. rudis*
(= *saxatilis*) have been well studied from this point of view. P. H. Fischer
et al. (1933) reported that the oxygen consumption of these animals
falls by five or six times when the animals are out of water, but their
figures refer to quiescent animals and the respiratory rate may be much
higher when the animals crawl about. Even when exposed to air the
shell valves of many bivalves do not close completely and the free edges
of the mantle protrude through the shell gape, but information is not
available to show whether or not cutaneous aerial respiration can play a
significant part in respiration. That some exchange between the "closed"

animal and the external medium can take place has been shown for
Scrobicularia plana by Freeman and Rigler (1957), the osmotic pressure
of the blood decreasing by about 1.5% per hour when the animal is
placed in dilute sea water—a much slower rate than when the shell is
open. Nevertheless, provided that the integument is permeable to oxygen
and the oxygen tension of the tissues just below it is lower than that in
the air, some uptake of oxygen is inevitable. Similarly, carbon dioxide
would be lost. There is some evidence that to a varying degree bivalves
can respire anaerobically when the tide uncovers them. Obviously, facul-
tative anaerobiosis has great survival value to intertidal animals. Moore
(1931) found that *Syndosmya* (*Abra*) *alba* could survive in deoxygen-
ated water, with which it retained connection with its siphons, for 3½
days, while Ricketts and Calvin (1948) report that *Mya arenaria* can
survive for 8 days without oxygen during which period the glycogen of
its tissues decreased. L. Patané, (1946a,b, 1955) found that both *Littorina
neritoides* and *L. punctata* can survive for a duration of several weeks
in pure nitrogen. Normally, *Mya arenaria* does not remove more than
between 5 and 10% of the oxygen from the water passing through its
mantle cavity, but after being uncovered by the tide it gradually builds
up an oxygen debt and when reimmersed its rate of utilization rises. The
longer the period of exposure the higher is the utilization coefficient so
that after 20 hours' exposure it rises to 20%; moreover, the rate at which
water is passed through the body increases (van Dam, 1935). This may
be viewed as an adaptation to life on intertidal mudflats. Dugal (1939)
found that *Venus mercenaria* can respire anaerobically also. The subject
of anaerobiosis in animals is dealt with fully by von Brand (1946). Bivalves such as oysters and mussels (Dodgson, 1928) simply close down
completely under conditions of low oxygen and can live without oxygen
for long periods. The mussel, like *Mya*, builds up an oxygen debt to be
repaid by an increased rate of pumping when the tide returns (Schlieper,
1957). That not all bivalves behave in this way is shown by the work of
Morton *et al.* (1957) on *Lasaea rubra* which, although it does not take
up oxygen when exposed to air for 3 hours, resumes respiration at the
normal rate when reimmersed in water.

Most, probably all, shore prosobranchs have hemocyanin as a respiratory pigment but at best this serves to increase the oxygen carrying
capacity of the blood by only about 3% (Carter, 1931). Many also have
hemoglobin in certain muscles which may act as an oxygen store (Ball and
Meyerhof, 1940). As shown by Redfield *et al.* (1926), the blood of the
stenoglossan, *Busycon canaliculatum*, shows a reversed Bohr effect, i.e.,
its blood when oxygenated will combine with more carbon dioxide than
will reduced blood under comparable conditions, and the presence of
carbon dioxide increases the affinity of the hemocyanin for oxygen.

This is the reverse of what happens in bloods containing hemoglobin, or, indeed, in the hemocyanin-containing blood of cephalopods. The ecological repercussions of this are not clear. As Redfield (1934) remarks "It may be argued that this property of the blood favours absorption of oxygen at the gill. The ease with which the phenomenon may be shown to be an advantage, irrespective of which way the system works, makes one very sceptical of the teleological argument." On the other hand, Scheer (1948) concludes that this property of the blood is advantageous since oxygen deficiency "even down to 10–20 mm tension" will not seriously reduce the oxygen supply to the *Busycon* tissues. Certain it is that the hemocyanins of such prosobranchs as have been studied have low loading tensions; i.e., they are saturated at low oxygen tensions and this can be regarded as an adaptation for life under poorly oxygenated conditions (as, for example, when the animals withdraw into their shells when the tide is out). On the other hand, this property of the blood means that the oxygen tension of the blood must be low all the time it is giving up oxygen to the tissues. But it must be remembered that when uncovered by the tide most shore molluscs become relatively inactive and their oxygen requirements correspondingly small.

B. Excretion

Delaunay (1931), Needham (1935, 1938, 1950), Spitzer (1937), and Heidermanns (1937) have shown that the nature of the end products of nitrogen metabolism of any species is related to the relative toxicity of ammonia (the primary product of deamination), urea, and uric acid, and to the ease with which these can be eliminated, bearing in mind the availability of water, particularly during embryonic development. Ammonia, the most toxic of the three, can be got rid of in the requisite extreme dilution only by aquatic animals. Urea, very soluble, must also be eliminated along with water, but uric acid is almost insoluble and practically innocuous in the concentrations in which it can occur dissolved. Moreover, it can be eliminated in the solid state with practically no water loss. Molluscs are no exception to the general rule that aquatic species tend to be ammoniotelic or ureotelic and that terrestrial species tend to be uricotelic. But in all molluscs a high but variable proportion of the nonprotein nitrogen is excreted as amino acids, purines, and other compounds (Vol. II, Chapter 7) as well as ammonia. Tables I–IV given by Needham (1935) show that terrestrial pulmonates excrete more uric acid than do aquatic species and that high level species of littorinids excrete more uric acid than do species living lower down the shore. Yet the correlation between shore level and degree of uricotely is not very exact for other series and more information is required before the rule can be extended to all shore molluscs. Moreover, the correlation between the degree of uricotely and the type of embryonic development does not hold even for the littorinid series for, *contra* Needham, *L. neritoides* (the littorinid living in the "splash zone") is oviparous; *L. littoralis* (= *obtusata*) (found on the middle shore) hatches as a miniature adult from large yolked eggs laid in a "cocoon"; and *L. littorea* (the lowest level littorinid) is oviparous, with a lengthy pelagic life. From the type of embryonic development it might be expected that *L. neritoides* would be less uricotelic than *L. littoralis*, but it is not so. Earlier references (by author, name and date only) to excretion in molluscs are given by Pelseneer (1935).

IV. PHYSIOLOGICAL VARIATIONS IN INTERTIDAL MOLLUSCS

A. *Variations with Latitude and Temperature*

Compared with some of the basic concepts of ecology, the idea that many poikilotherms vary physiologically with latitude both at the inter- and intraspecific level and with differing conditions even within a single large habitat is a comparatively new one. Its growth has been traced by Bullock (1955) and Dehnel (1955) to whose papers reference should be made for a summary of such information as was then available and also for their extensive bibliographies. These two works deal only with variations which directly or indirectly can be regarded as physiological compensations for differences in temperature, but the wider aspects of physiological variations are fully reviewed by Prosser (1955), who also gives a full discussion of the possible mechanisms underlying physiological adjustments or "acclimations," as they are often called (Bullock, 1955).

The observable activities of different populations of most eurythermal species do not differ materially with those differences in temperature which they experience (which often vary with latitude) although, of course, the rates of activity of individuals drawn from any one population will vary with temperature, as may be conveniently expressed by the Q_{10} or as rate/temperature curves. In some instances the difference in activity in the same or between related species, living at different temperatures, is less than would be expected from the Q_{10} measured for each population. Mayer (1914) pointed out that the rate of pulsation of the medusa, *Aurelia aurita*, is about the same at 29°C in the tropical Atlantic as at 14°C off Nova Scotia. Fox (1936), who discussed the same kind of phenomenon for a variety of equivalent species in cold and warmer waters and measured their oxygen consumptions at different temperatures, was the first to place such studies on an experimental basis. He found that the oxygen consumption of the warmer water species is greater than that of the colder water species when measured at the temperatures at which each normally lives, although the locomotory activity of the former is apparently no greater. He suggested that the two equivalent species require approximately equal amounts of oxygen for their locomotion but that the nonlocomotory oxygen consumption of the warmer water species is higher than that of the colder water ones.

Molluscs are among the many different types of animals which have been studied from this point of view, but information on the effects of environmental factors other than temperature is meager; for other kinds of animals, particularly insects, much is known about the repercussions of other "environmental stresses" (Prosser, 1955). A short summary of physiological variation in shore molluscs follows. Spärck (1936) found that species of bivalves from Greenland and Denmark had a higher oxygen consumption at any particular temperature than corresponding species from the Mediterranean. Thorson (1936, 1946, 1950) showed that species of bivalves from one genus but from arctic, boreal, and tropical waters have about the same rates of metabolism at the temperatures at which they normally live. Hopkins (1946) found that the oxygen consumption of tissues of populations of *Venus mercenaria* acclimated to cold water is higher at any given temperature than of those from warm-acclimated populations. Stauber (1950) investigated the behavior of the oyster drill, *Urosalpinx cinerea*, from waters with different temperatures and reports that those from Delaware will drill only above 10°C while those from Virginia require a temperature of 15°C or over before drilling. Their spawning temperatures also vary (see also Carriker, 1955; Hanks, 1957). Rao (1953a) compared the pumping rates of *Mytilus californianus* from three widely spaced latitudes, Friday Harbor, Fort Ross, and Los Angeles, and found that they were the same in populations living at 6.5°C, 10°C, and 12°C, while the Q_{10} was lower for specimens of the same size collected from higher than from lower latitudes. The ratio of body weight/weight of shell is greater in higher latitude populations.

Studies on the rate of growth of molluscs at different latitudes dates back to Weymouth *et al.* (1931), who found that growth in populations of the razor clam, *Siliqua patula*, along the Pacific Coast of North America is initially more rapid but stops sooner in the southern than in northern populations. Newcombe (1936) and Newcombe and Kessler (1936) obtained similar results for *Mya arenaria*. Swan (1952) also reports that southern populations of *Mya arenaria* grow more rapidly than northern ones, while Thorson's (1936) results indicate the same phenomenon for a variety of molluscs. On the whole, southern species have a shorter life and attain a smaller final size than northern ones. Carefully controlled experiments by Dehnel (1955) on four species of prosobranchs which have a range from Alaska to California show that the rates of growth of embryos and larvae from northern populations are from two to nine times as great at a given comparable temperature. Each of these species lays encapsulated telolecithal eggs (so ruling out effects due to differences in food supply). Dehnel's results are of the greatest interest since they show that, as for other activities, there is a compensatory effect in rates of growth (not brought out by previous studies) in a series of molluscs, the northern populations always growing faster than the southern ones when reared at the same temperature. Loosanoff and Nomejko (1951) report that American oysters (*Crassostrea virginica*) are divisible into different geographical races, with the more northern ones breeding at lower temperatures than the more southern ones. Korringa (1952, 1957) discusses this problem for the European oyster, *Ostrea edulis*.

B. Variations with Salinity

Only a few references can be traced to works dealing with physiological variations correlated with differences in salinity, although many species of euryhaline molluscs are known. For example, Schlieper (1957) reports the results of comparative studies on *Mytilus edulis* (which seems to be poikilosmotic, i.e., incapable of active regulation) acclimated to the North Sea (30‰ salinity) and Western Baltic (15‰ salinity). The brackish water mussels have less active gill cilia, a slower heartbeat and less resistance to heat, but their gills have a higher oxygen consumption. After a time, which varies with temperature but is not complete until after several weeks, these physiological differences disappear when specimens from the two populations are transposed, suggesting that they do not belong to genetically or physiologically distinct races (see also Schlieper and Kowalski (1956, 1957).

An excellent and compact account with a good bibliography of the ecological repercussion of variations in salinity is given by Pearse and Gunter (1957) and a fuller one by Pearse (1950).

C. Variations with Shore Level and Habitat

Instances of physiological variation within a single large habitat are less numerous than those recorded for variations with latitude but are no less convincing. For instance, Segal *et al.* (1953) and Segal (1956) discovered that the heartbeat of specimens of *Acmaea limatula* taken from low down the shore is consistently faster than that of those from higher shore levels. This difference is attributed to temperature differences between the two habitats, the upper shore animals experiencing both higher and lower temperatures but being acclimated to the higher (average) temperature. When low level "limpets" are transplanted to higher levels their heartbeat slows down and in about 29 days is fully acclimated, and vice versa. Comparisons between winter and summer show that both high and low level animals have faster heartbeats in winter at any temperature between 9° and 29°C. Low level limpets have a heart rate less dependent on temperature changes than high level ones in the range of 9°–19°C, and low level specimens are "cold-depressed" at higher temperatures than the warm-adapted, high level ones. The size of the gonads also varies with tidal level, and low level animals have a larger gonad in the winter than higher level animals. The two groups spawn out of phase and high level animals do not contribute to the breeding population. Rao (1953b, 1954) obtained similar results in study of *Mytilus californianus* and *M. edulis*, the pumping rate and the shell weight/body weight ratio being higher for specimens at low than for those at high levels on the shore. Much the same story can be told for *Lasaea rubra* (Ballantine and Morton, 1956); specimens from high up the shores as a rule are smaller in absolute size but have a higher pumping rate than those from lower down the shore. Indeed, during the first hour of immersion, high level specimens filter and respire at about twice the rate of those from low down the shore, can tolerate a greater range of salinity, and more quickly become active in response to splashing by waves, all of which are obviously adaptive compensations (Morton *et al.*, 1957). Berry (1961), in a study of a population of *Littorina saxatilis* (= *rudis*) on a stony beach, has shown that animals high up the shore grow faster, mature quicker, and produce more young than those at lower levels.

Some of the earlier evidence for physiological variations within a single species with position on the shore has already been alluded to. Some of this needs reinvestigation as, for example, that presented for *Littorina* by Gowanloch and Hayes (1926), who reported differences in behavioral responses between high and low level winkles, an alternative explanation of which is offered by Newell (1958a,b).

D. *The Underlying Causes for Physiological Variation*

While the adaptive nature of the physiological variations reported can hardly be questioned, their underlying causes await full investigation. In most instances the evidence clearly points to phenotypic variations, although Prosser (1955) quotes many examples from other groups of animals for which genetic differences must be invoked. Also, as he points out, "It is probable that if populations were examined for physiological variations as carefully as they have been for minute structural variations, many more races and subspecies would be found than are now recognised." A most interesting pointer for future investigations lies in the work of Staiger (1957), who showed that the very variable species *Nucella lapillus* has two main forms which are fully interfertile, one having a haploid chromosome number of 13 and the other of 18. When interbred any possible combination is possible in the diploid condition, and somatic variation in local and regional populations has a genetic basis. The form with 13 chromosomes occupies exposed situations and that with 18 chromosomes, sheltered places, but all sorts of intermediate habitats are colonized in which both types live and interbreed to give chromosomally heterogeneous populations. Pure types attain the largest size whereas shell thickness and weight/size ratio is greatest in heterogeneous populations.

REFERENCES

Baker, S. M. (1909). On the causes of zoning of brown seaweeds on the sea-shore I. *New Phytologist* **8**, 196–202.

Baker, S. M. (1910). On the causes of zoning of brown seaweeds on the sea-shore II. *New Phytologist* **9**, 54–67.

Bakker, K. (1959). Feeding habits and zonation in some intertidal snails. *Arch. néerl. zool.* **13**, 230–257.

Ball, E. G., and Meyerhof, O. (1940). The occurrence of iron porphyrin compounds and succinic dehydrogenase in marine organisms possessing the copper blood pigment, hemocyanin. *J. Biol. Chem.* **134**, 483–493.

Ballantine, D., and Morton, J. E. (1956). Filtering, feeding and digestion in the lamellibranch, *Lasaea rubra*. *J. Marine Biol. Assoc. U.K.* **35**, 241–274.

Barry, R. J. C., and Munday, K. A. (1959). Carbohydrate levels in *Patella*. *J. Marine Biol. Assoc. U.K.* **38**, 81–95.

Berry, A. J. (1961). Some factors affecting the distribution of *Littorina saxatilis* (Olivi). *J. Animal Ecol.* **30**, 27–45.

Beveridge, A. E., and Chapman, V. J. (1950). The zonation of marine algae at Piha, New Zealand, in relation to the tidal factor (studies in intertidal zonation 2). *Pacific Sci.* **4**, No. 3, 188–201.

Biebl, R. (1952). Ecological and non-environmental constitutional resistance of the protoplasm of marine algae. *J. Marine Biol. Assoc. U.K.* **31**, 307–315.

Boney, A. D., and Corner, E. D. S. (1959). Application of toxic agents in the study of the ecological resistance of intertidal red algae. *J. Marine Biol. Assoc. U.K.* **38**, 267–275.

Boney, A. D., and Corner, E. D. S. (1962). The effect of light on the growth of sporelings of the intertidal red alga *Plumaria elegans* (Bonnem.) Schm. *J. Marine Biol. Assoc. U.K.* **42**, 65–92.

Braams, W. G., and Geelen, H. J. F. M. (1953). The preference of some nudibranchs for certain coelenterates. *Arch. néerl. zool.* **10**, 241–264.

Brafield, A., and Newell, G. E. (1961). The behaviour of *Macoma balthica* (L.). *J. Marine Biol. Assoc. U.K.* **41**, 81–87.

Broekhuysen, G. J. (1940). A preliminary investigation of the importance of desiccation, temperature and salinity as factors controlling the vertical distribution of certain intertidal marine gastropods in False Bay, South Africa. *Trans. Roy. Soc. S. Africa* **28**, 255–292.

Brongersma-Sanders, M. (1957). Mass mortality in the sea. *Geol. Soc. Am. Mem.* **67**, No. 1, 941–1010.

Bullock, T. H. (1955). Compensation for temperature in the metabolism and activity of poikilotherms. *Biol. Revs. Cambridge Phil. Soc.* **30**, 311–342.

Burdon-Jones, C., and Charles, G. H. (1958). Light reactions of littoral gastropods. *Nature* **181**, 129–131.

Carnahan, J. A. (1952). Intertidal zonation at Rangitoto Island, New Zealand (studies in intertidal zonation 4). *Pacific Sci.* **6**, No. 1, 35–46.

Carriker, M. R. (1955). Critical review of biology and control of oyster drills *Urosalpinx* and *Eupleura*. *U.S. Fish Wildlife Serv., Spec. Sci. Rept., Fisheries Ser.* **148**, 150pp.

Carter, G. S. (1931). Aquatic and aerial respiration in animals. *Biol. Revs. Cambridge Phil. Soc.* **6**, 1–35.

Carter, G. S. (1957). Air breathing. *In* "The Physiology of Fishes" (M. E. Brown, ed.), Vol. 1, pp. 65–79. Academic Press, New York.

Chapman, V. J., and Trevarthen, C. B. (1953). General schemes of classification in relation to marine coastal zonation. *J. Ecol.* **41**, No. 1, 198–204.

Cole, H. A., and Knight-Jones, E. W. (1939). Some observations and experiments on the setting behaviour of larvae of *Ostrea edulis*. *J. Conseil permanent intern. exploration mer* **14**, 86–105.

Colgan, N. (1910). Notes on the adaptability of certain littoral mollusca. *Irish Naturalist* **19**, No. 7, 127–133.

Colman, J. (1933). The nature of the intertidal zonation of plants and animals. *J. Marine Biol. Assoc. U.K.* **18**, 435–476.

de Blok, J. W., and Geelen, H. J. F. M. (1958). The substratum required for the settling of Mussels (*Mytilus edulis* L.). *Arch. néerl. zool.* **13**, 446–460.

Dehnel, P. A. (1955). Rate of growth of gastropods as a function of latitude. *Physiol. Zoöl.* **28**, 115–144.

Delaunay, H. (1931). L'excrétion azotée des invertébrés. *Biol. Revs. Cambridge Phil. Soc.* **6**, 265–301.

Delf, E. M. (1942). The significance of the exposure factor in relation to zonation. *Proc. Linnean Soc. London* **154**, 234–236.

Dellow, U. (1950). Intertidal ecology at Narrow Neck Reef, New Zealand (studies in intertidal zonation 3). *Pacific Sci.* **4**, No. 4, 355–374.

Dodgson, R. W. (1928). Report on mussel purification. *Gt. Brit. Fishery Invest., Ser. II* **10**, No. 1, 498pp.

Doty, M. S. (1946). Critical tide factors that are correlated with the vertical distribution of marine algae and other organisms along the Pacific Coast. *Ecology* **27**, 315–328.

Doty, M. S. (1957). Rocky intertidal surfaces. *Geol. Soc. Am. Mem.* **67**, No. 1, 535–585.

Doty, M. S., and Archer, J. G. (1950). An experimental test of the tide-factor hypothesis. *Am. J. Botany* **37**, No. 6, 458–464.

Dugal, L. P. (1939). The use of calcareous shell to buffer the product of anaerobic glycolysis in *Venus mercenaria*. *J. Cellular Comp. Physiol.* **13**, 235–251.

Evans, F. (1961). Responses to disturbance of the periwinkle *Littorina punctata* (Gmelin) on a shore in Ghana. *Proc. Zool. Soc. London* **137**, 393–402.

Evans, F. G. C. (1951). An analysis of the behaviour of *Lepidochitona cinereus* in response to certain physical features of the environment. *J. Animal Ecol.* **20**, 1–10.

Evans, R. G. (1947a). The intertidal ecology of Cardigan Bay. *J. Ecol.* **34**, 273–309.

Evans, R. G. (1947b). The intertidal ecology of selected localities in the Plymouth neighbourhood. *J. Marine Biol. Assoc. U.K.* **17**, 173–218.

Evans, R. G. (1948). The lethal temperatures of some common British littoral molluscs. *J. Animal Ecol.* **45**, 165–173.

Evans, R. G. (1949). The intertidal ecology of rocky shores in south Pembrokeshire. *J. Ecol.* **37**, No. 1, 120–139.

Evans, R. G. (1957). The intertidal ecology of some localities on the Atlantic coast of France. *J. Ecol.* **45**, 245–271.

Ewer, D. W. (1956). Animal ecology and behaviour. *S. African J. Sci.* **52**, 211–215.

Fischer, E. (1929). Recherches de bionomie et d'océanographie littorales sur la Rance et le littoral de la Manche. *Ann. inst. océanogr. Monaco* [N.S.] **5**, 201–429.

Fischer, P. H. (1950). "Vie et moeurs des mollusques," 312pp. Payot, Paris.

Fischer, P. H., Duval, M., and Raffy, A. (1933). Études sur les échanges respiratoires des Littorines. *Arch. zool. exptl. et gén.* **74**, 627–634.

Fox, H. M. (1936). The activity and metabolism of poikilothermal animals in different latitudes. I. *Proc. Zool. Soc. London* **107**, 945–955.

Fraenkel, G. S. (1927). Beiträge zur Geotaxis und Phototaxis von *Littorina*. *Z. vergleich. Physiol.* **5**, 585–597.

Fraenkel, G. S. (1960). Lethal high temperatures for three marine invertebrates, *Limulus polyphemus*, *Littorina littorea* and *Pagurus longicarpus*. *Oikos* **11**, 171–182.

Fraenkel, G. S., and Gunn, D. L. (1940). "The Orientation of Animals—Kineses, Taxes and Compass Reactions," 352pp. Oxford Univ. Press, London and New York.

Freeman, R. F. H., and Rigler, F. H. (1957). The responses of *Scrobicularia plana* (da Costa) to osmotic pressure change. *J. Marine Biol. Assoc. U.K.* **36**, 553–567.

Fretter, V. (1941). The genital ducts of some British stenoglossan prosobranchs. *J. Marine Biol. Assoc. U.K.* **25**, 173–211.

Fretter, V. (1946). The pedal sucker and anal gland of some British stenoglossa. *Proc. Malacol. Soc. London* **27**, 126–130.

Fretter, V. (1948). The structure and life history of some minute prosobranchs of rock pools: *Skeneopsis planorbis* (Fabricius), *Omalogyra atomus* (Philippi), *Rissoella diaphana* (Alder) and *Rissoella opalina* (Jeffreys). *J. Marine Biol. Assoc. U.K.* **28**, 597–632.

Gail, F. W. (1918). Some experiments with *Fucus* to determine the factors controlling its vertical distribution. *Publ. Puget Sound Marine (Biol.) Sta.* **2**, 139–151.

Gail, F. W. (1922). Photosynthesis in some of the red and brown algae as related to light. *Publ. Puget Sound Marine (Biol.) Sta.* **3**, 177–193.

Gowanloch, J. N. (1926). Contributions to the study of marine gastropods. II. The intertidal life of *Buccinum undatum*, a study in non-adaptation. *Contribs. Can. Biol. and Fisheries* **3**, 167–178.

Gowanloch, J. N., and Hayes, F. R. (1926). Contributions to the study of marine gastropods. I. The physical factors, behaviour and intertidal life of *Littorina*. *Contribs. Can. Biol. and Fisheries* **3**, 133–166.

Graham, A. (1955). Molluscan diets. *Proc. Malacol. Soc. London* **31**, 144–159.

Graham, A., and Fretter, V. (1947). The life history of *Patina pellucida* (L.). *J. Marine Biol. Assoc. U.K.* **26**, 590–601.

Guiler, E. R. (1952). The nature of intertidal zonation in Tasmania. *Papers & Proc. Roy. Soc. Tasmania* **86**, 31–61.

Gunter, G. (1957). Temperature. *Geol. Soc. Am., Mem.* **67**, No. 1, 159–184.

Hanks, J. E. (1957). The rate of feeding of the common oyster drill. *Urosalpinx cinerea* (Say), at controlled water temperatures. *Biol. Bull.* **112**, 330–331.

Heidermanns, C. (1937). *Tabulae Biol.* **14**, 209.

Henderson, J. T. (1929). Lethal temperatures of lamellibranchiata. *Contribs. Can. Biol. and Fisheries* **4**, No. 25, 399–411.

Herdman, W. (1890). *Proc. Liverpool Biol. Soc.* **4**, 36–79.

Hodgkin, E. P. (1959). Catastrophic destruction of the littoral fauna and flora near Fremantle, January 1959. *West Australian Naturalist* **7**, 6–11.

Hopkins, H. S. (1946). The influence of season, concentration of seawater and environmental temperature upon the O_2 consumption of tissues in *Venus mercenaria*. *J. Exptl. Zool.* **102**, 143–158.

Hunter, W. Russell (1949). The structure and behaviour of *"Hiatella gallicana"*

(Lamarck) and *"H. arctica"* (L.) with special reference to the boring habit. *Proc. Roy. Soc. Edinburgh* **B63**, 271–289.

Huntsman, A. G., and Sparks, M. I. (1924). Limiting factors for marine animals. III. Relative resistance to high temperatures. *Contribs. Can. Biol. and Fisheries* **2**, 95–114.

Isaac, W. E. (1933). Some observations and experiments on the drought resistance of *Pelvetia canaliculata*. *Ann. Botany (London)* **47**, 343–348.

Isaac, W. E. (1935). A preliminary study of the water loss of *Laminaria digitata* during intertidal exposure. *Ann. Botany (London)* **49**, 109–117.

Jones, W. E. (1959). Experiments on some effects of certain environmental factors on *Gracilaria verrucosa* (Hudson) Papenfuss. *J. Marine Biol. Assoc. U.K.* **38**, 153–167.

Kanwisher, J. W. (1955). Freezing in intertidal animals. *Biol. Bull.* **109**, 56–63.

Kanwisher, J. (1959). Histology and metabolism of frozen intertidal animals. *Biol. Bull.* **116**, 258–264.

Knight-Jones, E. W. (1951). Gregariousness and some other aspects of the setting behaviour of *Spirorbis borealis* (Serpulidae). *J. Marine Biol. Assoc. U.K.* **30**, 201–222.

Knight-Jones, E. W. (1953a). Laboratory experiments on gregariousness during setting in *Balanus balanoides* and other barnacles. *J. Exptl. Biol.* **30**, 584–598.

Knight-Jones, E. W. (1953b). Some further observations on gregariousness in marine larvae. *Brit. J. Animal Behaviour* **1**, 81–82.

Knight-Jones, E. W., and Crisp, D. J. (1953). Gregariousness in barnacles in relation to the fouling of ships and to anti-fouling research. *Nature* **171**, 1109–1110.

Knox, G. A. (1953). The intertidal ecology of Taylor's Mistake, Banks Peninsula. *Trans. Roy. Soc. New Zealand* **81**, 189–220.

Korringa, P. (1952). Recent advances in oyster biology. *Quart. Rev. Biol.* **27**, 339–365.

Korringa, P. (1957). Water temperature and breeding throughout the geographical range of *Ostrea edulis*. *Année biol.* [3] **33**, 109–116.

Lewis, J. R. (1954). Observations on a high-level population of limpets. *J. Animal Ecol.* **23**, 85–100.

Lewis, J. R. (1955). The mode of occurrence of the universal intertidal zones in Great Britain. *J. Ecol.* **43**, No. 1, 270–289.

Loosanoff, V. L., and Nomejko, C. A. (1951). Existence of physiologically different races of oysters, *Crassostrea virginica*. *Biol. Bull.* **101**, 151–156.

Mayer, A. G. (1914). The effects of temperature on tropical animals. *Papers Tortugas Lab.* **6**, 3–24.

Moore, H. B. (1931). The muds of the Clyde Sea Area. III. Chemical and physical conditions; rate and nature of sedimentation; and fauna. *J. Marine Biol. Assoc. U.K.* **17**, 325–358.

Morton, J. E., Boney, A. D., and Corner, E. D. S. (1957). The adaptations of *Lasaea rubra* (Montagu), a small intertidal lamellibranch. *J. Marine Biol. Assoc. U.K.* **36**, 383–405.

Needham, J. (1935). Nitrogen catabolism in invertebrates. *Biochem. J.* **29**, 238–251.

Needham, J. (1938). Contributions of chemical physiology to the problem of reversibility in evolution. *Biol. Revs. Cambridge Phil. Soc.* **13**, 225–251.

Needham, J. (1950). "Biochemistry and Morphogenesis," 785pp. Cambridge Univ. Press, London and New York.

Newcombe, C. L. (1936). A comparative study of the abundance and the rate of growth of *Mya arenaria* L. in the Gulf of St. Lawrence and the Bay of Fundy regions. *Ecology* **17**, 418–428.

Newcombe, C. L., and Kessler, H. (1936). Variations in growth indices of *Mya arenaria* L. on the Atlantic coast of North America. *Ecology* **17**, 429–443.

Newell, G. E. (1954). Animal zones of the North Kent Coast. *South Eastern Naturalist and Antiquary* **49**, 34–54.

Newell, G. E. (1958a). The behaviour of *Littorina littorea* (L.) under natural conditions and its relation to position on the shore. *J. Marine Biol. Assoc. U.K.* **37**, 229–239.

Newell, G. E. (1958b). An experimental analysis of the behaviour of *Littorina littorea* (L.) under natural conditions and in the laboratory. *J. Marine Biol. Assoc. U.K.* **37**, 241–266.

Newell, R. (1960). The behaviour of *Hydrobia ulvae*. *Ann. Rept. Challenger Soc.* **3**, No. 12.

Newell, R. (1962). Behavioural aspects of the ecology of *Peringia* (= *Hydrobia*) *ulvae* (Pennant) Gasteropoda, Prosobranchia). *Proc. Zool. Soc. London* **138**, 49–75.

Orr, P. R. (1955). Heat death. I. Time-temperature relationships in marine animals. *Physiol. Zoöl.* **28**, 290–294.

Patané, L. (1946a). Sulla biologia di *Littorina punctata* (Gm.). *Boll. soc. ital. biol. sper.* **21**, No. 7, 928–929.

Patané, L. (1946b). Anaerobiosi in *Littorina neritoides* (L.). *Boll. soc. ital. biol. sper.* **22**, No. 7, 929–930.

Patané, L. (1955). Cinesi e tropismi, anidro-e anaerobiosi in *Littorina neritoides* (L.). *Boll. accad. sci. nat. Gioenia, sper. IV* **3**, 65–73.

Pearse, A. S. (1950). "The Emigrations of Animals from the Sea," 210pp. Dryden, New York.

Pearse, A. S., and Gunter, G. (1957). Salinity. *Geol. Soc. Am. Mem.* **67**, No 1, 129–158.

Pelseneer, P. (1935). "Essai d'ethologie zoologique d'après l'étude des mollusques," Publ. Fond. Agathon Potter, No. 1, 622pp. Palais des Académies, Brussels.

Prosser, C. L. (1955). Physiological variation in animals. *Biol. Revs. Cambridge Phil. Soc.* **30**, 229–262.

Rao, K. P. (1953a). Rate of water propulsion in *Mytilus californianus* as a function of latitude. *Biol. Bull.* **104**, 171–181.

Rao, K. P. (1953b). Shell weight as a function of intertidal height in a littoral population of pelecypods. *Experientia* **9**, 465.

Rao, K. P. (1954). Tidal rhythmicity of rate of water propulsion in *Mytilus* and its modifiability by transplantation. *Biol. Bull.* **106**, 353–359.

Redfield, A. C. (1934). The haemocyanins. *Biol. Revs. Cambridge Phil. Soc.* **9**, 175–212.

Redfield, A. C., Coolidge, T., and Hurd, A. L. (1926). The transport of oxygen and carbon dioxide by some bloods containing hemocyanin. *J. Biol. Chem.* **69**, 475–509.

Ricketts, E. F., and Calvin, J. (1948). "Between Pacific Tides," 365pp. Stanford Univ. Press, Stanford, California.

Rudall, K. M. (1955). The distribution of collagen and chitin. *Symposia Soc. Exptl. Biol.* **9**, 49–71.

Scheer, B. T. (1948). "Comparative Physiology," 563pp. Wiley, New York.

Schlieper, C. (1957). Comparative study of *Asterias rubens* and *Mytilus edulis* from the North Sea (30 per 1000 S) and the Western Baltic Sea (15 per 1000 S). *Année biol.* [3] **33**, fasc. 3–4, 117–127.

Schlieper, C., and Kowalski, R. (1956). Über den Einfluss des Mediums auf die thermische und osmotische Resistenz des Kiemen gewebes der Mieschschel, *Mytilus edulis* L. *Kiel. Meeresforsch.* **12**, 154–155.

Schlieper, C., and Kowalski, R. (1957). Weitere Beobachtungen zur ökologischen Physiologie der Miesmuschel, *Mytilus edulis* L. *Kiel. Meeresforsch.* **13**, 3–10.

Segal, E. (1956). Microgeographic variation as thermal acclimation in an intertidal mollusc. *Biol. Bull.* **111**, 129–152.

Segal, E., Rao, K. P., and James, T. W. (1953). Rate of activity as a function of intertidal light within populations of some littoral Mollusca. *Nature* **172**, 1108–1111.

Simkiss, K. (1960). Some properties of the organic matrix of the shell of the cockle (*Cardium edule*). *Proc. Malacol. Soc. London* **34**, 88–95.

Sinel, J. (1906). "An Outline of the Natural History of Our Shores," 344pp. Swan Sonnenschein, London.

Smith, A. U. (1958). The resistance of animals to cooling and freezing. *Biol. Revs. Cambridge Phil. Soc.* **33**, 197–253.

Smith, J. E. (1959). Private communication.

Smith, J. E., and Newell, G. E. (1955). The dynamics of the zonation of the common periwinkle (*Littorina littorea* (L.)), on a stony beach. *J. Animal Ecol.* **24**, 35–56.

Southward, A. J. (1958). The zonation of plants and animals on rocky shores. *Biol. Revs. Cambridge Phil. Soc.* **33**, 137–177.

Spärck, R. (1936). On the relation between metabolism and temperature in some marine lamellibranchs and its zoogeographical significance. *Kgl. Danske Videnskab. Selskab, Biol. Medd.* **13**, No. 5, 1–27.

Spärck, R. (1957). The importance of metabolism in the distribution of marine animals. Coll. intern. biol. mar. St. Ruscoff. *Année biol.* [3] **33**, fasc. 5–6, 233–235.

Spitzer, J. M. (1937). Physiologisch-ökologische Untersuchungen über den Exkretstoffwahsel der Mollusken. *Zool. Jahrb., Abt. allgem. Zool. u. Physiol.* **57**, 457–496.

Staiger, H. (1957). Genetical and morphological variation in *Purpura lapillus* with respect to local and regional differentiation of population groups. Coll. intern. biol. mar. St. Roscoff. *Année biol.* [3] **33**, fasc. 5–6, 252–258.

Stauber, L. A. (1950). The problem of physiological species with special reference to oysters and drills. *Ecology* **31**, 108–118.

Stephenson, T. A. (1942). The causes of the vertical and horizontal distribution of organisms between tidemarks in South Africa. *Proc. Linnean Soc. London* **154**, 219–232.

Stephenson, T. A., and Stephenson, A. (1949). The universal features of zonation between tide-marks on rocky coasts. *J. Ecol.* **37**, 289–305.

Swan, E. F. (1952). The growth of the clam, *Mya arenaria* as affected by the substratum. *Ecology* **33**, 530–534.

Thompson, T. E. (1958). The natural history, embryology, larval biology and post-larval development of *Adalaria proxima* (Alder and Hancock) (Gastropoda Opisthobranchia). *Phil. Trans. Roy. Soc.* **B242**, 1–58.

Thompson, T. E. (1960a). Defensive acid-secretion in marine gastropods. *J. Marine Biol. Assoc. U.K.* **39**, 115–122

Thompson, T. E. (1960b). Defensive adaptations in opisthobranchs. *J. Marine Biol. Assoc. U.K.* **39**, 123–134.

Thompson, T. E. (1962). Studies on the ontogeny of *Tritonia hombergi* Cuvier (Gastropoda Opisthobranchia). *Phil. Trans. Roy. Soc.* **B245**, 171–218.

Thorpe, W. H. (1956). "Learning and Instinct in Animals," 493pp. Methuen, London.

Thorson, G. (1936). On larval development, growth and metabolism of arctic bottom invertebrates compared with those of other seas. *Medd. Grønland* **100**, No. 6, 1–155.

Thorson, G. (1946). Reproduction and larval development of Danish marine bottom invertebrates. *Medd. Komm. Havundersøg., Kbh. (Plankton)* **4**, 1–523.

Thorson, G. (1950). Reproductive and larval ecology of marine bottom invertebrates. *Biol. Revs. Cambridge Phil. Soc.* **25**, 1–45.

van Dam, L. (1935). On the utilization of oxygen by *Mya arenaria*. *J. Exptl. Biol.* **12**, 86–94.

van Dongen, A. (1956). The preference of *Littorina obtusata* for Fucaceae. *Arch. néerl. zool.* **11**, 373–386.

Verwey, J. (1952). On the ecology of distribution of cockle and mussel in the Dutch Waddensea. Their role in sedimentation and the source of their food supply. With a short review of feeding behaviour in bivalve molluscs. *Arch. néerl. zool.* **10**, 171–239.

Verwey, J. (1954). De mossel in zijn eisen. Averdruk uit: *Faraday, 24e Jaargang* No. 2, 13pp. Grøningen.

Verwey, J. (1957). Discussion. Coll. intern. biol. mar. St. Roscoff. *Année biol.* [3] **33**, 238.

von Brand, T. (1946). Anaerobiosis in invertebrates. *Biodynamica Monographs* **4**, 328pp.

Weymouth, F. W., McMillin, H. C., and Rich, W. H. (1931). Latitude and relative growth in the razor clam. *Siliqua patula. J. Exptl. Biol.* **8**, 228–249.

Williamson, D. I. (1951). Studies in the biology of Talitridae (Crustacea, Amphipoda): visual orientation in *Talitrus saltator. J. Marine Biol. Assoc. U.K.* **30**, 91–99.

Wilson, D. P. (1952). The influence of the nature of the substratum on the metamorphosis of the larvae of marine animals, especially the larvae of *Ophelia bicornis* Savigny. *Ann. inst. océanogr. (Paris)* [N.S.] **27**, 49–156.

Womersley, H. B. S., and Edmonds, S. J. (1952). Marine coastal zonation in southern Australia in relation to a general scheme of classification. *J. Ecol.* **40**, 84–90.

Yonge, C. M. (1947). The pallial organs in the Aspidobranch Gastropoda and their evolution throughout the mollusca. *Phil. Trans. Roy. Soc.* **B232**, 443–518.

Yonge, C. M. (1949). "The Sea Shore." Collins, London.

Yonge, C. M. (1951). Marine boring organisms. *Research* **4**, 162–167.

Yonge, C. M. (1952). The mantle cavity in *Siphonaria alternata* Say. *Proc. Malacol. Soc. London* **29**, 190–199.

Yonge, C. M. (1955). Adaptation to rock boring in *Botula* and *Lithophaga* (Lamellibranchia, Mytilidae) with a discussion on the evolution of this habit. *Quart. J. Microscop. Sci.* **96**, 383–410.

Yonge, C. M. (1958). Observations on the pulmonate limpet *Trimusculus (Gadinia) reticulatus* (Sowerby). *Proc. Malacol. Soc. London* **33**, 31–37.

Yonge, C. M. (1960). Mantle cavity, habits and habitat in the blind limpet, *Lepeta concentrica* Middendorff. *Proc. Calif. Acad. Sci.* **31**, 103–110.

Zeuthen, E. (1947). Body size and metabolic rate in the animal kingdom with special regard to the marine microfauna. *Compt. rend. trav. lab. Carlsberg, Sér. chim.* **26**, 17–161.

CHAPTER 3

Physiological Aspects of Ecology
in Nonmarine Molluscs

W. Russell Hunter*

DEPARTMENT OF ZOOLOGY, UNIVERSITY OF GLASGOW, SCOTLAND

I. INTRODUCTION

Molluscs are largely marine: the number of species living on land is between one-quarter and one-third of that for the sea, and the number of fresh-water species is very much less (Thiele, 1931; Winckworth, 1950). No amphineuran, scaphopod, or cephalopod has ever colonized land or fresh waters. Terrestrial gastropods consist of the order Stylommatophora (Pulmonata) and (particularly in the tropics) certain genera in the prosobranch superfamilies Neritacea, Archaeotaenioglossa, Littorinacea, and Rissoacea which constitute the "land operculates." Primary physiological adaptations for life on land concern water control, air-breathing, and temperature regulation. In brackish and fresh waters there are a small number of bivalve genera, and both prosobranch and pulmonate gastropods. The primary physiological requirement of the bivalves and the gill-bearing prosobranchs is capacity for osmoregulation. But the majority of fresh-water snails belong to the order Basommato-

* Present address: Department of Zoology, Syracuse University, Syracuse, New York.

phora (Pulmonata), and are primarily air-breathers showing varying degrees of readaptation to aquatic life (Hunter, 1957). In general, non-marine molluscs also possess appropriate reproductive and excretory adaptations.

II. ESTUARINE MOLLUSCS

Bivalves and gastropods found on tidal mud flats in estuaries, and in other brackish-water habitats, include both marine littoral species and specifically estuarine forms. These molluscs must not only be capable of living in lowered salinities but also of withstanding considerable osmotic fluctuation within each tidal cycle. As noted by Milne (1938, 1940) and Bassindale (1940, 1943), salinity fluctuations of the order of 10‰ can occur in one tide in regions where molluscan species are abundant.

Although capacity for osmoregulation is the primary physiological requirement for life in estuaries, recent work on the energetics of osmotic control (Potts, 1954b) has shown that, contrary to early assumptions, only a small part (usually $<1\%$) of the metabolic energy of a nonmarine animal is involved in the osmotic work required (see also Section III below, and Chapter 9 of this volume). Work on certain crustaceans (Beadle and Cragg, 1940) suggested a two-stage adaptation of marine animals to fresh waters, with the immigrant first maintaining blood salts at concentrations near sea-water level by active uptake, and only later acquiring tissue toleration of lower concentrations and the ability to regulate with a hypotonic urine. This hypothesis is untenable in animals like bivalves, in which the first stage in the adaptation must have been the ability to tolerate a lower blood concentration, and thus bring the osmotic work within their capabilities (Potts, 1954b). The intermediate stage first capable of estuarine life could be still poikilosmotic but with tissues tolerant of lower blood salts. Significantly, *Mytilus edulis* seems to be incapable of active osmotic regulation (i.e., is poikilosmotic) but populations are found in many estuaries, in the outer Baltic at 15‰ salinity (Schlieper, 1957; Schlieper and Kowalski, 1957), and as a dwarfed form in the inner Baltic at about 5‰ (Segerstråle, 1949, 1953, 1957). Potts (1954b) also points out that, in a brackish-water animal, the production of urine hypotonic to the blood offers only a very small saving in osmotic work. Apart from salinities, range of temperatures—both diurnally and seasonally—and ranges of pH and of oxygen tensions are much wider in estuaries than in the sea (in temperate regions). Estuarine molluscs are also subjected to variable water currents, much suspended matter in the water, and, in many typical habitats, sustained precipitation of silt.

A general feature of the ecology of estuarine faunas is illustrated by the molluscs: the occurrence in each habitat of relatively few species (in contrast to the faunas of open shores), but these species numerically abundant as individuals. Many estuarine habitats have a macrofauna of only four or five species (Bassindale, 1938; Rees, 1940; Spooner and Moore, 1940). Of the essentially marine species living in estuaries, the cockle, *Cardium edule,* can occur at densities up to 383 per square meter in the Tamar, England (Spooner and Moore, 1940), and 1360–4675 per square meter at Skalling, Denmark (Thamdrup, 1935), and the periwinkle *Littorina littorea* at 320 per square meter in patches in the Clyde. More typically estuarine molluscs include *Scrobicularia plana* with densities up to 1094 per square meter in the Tamar (Spooner and Moore, 1940) and 1025 in the Gwendraeth (Green, 1957), and *Macoma balthica* with 5900 per square meter in the Mersey (Fraser, 1932; Bassindale, 1938). One of the more characteristic estuarine molluscs, the prosobranch snail *Hydrobia ulvae (Peringia ulvae* and *Sabanea ulvae* of some authors), exists in almost "pure culture" reaching densities of 10,000–18,000 per square meter near Cardiff (Rees, 1940); 10,000–28,000 in the Tamar (Spooner and Moore, 1940); 27,000–32,500 in the Forth (Nicol, 1935); 5,400–20,500 (and exceptionally 42,000) in the Clyde (Hunter and Hunter, 1962); and 46,000–60,000 per square meter at Skalling, Denmark (Thamdrup, 1935). A recent attempt at a census of a Clyde population (Hunter and Hunter, 1962), living in an area of less than 2.5 square miles (6.08 sq km) of tidal sands, gave an estimate of 3×10^{10} individuals. The evolutionary significance of such enormous estuarine populations is considerable, especially as each may be potentially panmictic. The existence of biological races in *H. ulvae* having varying resistance to lowered salinity has been suggested (McMillan, 1948). The paucity of species is illustrated in the Exe Estuary (Holme, 1949), where at one station over 61% and at another 73% of the biomass[1] consisted of the two bivalves, *S. plana* and *C. edule.* In *S. plana,* the success of further spatfall may be greatly reduced by the density of adults already present (Green, 1957).

Tropical estuaries usually support a much wider range of species more comparable to the marine facies of a typical open shore. Brackish (even fresh) waters around the Gulf of Bengal, in the East Indies, and in tropical America are rich in recent immigrants from the sea, including molluscs (Annandale, 1923; Hesse, 1924; Hesse *et al.,* 1937). The transition of a marine mollusc to brackish or fresh water seems less difficult under tropical conditions (Panikkar, 1940). Ecological features include the high and relatively constant temperatures of tropical rivers, regular seasonal dilution of surface waters of the sea by rainstorms, and, in many areas, high calcium content of the fresh waters.

---

[1] In this case, the biomass is the total weight of organisms per unit area of the bottom.

III. FRESH-WATER MOLLUSCS

A. General Ecological Factors

1. TEMPERATURE CONDITIONS

In environments provided by fresh waters, physical, chemical, and biotic-trophic conditions vary more widely than in the sea. The temperature range within which some fresh-water molluscs can live practically corresponds to the absolute limits for metabolism in metazoan tissues. A minute bivalve *Pisidium conventus* is found in the fresh waters of Novaya Zemlaya during the brief summer, and thus survives long periods below 0°C (Odhner, 1923). In America, the pulmonate snails, *Stagnicola palustris nuttalliana* and *Fossaria perplexa*, survive over winter in drained canals, including at least 55 days when the maximum temperature was 0°C or below (McNeil and Walter, 1957). The prosobranch snail *Paludestrina aponensis* was reported living at 32°–36°C, and surviving at 46°C, in thermal waters at Abbano in northern Italy (Issel, 1908). The common pulmonate snail *Lymnaea peregra* is also said to survive up to 45°C in thermal waters in the Pyrenees (Issel, 1908), yet the same species can be found actively moving and feeding under ice in ponds in Scotland (Hunter, unpublished). *Physa virginea* was found living in three localities, temperatures 35.5° to 38.7°C, during a detailed survey of the fauna of hot springs in the western United States (Brues, 1928). Recent studies on snail hosts of schistosomes (WHO Study Group, 1957) have shown that adult *Australorbis glabratus* survive temperatures from 0° to 42°C (even 52°C for a few minutes), and can breed at temperatures up to 32°C. Range of temperature experienced in a single fresh-water habitat can be considerable: some tropical swamp waters range from 10° to 42°C. Temperate fresh waters with molluscan populations can range from 0° to 29°C annually, and with a diurnal temperature range of more than 11°C (Boycott, 1936; Hunter, 1953b).

2. CALCIUM CONCENTRATION AND pH

The most important chemical variable is dissolved calcium, varying more than 100-fold in fresh waters with molluscs. In Britain, waters with calcium values of <3 mg/liter can usually support only *Lymnaea peregra*, *Ancylus fluviatilis*, and about 4 species of *Pisidium;* several lakes at 8–10 mg/liter calcium support up to 17 molluscan species each; and an Irish lake at *ca.* 50 mg/liter calcium contains 32 species (Phillips, 1915; Boycott, 1936; Macan, 1950; Hunter, 1957). Of the 62 species of fresh-water molluscs in Britain, 26 can live in soft waters (<10 mg/liter calcium), 6 are found only in harder waters, and the other 30 are all calciphile, requiring water with at least 20 mg/liter calcium (Boycott, 1936). Throughout the world—other environmental factors being equal— "harder" fresh waters undoubtedly support more molluscs than low calcium waters. However, most of those species tolerant of low calcium could survive in, and are found in, harder waters. Attempts have been made to relate molluscan distribution directly with pH (in Britain, few molluscs live at pH lower than 6.0), but clearer correlation is found with calcium content or total alkalinity (Boycott, 1936; Macan, 1950). Significantly, laboratory work has shown that four of the pulmonates transmitting schistosomes can breed between pH 4.8 and 9.8 (WHO Study Group, 1957).

3. TROPHIC STATE OF ENVIRONMENT

It is conventional to classify the larger lakes of the world as ranging from eutrophy, with rich concentrations of plant nutrients, organic bottom muds, and sometimes low oxygen tensions, to oligotrophy with waters lacking plant nutrients and usually highly oxygenated. Complicating this classification are "dystrophic" waters with a relatively high content of acidic organic materials (so-called "humic acid") in solution inhibiting bacterial breakdown and resulting in nutrient sterility. In general, molluscs are most plentiful in eutrophic lakes with hard water, less common in oligotrophic lakes, and absent from certain dystrophic waters with little calcium. Certain species are limited to eutrophic waters, but (as with calcium content) most of those tolerant of oligotrophy can also live in richer conditions. Even within Loch Lomond, the northern "highland" section of the loch is both more dystrophic and more oligotrophic than the southern "lowland" section. Fourteen species of fresh-water gastropods occur in the lowland part, only seven of which extend into the highland section (Hunter, 1957). Of the bivalves, at least three species are limited to the southern part (Hunter, 1955b, 1958b), while significantly the only molluscan species limited to the poorer conditions in deep water in the highland section is the arctic relict bivalve, *Pisidium conventus* (Hunter and Slack, 1958; Hunter, 1958a). Few other molluscs prefer more oligotrophic, or softer, waters. In Sweden, Agrell (1949) notes that with two species of *Unio* and one of *Anodonta*, as with almost all such fresh-water molluscs, both numerical abundance and individual shell weights increase with "rising trophic degree" (i.e., toward eutrophy), but with *Unio tumidus*, maximum population densities are found in oligotrophic waters and shell weights decrease with eutrophy.

A good account of ecological factors affecting the general distribution of fresh-water molluscs is that of Boycott (1936) dealing only with Britain; further data on distributional ecology are included in Alsterberg (1930), Frömming (1936, 1938, 1956), Boettger (1944), Hubendick

(1947), Macan (1950), Hunter (1953b, 1957), WHO Study Group (1957), Deschiens (1957), Mirolli (1958), and van Benthem Jutting (1959a,b). As Macan noted, such studies permit correlations between certain ecological factors and distribution, but little experimental analysis has yet been attempted.

B. Fresh-Water Bivalve Ecology

Adaptation of osmoregulation for life in fresh waters is necessarily more drastic in bivalves, with their method of feeding, than in other invertebrates such as crustaceans. The salt concentration in the blood of *Anodonta cygnea* is only equivalent to about 4% sea water (Potts, 1954a). In molluscs, as in several other invertebrate groups, drastic reduction of the blood concentration is probably essential for colonization of brackish and fresh waters. The energetics of osmotic regulation have been discussed by Potts (1954b), who considers that in *Anodonta* only 1.2% of the total metabolic energy is used for this. The production of urine, hypotonic to the blood but still *ca.* 100 times more concentrated than the medium, can give high efficiency in osmoregulation and reduced osmotic work. Hiscock (1953) has shown that the Australian freshwater bivalve *Hyridella australis* can, by closure of the shell valves, be effectively sealed off from short-term changes in the external medium (but see Chapter 2). This mechanism had been invoked to explain the survival of the poikilosmotic *Mytilus edulis* in estuarine conditions (Milne, 1940), but the tissues of *M. edulis* are clearly euryhaline (Schlieper, 1957; Segerstråle, 1957; see Section II above).

Hiscock (1953) also notes that shell closure allows *H. australis* to survive desiccation for 3 months. There are many older records of prolonged drought resistance in fresh-water bivalves (see Kew, 1893), and a recent authenticated case (Dance, 1958) of an African unionid *Aspatharia petersi* surviving for 12.5 months in dry air. Ability to withstand desiccation probably represents adaptation to the discontinuities in space and time of many bodies of fresh water. Similarly directed adaptations concern larval development in bivalves.

Only *Dreissena polymorpha* has free veligers and is probably a recent immigrant to fresh water, having spread westward through Europe from the Black Sea area during the nineteenth century. All others retain the developing embryos in a "marsupium" in the exhalent part of the mantle cavity, often within the outer demibranch of each gill. The Sphaeriidae produce only few young, more or less serially (Boycott, 1936; Thiel, 1926a,b), and liberate these when relatively large and almost adult in structure. The larger fresh-water mussels spawn young in enormous numbers (10^5 to 10^6), as relatively small "glochidia." These larvae, in many species armed with hooks and hinged spines, show obligatory parasitism of aquatic vertebrates as a necessary stage in their life cycle (Arey, 1932a,b,c; Baer, 1952). After attachment by their spines or a byssus thread to the host's gills or fins, these larval parasites become enclosed by growth of the host epidermis; then the embryonic mantle secretes enzymes and digests and assimilates part of the host tissue (Arey, 1932a). Subsequently the glochidium undergoes a metamorphosis involving complete histolysis of the larval organs. Once the adult organs are formed, the young mussel breaks out of the host "cyst" and falls to the bottom to grow to adult size. For several species, there is clear evidence that specific hosts, either fish or urodeles, are required for successful metamorphosis. Newly spawned glochidia will attach to a wide variety of hosts, but are sloughed off by most before metamorphosis. Further, even the normal species of vertebrate host can acquire an immunity to subsequent glochidial infection (Arey, 1932c; Baer, 1952).

An even more specialized parasitic development has been elucidated in an African fresh-water mussel, *Mutela bourguignati* (Fryer, 1959). The larvae are released each with a temporary filamentous tentacle more than 70 times the length of the larva; they attach to the fins of a cyprinid fish, *Barbus,* and then develop a pair of long tubes which penetrate the host. The parasitic postlarva is then not only unlike any mollusc but could be mistaken for a fungal hypha (Fryer, 1959). Later growth and differentiation of the outer end of the protruding stalk produce a typical small bivalve, which becomes capable of normal ciliary feeding before dropping off, leaving the stalk and "feeding tubes" attached to the host.

Even in the commoner species of *Anodonta* and *Unio,* young postglochidial bivalves have rarely been found, and practically nothing is known about the development, growth, or ecology of newly metamorphosed fresh-water mussels.

Again in some fresh-water habitats a single species of bivalve may be abundant. In a suitable locality densities of *Sphaerium corneum* up to 1420 per square meter occur in patches (Hunter, unpublished), and there are hard water rivers in many parts of the world where areas of the stream bottom are "paved" with larger unionids. Examples of distributional ecology in relation to eutrophy and calcium content are quoted above (Section III,A), and there are many "poor" or temporary fresh waters where the only mollusc is a species of *Pisidium* (e.g., in acid moorland waters of Scotland, usually *P. casertanum*—Hunter, unpublished). A survey of the *Pisidium* spp. of 466 localities in the British Isles was made by C. Oldham (reported in Boycott, 1936; see also Ellis, 1940; Macan, 1950), and provides data, for each of 15 species, on frequency of occurrence (1 to 42% of localities), on concurrence with other species (from <1 to 100%), and on habitat limitation. Specific anatomical modifications for particular habitats are not shown,[2] but some specific physiological adaptation may occur, e.g., probable temperature limitation of the arctic relict *P. conventus* (Odhner, 1923; Hunter and Slack, 1958). Bivalves of fresh waters show little of the adaptive radiation that gives particular interest to functional morphology in most groups of marine bivalves. The four major fresh-water families are remarkably uniform in structure: the larger fresh-water "mussels" belong to the nearly world-wide Unionidae (including *Anodonta* and *Unio*) and to the Mutelidae of the southern hemisphere; the smaller bivalves to the Corbiculidae and Sphaeriidae (the latter including the cosmopolitan and ubiquitous genera *Pisidium* and *Sphaerium*). However, great numbers of museum and geographical species have been described, although the validity of many of these is doubtful. There are probably less than 10 valid species of *Anodonta* and *Unio* living in Switzerland and France (Schnitter, 1922; Germain, 1931), although 458 species were once distinguished. Similarly, modern systematic revision of the Australasian fresh-water mussels has drastically reduced that list to 27 species in 8 genera (McMichael and Hiscock, 1958). In a region where systematics have stabilized, there are 84 genera (over 180 species) of British marine bivalves (Winckworth, 1932, 1951), but only 6 genera (27 species) in British fresh waters (Ellis, 1951). As with other fresh-water animals, within bivalve species there is much ecophenotypic variation, and also some genetic differences between populations.

C. Fresh-Water Prosobranch Ecology

As with bivalves, the primary physiological adaptation of prosobranch snails for fresh-water life is capacity for osmotic regulation (see Sections II and III,B). It is significant that several genera of fresh-water prosobranchs are closely related to estuarine or to littoral marine forms, and in a few cases, fresh-water species have marine congeners. As already noted, little of the metabolic energy of a fresh-water mollusc is required for osmoregulation (Potts, 1954b; Sections II and III,B above). This is borne out by comparative studies (Lumbye, 1958) of respiration under different conditions in two fresh-water prosobranchs: *Theodoxus fluviatilis*, believed to be an immigrant species which colonized fresh waters recently in a geological time-scale (i.e., during a Günz/Mindel interglacial), and *Potamopyrgus jenkinsi*, an immigrant to fresh water within recent historical time. *Theodoxus fluviatilis* shows the same oxygen consumption in brackish (11.1‰ salinity) as in fresh waters, while *P. jenkinsi* shows a

---

[2] With the notable exception of the Etheriidae (Unionacea), the four genera of which are specialized for life in moving, often turbulent, river waters largely within the tropics (Yonge, 1962).

slightly higher oxygen consumption in brackish water. Boycott (1936) has generalized that fresh-water prosobranch snails, as gill-breathers, are more limited to running, or at least well-oxygenated, waters than are fresh-water pulmonates. Lumbye (1958) found that neither of his proso-branchs could maintain a constant level of oxygen consumption in waters of lowered oxygen tension, and thus contrast with the respiratory inde-pendence shown by the pulmonate limpet *Ancylus fluviatilis* (Berg, 1952; see Section III,D below).

Once a prosobranch species has sufficient powers of osmotic regulation for fresh-water life, rapid colonization of available fresh waters is ap-parently possible. The best-known case is that of the hydrobiid snail *Potamopyrgus jenkinsi* (*Hydrobia jenkinsi* and *Paludestrina jenkinsi* in earlier literature), which has additional advantages for dispersal in being both parthenogenetic and viviparous. Its European distribution was en-tirely confined to brackish waters until near the end of last century. Colonization of fresh waters in England and Wales was followed in detail: first recorded in 1893, it was abundant throughout the area by about 1921 (Roebuck, 1921; Robson, 1923; Ellis, 1926). Colonization of other parts of Europe has followed, in most cases less rapidly: e.g., through parts of Denmark during thirty-five years (Bondesen and Kaiser, 1949); see Hubendick (1950) for dispersal elsewhere in the Baltic area. Established in Scotland in 1906, the species had not completed coloniza-tion of inland fresh waters fifty years later (Hunter and Warwick, 1957). The contrast between the rapid spread through England and Wales, and slower dispersal in Scotland and elsewhere, may result from the extensive canal system linking the natural fresh waters of the former area (Boycott, 1936; Hunter and Warwick, 1957; Hunter, 1957). This contrast may re-flect the relative rates of active migration and of chance passive dispersal. Both Hubendick (1950) and Moon (1956) have suggested that dispersal may be synanthropic, i.e., may correspond to some human activity. The more isolated colonies in Scotland lie on routes taken by migrating geese (Nicol, 1936; Hunter and Warwick, 1957). Complete assessment of the speed of colonization in *P. jenkinsi* is handicapped by lack of knowledge of its geographic origin, and by the probability that distinct races exist (Sanderson, 1940; Warwick, 1944, 1952). Work on active migrations in the American prosobranch *Campeloma decisum* by Bovbjerg (1952) has shown that this species can maintain its position in streams by a positive reaction to currents.

In fresh waters are found species belonging to about 10 unrelated groups of the Prosobranchia, and it is notable that more occur in tropical and subtropical regions (Pelseneer, 1906; Thiele, 1925). Although mor-phological differences between these groups are as large as any within the Prosobranchia, Yonge (1947) has pointed out that they are all alike in having complex genital ducts associated with suppression of the right kidney. Internal fertilization, followed by viviparity or the production of relatively large yolky eggs with protective capsules, is necessary for colonization of fresh water (or land). The recent monograph on the British prosobranchs by Fretter and Graham (1962) includes extensive data on reproductive physiology and general ecology besides an excellent and detailed synthesis of existing knowledge of functional morphology in the group. Growth and life cycle have been studied in natural populations of *Viviparus contectoides* (Van Cleave and Lederer, 1932), *Campeloma rufum* (Van Cleave and Altringer, 1937), and *Pomatiopsis cincinnatiensis* (van der Schalie and Dundee, 1955) in America; of *Bithynia tentaculata* (Lilly, 1953) and *Valvata piscinalis* (Cleland, 1954; Hunter, 1961b) in Britain; and of *Oncomelania* spp., vectors of schistosomes, in Japan and the Philippines (WHO Study Group, 1957). In temperate regions, most of the smaller species, including *Oncomelania*, have an annual life cycle with a single breeding season. However, *Oncomelania* is known to breed all the year round in a warmer climate (WHO Study Group, 1957). In nitrogenous excretion (Needham, 1938, 1942), *Potamopyrgus jenkinsi* (see above), with no detectable uric acid content, differs markedly from *Bithynia tentaculata* with 5 mg uric acid per gram dry body weight, and *Viviparus* sp. with 2–5 mg uric acid per gram dry body weight, values as high as those for some terrestrial pulmonates. This does not correlate with the evidence for estuarine ancestry in *Bithynia* and *Viviparus*. Among secondary adaptations to particular habitats, Bondesen (1940) has noted varying food provision in the form of nurse eggs in the egg capsules of *Theodoxus fluviatilis*. Ciliary feeding occurs in *Viviparus* (Cook, 1949), and in some populations of *Bithynia tentaculata*. Mori (1946) has described diurnal rhythms in the behavior patterns of two species of *Melanoides* on a lake shore, involving changes of response to gravity and light, and modification with temperature change.

More elaborate secondary adaptations are found in the peculiar prosobranchs of certain large lakes. Best known is Lake Tanganyika, the snails of which show radiation into a variety of forms (probably over 84 species, 66 endemic), capable of living at different depths and on different substrata. It was once suggested (Moore, 1903) that they were derived from a marine fauna isolated in the lake from the Jurassic, but there are fallacies in this theory (Cunnington, 1920; Yonge, 1938). All available evidence suggests that the separate types have been evolved *in situ* from forms already adapted to fresh waters. Peculiar gastropods are also found in other lakes, including Lake Baikal, certain lakes in Celebes (Sarasin and Sarasin, 1894–1896; Bollinger, 1914), and Lake Ochrida in the Balkans (Polinski, 1932; Radoman, 1955a,b, 1960; Stankovic, 1932, 1960). The greatest significance lies in the great age (in a geological time-scale) of these lakes as contrasted with the transitory nature of the *majority* of fresh-water habitats (Hubendick, 1952, 1954; Hunter, 1952, 1957).

D. Fresh-Water Pulmonate Ecology

1. AQUATIC READAPTATION

The pulmonate snails of fresh water—the "higher" Basommatophora—are primarily air breathing and show varying degrees of readaptation to aquatic life (Hunter, 1953c, 1957). The most important feature of the Pulmonata (including all the fresh-water families) is the absence of ctenidia—the characteristic gills, present and structurally homologous in all other major groups of the Mollusca (see Yonge, 1947, and Chapter 1 of this volume). The gill-less mantle cavity has a roof richly vascularized with thin-walled vessels, its opening to the exterior is narrow and muscular, and the rectum and kidney duct do not open into it; the mantle cavity is a lung. Evolutionary trends in the fresh-water pulmonates thus contrast with the more usual patterns in other groups (cf. Carter, 1931), wherein fresh-water life leads to preadaptations subsequently allowing transition to the land. The most primitive pulmonates are clearly amphibious air-breathers (Morton, 1955a,b).

The fresh-water species can be ranked as a series showing progressively greater degrees of adaptation to aquatic life (Hunter, 1953c, 1957). At one end of the series in Britain are such marsh-dwelling snails as *Lymnaea truncatula* and *L. palustris* (Basommatophora) and *Succinea* spp. (primitive Stylommatophora), species primarily air-breathing and nonaquatic, whose habits result in their occasional submergence in water. At the other end are the aquatic species; e.g., some ancylid limpets, where the pulmonate mantle cavity is completely absent and neomorphic gill-lobes are developed. "Intermediate" species are those which are completely aquatic in habit, while retaining the mantle cavity of characteristic "lung" form, and include the Physidae and most Lymnaeidae. Some retain aerial respiration though living submerged. For example, in many natural populations of *L. stagnalis*, the snails visit the surface regularly to take in air, at least during summer conditions.

2. RESPIRATORY ECOLOGY AND ADAPTATIONS

Surface breathing may occur in populations living in large lakes in seasonal (Cheatum, 1934) or in short-term (Hunter, 1953b) migrations. The latter occur at high water temperatures in littoral populations of *L. peregra* in Loch Lomond, where the respiratory needs of adult snails may result in their temporary starvation (by forcing migration on to near-sterile substrata), or may cause them to migrate away from young they have produced (Hunter, 1953b, 1957). The physiology of such periodic aerial respiration in pulmonates has long been studied in the laboratory, culminating in such detailed investigations as those of Precht (1939), Müller (1943) and Füsser and Krüger (1951). However, the same pulmonate species are known to occur in large lakes at depths from which periodic excursions to the surface are impossible. The classic case of the Lake of Geneva with *Lymnaea* spp. at depths of 40 to 200 meters is extreme, but far from unique. A survey of the condition of the mantle cavity in *Lymnaea peregra* and *Physa fontinalis* living in Loch Lomond has revealed several distinct physiological states in different populations (Hunter, 1953c). Some populations of each species living near the margin of the lake surface regularly, but only when the water temperature is relatively high, and then much less frequently than in laboratory experiments. Other populations of the two species live up to 1 km offshore, although they have not been found in depths of over 6 meters. In many populations, including some in relatively shallow water, the mantle cavity remains water-filled throughout life. In others the cavity contains a gas bubble, and micro-gas-analysis has revealed that in some cases the gas composition is such that the bubble could be used as an *exposed* physical gill, while in others this is unlikely and a hydrostatic function as an *internal* bubble more probable (Hunter, 1953c). The respiratory behavior of these and other species shows considerable adaptive plasticity, and snails from all the above populations took up a pattern of surface breathing after being brought into the laboratory (Hunter, 1953c). Earlier evidence on the probable hydrostatic function of the pallial bubble in some species was contradictory (Jacobs, 1941; Precht and Otto, 1948). However, Henderson (1961) believes that, in such larger species as *Lymnaea stagnalis* and *Planorbarius corneus,* the hydrostatic function may determine the amount of air taken in at surfacing. Henderson has shown in the laboratory that the normal duration of a dive in such species is of the same order as the time taken to use up oxygen from the bubble until the snail loses its buoyancy, but that much longer dives are possible.

Obviously populations of snails with water-filled mantle cavities, and certain others, are dependent on cutaneous respiration through exposed surfaces. Growth changes in the surfaces available for such respiration differ in *L. peregra* and *Physa fontinalis* (Hunter, 1953c). Similar relative changes between shell weight and tissue weight for three other pulmonate species (Nolan and von Brand, 1954) probably also affect available respiratory surfaces. These changes modify the relationship:

$$S = \chi V^{\frac{2}{3}} \qquad (1)$$

where S is the available respiratory surface, V is the volume of the snail's tissues, and χ a constant for each species. However, in several species, decrease in the surface/volume ratio consequent on growth clearly limits the size of an individual that can live submerged (Hunter, 1953b, 1957). Cutaneous respiration under water replaces surface breathing most completely in two basommatophoran families, the Planorbidae and the Ancylidae, in which secondary gills have been developed (Hunter, 1957). These gill-lobes are neomorphic—clearly not homologous with any part of the ctenidium of other molluscs—and lie outside the original mantle cavity. Cilia are almost totally absent from the pallial organs of most fresh-water pulmonates (Hunter, 1953c, and unpublished work), and similarly lacking on surfaces outside the mantle cavity in *Siphonaria* spp., pulmonate limpets of the marine littoral (Yonge, 1952, 1960). This absence of cilia may reflect *incomplete* readaptation from terrestrial life. In fresh-water pulmonates, well-ciliated surfaces could increase the respiratory efficiency of the neomorphic gill in *Ancylus* and of general cutaneous respiration in forms like *Physa*.

In the series of pulmonates considered above, the snails which are air-breathing and amphibious are structurally unspecialized and often more primitive, while those most completely adapted for aquatic life (e.g., ancylid limpets) are most specialized structurally (e.g., in pallial morphology, in renal and genital organs, and even in nervous system). The opposite would be the case if the group followed the more usual pattern (Carter, 1931) of preadaptation in fresh waters leading to terrestrial life. Data on nitrogenous excretion of fresh-water pulmonates are not really helpful. Needham (1938, 1942) gives the following values for uric acid, in mg per gram dry body weight: *Lymnaea stagnalis*, 3.5; *Planorbarius corneus*, 2.0; *Ancylus fluviatilis*, 0.6; and *Lymnaea peregra*, 0.2. Comparatively, the values for the first two species are about half those for representative terrestrial pulmonates, and for the latter two are about equal to values for unspecialized marine gastropods. This would imply a longer history of readaptation to aquatic life in the latter two species, which is very unlikely.

3. NORMAL AQUATIC RESPIRATION

Studies of oxygen consumption in ancylids (Berg, 1952, 1953; Berg *et al.*, 1958), and other fresh-water snails (Lumbye, 1958; Berg and Ockelmann, 1959), have provided valuable data on the ecological factors which can cause changes in purely aquatic respiration. The respiratory rates of *Acroloxus lacustris*, usually found in standing water, and *Ancylus fluviatilis*, usually in streams, are of the same order, but the former survives better under anaerobic conditions (Berg, 1952). This seems ecologically significant, but surprisingly *Acroloxus* cannot maintain its normal oxygen consumption at lowered oxygen tension, while *Ancylus* shows considerable respiratory independence, maintaining its normal oxygen consumption at lowered tensions (even one-third saturation values). All species studied show increase in oxygen consumption with increasing temperature, but the precise relationship varies from species to species and at different seasons within a species (Berg, 1953; Berg and Ockelmann, 1959). Two populations of *Ancylus* living at different temperatures showed a "reversed" respiratory acclimatization, the limpets from a "summer-warm" habitat (about 18°C) having greater oxygen consumption than those from a "summer-cold" one (about 11°C), when measured at the same temperatures (Berg, 1953). This is the opposite of the temperature compensation classically found in poikilotherms (Bullock, 1955, and references therein). Seasonal variations are found in the oxygen consumption of *Ancylus* (Berg *et al.*, 1958), and can be correlated with reproduction. Berg *et al.* (1958) point out a further correlation with the changing growth rates of this species, using data from Hunter (1953a). Even "partial" starvation has a marked effect on respiratory rate in *Ancylus*, some effect in *Lymnaea palustris* and in the prosobranch *Bithynia leachi*, and little or no effect in six other species (Berg and Ockelmann, 1959). Decrease in available oxygen causes lowered oxygen consumption in all species; this reduction is immediate but gradual in some species, and in others falls sharply but only at a critical level of oxygen tension (Berg and Ockelmann, 1959). As a group, fresh-water snails seem to have a fairly uniform respiratory rate, and the interspecific (and infraspecific) differences found cannot always be correlated with known ecology. These studies of Berg and his colleagues (references above) again confirm that physiological plasticity is characteristic of fresh-water snails.

4. Anaerobic Respiration, Hemoglobin, Desiccation

Recently, capacity for anaerobic respiration in certain pulmonate snails has been investigated. Mehlman and von Brand (1951) showed biochemical differences in end products resulting from anaerobic tissue respiration, and von Brand and Mehlman (1953) examined respiration during the recovery period, involving "repayment of an oxygen debt." Disposal of postanaerobic metabolites appears to be carried out in two ways: a fraction of the accumulated end products (both lactate and volatile fatty acids) is excreted, while another fraction undergoes chemical changes. There are differences in anaerobic capacity between species (von Brand *et al.*, 1950, 1955) and differences within species which are related to temperature and varying degrees of tissue hydration (von Brand, 1955). Correlation of these differences with known ecology is not yet possible, but von Brand *et al.* (1955) state that snails resistant to lack of oxygen (*Australorbis glabratus* and *Helisoma duryi*) remove anaerobic metabolites faster from their tissues than do more sensitive species (*Aplexa nitens* and *Lymnaea stagnalis*).

Similarly, no clear relationship has yet emerged between specific ecological limitations and the occurrence of hemoglobin as a blood pigment in certain planorbid snails. (Muscle hemoglobins are found in a much wider range of gastropods in the buccal mass.) In the species with blood hemoglobin the blood can have high oxygen affinity, and may show variable oxygen loading tensions and even significant oxygen storage (Leitch, 1916; Borden, 1931; Wolvekamp, 1932; Fox, 1945; Zaaijer and Wolvekamp, 1958). Unfortunately, detailed ecology and respiratory behavior under natural conditions is little known for these planorbids, although Zaaijer and Wolvekamp (1958) discuss considerable diurnal changes in oxygen tension in one habitat. Work on various invertebrates, including *Planorbarius corneus*, has shown that respiratory pigment synthesis may vary with environmental oxygen (Fox, 1948, 1955; Fox et al., 1951; Fox and Phear, 1953). Temperature is claimed to affect formation and distribution of hemoglobin in var. *rubra* of *P. corneus* (van Dalsum, 1947, 1951), and type of food may also be important.

Fresh-water pulmonates also show varying capacity to survive desiccation (for temperature limits, see Section III,A), and work on schistosome hosts (WHO Study Group, 1957; Olivier, 1956) shows that different races of a species can vary greatly in resistance to desiccation. Studies on *Australorbis glabratus* and *Tropicorbis centimetralis* demonstrate long survival in air at high humidities (Olivier, 1956), and survival for months (even over a year) in or on dry soil in simulated field conditions (Olivier and Barbosa, 1956). Seasonal field studies in Brazil show that populations of these species are maintained at temporary pools in spite of a dry season of 5–7 months each year (Olivier and Barbosa, 1955a,b; Olivier, 1956). In Britain about 7 species out of 36 fresh-water gastropods can tolerate drying loci, and all are species more abundant elsewhere (Boycott, 1936), but in Canada, Mozley (1932, 1939) believes that certain molluscan species are characteristic of ephemeral waters.

5. GROWTH AND REPRODUCTIVE ECOLOGY

Considerable infraspecific variation occurs in growth rates, reproduction, and course of life cycle in fresh-water pulmonates in temperate regions (Hunter, 1961b). Recent field studies on populations include those of W. F. De Wit (1955, Holland), R. M. De Witt (1955, U.S.A.), Geldiay (1956), Duncan (1959), and Hunter (1953a, 1957, 1961a,b); the most common pattern is a simple annual life cycle with breeding in late spring or early summer. Using dredged samples from an isolated bank in Loch Lomond to provide standards, Hunter (1961b) has surveyed inter-

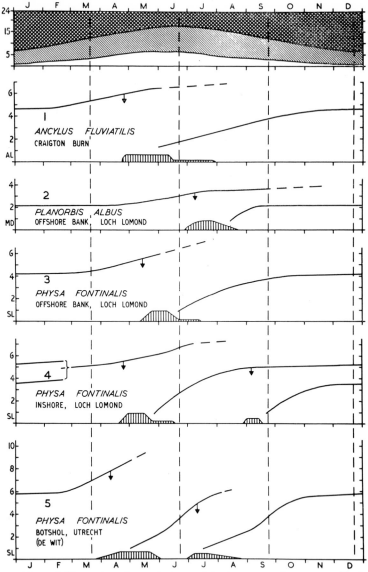

F‍ɪɢ. 1. Natural life cycles of populations of fresh-water pulmonate snails showing seasonal changes of mean shell size in populations, the onset of egg-laying (downward arrows), and the presence of developing egg-masses. Months are indicated on each horizontal axis, broken lines mark the solstices and equinoxes, and the vertical size scales (which differ) are in millimeters. At the top of each series are shown, in hours per day throughout the year, the potential period of sunlight (light shading), and the average actual sunshine (white), the latter being based on mean figures for the Glasgow area in the years 1948–1957. The mean size curves are smoothed; where data for several years are available, an over-all mean is used. From Hunter (1961b), which see for the sources of the data and further details.

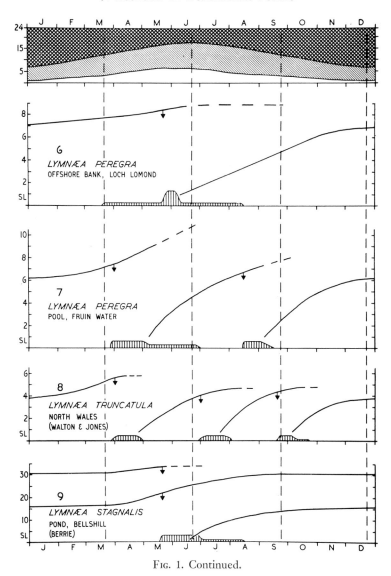

FIG. 1. Continued.

species ubiquitous elsewhere, e.g., the extremely euryoecic form, *Lymnaea peregra.*

E. Evolution in Fresh Waters

Hubendick (1952, 1954) and Hunter (1952, 1957, 1961b) have pointed out independently, and from different bases, that the process of evolution in molluscs living in fresh waters has been markedly different from evolution in similar animals living in the sea or on land. This results from the

population variations in growth and reproduction in five species. Infraspecific differences between populations in *Planorbis albus* and the prosobranch *Valvata piscinalis* involve only growth rates and the time and
intensity of the breeding season. In *Physa fontinalis, Lymnaea peregra*,
and *Ancylus fluviatilis*, interpopulation differences also involve the seasonal course of the reproductive cycle (and number of generations per
year). Four main patterns of life cycle found in temperate populations
are detailed by Hunter (1961b; see Fig. 1): two simple annual patterns,
with spring breeding and with late summer breeding; and two patterns
each involving a second generation annually, one of them showing complete replacement. All four patterns have been found in different populations of *P. fontinalis* and *L. peregra*. Variations in breeding are dependent
both on environmental factors (water temperature being most important),
and on endogenous causes involving the growth of the snails (Duncan,
1959; Hunter, 1961a,b). Variations in mortality may involve environmental limitation (Hunter, 1953a, 1961a). Most interpopulation variations can be environmentally evoked, but some differences seem genetically determined (Hunter, 1961b). Bred in the laboratory, "races" of
Lymnaea spp. can show genetically determined variations in fecundity
and in growth rates (Boycott *et al.,* 1930; Boycott, 1936; Forbes and
Crampton, 1942a).

Even in relatively stable populations, species with an annual life cycle
show considerable variation from year to year in mean adult size and in
population density at breeding, and these variations reflect weather
conditions during the preceding year (Hunter, 1953a, 1961a). A study
through 9 years of stable populations of *A. fluviatilis, Physa fontinalis*,
and *L. peregra* in Scotland shows that annual variations in assessed pro-
ductivity (as volumes of molluscan tissue per unit habitat) of molluscan
tissue can be over 7-fold, more than 3-fold, and over 8-fold, respectively,
in these species (Hunter, 1961a).

Under those tropical conditions with an annual dry season, natural
populations of pulmonates can have an average life span of under 1 year
(maximum *ca.* 15 months), and a life cycle extending over one dry and
two rainy seasons, or through one rainy season only (Olivier and Barbosa,
1955a,b). In more stable fresh waters in the tropics—as in the waters of
limestone caves—reproduction in pulmonates may occur all the year
round, as a result of high and relatively constant water temperatures.
There exist many accounts of life cycle in fresh-water snails in laboratory culture (e.g., for temperate species see references in Boycott *et al.,*
1930; Noland and Carriker, 1946; W. F. De Wit, 1955; Frömming, 1956).
Because of the plasticity noted in growth and reproduction in these snails,
culture results are usually difficult to correlate with observations on natural populations. For example, it has long been known that, other condi-

tions being equal, more dense laboratory populations show reduction of growth rates and fecundity (e.g., references in Taylor, 1900; Boycott *et al.*, 1930; Forbes and Crampton, 1942b; Noland and Carriker, 1946). Laboratory work on possible biological control of schistosome hosts has included extensive experiments, again proving these "crowding" effects in *Australorbis glabratus* (Chernin and Michelson, 1957a,b). Natural populations of three pulmonates did not show the expected inverse relationship between adult size and population density, though density varied greatly (up to 5-fold), and adult size considerably (up to ±17.5%), when surveyed over 9 years (Hunter, 1961a). Field data on fecundity (for *Ancylus* only) suggest a more complex relationship with population density: number of egg capsules per limpet is lower both at very high adult densities and at low densities.

6. SPECIFIC ADAPTATIONS AND HABITATS

Secondary adaptations to specific habitats are less common in fresh-water pulmonates, and only rarely involve much anatomical modification. However, several pulmonates are limpet-shaped: the family Ancylidae, the Australasian family Latiidae (which may not be related), one genus in the Planorbidae [*Patelloplanorbis* (Hubendick, 1957)], and one in the Lymnaeidae (*Lanx*). Several limpets live in swift streams, and their form in fresh water is supposed to represent adaptation for this habit by stream-lining and improved attachment. Of the two common European ancylids, *Ancylus fluviatilis* lives typically in swift streams and occasionally on the wave-swept shores of large lakes, but *Acroloxus lacustris* lives on reeds and similar plants in the stillest eutrophic waters. More generally in fresh waters, limpet form seems associated with lack of silt in the water and with hard substrata.

Many fresh-water pulmonates show temporary adaptations to particular habitats, by behavioral or physiological rather than structural changes. Patterns of respiratory behavior corresponding to particular depth zonation in a large lake are discussed above. *Physa fontinalis* and several species of *Lymnaea* and *Planorbis* can live temporarily as members of the "neuston," floating upside down under the surface film and using the ciliated foot-sole to collect microscopic organisms and chains of free protein molecules from it. The food available in such surface films in fresh waters is discussed by Goldacre (1949), and Cheeseman (1956) describes such pedal ciliary feeding in the prosobranch *Ampullarius*. Wright (1956) suggests that microhabitats, with microclimatic differences in temperatures and oxygen tensions, are more likely in tropical fresh waters, and gives as an example the snail microhabitat on the underside of water-lily leaves. As mentioned earlier, pulmonate snails found in special habitats in fresh water (e.g., hot springs) usually belong to transience of fresh-water environments and the high degree of small-scale, short-term isolation which can occur within them. The duration of most lakes is of the order of 10^3–10^4 years, whereas a relatively constant environment may persist on land for up to 10^6 years, and in the sea for many times this period. Inland waters lack the geographical continuity of environment afforded by the sea and even the largest lakes are of relatively small extent. These limitations in space and time are true of Loch Lomond—a "good" habitat of considerable permanency—yet the majority of populations of fresh-water molluscs live in bodies of water which are more variable in extent and more transitory (Hunter, 1957, 1961b).

Modern systematic revision of groups of fresh-water gastropods (e.g., of the Lymnaeidae by Hubendick, 1951) reveals a characteristically small number of species, almost world-wide in distribution, but with a high degree of infraspecific interpopulation variation. This is broadly true of fresh-water bivalves although individual species are usually less cosmopolitan in spite of being widely distributed (see Schnitter, 1922; Germain, 1931; McMichael and Hiscock, 1958). An exception noted above (Section III,C) is that those few lakes known to be of considerable age in a geological time-scale support a diversity of molluscan species not found elsewhere. As already stressed the greatest significance lies in the transitory nature of most fresh-water habitats, and thus specific radiation has been permitted only in the unusual permanence of these ancient lakes. The diversity of prosobranch species in Lake Tanganyika was noted above; recently Hubendick (1960) has discussed similar, though small-scale, intralacustrine radiation in the endemic ancylids of Lake Ochrida (see Stankovic, 1960, for other groups). These ancient lakes are exceptional; elsewhere species are widespread, with much infraspecific variation.

Interpopulation variation in shell form in fresh-water molluscs has been studied by several workers (e.g., Mozley, 1935; Diver, 1939, and references therein), but perhaps the most thorough survey has been carried out by Hubendick (1951) on *Lymnaea peregra*. One feature of almost all such studies is that the amount of variation within any single population is much less than the range of variation found in the species as a whole [Mozley (1935) found this true in Canadian populations of *L. emarginata* but not of *L. palustris*]. But interpopulation variation within a fresh-water species can be either ecophenotypic or genetically determined, e.g., variation in shell form. It is unlikely, however, that the fine structure of teeth in the radulae of snails show much environmentally controlled variation. A study of radulae in different populations of *L. peregra* from northwestern Europe (Berrie, 1959) shows that much variation occurs in the ratios between standard measurements on certain lateral teeth; such ratios are relatively constant for each individual. The variation within each population is very much less than the total variation of the species, and populations can differ very significantly from each other. However, interpopulation variation appears to be geographically random. The capacity of pulmonates, especially Lymnaeidae, for self-fertilization has been regarded (Hubendick, 1951) as contributing to the apparent genetic uniformity occurring within populations. Hubendick further suggested that this capacity could have had a retarding effect on lymnaeid evolution. However, existing field data suggest that self-fertilization is rare in natural populations. Some apparent population uniformity, e.g., in shell proportions, is clearly environmentally evoked. Examples of occurrence within a species of fresh-water mollusc of a particular character, in many populations as an ecophenotypic modification, but in occasional populations genetically fixed, are discussed by Hunter (1961b).

The type of selection occurring in fresh waters is a consequence of the nature of the environment. The transience of most fresh-water habitats limits the number of generations for which any separate population of fresh-water animals can exist. But, much short-term, small-scale isolation can occur, as fresh-water habitats are geographically discontinuous and mostly small. Genetic isolation can be sufficient to produce some interpopulation diversity, but even limited transfer of individuals between populations by passive dispersal (see Section III,C) usually results in sufficient gene exchange to prevent full speciation. Thus, a genetically determined character like the above radula-tooth ratios, presumably without significant selective value, is nearly constant within populations, but varies greatly between populations in a random manner. In the case of inheritable characters of selective value, infraspecific variation could form geographic clines, but this would depend on the nature of the interpopulation dispersal. In general, much interpopulation diversity occurs but little full speciation. Further, fresh-water snails show much adaptive plasticity in respiration (Hunter, 1953c, 1957, and references therein; see Section III,D,2 above), in growth cycles and reproduction (Hunter, 1961a,b, and references therein; see Section III,D,5), and in other aspects of their physiology. Hunter (1961b) suggests that this adaptive plasticity is of fundamental selective value. Particularly in many pulmonates, selection has produced genotypes which can show phenotypic flexibility. What appears to have been most strongly selected *for* is the capacity to vary, the possession of adaptive plasticity.

IV. LAND MOLLUSCS

A. General Considerations

Primarily, adaptation for terrestrial life involves maintenance of internal water in an aerial environment of variable humidity, respiration of gaseous oxygen, and resistance to (or avoidance of) a range of temperatures wider than any in aquatic environments. Problems of terrestrial locomotion, reproduction, excretion, etc., follow. As in fresh waters, molluscs living on land do not exhibit the structural and phyletic diversity of marine forms. Only snails are found—the order Stylommatophora (Pulmonata) and certain prosobranch genera of four distinct superfamilies. Although they belong to phyletically distinct stocks (each related to comparatively unspecialized marine forms), the adaptations which they show for life on land—in respiration, locomotion, excretion, reproduction, and even behavior—show considerable convergence. In almost all stocks the mantle cavity is a gill-less, vascularized lung. All have complex genital ducts, associated with internal fertilization and the production of large eggs or viviparity. Nitrogenous excretion is largely uricotelic in all; Helicid pulmonates, for example, have between 4 and 9 mg uric acid per gram dry body weight (Needham, 1938, 1942). In general, land snails are not as perfectly adapted to a terrestrial environment as are insects and amniote vertebrates, and thus are more limited in distribution. Many snails are cryptozoic in ecology, and many show nocturnal activity; terrestrial habitats with extreme ranges of temperature or very low humidity do not support snails.

The temperature limits over which land snails survive are difficult to define. Many species are known to be active at temperatures just above 0°C, and to survive lower temperatures in hibernation. Some species of the pulmonate genera *Vitrina* and *Radiodiscus* occur in Greenland or live close to the permanent snow line of mountains (Ellis, 1926; Winckworth, 1950; Hubendick, 1953). At higher temperatures, unlike snails in fresh water, the body temperature of land snails may differ from that of the air around them. As Hogben and Kirk (1944b) point out, slugs and snails are not truly poikilothermous but can, and usually do, maintain an internal temperature below that of the environment by continuous water loss from their surfaces. However, the slug *Arion ater* will survive and remain active at a body temperature of 31°C. In fully saturated air (100% relative humidity), body temperature usually corresponds to air temperature. Under such conditions *Helix pomatia* will remain active for an hour at 43°C, and *H. aspersa* at 40°C; both remain active for days at 35°C (Hogben and Kirk, 1944b). These temperatures are *ca.* 10°C higher than those survived by amphibians which also regulate by evaporation (Mellanby, 1941; Hogben and Kirk, 1944a,b; Kirk and Hogben, 1946). Recently, it has been shown that *Limax flavus* can adapt to changed levels of maintained environmental temperatures (within the range 10°–30°C) by increasing or decreasing oxygen consumption by amounts up to 60% (Segal, 1959, 1961). More extensive work has been done on acclimation in intertidal molluscs (see Chapter 2 of this volume), than in nonmarine species. However, it seems clear that in many groups of poikilotherms which are "conformers" as regards body temperature, among them the land snails, there is considerable capacity for acclimation, in the form of compensating shifts in activity rates and even of levels of tolerance.

The major physiological problem of land snails is control of water loss, and high environmental humidities are thus desirable. But as a result of the method of temperature regulation, 100% relative humidity is not always optimum for all land molluscs. With short periods of exposure, a lower relative humidity can allow sufficient regulation for survival at higher environmental temperatures. This can determine the preferred habitat for a snail species. Similar ecological problems of temperature and water control in the adaptation of isopod Crustacea to life on land have been discussed by Edney (1960). In the distribution of 102 species of land snails in Britain, Boycott (1934) considered only 12 as obligatory hygrophiles but at least 8 as xerophiles.

Apart from temperature and humidity, physicochemical factors obviously limiting molluscan life on land are few. Again, available calcium is important. In Britain, Boycott (1934) listed 9 species as obligatory calcicoles, 11 as almost limited to calcareous soils, 16 as preferring calcareous localities, 58 as indifferent to the presence or absence of lime (but still more prevalent in calcareous localities), and only 1 apparently calcifuge—Zonitoides excavatus. These last 59 species, which can live in relatively acid localities in Britain, include all the slugs (with shell reduced or absent), and only one snail with a substantial shell (Arianta arbustorum), the rest being relatively small and thin-shelled. Experiments on land snails in captivity show that the thickness and weight of the shell is directly dependent on the amount of calcium in food supplied (references in Boycott, 1934; Robertson, 1941). From distribution in Scotland, increase in latitude or in altitude (i.e., increasingly adverse climate) seems to raise the minimum calcium requirements of several species (Boycott and Oldham, 1936; Hunter and Hunter, 1956).

The nature of the vegetation obviously affects distribution of land snails, but it is difficult to define this clearly. Probably most species and more individual snails occur in evolved communities: in the climax associations of plant ecologists. In Britain, beech-ash woodlands support rich molluscan faunas. In the tropics, climax rain forests of various types offer the finest range of habitats for land snails, in a general environment of stable (not extremely high) temperature, high humidity, and lowered light intensity. These physical conditions of forest "climate," along with high level of organic turnover, provide an environment for numerous pulmonate species and most land prosobranchs. Exceptions to this relationship are those climax associations with soils of low pH and little calcium, such as coniferous woodland and heather moorland. The latter in western Scotland usually has only three species of slugs (Hunter, 1958a), and Boycott (1934) lists 8 British species of 102 as able to live on "the worst (acid dry exposed)" moorland. To the land snail, particular kinds of vegetation probably provide specific shelter (suitable micro-climates with stable temperature and high humidity), rather than specific plant foods. Boycott (1934) states that their normal food consists of decayed remains of higher plants, with fungi, lichens, and algae, and that living green plants are rarely important under natural conditions. However, in the laboratory, some pulmonate species can show definite preferences for specific higher plants (Frömming, 1953, 1954, and references therein). Few land snails are predatory carnivores. European testa-cellid slugs feed on live earthworms (Barnes and Stokes, 1951), as does the New Zealand genus *Paryphanta*, large snails with a discoid shell up to 4 inches across (Morton, 1958). The largely tropical family Oleaci-nidae, and some genera of the Streptaxidae, feed mostly on other land snails: a Jamaican species of *Varicella* attacks large pulmonates like *Pleuro-donte* spp. some 20 times heavier (Hunter, 1955a).

Detailed zoogeography of land snails in the British Isles is reviewed in the series of nonmarine census of the Conchological Society, the most recent edition being that of Ellis (1951). The habitats of British species are fully discussed by Boycott (1934). Data on distributional ecology are also given by Ellis (1926), Quick (1943, and 1960—slugs only), Pils-bry (1939–1948), Barnes and Weil (1944, 1945—slugs only), Frömming (1954) and Bruijns *et al.* (1959). The influence of man on snail distribu-tion is considered by Boycott (1934), Meeuse and Hubert (1949), Walden (1955), and Bruijns *et al.* (1959).

B. *Adaptations of Stylommatophora*

1. WATER RELATIONS

Unlike the best adapted land animals—land arthropods and amniote vertebrates—land snails have skin readily permeable to water. Künkel (1916) noted weight loss in pulmonate snails and slugs deprived of access to water. He found that in dry air *Limax variegatus*, if motionless, lost 2.4% of its initial weight per hour; if stimulated to move continually, it lost 16% per hour, death resulting in a few hours. Recent extensive work shows similar rates of loss in five British species of slugs (Dainton, 1954a). More is lost through general evaporation from the moist skin, but some loss results from the continued pedal secretion of watery mu-cus for locomotion. General statements that the mucous covering of the skin slows down water loss are fallacious. Apart from the circumstantial evidence that rapid water loss does occur from a mucus-covered slug or snail, Hogben and Kirk (1944b) showed that mucus obtained from *Arion ater* does not retain water at normal temperatures, unless the air humidity is near saturation. In *Helix pomatia*, rhythmic weight fluctuations of individual snails (up to 50% of lower weight), corresponding to variations in water content, were found by Howes and Wells (1934a). These fluctuations continue with an irregular periodicity of a few days, at 40–60% relative humidity, as long as the snails have access to free water. Similar fluctuations continued when they were kept in air saturated with water vapor (100% relative humidity) at similar periodicity but with smaller amplitude (Howes and Wells, 1934a). Thus some of the periodic weight decrease (i.e., loss of water) is not due to evaporation. As they grow after hatching, young snails (*H. pomatia*) undergo continued fluctuations in water content of greater amplitude than adults (Howes and Whellock, 1937). Less extensive experiments showed that similar weight fluctuations occur in *Arion ater* and *Limax flavus*, when they have access to water (Howes and Wells, 1934b). The nature of the periodic weight increases by water uptake is not clear. In discussion, Howes and Wells (1934a,b) imply active drinking, but Dainton (1954a) states that in her extensive experiments slugs were never seen drinking, and reports a single demonstration of cutaneous water uptake in *Limax maximus*. Shelled snails without water lose weight somewhat more slowly than slugs, and can greatly cut down water loss by withdrawal into the shell.

2. Temperature Regulation

As mentioned above, the continued evaporation from the moist skin of a slug or snail effects a degree of temperature regulation in all but fully saturated air. Using a skin thermocouple inserted in the musculature of the foot to measure the body temperature, Hogben and Kirk (1944b) demonstrated that the slug *Arion ater* maintains a body temperature lower than the surrounding air, in fact, "behaves as a well-nigh perfect wet-bulb thermometer." For example, at an external temperature of 33.7°C and at 24% relative humidity, the body temperature of a slug was found to be 21°C, i.e., well below its thermal death point. Even under more usual environmental conditions at lowered temperatures, significant downward regulation was found. Measurements on *Helix pomatia* showed similar internal temperatures in fully extended snails, and in living snails with shells removed. Snails, fully withdrawn into the shell (but without mucous occlusion of the opening), showed internal temperatures appreciably below those of the air around, but far above corresponding "wet-bulb" temperatures.

In relation to survival in different environments, therefore, a snail has a choice which the slug has not. Except in saturated air, both can protect themselves by evaporation from overheating, but this cannot continue indefinitely without access to water. The slug is compelled to lose water by evaporation from the body surface when external temperatures are low, that is, in circumstances which confer no advantage to offset depletion of its water reserve. In contrast, the snail can protect itself against overheating in excessively warm, but not too humid, surroundings (Hogben and Kirk, 1944b), but alternatively can cut the rate of water loss by withdrawal into its shell (Howes and Wells, 1934a).

3. Estivation, Survival, and Slug Form

Of course, most pulmonate snails, withdrawn into the shell and in a "resting phase," can close the mouth of the shell. They can use a layered secretion of calcareous material and hardened mucus, the "epiphragm," or thinner films of dried mucus either across the peristome or from it to some hard substratum, termed the "mucous veil" by Howes and Wells (1934a). Snails retain the former structure for a longer period (usually overwinter) and are said to be in *hibernation*. Snails with the latter kind of secreted occlusion are termed in *estivation*. This word is perhaps unfortunate since the phase is usually short-term, and may occur at any time of the year in most species. Measuring oxygen consumption, Wells (1944) showed that activity in *H. pomatia* fluctuated with cyclic changes in water content, hydrated snails (especially if fed) being most active. Further, estivation tends to occur—even if conditions are good—whenever water content is low (Howes and Wells, 1934a; Wells, 1944). Variations are found in the blood concentration of *Helix* spp., and Arvanitaki and Cardot (1932; see Chapter 9 of this volume) showed that tissue hydration took place only some 12 hours after rainwater and food became available. This clearly suggests a slow rate of gut uptake. Wells (1944) discusses these results in relation to the finding (Howes and Wells, 1934a) that greater fluctuations of water content occur in fed than in fasting snails. Many workers have observed that starved snails are less active and more likely to estivate. Feeding and digestion are thus incompatible with estivation. Hibernation is clearly determined by internal causes but needs a longer period of preparatory metabolic changes, possibly involving blood calcium, although clear experimental evidence is lacking. The temperature of a snail with an intact epiphragm corresponds closely to environmental temperature, there being no regulation even at low relative humidity (Hogben and Kirk, 1944b). Before either kind of diapause, the gut is usually empty; then all digestive processes cease, heartbeat is reduced, other muscular activity suspended, and respiration slowed.

Certain species burrow into the surface soil before estivating, achieving a microclimate of lower temperature. Surprisingly, others climb as high as possible on vegetation, and the hardened mucus closing the shell also attaches the snail to stem or twig. Such snails include the European species, *Helicella itala*, *H. virgata*, and *Cepaea hortensis*, the Central American *Oxystyla* (= *Zebra*) *undata*, and the African *Helix lactea* and *H. desertorum*. The last two estivate in colonies hanging on desert shrubs, and are said to survive a mid-day temperature of 43°C (Morton, 1958). Work on microclimates has suggested that, in some conditions, insects could keep cooler by climbing to the top of a grass crop (Waterhouse, 1955). Clearly, once in estivation a snail would not be subject to increased evaporation through stronger air currents, but would benefit from wind cooling. Evidence is lacking on the possible significance of light shell color in reflecting solar radiation, but *Helicella itala* and *H. virgata* are whitish. In some species diapause may be prolonged for years. In his critical study of lifespan, Comfort (1957) accepted certain older records of lengthy diapause, including 6 years in *Buliminus pallidor*, but doubted 23 years in *Oxystyla capax* (however, see Baker, 1935).

Although generally cryptic, few pulmonates burrow continually in the soil, but some lay eggs in soil cavities. These, although relatively large and yolky and usually uricotelic, are less cleidoic than amniote eggs, and easily lose water. However, normal development is possible after considerable (about 40%, and once 85%) desiccation (Needham, 1938), although Carrick (1938, 1942) found that *Agriolimax* required soil with water content of 40–80% saturation if oviposition followed by normal development was to take place. Thus, for eggs, two expressions of terrestrial adaptation are shown: in developmental indifference to water loss, and in adult behavior patterns at oviposition. Elaborate precopulatory behavior is found in slugs and helicid snails; as in other land animals, these are probably of adaptive value in ensuring specific internal fertilization on land. Slug body form can be regarded as an adaptation to life among narrow crevices, and even to burrowing; pulmonate slugs are certainly polyphyletic (Morton, 1958; see also Chapter 1 of this volume). The widely distributed Arionidae, Limacidae, and other families are all similar in form yet not closely related, but two aberrant slug families show anatomical peculiarities. The Australasian family Athoracophoridae (formerly Janellidae) have trachea-like tubules arising from a small pulmonary cavity (Pelseneer, 1906), but these await physiological investigation. The genus *Vaginula* (*Veronicella*), widespread throughout the tropics, consists of slugs with a caudal anus, no pallial cavity, and cutaneous respiration.

4. BEHAVIORAL PATTERNS

Behavior evoked by particular environmental changes is obviously important in maintaining land snails and slugs in appropriate microclimatic conditions. Activity of land molluscs is associated with high humidity, and in temperate countries occurs regularly by night and occasionally following rain by day. Increase of humidity, however, appears to have no direct effect as a stimulus. In *Helix pomatia*, Wells (1944) suggests that re-activation does not result from hydration, but from another sensory stimulus (such as mechanical stimulation by raindrops), and then hydration follows. Extent of activity depends on high water content; therefore, sustained activity is possible only at high humidity. Barnes and Weil (1945) believe that the extent of activity ultimately depends on there being a film of water over all surfaces which the slugs must traverse. In Palestine, Shalem (1949) relates activity in *Helicella bargesiana* directly to amount of dew, and maps "isoroses" (lines of equal dewfall). Humidity change alone does not induce activity in the slug *Agriolimax reticulatus*, but temperature change is the most important stimulus (Dainton, 1954a). This is probably true of most nocturnal pulmonates. Dainton (1954a) found that between 4° and 20°C activity is induced by falling temperatures and suppressed by rising temperatures. Assessed at different constant temperatures, the level of slug activity is very low, and is similar at all temperatures. Changes downward at rates of 0.1°C per hour are detected, and responses to falling temperatures account for occasional daytime activity after showers observed in the field, as well as the regular nocturnal rhythm. Significantly, daytime slug activity is not obvious if rain is continuous; i.e., although humidity conditions are good, the temperature-change stimulus is lacking. Further, no particular level of temperature is associated with slug activity in the field.

In a temperature gradient slugs aggregate about a preferred temperature: 17°–18°C for *A. reticulatus* in the laboratory (Dainton, 1954a). Ecologically this implies that only after nightfall, with no temperature gradients between the soil surface and vegetation, can prolonged slug activity be stimulated by fall of temperature. Should any earlier activity be induced by a temporary fall in ambient temperature, during the afternoon while a temperature gradient still exists, this activity soon ceases. This happens because any activity will cause slugs to move in a gradient toward higher temperatures, with consequent suppression of activity. Various species of slugs differ in duration, time of onset, and in peaks of nocturnal activity (Barnes and Weil, 1944, 1945), and there is some laboratory evidence of species differences in toleration of high and low temperatures and of desiccation (Getz, 1959). In the field, different species of "resting" slugs and snails resort by day to different preferred temperature levels. Migration of pulmonates deeper into cavities, leaf litter, or soil on the onset of cold weather may result from movement toward a preferred temperature.

The ecological significance of most other responses is that they move pulmonates away from desiccating conditions. Slugs turn away from strong air currents impinging on the head and tentacles, and then move downwind (Kalmus, 1942; Dainton, 1943, 1954b). Air currents on the body or tail induce activity from rest, or increase the speed of existing locomotion. Obviously this can remove them from draughty, drying situations. Most daytime microhabitats, where slugs hide, will be dark and therefore not affected by change in light intensity at nightfall. Thus, nocturnal activity of slugs bears no relation to the onset of darkness. On the contrary, dark-adapted slugs become active if illuminated (Dainton, 1954b), and this light reaction may temporarily increase activity at dawn, and thus decrease the chance of the slug resting in an illuminated (exposed) situation. It may also provide an escape reaction from desiccation and/or predation for pulmonates accidentally exposed during the day. At high temperatures (i.e., between 20° and 30°C), Dainton (1954a) found a reversal of responses: activity is induced by rising, and suppressed by falling, temperature. Although *level* of activity does not appear to vary at different constant temperatures, actual rate of locomotion in slugs varies directly with temperature (Crozier and Pilz, 1924; Dainton, 1954a). Ecologically, these again imply an escape reaction: high rising temperature stimulates activity which will take the slug down any temperature gradient toward its preferred temperature.

Such responses can lead a population of molluscs at the close of periods of activity toward suitable shelter places for "rest," but not an individual mollusc toward a unique resting place. Several land pulmonates show considerable homing ability, and the small-scale journeys made by them back to a regular diurnal resting place could involve chemoreception as well as the "tactile memory" involved in the homing of marine limpets and chitons. Large-scale seasonal homing in *Helix pomatia* may involve return to winter quarters from distances of 40–150 meters, and Edelstam and Palmer (1950) believe this behavior is dominated by "remembered" responses to chemoreception.

C. Other Land Snails

Terrestrial snails belonging to the Prosobranchia—"operculate" land snails—are most abundant as species and as individuals in the warm, damp forests of the tropics. Winckworth (1950) assesses the snail faunas of the world, and gives 133 genera of operculates, with approximately 4000 species, against 667 genera of pulmonates with 15,000 species. In Britain there are probably 103 species of land pulmonates and only 2 of operculates (Ellis, 1951). This proportion is not atypical of temperate land areas. In Jamaica there may be 450 ± 100 species of land snails, of which only about half are pulmonate (Hunter, 1955a). This proportion is roughly similar in Cuba and Hispaniola, but nowhere else in the world are operculates so numerous.

Land operculates are clearly polyphyletic. The diverse genera and families, while showing convergent evolution in adaptation for life on land, are each related to comparatively unspecialized marine forms, and placed systematically in four main prosobranch superfamilies. One of these, the Neritacea, including such land operculates as the Helicinidae, represent a group distinct from the Archaeogastropoda (see Chapter 1, this volume). As the anatomical studies of Bourne (1908, 1911) first showed, and as more recently discussed on functional grounds by Yonge (1947), this group (including marine, fresh-water, and land forms) has evolved completely independently of—though occasionally parallel to— the rest of the gastropods. Species of neritacean land snails belonging to the genus *Proserpina* have secondarily lost the operculum, developed ridges within the shell aperture, and extended the mantle to cover the shell. An extreme degree of evolutionary convergence occurs in Jamaica where a pulmonate genus, *Proserpinula* (of the family Sagdidae), shows great similarity of form and function to *Proserpina* and is found in the same ecotope (Hunter, 1955a). These two genera, of widely separate gastropod stocks—one of highly evolved Neritacea, the other of sagdid Pulmonata—have similar habits and even the extensible mantle seems to have the same texture and pigmentation in both.

Other groups of land operculates include the Cyclophoridae, developed from the most primitive stock of Mesogastropoda, and the land genera of the Hydrobiidae (a family which also includes estuarine and fresh-water genera). Yet another land stock comprises the family Pomatiasidae (Annulariidae), closely related to the Littorinidae—the world-wide family of intertidal periwinkles.

Less is known about the functional adaptations of land operculates, but in many ways they resemble those of Stylommatophora. The mantle cavity is a lung, and the genitalia are complex. The eggs produced are yolky and relatively large, and Creek (1951) found that in the British operculate, *Pomatias elegans*, uptake of water and salts from the surrounding soil occurred during development of the eggs. This species is markedly uricotelic in nitrogenous excretion, with 80 mg uric acid per gram dry body weight (Needham, 1938, 1942). Many operculates desiccate and die extremely readily, and of the few genera not living in the tropics, several are clearly soil-burrowing in habit. Little is known of diapause in most genera, although the operculum could be a preadaptation permitting successful sealing of the shell. Short-term estivation does occur in some annulariids. Jamaican species of *Tudora* climb upward, attach themselves to a vertical surface by byssus-like threads secreted from a pedal gland, and, after the threads have hardened, hang inactive with operculum closed (Hunter, unpublished). Land operculates secrete mucus for loco-motion as do pulmonates, lose water in air at less than 100% relative humidity, and so must regularly take up water. They seem more prone to accidental drowning than pulmonates, but in tropical rain forests sufficient free water for this is unusual.

D. *Natural Selection in Land Snails*

Among the few convincing demonstrations of selection in action on natural animal populations is recent work on the helicid genus *Cepaea*. Two European species are widespread and abundant: *Cepaea hortensis* and *C. nemoralis*. Both are polymorphic in shell characters, the latter perhaps more so. The basic shell color may be bright yellow, dull brown, or any shade from very pale fawn through pink and orange to red. Up to five longitudinal dark bands may be present, and all possible combinations of presence or absence of them, and of fusion between adjacent bands, have been described. All these variables are genetically determined, and something of the inheritance of color and banding variations is known. Earlier genetic work (Diver, 1932, 1939; Fisher and Diver, 1934) is reviewed and supplemented by Lamotte (1951), and Cain and Sheppard (1957). Natural populations of *Cepaea* usually consist of two or more different varieties living together. In *C. nemoralis*, Cain and Sheppard (1950, 1952, 1954; Sheppard, 1952) showed that there is a strong correlation between the proportions of varieties in each colony and the class of background on which the snails are living. They found that in woods where the ground is brown with decaying leaves and fairly uniform in appearance, unbanded brown or unbanded and 1-banded pink shells are more common. In hedgerows and on rough green herbage the yellow 5-banded form tends to be commoner. The less green the background the lower the proportion of yellow shells, and the more uniform the background the more common unbanded or 1-banded forms.

An important predator is the European song thrush, *Turdus ericetorum*, which breaks *Cepaea* and other helicids on stone "anvils," extracts the snails, and leaves the broken shells. Thus the proportion of each variety eaten by thrushes can be compared with the proportion present in the snail colony. Using this method, direct evidence was gained that, in typical rough herbage, unbanded shells were subject to significantly greater thrush predation than banded shells (Cain and Sheppard, 1954). As regards color, Sheppard (1951) was able to demonstrate, using marked snails as controls, that the proportions killed change with seasonal change in background vegetation. In a wood in early spring when the background was brown, proportionately more yellows (43%) were taken than in late spring when the background was green (14%). This is a particularly clear demonstration of natural selection by thrush predation.

Selection seems to act within as well as between the main banding and color classes. Not only the proportion of pinks and browns in a colony, but also the shade of the pink shells is determined by selection, richer reds being found on beech leaf litter, and paler fawns and pinks on oak leaf litter (Cain and Sheppard, 1952). Most populations, in which Cain and Sheppard (1954) counted proportions of different shellmorphs, yielded a good correlation with background. Of over 100 colonies studied, only four were exceptional—all of C. *nemoralis* living on sloping down-land with coarse grass. All four had high population densities, with an unexpectedly high proportion of pinks and browns and low proportion of yellows (for grassland). Rabbits were predators at the four localities and, from subsequent experiment, it is likely that they were exerting visual selection by tone alone, and not by color and tone as do thrushes and the other bird predators (Cain, 1953). Rabbits are color-blind and to them a rich pink shell could appear more like green grass than a yellow one. In general, these results of Cain and Sheppard provide a convincing demonstration of natural selection in action. Direct evidence of preda-tion rates was obtained from only a few localities, but is amply sup-ported by indirect evidence from many populations, which show a cor-relation between proportion of shellmorphs and habitat background.

Independently, Goodhart (1958) studied thrush predation on C. *hor-tensis*, noting that this occurred during two restricted periods annually: in January to March, and in June and July. He confirmed Sheppard's (1951) finding that proportionately more pinks and less yellows were taken in summer (i.e., from greener grass), but could not demonstrate differential predation of banding patterns. Lamotte (1950, 1951) found that, in colonies of *Cepaea* in France, a greater proportion of unbanded snails were attacked by predators (both birds and small mammals). How-ever, Lamotte (1951) claimed to find no widespread correlation between the shellmorphs of colonies and their environment, although Cain and Sheppard (1954) have pointed out that Lamotte's grouping of environ-ments was not based on their visual background. In Western Australia, Main and Carrigy (1953) found a correlation in shell colors of *Bothriem-bryon* spp. apparently resulting from differential visual predation. The proportion of a melanic to a yellow form is greater in areas of vegetation subject to fires.

There is some evidence of metabolic differences between different shellmorphs in *Cepaea* spp., including preferred temperatures, degree of activity after light and dark adaptation, and resistance to high tempera-tures (Boettger, 1954; Sedlmair, 1956). Goodhart (1958) discussed these differences and noted that they could increase the significance of the lower predation of yellow in summer. Thus, seasonal changes in propor-tion of different shellmorphs taken are due to differential visual selection by predator, not to differential behavior of prey. Metabolic differences have been invoked to explain differences in distribution of *C. nemoralis* and *C. hortensis*. The latter extends throughout Britain, while *C. nemoralis* does not occur in northern Scotland (Ellis, 1951). Although in some habitats mixed colonies of the two are found, in England populations of *C. nemoralis* alone are abundant on sand dunes and the grass of sea cliffs (Boycott, 1934). Sand dunes are occupied by *C. hortensis* in northern Scotland, and Boycott regards this as due to absence of competition. Williamson (1959) noted, in a mixed colony of *C. nemoralis* and *C. hortensis*, that each species was damaged more frequently in that part of the colony where the other was most common. The significance of such differential damage for species segregation is obvious.

Cain and Sheppard (1954) note that different colonies of *C. nemoralis* with differing distinctive characters are often adjacent. Lamotte (1951) found that migration in *Cepaea* was on a very small scale, and suggested that no colony of more than 30-meter radius can be considered a panmictic unit. Cain and Sheppard record cases where hedgerow colonies approach within a few feet of woodland ones without either losing its distinctive characters. The existence of such situations is itself strong evidence both for visual selection and for lack of migration. A series of colonies of *Cerion* in the Bimini group of the Bahamas provides an interesting parallel in infraspecific differentiation (Mayr and Rosen, 1956). Each colony has its own diagnostic shell characters in size, shape, sculpture, and coloration, which may correspond to different substrates. They can all interbreed, and Mayr and Rosen suggest that the pronounced but irregular geographic variation results from two opposed trends: ". . . a high degree of sedentariness and infrequent long-distance dispersal by hurricanes."

Finally, if selection of these polymorphic snails were entirely due to predators, variation would be reduced to a few pure stocks—one suitable for woods, one for rough grasslands, and so on. This does not occur. Thus other selective agents must tend to maintain the complex polymorphism; Sheppard (1958; see also Lamotte, 1951, 1952; Cain and Sheppard, 1954; Goodhart, 1956) discusses several hypotheses and suggests that genetic differences in viability or fertility advantageous to heterozygotes are important. Selection in favor of these can maintain the polymorphism, but allow the relative frequency of the polymorphic types to vary as a result of visual predation. Shell polymorphism is undeniably stable. Evidence from subfossil and fossil populations of *Cepaea* (Diver, 1929) shows that the range of shell banding has persisted for tens of thousands of years. Sheppard (1958) suggests that the ancestral stock which gave rise to the closely related species pair, *Cepaea nemoralis* and *C. hortensis*, was polymorphic for the same genes; i.e., the genes and the polymorphism are older than either species.

References

Agrell, I. (1949). The shell morphology of some Swedish Unionides as affected by ecological conditions. *Arkiv. Zool.* **41A**, No. 15, 1–30.

Alsterberg, G. (1930). "Wichtige Züge in der Biologie der Süsswassergastropoden." Lund.

Annandale, N. (1923). Advances in our knowledge of the fauna of the fresh and brackish waters of India, with a bibliography for the years 1912–1922. *J. Proc. Asiatic Soc. Bengal* [N.S.] **18**, 527–554.

Arey, L. B. (1932a). The nutrition of glochidia during metamorphosis: a microscopical study of the sources and manner of utilization of nutritive substances. *J. Morphol.* **53**, 201–221.

Arey, L. B. (1932b). The formation and structure of the glochidial cyst. *Biol. Bull.* **62**, 212–221.

Arey, L. B. (1932c). A microscopical study of glochidial immunity. *J. Morphol.* **53**, 367–379.

Arvanitaki, A., and Cardot, H. (1932). Sur les variations de la concentration du milieu intérieur chez les mollusques terrestres. *J. physiol. et pathol. gén.* **30**, 577–592.

Baer, J. G. (1952). "Ecology of Animal Parasites," 224pp. Univ. of Illinois Press, Urbana Illinois.

Baker, F. (1935). A conchological Rip van Winkle. *Nautilus* **48**, 5–6.

Barnes, H. F., and Stokes, B. M. (1951). Marking and breeding *Testacella* slugs. *Ann. Appl. Biol.* **38**, 540–545.

Barnes, H. F., and Weil, J. W. (1944). Slugs in gardens: their numbers, activities and distribution. Part 1. *J. Animal Ecol.* **13**, 140–175.

Barnes, H. F., and Weil, J. W. (1945). Slugs in gardens: their numbers, activities and distribution. Part 2. *J. Animal Ecol.* **14**, 71–105.

Bassindale, R. (1938). The intertidal fauna of the Mersey estuary. *J. Marine Biol. Assoc. U.K.* **23**, 83–98.

Bassindale, R. (1940). Studies on the biology of the Bristol Channel. IV. The invertebrate fauna of the southern shores of the Bristol Channel and Severn Estuary. *Proc. Bristol Naturalists Soc.* [4] **9**, 143–201.

Bassindale, R. (1943). Studies on the biology of the Bristol Channel. XI. The physical environment and intertidal fauna of the southern shores of the Bristol Channel and Severn Estuary. *J. Ecol.* **31**, 1–29.

Beadle, L. C., and Cragg, J. B. (1940). Studies on adaptation to salinity in *Gammarus* spp. I. Regulation of blood and tissues and the problem of adaptation to fresh water. *J. Exptl. Biol.* **17**, 153–163.

Berg, K. (1952). On the oxygen consumption of Ancylidae (Gastropoda) from an ecological point of view. *Hydrobiologia* **4**, 225–267.

Berg, K. (1953). The problem of respiratory acclimatization, illustrated by experiments with *Ancylus fluviatilis* (Gastropoda). *Hydrobiologia* **5**, 331–350.

Berg, K., and Ockelmann, K. W. (1959). The respiration of freshwater snails. *J. Exptl. Biol.* **36**, 690–708.

Berg, K., Lumbye, J., and Ockelmann, K. W. (1958). Seasonal and experimental variations of the oxygen consumption of the limpet *Ancylus fluviatilis* (O. F. Müller). *J. Exptl. Biol.* **35**, 43–73.

Berrie, A. D. (1959). Variation in the radula of the freshwater snail *Lymnaea peregra* (Müller) from northwestern Europe. *Arkiv. Zool.* [2] **12**, 391–404.

Boettger, C. R. (1944). Basommatophora. *Tierwelt Nord-Ostsee* **9**, 241–478.

Boettger, C. R. (1954). Zur Frage der Verteilung bestimmter Varianten bei der Landschneckengattung *Cepaea* Held. *Biol. Zentr.* **73**, 318–333.

Bollinger, G. (1914). Süsswasser-Mollusken von Celebes. Ausbeute der zweiten Celebes-Reise der Herren Dr. P. and Dr. F. Sarasin. *Rev. suisse zool.* **22**, 557–579.

Bondesen, P. (1940). Preliminary investigations into the development of *Neritina fluviatilis* L. in brackish and fresh water. *Dansk. Naturhist. Foren., Videnskab. Medd.* **104**, 283–318.

Bondesen, P., and Kaiser, E. W. (1949). *Hydrobia* (*Potamopyrgus*) *jenkinsi* Smith in Denmark illustrated by its ecology. *Oikos* **1**, 252–281.

Borden, M. A. (1931). A study of the respiration and of the function of haemoglobin in *Planorbis corneus* and *Arenicola marina*. *J. Marine Biol. Assoc. U.K.* **17**, 709–738.

Bourne, G. C. (1908). Contributions to the morphology of the group Neritacea of aspidobranch gastropods—Part I. The Neritidae. *Proc. Zool. Soc. London* pp. 810–887.

Bourne, G. C. (1911). Contributions to the morphology of the group Neritacea of the aspidobranch gastropods—Part II. The Helicinidae. *Proc. Zool. Soc. London* pp. 759–809.

Bovbjerg, R. V. (1952). Ecological aspects of dispersal of the snail *Campeloma decisum*. *Ecology* **33**, 169–176.

Boycott, A. E. (1934). The habitats of land Mollusca in Britain. *J. Ecol.* **22**, 1–38.

Boycott, A. E. (1936). The habitats of fresh-water Mollusca in Britain. *J. Animal Ecol.* **5**, 116–186.

Boycott, A. E., and Oldham, C. (1936). A conchological reconnaissance of the limestone in West Sutherland and Ross. *Scot. Naturalist* pp. 47–52 and 65–71.

Boycott, A. E., Diver, C., Garstang, S., and Turner, F. M. (1930). The inheritance of sinistrality in *Limnaea peregra* (Mollusca, Pulmonata). *Phil. Trans. Roy. Soc. London* **B219**, 51–131.

Brues, C. T. (1928). Studies on the fauna of hot springs in the western United States and the biology of thermophilous animals. *Proc. Am. Acad. Arts Sci.* **63**, 139–228.

Bruijns, M. F. M., Altena, C. O. van Regteren, and Butot, L. J. M. (1959). The Netherlands as an environment for land Mollusca. *Basteria* **23**, Suppl., 132–174.

Bullock, T. H. (1955). Compensation for temperature in the metabolism and activity of poikilotherms. *Biol. Revs. Cambridge Phil. Soc.* **30**, 311–342.

Cain, A. J. (1953). Visual selection by tone of *Cepaea nemoralis* (L.). *J. Conchol.* **23**, 333–336.

Cain, A. J., and Sheppard, P. M. (1950). Selection in the polymorphic land snail *Cepaea nemoralis*. *Heredity* **4**, 275–294.

Cain, A. J., and Sheppard, P. M. (1952). The effects of natural selection on body colour in the land snail *Cepaea nemoralis*. *Heredity* **6**, 217–231.

Cain, A. J., and Sheppard, P. M. (1954). Natural selection in *Cepaea*. *Genetics* **39**, 89–116.

Cain, A. J., and Sheppard, P. M. (1957). Some breeding experiments with *Cepaea nemoralis* (L.). *J. Genet.* **55**, 195–199.

Carrick, R. (1938). The life-history and development of *Agriolimax agrestis* L., the gray field slug. *Trans. Roy. Soc. Edinburgh* **59**, 563–597.

Carrick, R. (1942). The grey field slug *Agriolimax agrestis* L., and its environment. *Ann. Appl. Biol.* **29**, 43–55.

Carter, G. S. (1931). Aquatic and aerial respiration in animals. *Biol. Revs. Cambridge Phil. Soc.* **6**, 1–35.

Cheatum, E. P. (1934). Limnological investigations on respiration, annual migratory cycle, and other related phenomena in fresh-water pulmonate snails. *Trans. Am. Microscop. Soc.* **53**, 348–407.

Cheeseman, D. F. (1956). The snail's foot as a Langmuir trough. *Nature* **178**, 987–988.

Chernin, E., and Michelson, E. H. (1957a). Studies on the biological control of schistosome-bearing snails. III. The effects of population density on growth and fecundity in *Australorbis glabratus. Am. J. Hyg.* **65**, 57–70.

Chernin, E., and Michelson, E. H. (1957b). Studies on the biological control of schistosome-bearing snails. IV. Further observations on the effects of crowding on growth and fecundity in *Australorbis glabratus. Am. J. Hyg.* **65**, 71–80.

Cleland, D. M. (1954). A study of the habits of *Valvata piscinalis* (Müller) and the structure and function of the alimentary canal and reproductive system. *Proc. Malacol. Soc. London* **30**, 167–203.

Comfort, A. (1957). The duration of life in molluscs. *Proc. Malacol. Soc. London* **32**, 219–241.

Cook, P. M. (1949). A ciliary feeding mechanism in *Viviparus viviparus* (L.). *Proc. Malacol. Soc. London* **27**, 265–271.

Creek, G. A. (1951). The reproductive system and embryology of the snail *Pomatias elegans* (Müller). *Proc. Zool. Soc. London* **121**, 599–640.

Crozier, W. J., and Pilz, G. F. (1924). The locomotion of *Limax*. I. Temperature coefficient of pedal activity. *J. Gen. Physiol.* **6**, 711–721.

Cunnington, W. A. (1920). The fauna of the African lakes: a study in comparative limnology with special reference to Tanganyika. *Proc. Zool. Soc. London* pp. 507–622.

Dainton, B. H. (1943). Effect of air currents, light, humidity and temperature on slugs. *Nature* **151**, 25.

Dainton, B. H. (1954a). The activity of slugs. I. The induction of activity by changing temperatures. *J. Exptl. Biol.* **31**, 165–187.

Dainton, B. H. (1954b). The activity of slugs. II. The effect of light and air currents. *J. Exptl. Biol.* **31**, 188–197.

Dance, S. P. (1958). Drought resistance in an African freshwater bivalve. *J. Conchol.* **24**, 281–283.

Deschiens, R. (1957). Les facteurs conditionnant l'habitat des mollusques vecteurs des bilharzioses, leurs incidences épidémiologiques. I. Generalités. Facteurs physiques. *Ann. inst. Pasteur* **92**, 576–585; II. Facteurs chimiques. Nutrition. *Ibid.* pp. 711–727; III. Flore et faune des gites, ennemis naturels, maladies compétitions, fluctuations. *Ibid.* **93**, 1–12; IV. Constantes physiologiques de la reproduction et particularités en fonction des especes. Conclusions. *Ibid.* pp. 153–167.

De Wit, W. F. (1955). The life cycle and some other biological details of the freshwater snail *Physa fontinalis* (L.). *Basteria* **19**, 35–73.

De Witt, R. M. (1955). The ecology and life history of the pond snail *Physa gyrina*. *Ecology* **36**, 40–44.

Diver, C. (1929). Fossil records of Mendelian mutants. *Nature* **124**, 183.

Diver, C. (1932). Mollusca genetics [description of exhibits]. *Proc. 6th Intern. Congr. Genetics, Ithaca, N.Y., 1932* **2**, 236–238.

Diver, C. (1939). Aspects of the study of variation in snails. *J. Conchol.* **21**, 91–141.

Duncan, C. J. (1959). The life cycle and ecology of the freshwater snail *Physa fontinalis* (L.). *J. Animal Ecol.* **28**, 97–117.

Edelstam, C., and Palmer, C. (1950). Homing behaviour in gastropods. *Oikos* **2**, 259–270.

Edney, E. B. (1960). Terrestrial adaptations. *In* "Physiology of Crustacea" (T. H. Waterman, ed.), Vol. I, pp. 367–393. Academic Press, New York.

Ellis, A. E. (1926). "British Snails," 275pp. Oxford Univ. Press, London and New York.

Ellis, A. E. (1940). The identification of the British species of *Pisidium*. *Proc. Malacol. Soc. London* **24** 44–88.

Ellis, A. E., ed. (1951). Census of the distribution of British non-marine Mollusca. *J. Conchol.* **23**, 171–244.

Fisher, R. A., and Diver, C. (1934). Crossing-over in the land snail *Cepaea nemoralis* L. *Nature* **133**, 834–835.

Forbes, G. S., and Crampton, H. E. (1942a). The differentiation of geographical groups in *Lymnaea palustris*. *Biol. Bull.* **82**, 26–46.

Forbes, G. S., and Crampton, H. E. (1942b). The effects of population density upon growth and size in *Lymnaea palustris*. *Biol. Bull.* **83**, 283–289.

Fox, H. Munro (1945). The oxygen affinities of certain invertebrate haemoglobins. *J. Exptl. Biol.* **21**, 161–165.

Fox, H. Munro (1948). The haemoglobin of *Daphnia*. *Proc. Roy. Soc.* **B135**, 195–212.

Fox, H. Munro (1955). The effect of oxygen on the concentration of haem in invertebrates. *Proc. Roy. Soc.* **B143**, 203–214.

Fox, H. Munro, Gilchrist, B. M., and Phear, E. A. (1951). Functions of haemoglobin in *Daphnia*. *Proc. Roy. Soc.* **B138**, 514–528

Fox, H. Munro, and Phear, E. A. (1953). Factors influencing haemoglobin synthesis by *Daphnia*. *Proc. Roy. Soc.* **B141**, 179–189.

Fraser, J. H. (1932). Observations on the fauna and constituents of an estuarine mud in a polluted area. *J. Marine Biol. Assoc. U.K.* **18**, 69–85.

Fretter, V., and Graham, A. (1962). "British Prosobranch Molluscs, Their Functional Anatomy and Ecology," 755pp. Ray Society, London.

Frömming, E. (1936). Über den Einfluss der Wasserstoffionenkonzentration auf unsere Süsswasserschnecken. *Intern. Rev. Hydrobiol.* **33**, 25–37.

Frömming, E. (1938). Untersuchungen über den Einfluss der Härte des Wohngewässers auf das Vorkommen unserer Süsswassermollusken. *Intern. Rev. Hydrobiol.* **36**, 531–561.

Frömming, E. (1953). Ist der Vitamin C-Gehalt der Pflanzen ein Faktor, welcher die Nahrungswahl der Schnecken beeinflusst? *Basteria* **17**, 9–15.

Frömming, E. (1954). "Biologie der mitteleuropäischen Landgastropoden," 404pp. Duncker & Humblot, Berlin.

Frömming, E. (1956). "Biologie der mitteleuropäischen Süsswasserschnecken," 313pp. Duncker & Humblot, Berlin.

Fryer, G. (1959). Development in a mutelid lamellibranch. *Nature* **183**, 1342–1343.

Füsser, H., and Krüger, F. (1951). Vergleichende Versuche zur Atmungsphysiologie von *Planorbis corneus* und *Limnaea stagnalis* (Gastropoda Pulmonata). *Z. vergleich. Physiol.* **33**, 14–52.

Geldiay, R. (1956). Studies on local populations of the freshwater limpet *Ancylus fluviatilis* Müller. *J. Animal Ecol.* **25**, 389–402.

Germain, L. (1931). Mollusques terrestres et fluviatiles (deuxieme partie). *Faune France* **22**, 479–893.

Getz, L. L. (1959). Notes on the ecology of slugs: *Arion circumscriptus, Deroceras reticulatum* and *D. laeve*. *Am. Midland Naturalist* **61**, 485–498.

Goldacre, R. J. (1949). Surface films on natural bodies of water. *J. Animal Ecol.* **18**, 36–39.

Goodhart, C. B. (1956). Genetic stability in populations of the polymorphic snail, *Cepaea nemoralis* (L.). *Proc. Linnean Soc. London* **167**, 50–67.

Goodhart, C. B. (1958). Thrush predation on the snail *Cepaea hortensis*. *J. Animal Ecol.* **27**, 47–57.

Green, J. (1957). The growth of *Scrobicularia plana* (da Costa) in the Gwendraeth estuary. *J. Marine Biol. Assoc. U.K.* **36**, 41–47.

Henderson, A. E. (1961). Studies on the respiratory and hydrostatic functions of the mantle cavity in two freshwater pulmonate snails. Thesis, University of Glasgow.

Hesse, R. (1924). "Tiergeographie auf ökologischer Grundlage," 613pp. Fischer, Jena.

Hesse, R., Allee, W. C., and Schmidt, K. P. (1937). "Ecological Animal Geography," 597pp. [Translation and revised edition of Hesse, 1924.] Wiley, New York.

Hiscock, I. D. (1953). Osmoregulation in Australian freshwater mussels (Lamellibranchiata). I. Water and chloride ion exchange in *Hyridella australis* (Lam.). *Australian J. Marine and Freshwater Research* **4**, 317–329.

Hogben, L., and Kirk, R. L. (1944a). The pigmentary effector system. X. Relation of colour change to surface absorption of radiation. *Proc. Roy. Soc.* **B132**, 68–82.

Hogben, L., and Kirk, R. L. (1944b). Studies on temperature regulation. I. The Pulmonata and Oligochaeta. *Proc. Roy. Soc.* **B132**, 239–252.

Holme, N. A. (1949). The fauna of sand and mud banks near the mouth of the Exe estuary. *J. Marine Biol. Assoc. U.K.* **28**, 189–237.

Howes, N. H., and Wells, G. P. (1934a). The water relation of snails and slugs. I. Weight rhythms in *Helix pomatia* L. *J. Exptl. Biol.* **11**, 327–343.

Howes, N. H., and Wells, G. P. (1934b). The water relations of snails and slugs. II. Weight rhythms in *Arion ater* L. and *Limax flavus* L. *J. Exptl. Biol.* **11**, 344–351.

Howes, N. H., and Whellock, R. B. (1937). A semisynthetic diet for *Helix pomatia*. *Biochem. J.* **31**, 1489–1498.

Hubendick, B. (1947). Die Verbreitungsverhältnisse der limnischen Gastropoden in Südschweden. *Zool. Bidrag Uppsala* **24**, 419–559.

Hubendick, B. (1950). The effectiveness of passive dispersal in *Hydrobia jenkinsi*. *Zool. Bidrag Uppsala* **28**, 493–504.

Hubendick, B. (1951). Recent Lymnaeidae, their variation, morphology, taxonomy, nomenclature, and distribution. *Kgl. Svenska Vetenskapsakad. Handl.* [4] **3**, 1–223.

Hubendick, B. (1952). On the evolution of the so-called thalassoid molluscs of Lake Tanganyika. *Arkiv Zool.* [2] **3**, 319–323.

Hubendick, B. (1953). The relationships of the East African Vitrinae with notes on the taxonomy of *Vitrina*. *Arkiv. Zool.* [2] **6**, 83–96.

Hubendick, B. (1954). Viewpoints on species discrimination with special attention to medically important snails. *Proc. Malacol. Soc. London* **31**, 6–11.

Hubendick, B. (1957). *Patelloplanorbis*, a new genus of Planorbidae (Mollusca Pulmonata). *Proc. Koninkl. Ned. Akad. Wetenschap.* **C60**, 90–95.

Hubendick, B. (1960). The Ancylidae of Lake Ochrid and their bearing on intra-lacustrine speciation. *Proc. Zool. Soc. London* **133**, 497–529.

Hunter, W. Russell (1952). The adaptations of freshwater Gastropoda. *Glasgow Naturalist* **16**, 84–85.

Hunter, W. Russell (1953a). On the growth of the freshwater limpet, *Ancylus fluviatilis* Müller. *Proc. Zool. Soc. London* **123**, 623–636.

Hunter, W. Russell (1953b). On migrations of *Lymnaea peregra* (Müller) on the shores of Loch Lomond. *Proc. Roy. Soc. Edinburgh* **B65**, 84–105.

Hunter, W. Russell (1953c). The condition of the mantle cavity in two pulmonate snails living in Loch Lomond. *Proc. Roy. Soc. Edinburgh* **B65**, 143–165.

Hunter, W. Russell (1955a). Endemicism in the snails of Jamaica. *Glasgow Naturalist* **17**, 173–183.

Hunter, W. Russell (1955b). New and newly-confirmed distribution records of non-marine molluscs in the West of Scotland (IIIrd paper). *Glasgow Naturalist* **17**, 207–211.

Hunter, W. Russell (1957). Studies on freshwater snails at Loch Lomond. *Glasgow Univ. Publ., Stud. Loch Lomond* 1, 56–95.

Hunter, W. Russell (1958a). Biology in the Clyde and its associated waters, with a note on land animals in the Clyde area. *Brit. Assoc. Handb. (Glasgow, 1958)* 5, 97–118.

Hunter, W. Russell (1958b). New and newly-confirmed distribution records of non-marine molluscs in the West of Scotland (IVth paper). *Glasgow Naturalist* 18, 37–44.

Hunter, W. Russell (1961a). Annual variations in growth and density in natural populations of freshwater snails in the West of Scotland. *Proc. Zool. Soc. London* 136, 219–253.

Hunter, W. Russell (1961b). Life cycles of four freshwater snails in limited populations in Loch Lomond, with a discussion of infraspecific variation. *Proc. Zool. Soc. London* 137, 135–171.

Hunter, W. Russell, and Hunter, M. Russell (1956). Mollusca on Scottish mountains. *J. Conchol.* 24, 80.

Hunter, W. Russell, and Hunter, M. Russell (1962). On a population of *Hydrobia ulvae* in the Clyde estuary. *Glasgow Naturalist* 18, 198–205.

Hunter, W. Russell, and Slack, H. D. (1958). *Pisidium conventus* Clessin in Loch Lomond. *J. Conchol.* 24, 245–247.

Hunter, W. Russell, and Warwick, T. (1957). Records of *Potamopyrgus jenkinsi* (Smith) in Scottish fresh waters over fifty years (1906–1956). *Proc. Roy. Soc. Edinburgh* B66, 360–373.

Issel, R. (1908). Sulla biologia termale. *Intern. Rev. Hydrobiol.* 1, 29–36.

Jacobs, W. (1941). Die hydrostatische Bedeutung der Atmungsorgane von Wassertieren. *Sitzber. Ges. Morphol. Physiol. München* 50, 45–52.

Kalmus, H. (1942). Anemotaxis in soft-skinned animals. *Nature* 150, 524.

Kew, H. W. (1893). "The Dispersal of Shells. An Inquiry into the Means of Dispersal Possessed by Freshwater and Land Mollusca," 291pp. London.

Kirk, R. L., and Hogben, L. (1946). Studies on temperature regulation. II. Amphibia and reptiles. *J. Exptl. Biol.* 22, 213–220.

Künkel, K. (1916). "Zur Biologie der Lungenschnecken." Carl Winter, Heidelberg.

Lamotte, M. (1950). Observations sur la sélection par les prédateurs chez *Cepaea nemoralis*. *J. Conchyliol.* 90, 180–190.

Lamotte, M. (1951). Recherches sur la structure génétique des populations naturelles de *Cepaea nemoralis* (L.). *Bull. biol. France* Suppl. 35, 1–239.

Lamotte, M. (1952). Le rôle des fluctuations fortuites dans la diversité des populations naturelles de *Cepaea nemoralis* (L.). *Heredity* 6, 333–343.

Leitch, I. (1916). The function of haemoglobin in invertebrates with special reference to *Planorbis* and *Chironomus* larvae. *J. Physiol. (London)* 50, 370–379.

Lilly, M. M. (1953). The mode of life and structure and functioning of the reproductive ducts of *Bithynia tentaculata* (L.). *Proc. Malacol. Soc. London* 30, 87–110.

Lumbye, J. (1958). The oxygen consumption of *Theodoxus fluviatilis* (L.) and *Potamopyrgus jenkinsi* (Smith) in brackish and fresh water. *Hydrobiologia* 10, 245–262.

Macan, T. T. (1950). Ecology of fresh-water Mollusca in the English Lake District. *J. Animal Ecol.* 19, 124–146.

McMichael, D. F., and Hiscock, I. D. (1958). A monograph of the freshwater mussels (Mollusca: Pelecypoda) of the Australian region. *Australian J. Marine and Freshwater Research* 9, 372–508.

McMillan, N. F. (1948). Possible biological races in *Hydrobia ulvae* (Pennant) and their varying resistance to lowered salinity. *J. Conchol.* 23, 14–16.

McNeil, C. W., and Walter, W. M. (1957). Surface-wintering of aquatic snails in central Washington. *J. Parasitol.* **43**, 114–115.

Main, A. R., and Carrigy, M. A. (1953). Native snails of the genus *Bothriembryon* in King's Park, Perth. *West. Australian Naturalist* **4**, 49–59.

Mayr, E., and Rosen, C. B. (1956). Geographic variation and hybridization in populations of Bahama snails (*Cerion*). *Am. Museum Novitates* **1806**, 1–48.

Meeuse, A. D. J., and Hubert, B. (1949). The mollusc fauna of glasshouses in the Netherlands. *Basteria* **13**, 1–30.

Mehlman, B., and von Brand, T. (1951). Further studies on the anaerobic metabolism of some fresh water snails. *Biol. Bull.* **100**, 199–205.

Mellanby, K. (1941). The body temperature of the frog. *J. Exptl. Biol.* **18**, 55–61.

Milne, A. (1938). The ecology of the Tamar estuary. III. Salinity and temperature conditions in the lower estuary. *J. Marine Biol. Assoc. U.K.* **22**, 529–542.

Milne, A. (1940). The ecology of the Tamar estuary. IV. The distribution of the fauna and flora on buoys. *J. Marine Biol. Assoc. U.K.* **24**, 69–87.

Mirolli, M. (1958). I Gasteropodi costieri del Lago Maggiore e di alcuni Laghi vicini. *Mem. ist. ital. idrobiol. Dott. Marco de Marchi* **10**, 209–316.

Moon, H. P. (1956). The distribution of *Potamopyrgus jenkinsi* (E. A. Smith) in Windermere. *Proc. Malacol. Soc. London* **32**, 105–108.

Moore, J. E. S. (1903). "The Tanganyika Problem." London.

Mori, S. (1946). Daily rhythmic activities of two species of Japanese freshwater snails (in Japanese). *Physiol. Ecol. Contr. Otsu Hydrobiol. Sta.* (*Kyoto Univ.*) **60**, 1–17. (Not seen in the original, quoted from author's English abstract.)

Morton, J. E. (1955a). The functional morphology of the British Ellobiidae (Gastropoda Pulmonata) with special reference to the digestive and reproductive systems. *Phil. Trans. Roy. Soc.* **B239**, 89–160.

Morton, J. E. (1955b). The evolution of the Ellobiidae with a discussion on the origin of the Pulmonata. *Proc. Zool. Soc. London* **125**, 127–168.

Morton, J. E. (1958). "Molluscs," 232pp. Hutchinson, London.

Mozley, A. (1932). A biological study of a temporary pond in Western Canada. *Am. Naturalist* **66**, 235–249.

Mozley, A. (1935). The variation of two species of *Lymnaea*. *Genetics* **20**, 452–465.

Mozley, A. (1939). The Quill Lakes basin, Saskatchewan, Canada, and its molluscan fauna. *Intern. Rev. Hydrobiol.* **38**, 243–249.

Müller, I. (1943). Die Abhängigkeit des Stoffwechsels von der Körpergrösse und der Zusammenhang von Stoffwechseltypen und Wachstumstypen. *Riv. Biol.* (*Perugia*) **35**, 48–95.

Needham, J. (1938). Contributions of chemical physiology to the problem of reversibility in evolution. *Biol. Revs. Cambridge Phil. Soc.* **13**, 225–251.

Needham, J. (1942). "Biochemistry and Morphogenesis," 785pp. Cambridge Univ. Press, London and New York.

Nicol, E. A. T. (1935). The ecology of a salt-marsh. *J. Marine Biol. Assoc. U.K.* **20**, 203–261.

Nicol, E. A. T. (1936). The brackish-water lochs of North Uist. *Proc. Roy. Soc. Edinburgh* **56**, 169–195.

Nolan, M. O., and von Brand, T. (1954). The weight relations between shell and soft tissues during the growth of some fresh-water snails. *J. Wash. Acad. Sci.* **44**, 251–255.

Noland, L. E., and Carriker, M. R. (1946). Observations on the biology of the snail *Lymnaea stagnalis appressa* during twenty generations in laboratory culture. *Am. Midland Naturalist* **36**, 467–493.

Odhner, N. H. (1923). Mollusca: *Pisidium conventus* Clessin (*P. clessini* Surbeck, partim). *Rept. Sci. Research Norweg. Exped. Novaya Zemyla 1921* 1, No. 6, 1–6.

Olivier, L. (1956). Observations on vectors of schistosomiasis mansoni kept out of water in the laboratory, I. *J. Parasitol.* 42, 137–146.

Olivier, L., and Barbosa, F. S. (1955a). Seasonal studies on *Australorbis glabratus* Say from two localities in eastern Pernambuco, Brazil. *Publs. avulsas inst. Aggeu Magalhães* 4, 79–103.

Olivier, L., and Barbosa, F. S. (1955b). Seasonal studies on *Tropicorbis centimetralis* in northeastern Brazil. *Publs. avulsas inst. Aggeu Magalhães* 4, 105–115.

Olivier, L., and Barbosa, F. S. (1956). Observations on vectors of schistomiasis mansoni kept out of water in the laboratory, II. *J. Parasitol.* 42, 277–286.

Panikkar, N. K. (1940). Influence of temperature on osmotic behaviour of some crustacea and its bearing on problems of animal distribution. *Nature* 146, 366–367.

Pelseneer, P. (1906). Part 5: Mollusca, 355pp. *In* "A Treatise on Zoology" (E. R. Lankester, ed.). Adam and Charles Black, London.

Phillips, R. A. (1915). The non-marine Mollusca of south Galway. *Irish Naturalist* 24, 137–150.

Pilsbry, H. A. (1939–1948). "Land Mollusca of North America (North of Mexico)," Vols. 1 and 2. Acad. Natural Sciences, Philadelphia, Pennsylvania.

Polinski, W. (1932). Die reliktäre Gastropodenfauna des Ochrida-Sees. *Zool. Jahrb., Abt. System. Ökol. u. Geogr. Tiere* 62, 611–666.

Potts, W. T. W. (1954a). The inorganic composition of the blood of *Mytilus edulis* and *Anodonta cygnea. J. Exptl. Biol.* 31, 376–385.

Potts, W. T. W. (1954b). The energetics of osmotic regulation in brackish- and fresh-water animals. *J. Exptl. Biol.* 31, 618–630.

Precht, H. (1939). Die Lüngenatmung der Süsswasserpulmonaten (zugleich ein Beitrag zur Temperaturabhangigheit der Atmung). *Z. vergleich Physiol.* 26, 696–739.

Precht, H., and Otto, E. (1948). Hat die Lunge der Süsswasserpulmonaten hydrostatische Bedeutung? *Verhandl. deut. zool. Keil.* (*1948*) 60, 381–387 (*Zool. Anz.* Suppl. 13).

Quick, H. E. (1943). Land snails and slugs of west Glamorgan. *J. Conchol.* 22, 4–12.

Quick, H. E. (1960). British slugs (Pulmonata; Testacellidae, Arionidae, Limacidae). *Bull. Brit. Museum* (*Nat. Hist.*), *Zool.* 6, 103–226.

Radoman, P. (1955a). Recherches morphologiques et systématiques sur les Hydrobiides du lac d'Ohrid (text in Yugoslav, summary in French). *Soc. serbe biol., Beograd Ed. spéc.* 1, 1–106.

Radoman, P. (1955b). Contribution à la connaissance des gastéropodes du bassin d'Ohrid (text in Yugoslav, summary in French). *Rec. trav. sta. hydrobiol., Ohrid* 3, 23–39.

Radoman, P. (1960). Two sibling species of *Pseudammicola* in Ohrid Lake. *Basteria* 24, 1–9.

Rees, C. B. (1940). A preliminary study of the ecology of a mud-flat. *J. Marine Biol. Assoc. U.K.* 24, 185–199.

Robertson, J. D. (1941). The function and metabolism of calcium in the invertebrata. *Biol. Revs. Cambridge Phil. Soc.* 16, 106–133.

Robson, G. C. (1923). Parthenogenesis in the mollusc *Paludestrina jenkinsi*: Part I. *Brit. J. Exptl. Biol.* 1, 65–78.

Roebuck, W. D., ed. (1921). Census of the distribution of British land and freshwater Mollusca. *J. Conchol.* 16, 165–212.

Sanderson, A. R. (1940). Maturation in the parthenogenetic snail, *Potamopyrgus jenkinsi* Smith, and in the snail *Peringa ulvae* (Pennant). *Proc. Zool. Soc. London* **110**, 11–15.

Sarasin, P., and Sarasin, F. (1894–1896). Reiseberichte aus Celebes. *Z. Ges. Erdk. Berlin* **29**, 351–401; **30**, 226–234, 311–352; **31**, 21–49.

Schlieper, C. (1957). Comparative study of *Asterias rubens* and *Mytilus edulis* from the North Sea (30 per 1,000 S) and the western Baltic Sea (15 per 1,000 S). *Année biol.* [3] **33**, 117–127.

Schlieper, C., and Kowalski, R. (1957). Weitere Beobachtungen zur ökologischen Physiologie der Miesmuschel *Mytilus edulis* L. *Kiel. Meeresforsch.* **13**, 3–10.

Schnitter, H. (1922). Die Najaden der Schweiz. *Z. Hydrol.* Suppl. 2, 1–202.

Sedlmair, H. (1956). Verhaltens-, Resistenz- und Gehäuseunterschiede bei den polymorphen Bänderschnecken *Cepaea hortensis* (Müll.) und *Cepaea nemoralis* (L.). *Biol. Zentr.* **75**, 281–313.

Segal, E. (1959). Respiration and temperature acclimation in slugs. *Anat. Record* **134**, 636.

Segal, E. (1961). Acclimation in molluscs. *Am. Zoologist* **1**, 235–244.

Segerstråle, S. G. (1949). The brackish-water fauna of Finland. *Oikos* **1**, 127–141.

Segerstråle, S. G. (1953). Further notes on the increase in salinity of the inner Baltic and its influence on the fauna. *Soc. Sci. Fennica Comment. Biol.* **13**, No. 15, 1–7.

Segerstråle, S. G. (1957). Baltic Sea. *Geol. Soc. Am., Mem.* **67**, 751–800.

Shalem, N. (1949). L'influence de la rosée et des brouillards sur la répartition des escargots. *J. Conchyliol.* **89**, 95–107.

Sheppard, P. M. (1951). Fluctuations in the selective value of certain phenotypes in the polymorphic land snail *Cepaea nemoralis* (L.). *Heredity* **5**, 125–134.

Sheppard, P. M. (1952). Natural selection in two colonies of the polymorphic land snail *Cepaea nemoralis*. *Heredity* **6**, 233–238.

Sheppard, P. M. (1958). "Natural Selection and Heredity," 212pp. Hutchinson, London.

Spooner, G. M., and Moore, H. B. (1940). The ecology of the Tamar estuary. VI. An account of the macrofauna of the intertidal muds. *J. Marine Biol. Assoc. U.K.* **24**, 283–330.

Stankovic, S. (1932). Die Fauna des Ohrid-Sees und ihre Herkunft. *Arch. Hydrobiol. (u. Planktonk.)* **23**, 557–617.

Stankovic, S. (1960). The Balkan Lake Ohrid and its living world. *Monograph. Biol.* **9**, 1–357.

Taylor, J. W. (1900). "A Monograph of the Land and Freshwater Mollusca of the British Isles," Vol. I, Structural and General, 454pp. Taylor Bros., Leeds.

Thamdrup, H. M. (1935). Beiträge zur Okologie der Wattenfauna auf experimenteller Grundlage. *Medd. Komm. Havundersøg., Kbh. (Fiskeri)* **10**, No. 2, 1–125.

Thiel, M. E. (1926a). Vorläufige Mitteilung über das Wachstum und die Fortpflanzung von *S. corneum* im Hamburger Hafen. *Mitt. zool. Staatinst. Hamburg* **42**, 40–47.

Thiel, M. E. (1926b). Weitere Mitteilung zur Lebensweise von *S. corneum*. *Mitt. zool. Staatinst. Hamburg* **42**, 48–90.

Thiele, J. (1925). Prosobranchia in Kukenthal und Krumbach. *Handbuch Zool.* **5**.

Thiele, J. (1931). "Handbuch der systematischen Weichtierkunde," Parts 1 and 2, 778pp. Fischer, Jena.

van Benthem Jutting, W. S. S. (1959a). Ecology of brackish water Mollusca in the Netherlands. *Basteria* **23**, 77–105.

van Benthem Jutting, W. S. S. (1959b). Ecology of freshwater Mollusca in the Netherlands. *Basteria* **23**, 106–131.

Van Cleave, H. J., and Altringer, D. A. (1937). Studies on the life cycle of *Campeloma rufum*, a fresh-water snail. *Am. Naturalist* **71**, 167–184.

Van Cleave, H. J., and Lederer, L. G. (1932). Studies on the life cycle of the snail, *Viviparus contectoides*. *J. Morphol.* **53**, 499–522.

van Dalsum, J. (1947). De kleurvariëteiten van *Planorbis corneus* (L.). *Basteria* **11**, 100–109.

van Dalsum, J. (1951). Over de invloed van de temperatuur op de kleur van *Planorbis corneus* (L.) var. *rubra* Oldham. *Basteria* **15**, 59–61.

van der Schalie, H., and Dundee, D. S. (1955). The distribution, ecology and life history of *Pomatiopsis cincinnatiensis* (Lea), an amphibious operculate snail. *Trans. Am. Microscop. Soc.* **74**, 119–133.

von Brand, T. (1955). Anaerobiosis in *Australorbis glabratus:* Temperature effects and tissue hydration. *J. Wash. Acad. Sci.* **45**, 373–377.

von Brand, T., and Mehlman, B. (1953). Relations between pre- and post-anaerobic oxygen consumption and oxygen tension in some fresh water snails. *Biol. Bull.* **104**, 301–312.

von Brand, T., Baernstein, H. D., and Mehlman, B. (1950). Studies on the anaerobic metabolism and the aerobic carbohydrate consumption of some fresh water snails. *Biol. Bull.* **98**, 266–276.

von Brand, T., McMahon, P., and Nolan, M. O. (1955). Observations on the post-anaerobic metabolism of some fresh-water snails. *Physiol. Zoöl.* **28**, 35–40.

Walden, H. W. (1955). The land gastropods of the vicinity of Stockholm. *Arkiv Zool.* [2] **7**, 391–449.

Warwick, T. (1944). The inheritance of the keel in *Potamopyrgus jenkinsi* (Smith). *Nature* **154**, 798–799.

Warwick, T. (1952). Strains in the mollusc *Potamopyrgus jenkinsi* (Smith). *Nature* **169**, 551–552.

Waterhouse, F. L. (1955). Microclimatological profiles in grass cover in relation to biological problems. *Quart. J. Roy. Meteorol. Soc.* **81**, 63–71.

Wells, G. P. (1944). The water relations of snails and slugs. III. Factors determining activity in *Helix pomatia* L. *J. Exptl. Biol.* **20**, 79–87.

WHO Study Group (1957). Study group on the ecology of intermediate snail hosts of Bilharziasis: report. *World Health Organ. Tech. Rept. Ser.* **120**, 1–38.

Williamson, M. H. (1959). Differential damage in a mixed colony of the land snails *Cepaea nemoralis* and *C. hortensis*. *Heredity* **13**, 261–263.

Winckworth, R. (1932). The British marine Mollusca. *J. Conchol.* **19**, 211–252.

Winckworth, R. (1950). "Gastropoda," "Mollusca," and "Snail" in *Chamber's Encyclopaedia*.

Winckworth, R. (1951). A list of the marine Mollusca of the British Isles: Additions and corrections. *J. Conchol.* **23**, 131–134.

Wolvekamp, H. P. (1932). Untersuchungen über den Sauerstofftransport durch Blutpigmente bei *Helix, Rana* und *Planorbis*. *Z. vergleich. Physiol.* **16**, 1–38.

Wright, C. A. (1956). A note on the ecology of some molluscan intermediate hosts of African schistosomiasis. *Ann. Trop. Med. Parasitol.* **50**, 346–349.

Yonge, C. M. (1938). The prosobranchs of Lake Tanganyika. *Nature* **142**, 464–465.

Yonge, C. M. (1947). The pallial organs in the aspidobranch Gastropoda and their evolution throughout the Mollusca. *Phil. Trans. Roy. Soc.* **B232**, 443–518.

Yonge, C. M. (1952). The mantle cavity in *Siphonaria alternata* Say. *Proc. Malacol. Soc. London* **29**, 190–199.

Yonge, C. M. (1960). Further observations on *Hipponix antiquatus* with notes on north Pacific pulmonate limpets. *Proc. Calif. Acad. Sci.* [4] **31**, 111–119.

Yonge, C. M. (1962). On *Etheria elliptica* Lam. and the course of evolution, including assumption of monomyarianism, in the family Etheriidae (Bivalvia: Unionacea). *Phil. Trans. Roy. Soc. London* **B244**, 423–458.

Zaaijer, J. J. P., and Wolvekamp, H. P. (1958). Some experiments on the haemoglobin-oxygen equilibrium in the blood of the ramshorn (*Planorbis corneus* L.). *Acta Physiol. et Pharmacol. Neerl.* **7**, 56–77.

CHAPTER 4

Reproduction

V. Fretter and A. Graham
DEPARTMENT OF ZOOLOGY, UNIVERSITY OF READING, READING, ENGLAND

I. REPRODUCTIVE METHODS

In the great majority of animal species individuals are either male or female throughout their lifetime. They are said to show separate sexes, to be unisexual, gonochoristic or dioecious. Throughout the various phyla, however, a not inconsiderable number of cases is known in which an animal produces gametes of both male and female type, either at the same time or else first of one sort and later of another. These animals are called hermaphrodites, ambisexual or monoecious.

A. Gonochorism: Sexual Dimorphism and Proportion of the Sexes

In molluscs sexual dimorphism is rarely obvious; some differentiation, however, exists, the female gastropod being usually larger and with slightly more tumid shell whorls than the male. The mouth of the shell may be more open in the female. Otherwise the sex can be determined only by the presence or absence of a penis in mesogastropods and neogastropods or of a ventral pedal gland in many neogastropods. Except for the presence of a pair of vesiculae in the mantle cavity in the male phase of *Xylophaga*,

127

provision there for incubating eggs in some species of *Unio* and *Lamp-silis* and for minor shell differences in some *Astarte* species, there is no way of knowing the sex of a bivalve apart from examination of the gonad. In cephalopods the presence or absence of a hectocotylized arm permits recognition of sex and there are also differences in shape of the body and shell. Some cephalopods (*Argonauta*) show an exaggerated sexual dimorphism, with the males much smaller than the females and lacking the familiar paper nautilus shell.

Females tend to be more numerous than males in gonochoristic species and to become still more numerous as the age of the population increases. This disparity is not present in young animals and is therefore probably due to the early death of the males. Some figures expressed as percentage of males in a population follow (based on Pelseneer, 1926): *Lepidochitona cinereus*, 53; *Patina pellucida*, 50; *Margarites helicinus*, 43; *Viviparus bengalensis*, 28; *Littorina littorea* (young), 51 (old), 33; *Rissoa parva*, 63; *Bithynia leachi*, 20; *Pomatias elegans*, 61; *Turritella communis*, 37; *Nassarius reticulatus*, 40; *Mytilus edulis*, 54; *Cardium edule*, 40; *Donax vittatus*, 45; *Anodonta cygnea*, 46; *Nautilus pompilius*, 69; *Sepiola atlantica*, 47; *Loligo subulata*, 33; *Eledone moschata*, 30. These figures may be affected by parasitism.

B. *Hermaphroditism*

It is usually held that hermaphroditism is secondarily derived from a gonochoristic condition, but this may not be true, since there is some evidence for regarding the hermaphroditic state as the primitive one, particularly in the phylum Mollusca. Some classes of the phylum (e.g., cephalopods and scaphopods) are exclusively gonochoristic; in others, one species may be gonochoristic, a related species hermaphroditic; it is often difficult to discover physiological or ecological reasons for this. It sometimes appears, however, that a hermaphrodite is normally living in a habitat or ecological situation in which it is confronted by some difficulty in reproductive activity, and that this difficulty, to some extent at least, is eased by the adoption of the ambisexual state. Hermaphroditism has therefore been favored and perpetuated by natural selection. Thus, hermaphrodites are commoner among fresh-water than marine molluscs; they occur in terrestrial forms which are restricted by environmental factors to limited activity; and they are frequently sedentary or sessile species, whether free-living or parasitic. In all of these situations it is likely that the meeting of individuals is a sufficiently uncommon event for cross-fertilization of two hermaphrodites to be significantly more efficient from the point of view of natural selection than the meeting of male and female. A logical extension of this is the increased efficiency introduced when self-fertilization becomes possible if an individual fails to find a partner with which it may copulate. This is indeed found as a further development of hermaphroditism in a number of species.

The various types of hermaphroditism which occur in the phylum have been well reviewed by Coe (1943, 1944) and Bacci (1951). The classification of hermaphrodites proposed by these two workers is given in the following tabulation.

Coe	Bacci
Functional or simultaneous	Simultaneous (with synchronous ripening)
Consecutive	Successive (with asynchronous ripening) or consecutive
Rhythmical consecutive	Successive (with asynchronous ripening) or alternate
Alternative	Successive (with separate ripening) or alternate

1. BIVALVIA

Most of the hermaphrodite bivalves, as was noted by Pelseneer (1895, 1911), are also those which do not broadcast their eggs but incubate them in the mantle cavity or gill until they have developed as far as the larval stage, or until they are miniatures of the parent. Some of these are freshwater animals (e.g., *Cyclas, Pisidium, Sphaerium, Anodonta*) in which suppression of the larval stage seems clearly adaptive; others, which are marine (e.g., Erycinidae, Montacutidae, *Transennella, Ostrea* and some species of *Teredo*), live in restricted habitats where the same advantage accrues. The incubatory habit and hermaphroditism are both related to the stress of reproduction in a habitat in some way unfavorable. Perhaps because of the gastropod habit of laying eggs in capsules or shells the link between hermaphroditism and viviparity does not seem to have become established in that group of molluscs.

Taken as a whole, the bivalves may be regarded as a group characterized by gonochorism since, according to Coe (1943), about 96% of the species included in the class have separate sexes. The majority of the hermaphroditic bivalves fall into Coe's category of simultaneous or functional hermaphrodites. These species produce, simultaneously, male and female gametes, and in appropriate circumstances, self-fertilization may result. Such is the case in *Pecten irradians*, in which the two types of gamete, though developed in distinct parts of the gonad, are shed together along the same ducts. In the European *P. maximus* and *Chlamys opercularis*, the possibility of self-fertilization is negligible since the testicular part of the gonad is regularly spent before the eggs have ripened in the ovarian half.

This tendency toward protandry is frequent in simultaneous hermaphrodites. If the production of eggs overlaps the production of sperm there arises a type of life history which may be diagrammatically represented as $\delta \rightarrow \delta_+^\circ \rightarrow \circ$; but a period of sexual inactivity may separate the initial male from the later female phase. In some simultaneous hermaphrodites (e.g., *Teredo diegensis*) a certain number of young males never change sex and must therefore be regarded as true males. These are characterized by an absence of potential eggs in the gonad, and differ in that respect from the bulk of the males in the population, which have a hermaphrodite gonad. The following genera may be listed as simultaneous hermaphrodites: *Pecten, Chlamys, Anodonta, Montacuta, Lasaea, Sphaerium, Musculium, Pisidium, Cardium, Tridacna, Tivela, Gemma, Teredo, Thracia, Poromya,* and *Cetoconcha*. The label is not necessarily applicable to every species of these genera: thus, *Cardium edule*, the edible cockle of Europe, has separate sexes; whereas *Montacuta substriata* is a simultaneous hermaphrodite, *M. ferruginosa* is a consecutive one. Coe (1943) included *Kellia* in this list but Oldfield (1959) has shown that this species is a consecutive hermaphrodite.

Consecutive hermaphrodites change sex once in their lives, usually from a younger male to an older female phase, although a few (*Kellia suborbicularis, Montacuta ferruginosa*) reverse this sex sequence and are regularly protogynous (Oldfield, 1959). The change may take place in such a way as to render the animals of one sex early in the breeding season and of the other sex later, or there may be a winter pause between the two phases. In the former case there may be an overlapping of the male and female activity, giving a brief period of simultaneous hermaphroditism; this merges with the kind of hermaphroditism exhibited by *Teredo diegensis*. *Venus mercenaria* is the best-known example of this type, which also occurs in the wood-boring bivalves *Bankia setacea* and *Xylophaga dorsalis* (Purchon, 1941). In *Venus*, as in *Teredo diegensis*, a very small proportion of genuinely gonochoristic animals, both male and female, occurs.

A variation of consecutive hermaphroditism is to be found where the change of sex is repeated, either annually or at closer intervals, leading to a more or less regular alternation from male to female. This is rhythmical consecutive hermaphroditism and it is well known in *Ostrea*, particularly *O. edulis;* it was first described in the important work of Orton (1927a). Individual oysters may be out of phase so that there are always sufficient animals acting as males and females to ensure cross-fertilization. This is also true of the American species, *O. equestris* and *O. lurida* in which the sex may change and revert to the original within one year. As in *Venus* and *Teredo diegensis*, a small proportion of animals is not hermaphroditic. *Teredo navalis* also exhibits rhythmical consecutive hermaphroditism changing from male to female; but mortality in the latter phase is so great that it virtually marks the end of the animal's life.

In alternative hermaphroditism a sex change occurs but its timing is erratic. The nonincubatory oysters, *Crassostrea virginica*, *C. gigas* from Japan, and *C. cucullata* (India), exhibit it. In the American *C. virginica* 70% of the young are functionally male; at the second spawning the numbers of males and females are equal; while there is an excess of females in older animals. As in other cases a small proportion of apparently true males and females exists.

Since many bivalves change sex once or many times it cannot be assumed that an animal emitting sperm or eggs is a true male or female. This can be proved only by ascertaining that there are no immature gametes of the opposite sex in the gonad. So far this proof is lacking for most apparently gonochoristic bivalves and has been obtained only for the following: *Modiolus demissus*, *Brachyodontes bifurcatus*, *Mytilus californianus*, *Anomia simplex*, *Petricola pholadiformis*, *Donax gouldi*, *Mya arenaria*, and *Barnea truncata*. There is, however, no suggestion that most bivalves are not genuinely gonochoristic.

2. GASTROPODA

In gastropods the best-known hermaphrodites are the opisthobranchs and pulmonates, which are simultaneous hermaphrodites with synchronous ripening of male and female gametes. In many, spermatozoa and ova develop side-by-side in the same acini of the ovotestis as in the familiar helicids, but there are frequent instances among opisthobranchs (e.g., *Eubranchus pallidus*: Lloyd, 1952) where the gonad has separate areas of follicles for sperm and ova.

A rather limited number of prosobranch gastropods are hermaphroditic: *Diodora*, *Puncturella*, *Patella*, *Acmaea*, the Cocculinacea, *Valvata*, *Omalogyra*, *Rissoella*, Scalidae, Janthinidae, *Stilifer*, *Pelseneeria*, *Enteroxenos*, Pyramidellidae, *Trichotropis*, *Capulus*, as well as *Hipponyx*, Calyptraeidae, *Capulacmaea*, *Velutina*, *Onchidiopsis*, *Marsenina*, and *Ctenosculum*. Not all species of some of these genera are hermaphroditic. As in bivalves, the list includes animals living in situations where some difficulty may be thought to affect the reproductive process. Many of the animals are parasitic: one (*Valvata*) lives in fresh water, one group (Cocculinacea) includes prosobranchs from the deep sea, some are limpets with restricted mobility, others (*Janthina*) follow specialized modes of life. In the archaeogastropods change of sex involves little more than an alteration in the type of gamete that is made, but in the mesogastropods (the majority), not only must this occur but there must also be an extensive modification of the genital duct and of the external genital organs before the change can be effective. Bacci (1947) suggested that *Diodora*, though predominantly gonochoristic, showed about 12% protandrous hermaphrodites. Rammelmeyer (1925) assumed *Puncturella noachina* to be a simultaneous hermaphrodite on the basis of finding spermatogenesis occurring in the gonads of about 20 animals otherwise functioning as females. Willcox (1898) and Thorson (1935), on the other hand, stated that *Acmaea fragilis* and *A. rubella* were protandrous consecutive hermaphrodites. The same also appears to be true of some species of *Patella*. Orton (1920) claimed that at least 90% of a population of *P. vulgata* changes sex from male to female. Orton *et al.* (1956) found small specimens of this species (16–25 mm shell length) to be 90% male, those with shells 40 mm long were male and female in equal numbers, and larger animals (60 mm shell length) were 60–70% female. *P. coerulea* (from the Mediterranean) behaves similarly (Bacci, 1947; Pellegrini, 1948), with the change of sex restricted to the resting period between successive breeding seasons, but liable to affect the animals of any age (Pellegrini, 1949). As in many bivalves there is here a continuous spectrum of sexual condition ranging from the relatively rare gonochoristic male through more frequent grades of hermaphroditism, some favoring maleness, some femaleness, to the rare gonochoristic female.

Most of the information about hermaphroditism in prosobranchs relates to the family Calyptraeidae where an elaborate sexual biology has been well investigated. In *Calyptraea chinensis* males and females associate only during the breeding season. Young animals are purely male and their gonads lack oöcytes (Bacci, 1951), these only becoming visible later when the animal has matured and is acting as male. Later still the spermatic tissue is resorbed, the genital ducts are transformed, and the animal acts as a female during the second and any subsequent breeding season. All animals behave in the same way at the same age (Pellegrini, 1949). *Crepidula fornicata*, the slipper limpet, and other species of the genus differ in that the change from male to female may occur at different times in the life history according to the circumstances in which the individual happens to be living. Normally these animals are found in chains of up to twelve individuals, each clinging to the shell of the next in the chain so that the right lips of the shells are aligned. The basal members of the group are females, the apical members males, and those between are transitional from male to female. The groups persist in time with the death of the old females and the addition of young males. Almost all who have examined *Crepidula* have assumed that the grouping has a sexual basis, allowing young males to fertilize older females. A few workers, however, most recently Wilczynski (1955), have maintained that the basic reason underlying grouping is nutritional, permitting the production of a greater current of water for feeding (since they are ciliary feeders) than would be achieved by a solitary limpet.

Conklin (1897) discovered that *Crepidula* was hermaphroditic. At settling, the gonad has immature cells of male and female type of which at first only the male cells mature. A penis develops when ripe sperm fill the genital duct (Coe, 1948). Later, with the onset of oögenesis, the duct transforms from male pattern to female and the penis is slowly absorbed (Giese, 1915).[1] The ductal changes involve the conversion of an open seminal groove, running from the male pore within the mantle cavity to the penis, into a closed duct provided with glands for the elaboration of egg capsules, and the formation of sperm pouches and of a gonopericardial connection.

Much interest has centered on the circumstances in which the sex transformation occurs and on its apparent causes. Isolated young animals seem to develop rapidly through brief male and transitional phases into a female condition or even to arrive there directly, although they may remain male until a still younger animal settles on them, an event which apparently initiates a change of sex (Coe, 1948). These behavioral differences appear to be related to genetic differences in sexuality (Gould, 1952; Coe, 1953), or, in *C. plana*, to starvation (Gould, 1947; Coe, 1948). In *C. aculeata* and *C. walshi*, from Japan, solitary males become hermaphrodites (Ishiki, 1936). Most young animals of all these species, however, settle on one of the chains already referred to where they transform to a functional male and remain thus for some time. Coe (1944) showed that association with females prolonged the male phase and stimulated the production of sperm, although the view expressed earlier by Gould (1919) that the association was essential for provoking the male phase is clearly an exaggeration.

Gould (1919, 1947) and Coe (1938a, b, 1944, 1948) showed that sex change in *Crepidula* is, indeed, the result of an interaction between the various members of the social group which is the chain. As early as 1919 Gould suggested that the lower members of the chain, the mature females, secreted some substance into the surrounding water with the effect of maintaining the maleness of the upper members. He reiterated this in 1952. Coe at first denied this (1938b, 1944), though retaining the idea in a modified form by supposing that the sensory action and reaction between male and female kept the former as an actively functioning male. Later (1953) he accepted the idea of a species-specific hormone liberated into the water by females and responsible for maintaining the masculinity of the males.

Little is known of the conditions in the other hermaphroditic prosobranchs beyond the fact that most seem to be protandrous consecutive

[1] Except in *Trichotropis cancellata* where the penis continues to increase throughout life although the animals are all functional males at the end of the first year and become functional females in the second year (Yonge, 1962).

hermaphrodites. This has been shown for the minute mesogastropods *Omalogyra* and *Rissoella* by Fretter (1948), who also described the transformation of the genital duct from the early male pattern to the later female type. Graham (1954) made similar observations in *Janthina*. Pyramidellids, on the other hand, seem to be simultaneous hermaphrodites (Fretter and Graham, 1949; Fretter, 1951c). The scalids appear to change sex at each breeding season like some oysters.

The underlying causes of the hermaphroditic state in molluscs have been discussed by a number of authors, many of whom have supposed that two factors are involved, one external and environmental, the second internal and genetic. The latter perhaps acts primarily by making the animals sensitive to changes in the former, although more recent work tends to make it much the more important factor. That environmental factors are significant, however, is suggested by the relationship which Bloomer (1939) demonstrated between the proportion of males, females, and hermaphrodites in *Anodonta cygnea* and different geographical situations in England. It is also suggested by Awati and Rai's work (1931) on the Bombay oyster, *Crassostrea cucullata*, a species in which the proportion of males is raised from 41 to 82% by infection with the pea crab *Pinnotheres*. In slugs Rosenwald (1926) and Richter (1935) found that variation in environmental conditions, particularly moisture and food, affected the sexual development toward maleness or femaleness.

Orton (1927b) suggested that sex was related to the particular metabolic pathways followed by an animal; he associated maleness with a metabolism relying mainly on carbohydrate sources of energy and femaleness with one relying on protein. He thought that the rhythmical reversal of sex which he found in oysters was due to an accumulation of by-products of one type of metabolism swinging the economy of the bivalve over to the other.

In the last decade, however, the explanation of hermaphroditism and gonochorism has tended to become more genetic (Montalenti, 1950, 1960; Montalenti and Bacci, 1951). Hermaphroditic species fall into two main groupings, called by Bacci balanced and unbalanced, the difference between them being primarily genetic. In the former, one sex changes to the other at a regular time in the life history (e.g., calyptraeids) and most individuals behave identically. They are all supposed to have a uniform genotype, and departures from the norm of behavior are mainly due to environmental influences. Unbalanced hermaphroditic populations (e.g., *Patella*) include a great variety of genotypes, each of which has its own genetically controlled time for changing sex; this therefore happens earlier or later in life according to the genotype. This theory may be interpreted in terms of multiple genetic factors as originally suggested for *Lymantria* by Goldschmidt (1923) giving a range from pure gonochoristic males through varying degrees of hermaphroditism to gonochoristic females. Although the genotype itself is responsible for change of sex, its sensitivity to environmental conditions may have effect and cause sex reversal at critical stages in the life history; or, if the sensitivity is great enough, it may swing the animal from sex to sex from season to season. Montalenti and Bacci (1951) suggest a number of categories of sexuality based on the assumption that the genotypes are produced from the combinations of eight gene pairs. Table I presents their categories and the combination of genetic factors associated with each.

Either balanced or unbalanced hermaphroditism may be more appropriate according to the details of the environmental and ecological situation

TABLE I

GENETIC CATEGORIES OF SEXUALITY

Combinations of factors	Per cent of population	Corresponding categories of sexuality in			
		Patella coerulea	*Crepidula plana*	*Crassostrea virginica*	*Teredo navalis*
8D : 0r 7D : 1r	0.39 } 3.13	Primary ♂	♂ with ♂ phase indefinitely prolonged	♂ with ♂ gonad and successive ♂ phases	Primary phase ♂
6D : 2r 5D : 3r	10.93 } 21.87	⚥ with long ♂ phase	⚥ with long ♂ phase	♂ with ⚥ gonad, prevailing ♂ phase	⚥ with primary ♀ phase, later ♂
4D : 4r	27.34	⚥ with equal ♂ and ♀ phases	⚥ with equal ♂ and ♀ phases	♂ with ⚥ gonad, equal ♂ and ♀ phases	Simultaneous ⚥
3D : 5r 2D : 6r	21.87 } 10.93	⚥ with long ♀ phase	⚥ with short ♂ phase	♂ with ⚥ gonad, prevailing ♀ phase	Primary phase ♀, later alternate ♂, ♀
1D : 7r 0D : 8r	3.13 } 0.39	Primary ♀	♀ isolated, with no ♂ phase	♀ with ♀ gonad and successive ♀ phases	Primary phase ♀

KEY: D, dominant sex-determining gene; r, recessive sex-determining gene; ⚥, hermaphrodite (after Montalenti and Bacci, 1951).

in which a given species lives. Selection may therefore favor either the one or the other, sometimes to the extent of having one form in one part of the range of a species and another in another part (e.g., in the asteroid echinoderm, *Asterina:* Bacci, 1951). From such a condition a variety of genetic changes may occur to give rise to a gonochoristic condition (Montalenti, 1960), and one or another of these may have operated in the production of the genuinely unisexual molluscs from an ambisexual ancestral form. As in other evolutionary changes isolation may also affect the rate and nature of the result; this would explain how hermaphroditic races have often perpetuated themselves in isolated situations, as shown, for example, by Wiesensee (1916) for *Anodonta cygnea.*

C. *Self-Fertilization*

In hermaphrodites there always exists the possibility of self-fertilization. The barrier of autosterility may prevent this in some but not in others (particularly among the basommatophoran pulmonates). Even among the opisthobranchs and Stylommatophora, however, precautions may be taken against the possibility. Thus, Buresch (1912) has shown how, in *Helix arbustorum*, although sperm and eggs develop side-by-side, a layer of germinal epithelium lies over the developing eggs during the early part of the breeding season when spermatozoa lie free in the follicle, and it is only toward the end of the season that this breaks down and liberates the eggs. By then the spermatocytes and spermatozoa have degenerated, providing food used by the ripening eggs, and the only functional male cells in the genital system are those which have been received in copulation and which fertilize the eggs.

Self-fertilization may be direct, brought about by the union of an egg and sperm from the same gonad as both travel down the genital duct, or indirect, effected by a process of self-copulation, when the penis is thrust into the female duct of the same animal to discharge spermatozoa. As this is not always noticed, it is difficult to know whether instances of self-fertilization have also involved self-copulation. De Larambergue (1939) gives a comprehensive list of pulmonate species in which self-fertilization has been recorded and where alone it seems to occur. It is particularly widespread among basommatophorans, especially lymnaeids, physids, and planorbids, but is also known in *Ancylus fluviatilis* and two bulinids. Among the Stylommatophora some arionids, limacids, and helicids exhibit it as well as one zonitid and one vitrinid. Self-copulation has been observed only in some lymnaeids and *Planorbis planorbis* (Colton, 1918; Crabb, 1927; Boettger, 1944; Noland and Carriker, 1946). The following species are believed to be autosterile: *Agriolimax reticulatus, Helix aspersa, H. arbustorum, H. pomatia, H. vindobonensis, Cepaea hortensis, C. nemoralis.*

D. *Parthenogenesis*

Natural parthenogenetic reproduction has been described in several mesogastropods: *Potamopyrgus jenkinsi* (Boycott, 1919), *Campeloma rufum* (Van Cleave and Altringer, 1937), and melaniids (Jacob, 1957). A single male of *P. jenkinsi* with sex ducts resembling those of the related *Hydrobia ulvae* and apparently containing functional sperm has recently been described (Patil, 1958). The rare males of *Melanoides tuberculatus* and *M. lineatus* are sterile, degeneration of the gametes occurring mostly at the spermatid stage (Jacob, 1958). In *P. jenkinsi* and *C. rufum* gametogenesis is ameiotic with a single maturation division. Sanderson (1939, 1940) found 36–44 chromosomes in British populations of *P. jenkinsi*, twice that of a European race with 20–22 chromosomes described by Rhein (1935). In *C. rufum* the autosomal number is 12 and there is no suggestion of polyploidy. *Melanoides* spp. have an ameiotic gametogenesis with two equational maturation divisions. *M. tuberculatus* is not a homogeneous species: there are diploid races with 32 chromosomes and polyploid with 90–94, males making up about 3% of the latter group. *M. lineata* and *M. scabra* are both polyploid; in the former 0.01% are males.

Molluscs have not been as much used for experimental work on parthenogenesis as other animals. Their eggs, however, seem to be influenced by the same activating agents as are effective in other groups. Details will be found in papers by Morris (1917), Inaba (1936) and Pasteels (1938). (See also Chap. 5.)

II. THE GAMETES

A. *Spermatozoa*

1. TYPES OF SPERM

The morphology of molluscan sperm has been investigated by Retzius (1904, 1906, 1909, 1912), Tuzet (1928, 1930, 1939, 1940, 1950) and Franzén (1955, 1956), who have demonstrated that amphineurans, archaeogastropods, bivalves, and most cephalopods—external fertilization is the rule in all—possess sperm of one type, whereas the Neritacea, mesogastropods, neogastropods, opisthobranchs, pulmonates, and some octopod cephalopods—in which fertilization is internal—have sperm of another pattern. In the former, mitochondria gathered into spherical masses lie at or around the posterior end of the head, and the tail is very thinly covered with cytoplasm, whereas in the latter the mitochondria form a sheath around the middle piece and the tail is richer in cytoplasm. The head of the former, too, is short and broad, of the latter long and thin, ranging from 1/30 of the total length (primitive opisthobranchs) to about 1/2 (*Cingula semicostata*). Franzén associated these differences with the fact that the first type of sperm swims in sea- or fresh water of low viscosity, whereas the latter swims in more viscous prostatic or oviducal secretions. Fretter and Graham (1962), however, suggested that the change in shape also facilitated close packing in the sperm receptacles of the female.

Rothschild and Tyler (1955) and Dan and Wada (1955) have shown that in at least some molluscs (mainly chitons and bivalves) the sperm head contains droplets of material which can be extruded in the form of an acrosomal filament, as in echinoderms. This may measure twice the length of the head. The filament appears to be extruded when the sperm strike the vitelline membrane of the egg.

Some molluscs produce spermatozoa which are incapable of effecting fertilization, in addition to producing those which can. The former are distinguished from the normal (eupyrene) type by an abnormal, usually decreased, chromatin content (for which reason they are known as dyspyrene, oligopyrene, or apyrene) and by an excess of cytoplasm. Although valueless for fertilization apyrene sperm are not necessarily without importance in the sexual biology of such species as possess them, which are exclusively mesogastropods and neogastropods (see Section III,B,3). In *Bithynia tentaculata* Ankel (1924, 1933) has shown that two types occur, hyperpyrene and oligopyrene, but in other species only one kind is known. This may be vermiform and motile, with 8–16 tails (*Vermetus:* Hanson *et al.*, 1952), or spindle-shaped and immobile (*Nassarius, Fusus:* Pelseneer, 1935), or large and plate-like with a thick tail (Scalidae: Ankel, 1926, 1930; *Janthina:* Ankel, 1926; *Cerithiopsis:* Fretter and Graham, 1962). This last type carries large numbers of eupyrene sperm attached by their heads to its tail and is known as a spermatozeugma. It is possible that the origin of spermatozeugmata is to be sought in the association between developing spermatozoa and nurse cells or cytophores which has been described in *Littorina* spp. (Ankel, 1930) and *Montacuta* spp. (Oldfield, 1959). The cytophore may contain yolk and contribute toward the nourishment of the sperm. Hanson *et al.* (1952) suggested that the atypical sperm of *Viviparus* contribute toward the nutrition of the eupyrene sperm in the ducts of the female by dissolving and releasing reserve polysaccharide. In *Littorina* and *Montacuta* the sperm-cytophore association is not ended until after transference to the female. Aggregations of 250–2000 sperm also occur in the oyster *Ostrea lurida* (Coe, 1931), although not centered on a cytophore; they do not break up until after discharge.

2. Spermatophores

Sperm may be packeted into spermatophores before emission by certain gastropods and cephalopods: *Diodora nubecula* (von Medem, 1945);

Neritacea (Bourne, 1908); *Haminea* (Perrier and Fischer, 1914); *Ancylus* (Moquin-Tandon, 1855); many stylommatophorans and almost all cephalopods. They may be considered as portable seminal vesicles within which the sperm are preserved in optimal conditions of immobility by the provision of the appropriate physicochemical conditions. In *Diodora* Medem stated that the spermatophores are formed of groups of sperm surrounded by testicular epithelium (this is certainly not true of all species of this genus). In the slugs *Arion, Limax,* and *Parmacella* the spermatophores are made of secretion from the wall of the epiphallus surrounding the contained mass of sperm, while in the stylommatophoran snails the distal vas deferens, penis, and flagellum seem to share the process. The outer wall of the spermatophore has spinous processes or ridges molded by the duct in which it is formed and characteristic of the species (Phillips and Watson, 1930) or of local races in *Arion hortensis* (Quick, 1960).

The spermatophores of cephalopods have been investigated by many workers, the most important being Racovitza (1894), Marchand (1907, 1913), Drew (1919), Blancquaert (1925), Weill (1927), Fort (1937, 1941), and Hamon (1942). Each spermatophore (Fig. 1) consists of three sacs: a deeper sperm tube and a more superficial ejaculatory apparatus, both placed within an outer sheath closed at its mouth and provided with a terminal filament. The walls of the sacs are formed of glycoproteins (Hamon, 1942). Blancquaert (1925) showed that the sperm tube is secreted by the first seminal vesicle, the ejaculatory apparatus by the second and the proximal part of the third seminal vesicles, and the outer sheath by the distal part of the third vesicle. The terminal filament is formed by a gland in the appendix of the accessory gland. The contents of the spermatophore are under considerable hydrostatic pressure, exerted mainly by the middle of the three layers of which the sheath is composed.

Discharge of the spermatophore can be brought about in one of two ways: (*1*) The spermatophore can open at the upper end, either by mechanical traction on the filament (most decapods) or by local imbibition of water (most octopods and *Sepiola*). This allows the eversion of the ejaculatory apparatus, which turns inside out and pulls the sperm tube

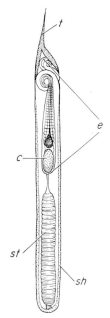

Fig. 1. Diagram of spermatophore of decapod cephalopod. *c,* cement sac; *e,* ejaculatory apparatus; *sh,* outer sheath; *st,* sperm tube; *t,* terminal filament.

forward as it does so. The ejaculatory apparatus often contains cement which fastens the sperm tube to the body of the female. (2) The spermatophore can break at any point and internal pressure then expresses its contents. This occurs especially with immature spermatophores.

The causes of the discharge of the spermatophores of cephalopods have been sought by Hamon, who concluded that imbibition of water was the most important single factor, low pH and the cations Na^+, K^+, and Ca^{++} (especially the last) lowering its rate and so delaying explosion, whereas high pH accelerated it and facilitated explosion; osmotic pressure and the secretions of the female genital tract were unimportant. Mucus from Needham's sac, where spermatophores are stored, tends to prevent explosion. The momentary nature of copulation in cephalopods is imposed by the rapidity of explosion of the spermatophores.

No comparable work has been done on spermatophores of opisthobranchs and pulmonates, but it is certain that the wall is dissolved in the female ducts by secretions from the spermatheca (Meisenheimer, 1912; Quick, 1960) or vagina (Rigby, 1960), taking 3–4 hours in *Oxychilus helveticus*, and 3–6 hours in *Helix pomatia*. The manufacture of spermatophores is not begun prior to the preliminary acts of mating, and only the one immediately to be transferred is actually prepared. The process of manufacture is complete in about 20 minutes in *Helix* and *Arion*.

The spermatophores of the cephalopod may explode in the female tract (*Eledone* and other octopods) or on the buccal membrane (most decapods) liberating the sperm tube (or spermatangium) from which the sperm escape. Later they may be found in the spermatheca, described in *Loligo vulgaris* by Van Oordt (1938) as a mammiform structure with internal lamellae between which lie the inactive sperm. How they reach this position is uncertain: the outer wall of the spermatheca is cuticularized and active sperm show no chemical attraction to it. They may be sucked in by the muscular walls. They are probably inactivated by the pH (6.06), perhaps caused by the acid secretion of the walls. How long they retain power to fertilize is unknown.

B. Eggs

1. SIZE AND NUMBER

As in other groups of the animal kingdom, the number of eggs produced by molluscs is related to their size and yolkiness, and to whether they are to be broadcast for external fertilization or retained in capsules or in the oviduct of the female during development.

When eggs are broadcast they are usually numerous and small, producing planktotrophic larvae. Some figures from Pelseneer (1935) are: *Ischnochiton magdalenensis:* $1.6–2.0 \times 10^5$; *Ostrea edulis:* 1.5×10^6; *My-*

tilus edulis: 10^7; *Tivela stultorum:* $7.5–9.8 \times 10^7$; *Haliotis tuberculata:* 10^4. When the eggs are laid in cases or mucous strings, either free or attached, the numbers tend not to reach such high levels: *Nucula delphinodonta:* 20–70; *Littorina littorea:* 4×10^3; *Littorina littoralis:* 50–350; *Hydrobia ulvae:* 12–25; *Crepidula fornicata:* 13×10^3; *Natica catena:* 7.5×10^4; *Nassarius reticulatus:* $5.2–11 \times 10^3$; *Neptunea antiqua:* 21–28; *Fusus islandicus:* $8–11 \times 10^4$; *Ocenebra erinacea:* $4.8–12 \times 10^3$; *Philine aperta:* 1.5×10^5; *Goniodoris castanea:* 5.6×10^4; *Tergipes despectus:* 65; *Lymnaea stagnalis:* 100–130; *L. peregra:* 60–300; *Planorbarius corneus:* 20–42; *Testacella haliotidea:* 6–15; *Helix pomatia:* 60–90; *H. aspersa:* 40–110; *Achatina fulica:* 1,500; *Arion hortensis:* 12–80; *Limax agrestis:* 28–70; *Loligo pealei:* 2,500; *Sepiola atlantica:* 20; *Sepia officinalis:* 60–300; *Octopus vulgaris:* 300; *Eledone cirrosa:* 800.

In the rachiglossan examples it is necessary to remember (see Section IV,B) that not all eggs in a capsule will hatch; some are used as food eggs.

Thorson (1950) has shown that a tendency toward suppression of free-swimming larval stages exists in prosobranchs of higher latitudes and that the production of planktotrophic larvae is most common toward the equator. This implies a correlated production of a smaller number of larger eggs in colder waters. Similarly, Bondesen (1940) has indicated that within a species individuals living in brackish or fresh water produce a smaller number of larger eggs than those found in the sea.

2. COVERINGS

The eggs are surrounded by a vitelline membrane which is the only covering in some species with external fertilization (e.g., bivalves), and may be rather thick (Unionidae, Anatinacea), or scarcely visible. In some species it is lost soon after the first cleavages (*Mytilus,* Pholadidae, *Dentalium, Patella*). An apparent opening indicates earlier attachment to the germinal epithelium. The membrane may be surrounded by a gelatinous layer, also derived from the ovum, which swells in water and protects the embryo during early development (Trochacea). A third primary egg membrane in *Diodora apertura* causes the eggs to cohere (Fretter and Graham, 1962). In the Polyplacophora, follicle cells in the ovary secrete a secondary egg membrane or chorion which becomes tough; the appearance of its external surface varies from species to species and may be spiny. Follicle cells also surround the large ova of *Pseudokellya cardiformis* and the much larger eggs of cephalopods in which the chorion finally appears as a tough membrane thickened at the animal pole and with a funnel-shaped micropyle. The presence of a secondary egg membrane is usually associated with external fertilization, although there are exceptions to this, as in some cephalopods (*Eledone*).

In gastropods, tertiary membranes are secreted around the eggs in the oviduct, where they are fertilized. In cephalopods, in which fertilization may occur in the oviduct, mantle cavity, or funnel, tertiary membranes are secreted by nidamental glands discharging to the mantle cavity (Drew, 1911; Grimpe, 1926). The membranes comprise albumen, enclosed in a more or less solid external layer which is gelatinous (some prosobranchs, opisthobranchs, aquatic pulmonates, cephalopods), calcareous (land pulmonates, *Ampullarius*), or made of fibers of conchiolin (mesogastropods, neogastropods). Each egg may be surrounded by a supply of albumen and separated from its fellows in an enveloping fluid or jelly by a membrane or shell (some prosobranchs, opisthobranchs, pulmonates); or all may share a common albumen (some mesogastropods, neogastropods). In either case the albumen is used as food. The albumen is not homogeneous; the part around the embryo is typically semifluid and clear, and the rest is more viscous and granular. In *Viviparus viviparus* the albumen contains mineral salts but neither carbohydrates nor fats (Charin, 1926), but in other gastropods it contains galactogen (Lilly, 1953; Horstmann, 1956). In *Succinea putris* (George and Jura, 1958) an outer skin of albumen, presumably the last food of the embryo, contains arginine, tyrosine, —SS— groups, and polysaccharides, while the inner albumen comprises simple protein, chiefly tyrosine, α-amino acids, —SS— groups, and polysaccharides other than mucopolysaccharides and glycogen. The jelly enclosing the eggs of pulmonates may not only have a protective function but the mucopolysaccharides, fat, protein, and calcium which it contains may well be utilized by the young snail (Jura and George, 1958).

III. THE UNION OF THE GAMETES

A. Spawning

In a population of molluscs of a single species it seems likely that the annual reproductive cycle is set according to the following pattern. Maturation of the gametes is set off by annual temperature fluctuations and is possibly correlated to some extent with changes in illumination. A combination of factors—thermal, mechanical, genetic, and hormonal—trigger the actual spawning of gametes in the more sensitive members of the community. As soon as this has occurred gamonic action begins; the spawning process builds up to a maximum. These factors will be dealt with separately.

1. Effect of Temperature and Lunar Periodicity

Emission of gametes in molluscs in which they are broadcast is narrowly controlled by activators of spawning and broadly by other factors. Of these, temperature is often regarded as the most important. Orton (1920) first directed attention to this by suggesting that some animals spawn when the temperature exceeds a critical level characteristic of the species, while others do so at a particular change in environmental temperature, either the local seasonal maximum or minimum. Loosanoff and Engle (1940) pointed out that there was a considerable lag in Long Island Sound between the time when the water reached the supposedly critical temperature (20°C) and the time of spawning of *Crassostrea virginica*. Later, Loosanoff and Davis (1950) showed that there was no definite temperature below which spawning did not occur in the oyster and suggested that the significant temperature was that at which maturation of the gonads occurred. This had already been suggested by Thorson (1946). They were able, however, to force oysters into double breeding by manipulation of the temperature, so emphasizing its importance as a factor controlling breeding (Loosanoff and Davis, 1952).

The work of Loosanoff and Engle (1942), Stauber (1947, 1950), Korringa (1957), Loosanoff (1960), and others has made it clear that the breeding time of the oysters *Ostrea edulis* and *Crassostrea virginica* is not a simple function of temperature acting on a population of homogeneous constitution throughout its whole geographical range, which is very wide for both species. In both there is evidence of the existence of physiological races, each with its own effective spawning temperature and correlated distribution. Thus, *C. virginica* has races with spawning temperatures of 17°, 20°, and 25°C, the first occurring at the northern and the last at the southern extremities of the range of the species. Sometimes, at the same latitude, one race may live in deeper, cooler waters, the other in shallower and warmer situations. Loosanoff (1960) has shown that 50% of oysters from Long Island Sound spawned after 18 days of conditioning at 21°C, while oysters from New Jersey required 78 days and those from still farther south never exhibited this degree of spawning. At 12°C Long Island oysters were 67% ripe after 68 days, New Jersey oysters failed to ripen after 78 days, and those from Florida and South Carolina could not even be sexed on examination of the gonad. Loosanoff and Nomejko (1951) have shown that this difference also affects other aspects of the physiology of the animals.

Certain molluscs—*Patella vulgata*, some trochids, pleurotomariids, and desert pulmonates—spawn in the winter as a reaction to changes in temperature about the minimum of the annual cycle; but the much more frequent spring and summer breeders may be reacting to a level reached as the water heats, or to salinity or food changes. Short spawning seasons result when all animals of a species react sensitively and simultaneously to the coordinating factors. Long spawning seasons may be due to a variety of causes: if a species lives over a considerable vertical range, then the critical temperature for spawning will be reached at different times at different depths (*Nassarius reticulatus, Akera bullata*, according to Thorson, 1946); different age groups may spawn at different times (*Mytilus edulis*); or each individual may spawn for short periods over the whole breeding season and, if this is arhythmical, it may result in a continuous production of young over a long period. Loosanoff and Engle (1942), however, found *Crassostrea virginica* at different depths and therefore at different temperatures, all spawning simultaneously.

Peaks in spawning may occur. These may be due in the first place to a lunar periodicity, as Grave (1922) showed for the chiton *Chaetopleura apiculata*, Amirthalingam (1928) for *Chlamys opercularis*, and Korringa (1947) for *Ostrea edulis*, which lays more eggs between full and new moon than between new and full, although it is uncertain whether it is light or pressure of water that is the critical factor. In other species a spawning migration may have to occur, as in *Littorina neritoides* (Fretter and Graham, 1962); in land molluscs there may be a cessation of breeding at the height of the hot or dry seasons so that there appear to be two separate breeding times, one vernal, the other autumnal (*Limax flavus, L. maximus, Lehmannia marginata*).

Other factors play some role in the discharge of the gametes, although they have not been studied at all carefully in molluscs. Heath (1905) showed that rough weather interfered with spawning in chitons, whereas *Mytilus californianus* (Young, 1946), *Patella vulgata* (Orton *et al.*, 1956), and some other molluscs appear to be stimulated by wave action or mechanical shock (Orton, 1924; Field, 1922).

2. Effect of Hormones and Neurosecretion

It is likely that hormones and neurosecretion play a more important part in the control of reproductive activity in molluscs than is at present suspected. The earliest suggestion of hormonal control was that of Sereni (1929), who believed that the production of such secondary sexual characters as the hectocotylus of *Octopus* was under endocrine control. This was denied by Callan (1940) on the grounds that after castration and later amputation of the arm a normal hectocotylus is regenerated. Wells and Wells (1959) have shown that sexual maturity in *Octopus vulgaris* is brought about by the secretion of a hormone by the optic gland. This is inhibited by a nervous control originating in the subpedunculate and dorsal basal area of the supraesophageal part of the brain. Since the result can also be achieved by section of the optic nerve it seems that this mechanism relates internal function to external conditions in the same way as the eye-hypophysis system of vertebrates. Since all cephalopods except *Nautilus* possess optic glands it may be that this method of control is general throughout the class.

In gastropods one undoubted and some probable examples of sex hormones are known. It was shown by Linke (1933) that in *Littorina littorea* males lose the penis after the end of the breeding season and regrow it before the beginning of the next. Similar but lesser changes affect the ovipositor in females, and the same happens to a small extent in *L. saxatilis* (Berry, 1956). Other changes also occur in relation to the sex cycle, as shown by Linke (1934b), in that material derived from the regression of the reproductive organs is stored over the winter in connective tissue cells and used later for their reelaboration. The prosobranchs do not lend themselves kindly to many types of experimental work and neither Linke (1934a) nor, more recently, Rohlack (1959) had any success in attempting to imitate these events by injection of sex hormones. All experimental animals died. Rohlack, however, did find an estrogen (not identical with vertebrate estrogen) in the ovary of *L. littorea*, though she failed to find evidence of androgen production in male winkles. Jenner and Chamberlain (1955) have recorded a similar seasonal resorption and redevelopment of the penis in the neogastropod *Nassa obsoleta*, and it seems likely that this phenomenon, as well as the transformation of the genital duct from male to female pattern which occurs in many consecutive hermaphrodites (see Giese, 1915) will prove to be under endocrine control. Retention of the penis in the female phase in *Trichotropis* may be due to the continuance of some production of sperm in the gonad (Yonge, 1962).

Laviolette (1950) successfully demonstrated that implantation of pieces of gonad in a number of immature slugs, particularly *Arion subfuscus*, brought about a rapid maturation of the genital glands and ducts, but did not affect penis or genital atrium. The parts affected were mainly those dealing with ova, or sperm received in copulation; this may be correlated with the fact that the implanted gonad was still functional as an ovary but was effete as a testis. The converse experiment, of implanting an immature duct in a mature host, also showed a development of the duct both in size and degree of histological differentiation. Total removal of the gonad in *Limax maximus* was followed 3 months later by a marked regression of the albumen gland and genital ducts, but not of the penis.

Neurosecretory control of spawning has been suggested by Lubet (1956, 1957) for *Mytilus edulis* and *Chlamys varia*, on the basis of his finding that the response of these bivalves to other spawning inducers is maximal when there has been a reduction of the neurosecretory products of the cerebropleural and visceral ganglia, after a maximum coincident with gametogenesis. Removal of the ganglia accelerated spawning. Lubet therefore suggested that the neurosecretion inhibits response to the factors which cause spawning.

3. Effect of Gamones in Fertilization

The existence of endocrine-like substances secreted by gametes and facilitating their union in external fertilization has been known for some time. In echinoderms at least four substances occur: gynogamone I, which activates spermatozoa and is antagonized by androgamone I; gynogamone II (G II) (= Lillie's fertilizin), which agglutinates sperm; and androgamone II, (AII) (antifertilizin) which inhibits the agglutinating effect and dissolves the jelly coat around the egg. The last action may be due to a separate lysin (Rothschild, 1956).

In molluscs both GII and AII may occur, but they are absent in certain animals where their presence might be expected. Thus the chiton *Katharina tunicata* possesses GII (Tyler, 1940b) as does the gastropod *Megathura crenulata*, but the gamone is absent from some other chitons and from *Haliotis* and *Cumingia* (Sampson, 1922). AII apparently occurs in *Patella vulgata* and *P. coerulea* (Hultin, 1947), and in *Megathura crenulata* and *Haliotis cracherodi* (Tyler, 1939); at least the sperm of these animals contain a lysin. GII has been recorded from the bivalves *Crassostrea virginica* (Glaser, 1921), *Ostrea circumpincta* (Terao, 1926), *Pecten varius* and *Ensis ensis*.

GII appears to be confined to the jelly in which the eggs lie (Tyler, 1940b) and which seems to be secreted either by follicle cells or by the egg only while it is still in the ovary since its removal stops all further agglutination (Runnström and Monné, 1945). The agglutinating substance is precipitated by ammonium sulphate and destroyed by trypsin and therefore seems to be protein (Tyler and Fox, 1940), although the nitrogen content (4.5%) is high for a simple protein. In most cases agglutination is reversible, but it is irreversible in *Megathura* and *Katharina*. The agglutinin is heat labile and stable at pH 4 in *Megathura*.

Antifertilizin (AII), which antagonizes GII, is also a protein in *Megathura* (Tyler, 1939, 1940a). In *Patella vulgata* and *P. coerulea* it is a basic protein contained in the sperm head (Hultin, 1947). The lysin which destroys the egg membrane was first demonstrated by Tyler (1939) in *Megathura crenulata* and *Haliotis cracherodi*. It is specific in its action, a protein and not hyaluronidase. It acts rapidly, dissolving the egg surface in 30 seconds if the jelly has been previously removed, but taking 4 to 6 times as long if the jelly is present. Dan and Wada (1955) suggest that it is carried in the acrosome.

In addition to these gamones some molluscs which broadcast their gametes seem to produce substances which activate spawning by other members of the same species: these have been shown to occur in chitons (Heath, 1905), oysters (Galtsoff, 1930), and mussels (Young, 1942). In oysters the spawning agent is heat stable and dialyzable (Galtsoff, 1930,

1938). The females respond only to sperm of the same species, and the activating agent may therefore be another aspect of the gamone AII since Tyler and Fox (1940) found the activating agent inseparable from the agglutinin in *Megathura*. Male oysters, however, are activated by other males, by a variety of eggs or egg waters, and by thyroxin and glutathione (Galtsoff, 1940). This sensitivity of the males to a heterogeneous collection of stimulants is of value in that it initiates a process of spawning which can then echo and re-echo throughout the population. Nelson and Allison (1940) have shown that the receptors in this case are placed on the gills and that their stimulation induces relaxation of a sphincter on the male duct, resulting in spawning. Experimentally, spermatozoa may be obtained by using sperm or egg water, by electrical stimulation (Iwata, 1949), or by heat (Wada, 1936).

Mention might be made at this point of diantlin, a hormone-like protein discovered by Nelson (1936) in oyster sperm. It has the effect of increasing the ventilation of the mantle cavity by increasing the size of the branchial pores, relaxing the adductors, and accelerating the rate of ciliary beat. Its secretion occurs prior to egg spawning and presumably allows the eggs to pass through the gill passages into the inhalant chamber more readily. Similar substances occur and act comparably in mussels. Young (1942, 1946) recorded that the testicular tissue of *Mytilus californianus* contains a substance causing spawning in females. A similar gonadal stimulant affects the discharge of sperm in *Tridacna* (Wada, 1954).

B. Courtship and Copulation

1. GASTROPODS

Copulation is preceded by a period of courtship which may last 2 hours or more in terrestrial pulmonates, whereas it is brief and sometimes hardly recognizable in aquatic gastropods. In some opisthobranchs the period of sexual union is extensive, lasting for several hours and even up to 4–5 days in *Archidoris pseudoargus*, although the actual emission of sperm is of short duration. In many mesogastropods and in hermaphrodites in which exchange of sperm cannot be reciprocal since male and female apertures are widely separate, the partners orientate themselves in the same direction and the male may mount the female, settle on the right side of the body, and even be carried about by her, as in *Littorina* spp., the markedly sexually dimorphic *Lacuna pallidula*, and *Assiminea grayana*. In some [*Aplysia, Akera, Dolabella, Lymnaea stagnalis* (Barraud, 1957)] chains of individuals are formed, each acting as male to the animal below. In the majority of hermaphrodites (Pleurobranchidae, Elysiidae, Limapontiidae, nudibranchs, stylommatophoran pulmonates) copulation is reciprocal. Two animals come to face in opposite directions, approximating the genital apertures on the right sides; this is often preceded by a preliminary recognition when the partners creep round one another. In some opisthobranchs the penis is armed with spines which stimulate the partner and secure a hold, and in the sacoglossans and some eolids (Pelseneer, 1894) the terminal part of the penial duct forms a stylet which in *Acteonia cocksi* and *Limapontia capitata* is driven through the body wall into the bursa (Gascoigne, 1956). Stimulating organs are more common in pulmonates. The familiar darts of snails such as *Helix, Cepaea, Helicella*, discharged after a period of courtship, rarely penetrate deeply or cause harm and are soon removed by muscular movements (Meisenheimer, 1912). In species of *Helminthoglypta* the dart is not freed, but the partner brings it into action more or less constantly during mating (Webb, 1942). Some pulmonates enhance precopulatory excitement by bodily contacts, by gnawing the partner's body and even the penis (Webb, 1950). During coition slugs may have not only the penis everted but also adjacent genitalia. *Agriolimax* (Quick, 1960) has a sarcobelum on the penis which in courtship plays over the surface of the partner; then the atrium is everted, bringing to the surface the duct of the spermatheca, which receives sperm, and also the penis appendage, which links the animals while sperm packets are simultaneously transferred. In *Arion* spp. no true penis occurs and spermatophore transfer is managed by the everted epiphallus with the help of the ligula, a special adhesive organ developed on the wall of the atrium or oviduct. In *Limax* the penis is large and complex with one specially thickened fold, the comb, which alone is everted; it may remain so for a period of 90 minutes in *L. tenellus* while the partners revolve clockwise (Gerhardt, 1933). *L. cinereoniger* and *L. maximus* copulate in mid-air suspended from a stout, mucous thread, hanging upside down from a tree or other support with bodies and penes intertwined. At the end of the process they separate, reclimb the mucous rope, and take their own ways. In all these pulmonates sexual biology has become extremely elaborate both anatomically and physiologically.

2. CEPHALOPODS

Because of the rapidity with which the spermatophores explode and because of the nature of the copulatory organ, copulation in cephalopods differs from that of gastropods in a number of ways. The copulatory organ is the hectocotylus, a modification of one or more arms (for list see Hoyle, 1907), or the spadix, a modification of four tentacles, in *Nautilus*. Only rare genera like *Vampyroteuthis* have no hectocotylus. Normally the hectocotylus receives spermatophores from the funnel and is then thrust into the mantle cavity or buccal region of the female where they are deposited; later it is withdrawn. In *Argonauta, Ocythoe,* and *Tremoctopus,* however, the hectocotylus (which in these genera carries sperm not enclosed in spermatophores) autotomizes and is left in the female. It contains the distal extremity of the vas deferens dilated into a seminal vesicle, and the whole, normally coiled in a special sac, may, when unrolled, be 10 times as long as the adult male. The hectocotylus may transfer sperm to the neighborhood of the sperm receptacle on the buccal membrane (*Sepia*), to the mantle cavity (*Loligo*), to a special receptacle near the oviducal opening (*Rossia, Sepiola*), or even into the genital duct itself (*Eledone, Octopus*). To some extent this is variable with the species or with the physiological state of the animal or its eggs. Arms other than the hectocotylus may be used to grip the female during copulation and the process is relatively brief (10 seconds in *Loligo pealei*, 2–5 minutes in *Sepia officinalis*, 10 minutes in *Sepiola atlantica*), although Racovitza (1894) saw a union which lasted for an hour in *Octopus vulgaris*. Speed is necessary not only because of the rapid explosion of the spermatophores but also because the insertion of the hectocotylus into the mantle cavity may interfere with respiration. Descriptions of the process will be found in papers by Racovitza (1894), Levy (1912), Drew (1919), Grimpe (1926), Bott (1938), and Tinbergen (1939).

Prior to actual union there is often some specialized courtship behavior, usually involving color displays (Levy, 1912; Grimpe, 1926; Tinbergen, 1939). This also helps in sex recognition since the behavior of the two sexes is different. Thus in *Sepia officinalis* a characteristic black and white pattern of zebra stripes is exhibited by males about to pair, along with an extension of the fourth arm and an opening of an eye toward another squid. If this be a male he displays similarly and this may provoke squabbling and biting, but ultimately one retires. This may happen anywhere in an aquarium, suggesting the absence of a territorial system. If the second animal be female it may display, but it is more likely to swim away, pursued by the male. A pair may then be formed with copulation following. Males treat any animal with resting color as female and any with a zebra display pattern as male.

Multiple copulations are known, and the process may be repeated up to 4 times in 12 hours (Grimpe, 1926).

3. Aphallic Transfer of Sperm

A number of gastropod species, mainly stylommatophoran pulmonates, show aphallic individuals among the normal euphallic. A small number of prosobranch species among an otherwise euphallic group may be wholly aphallic (Turritellidae, Janthinidae, Cerithiopsidae, Scalidae). This would seem to preclude the possibility of copulation, perhaps even of cross-fertilization; rarely, however, are the consequences so severe. Some prosobranch species achieve an internal cross-fertilization by making use of spermatozeugmata, devices elaborated from an apyrene sperm which has attached to it a large number of eupyrene sperm. In *Janthina* they have been seen to be emitted from the male (Wilson and Wilson, 1956), occur in all parts of the female tract (Graham, 1954), and seem to be a device for ferrying the eupyrene sperm to the female. They are limited to species which are aphallic and which have a gregarious habit. In other species (e.g., *Turritella communis*) aphallism necessitates the sperm being broadcast, but they seem to be collected by the female out of the same current which bears particulate food into her mantle cavity (since the animals are ciliary microphagous feeders) and stored in sperm receptacles. Fretter (1951b, 1953) has suggested that aphallism in prosobranchs is often associated with a narrow, tightly coiled shell which produces a narrow mantle cavity, the respiratory activity of which would be impeded if it had also to house a penis.

In pulmonates partial or complete atrophy of male copulatory apparatus occurs in a surprisingly large number of species (see de Larambergue, 1939) mostly in the stylommatophoran Vertiginacea and Zonitacea. These are slow, mainly small animals, not gregarious, and therefore with a reduced chance of copulation. It is also exhibited by a small number of basommatophorans. So long as self-fertilization can occur, atrophy, partial or complete, of the male organs does not embarrass the species and may permit the establishment of local races showing higher ecological adaptation. Even if self-fertilization is not possible aphallic animals can always act as females, euphallic animals behaving as males. This supposes a rather different copulatory behavior in those species from that of other stylommatophorans in which copulation may be abandoned if both animals do not act together as male and female; but if it is possible, it is one way in which a trend toward gonochorism could be initiated. Riedel (1955) stated that the absence of copulatory organs and male duct may not be an absolute barrier to copulation because sperm may be passed down the vagina which can evert to act as an intromittent organ allowing some transfer of sperm. The genera in which aphallism has been recorded are: *Physa*, *Lymnaea*, *Bulinus*, *Agriolimax*, *Vertigo*, *Truncatellina*, *Columella*, *Chondrina*, *Acanthinula*, *Vallonia*, *Retinella*, *Zonitoides* (Boettger, 1944; Riedel, 1955; Quick, 1960).

IV. OVIPOSITION

A. Spawn and Capsules

Methods of oviposition vary considerably within the phylum. Primitively the eggs are discharged into the surrounding water as in Amphineura, Archaeogastropoda, Scaphopoda, and most Bivalvia.

Bivalve eggs have only the protection of the vitelline membrane except in the few species in which they are also enclosed in egg sacs (*Nucula delphinodonta* (Drew, 1901), *Modiolaria discors* var. *laevigata*, *M. nigra*, *Loripes lacteus* (Myazaki, 1938), *Turtonia minuta*). The secretion for these egg sacs comes from the hypobranchial gland in *N. delphinodonta*, in which the capsules are attached to the posterior end of the valves. In *T. minuta* (Oldfield, 1955) special, seasonally developed cells in the mantle edge secrete the egg capsules which are attached to byssal threads.

Some archaeogastropods which agglutinate the eggs of one spawning manipulate them with the foot for attachment to the substratum. The secretion for agglutination comes from a variety of sources. In *Diodora apertura* it comes from the egg itself, swelling to a considerable thickness when shed. In *Acmaea tessulata* the secretion is from the pedal sole (Willcox, 1905), which plasters the eggs into a layer one cell thick as in *Diodora*. In *Margarites helicinus* and *Calliostoma zizyphinum* it comes from the enlarged urinogenital papilla and is more copious, protecting the young until they are small snails. Higher gastropods and cephalopods produce egg capsules even when the eggs are retained in a brood pouch, although the wall surrounding the albumen with which each egg is supplied is then very thin. The secretions for making all capsules come from the oviduct and, in cephalopods, also from the nidamental glands which are pallial in origin. The capsules are molded as they pass through the cephalopod funnel, and are then passed to the arms which fix them to a suitable substratum. In gastropods the foot manipulates the spawn, molding it to shape so accurately that for each species every capsule is a replica of the previous one. Some *Littorina* spp. (*littorea, neritoides*) have pelagic capsules extruded from an ovipositor situated near the genital aperture in a position comparable to that of the penis. Here the capsule receives its final form and its outer layers harden in contact with sea water. In other genera there may be a temporary groove on the right side of the foot which conducts the spawn mass from the oviduct to the sole. In the semi-terrestrial *Assiminea grayana* this groove is permanent and deposits the capsules on the mud as the animal creeps (Sander, 1950, 1952).

Land snails lay their eggs in clusters in places where the humidity is persistently high. This may be in burrows in soil (*Helix:* Meisenheimer, 1912), in moss (*Campylaea cingulata:* Künkel, 1910) or in a nest formed by fastening together the edges of a leaf (*Cochlostyla leucophthalma*). *Pomatias elegans* deposits them singly beneath the soil surface, each manipulated by the foot so that it is coated with soil particles (Creek, 1951). The pulmonate *Libera* of the Society Islands uses the umbilicus of its own shell as a brood chamber.

The greatest variety of spawn occurs in aquatic gastropods. In opisthobranchs the thin-walled capsules, small and numerous, are embedded in gelatinous secretions which offer sufficient protection for a rather brief embryonic period. In some tectibranchs the spawn is attached by the foot, which grips it as it protrudes from the oviduct. In *Philine* and *Scaphander* spiral strings of eggs in the spawn jelly reflect the circuitous route they have taken through the female duct (Lloyd, 1952). In *Bullaria gouldiana*, *Tethys*, and *Aplysia* a tangled egg cord is produced, taking 1–2 hours to leave the oviduct. *Tethys* grips it in a fold of the upper lip, where it is coated with mucus; as the head moves to and fro, the secretion sticks the coils to one another and to the substratum. In the tectibranch *Navanax inermis* the egg string travels forward from the genital aperture between the upturned parapodium and the body, round the anterior part of which it is coiled by rotation of the head; each loop sticks to the preceding to form a skein of threads from which the mollusc later withdraws. Many eolids and dorids gyrate slowly as the spawn leaves the body so that it is anchored in a tight spiral; eolids may attach it to hydroids, seaweed, or bryozoans. In dorids a flat ribbon is formed because the mass is gripped between mantle and foot and the basal edge is plastered to the substratum. In *Archidoris pseudoargus* a ribbon 38 × 2 cm contains 5×10^4 eggs. Differences in the body color of nudibranchs are also present in their spawn. Many sublittoral species migrate onshore to spawn.

Prosobranch capsules have resistant walls and each contains relatively few eggs; with few exceptions the capsules are attached. They may be lens-shaped, globular, triangular in outline, or vase-shaped, sometimes linked to one another in a chain (*Clathrus*), or bunch (*Crepidula*), or piled on one another to form a ball (*Buccinum*). The wall is often divided by a suture into two halves and sometimes there is also an area plugged with different material. These characteristics derive from features of the glandular oviduct.

The oviduct presumably originated as an open pallial groove with walls thickened, especially laterally, by gland cells. In these features it resembles the prostate of *Littorina littorea*, but is more complicated in all females. Production of capsules requires that fertilization occur before the wall is elaborated, so that sperm pouches are associated with the duct. These may be of two types (*1*) the bursa (copulatrix) into which the penis discharges seminal fluid, and (2) the receptaculum (seminis) where sperm are stored till the time of fertilization. A variety of anatomical relationships may exist between the duct and these pouches (Fretter and Graham, 1962). The duct also produces materials to feed and protect the embryos, in areas comprising the albumen, shell, and capsule glands. In some mesogastropods (*Bittium reticulatum, Cerithiopsis tubercularis, Turritella communis, Clathrus clathrus*) these elaborations occur but the duct is an open one resembling the primitive condition; in the male there is no penis, and sperm are carried in the pallial water current. This condition is probably secondary (see Section III,B,3). Evidence of the closure of the pallial genital duct may be seen in the prostate of *Ocenebra* and *Nucella* (Fretter, 1941). It is incomplete posteriorly, however, leaving an outlet to the mantle cavity in addition to the normal genital pore, perhaps a safety valve for the escape of semen (Fretter and Graham, 1962). Actual closure may be witnessed in the protandrous hermaphrodites *Calyptraea*, *Capulus*, and *Crepidula*, where the open groove of the male becomes the closed oviduct of the female (Giese, 1915). The ventral wall of the pallial oviduct usually fails to develop glands and so provides an easy pathway for the penis in copulation (rissoids, calyptraeids, *Lamellaria*) or for sperm (*Littorina*, *Nucella*, *Buccinum*).

Sperm received in copulation are stored in the receptaculum or, if that is absent, in a region of oviduct proximal to the glands (*Cremnoconchus*, *Pomatias*, *Lacuna pallidula*). They lie closely packed, their heads embedded in the cytoplasm of the epithelial cells and perhaps deriving nourishment from them. They remain healthy for several weeks; in *Viviparus*, Ankel (1925) found viable sperm in the receptaculum after 5 months and, in the albumen gland where they are less crowded, after 11 months. Sperm remain functional in the receptaculum of *Crepidula* for more than a year (Coe, 1942). In *Littorina littorea*, Tattersall (1920) recorded five layings after one copulation. In *Cepaea hortensis*, Lang (1896) observed successful oviposition 2 years after copulation and Taylor (1900) mentioned a specimen of *Helix aspersa* which laid fertile eggs after 4 years in isolation (these are stylommatophoran species which are believed to be self-sterile).

In some prosobranchs special ingesting cells near the receptaculum deal with effete or superfluous spermatozoa (*Acicula*, *Trivia*, *Cerithiopsis*, *Nucella*, *Ocenebra*, *Buccinum*, *Mangelia*). Excess sperm are also used as nourishment by males: ingestion by the epithelium of the seminal vesicle occurs in the breeding season (*Littorina*: Linke, 1933) and during oviposition (*Oxychilus cellarius*: Rigby, 1960). Other unwanted material may be dealt with in a variety of ways. Yolk from an egg not included in a capsule is taken up by the sperm-ingesting gland (*Ocenebra*, *Buccinum*: Fretter, 1941). Secretion not used in producing capsules fills a large pouch preceding the brood pouch in *Potamopyrgus jenkinsi* and corresponding to the bursa of related forms, while in *Rissoella diaphana* a muscular sac at the upper end of the pallial duct collects unused secretions and sperm for discharge to the mantle cavity by a special duct (Fretter, 1948). In many gastropods the bursa is important in this respect. It has a double function, for it harbors the sperm till they transfer to the receptaculum and also retains the secretions in which they were received. In tectibranchs and pulmonates, where the bursa lies freely in the hemocoele with a long duct, the functions may be separate, sperm being deposited in the duct and superfluous sperm, prostatic and other debris being dealt with by the pouch. In *Buccinum* amoebocytes scavenge the prostatic fluid, in Neritacea waste may escape by a special duct (Bourne, 1908), and in some opistho-branchs and pulmonates the bursal epithelium produces a secretion with digestive properties. In *Oxychilus* and *Succinea* unwanted sperm and pro-static fluid are disposed of in the bursa in 24 hours (Rigby, 1960). In the latter digestion occurs in the lumen; in the former in the epithelium as well. In dorids the bursa receives sperm in copulation and later, at ovipo-sition, collects all kinds of superfluous material from the ducts. In opistho-branchs and pulmonates its contents are frequently red, orange, or brown with carotenoid pigments.

Other elaborations of the ducts of higher gastropods are linked with hermaphroditism (Fretter, 1946); with the separation of glands from the main ducts so that eggs no longer pass through the albumen gland or are diverted along a circuitous route concerned with concentrating them (mucous gland of opisthobranchs); and with hypertrophy at breeding, when they fill all available space in the hemocoele so that even feeding may cease. In dorids and elysiids the bursa has acquired a separate ex-ternal opening although connected to the oviduct at its inner end; this causes minimal disturbance of the enlarged ducts at copulation. In con-trast, the cephalopods have no enlarged vascular spaces, and the nidamen-tal glands, which produce the bulk of the secretion for the spawn, are associated with the mantle cavity and open to it.

The vase-shaped egg capsules of some neogastropods are deposited in-tertidally (*Ocenebra*, *Nucella*) and withstand exposure for weeks. The wall is made of protein fibers separated (when weathered) by spaces pre-viously filled with mucus. These two secretions from the capsule gland are intermingled by cilia and by movement of the egg mass through the secretion (Fretter, 1941; Hancock, 1956). The thin, nonsecreting dorsal and ventral walls of the gland account for the sutures characteristic of the capsule, and its inner end for the mucous plug which is molded into posi-tion by local muscles. Each capsule, roughly formed in the oviduct, is passed to a gland in the middle of the pedal sole, developed in females only. It is held with the plug towards the inner end of the gland, the base toward the opening. Here it is retained 15–20 minutes, manipulated into definite shape, and the walls hardened and cemented to the substratum. Specific differences in capsular shape originate in differences in this gland.

Lamellariacea and Cypraeacea also possess a ventral pedal gland, put to a slightly different use in that the capsules are sunk in holes made by the radula in the test of compound ascidians; the gland pushes them into place and molds the exposed areas (Fretter, 1951a; Ankel, 1935). In other mesogastropods oviposition is lubricated by the sole gland.

B. Food Eggs

In capsules of prosobranchs with common albumen the occasional un-healthy embryo may be eaten by others (e.g., *Rissoa membranacea*); in other species the embryos can complete development only by feeding on other eggs. These food eggs or nurse cells are ova arrested in development (Staiger, 1951), commonly unfertilized (*Pisania maculosa, Fasciolaria tulipa, F. lignaria*) or fertilized without syngamy (*Nucella lapillus, Murex trunculus, Buccinum undatum*). The ova may cleave to groups of cells with haploid nuclei (*F. lignaria, M. trunculus*). Atypical fertiliza-tion by oligopyrene sperm has been regarded as the origin of these sterile ova. The fact that in *F. tulipa* the ratio of eggs to nurse cells (1:59) is remarkably close to that of eupyrene to oligopyrene sperm (1:50) has lent support to this speculation (Hyman, 1923) although most food eggs in this species are now thought to be unfertilized. Moreover, in *Natica catena* only one type of sperm has been found but food eggs are common. Their origin may be inherent (Glaser, 1906; Burger and Thornton, 1935). Staiger (1950) has shown that in *P. maculosa* 90% of the eggs are not fertilized; of the remainder, 2% develop normally and 8% become food eggs arrested at four different developmental stages; in one of these poly-spermy occurs. This indicates that in a given species the ova which fail to undergo normal development are not a homogeneous population; they are perhaps genetically determined by a multifactorial system, a suggestion supported by the constant proportion of the various types within the cap-sules of a given female and, more broadly, within a given species. In *Buccinum* eggs are rarely unfertilized and no atypical sperm seem to be involved; the suggestion that there are two visibly indistinguishable types, only one of which ensures proper fertilization, is therefore plausible.

C. Incubation, Ovoviviparity, and Viviparity

Although most molluscs release their eggs and pay no further attention to them, some exhibit varying degrees of parental care. They may brood over eggs located external to the body [Calyptraeidae, *Hipponyx* (= *Amalthea*) (Yonge, 1953)]; eggs may be retained in the mantle cavity (*Ostrea* spp., *Teredo* spp., *Entovalva, Chiton polii, Acmaea rubella*), the pseudopallial cavity (*Gasterosiphon*), or the marsupium provided by the gills of bivalves. This may be either the interlamellar spaces of inner and outer demibranch (*Margaritana margaritifera*) or of only one (Unionidae, *Lasaea, Pseudokellya, Transennella*). Alternatively, the animals may adopt degrees of ovoviviparity (*Littorina saxatilis, Melania* spp., *Potamopyrgus jenkinsi, Viviparus* spp., many stylommatophorans) or viviparity (*Janthina* spp.). This is presumably adopted by gastropods because of their inability to use the mantle cavity as a brood pouch with the same ease as a bivalve. In the majority of these animals the most that the eggs receive is protection, but in some provision is made for the secretion of a histotrophe (*Janthina:* Graham, 1954).

REFERENCES

Amirthalingam, C. (1928). On lunar periodicity in reproduction of *Pecten opercularis* near Plymouth in 1927–28. *J. Marine Biol. Assoc. U.K.* **15**, 605–641.

Ankel, W. E. (1924). Spermatozoen-Dimorphismus und Befruchtung bei *Bythinia tentaculata* L. und *Viviparus viviparus* L. *Senckenbergiana* **6**, 1–12.

Ankel, W. E. (1925). Zur Befruchtungsfrage bei *Viviparus viviparus* L. nebst Bemerkungen über die erste Reifungsteilung des Eies. *Senckenbergiana* **7**, 37–54.

Ankel, W. E. (1926). Spermiozeugmenbildung durch atypische (apyrene) und typische Spermien bei *Scala* und *Janthina. Verhandl. deut. zool. Ges.* **31**, 193–202.

Ankel, W. E. (1930). Die atypische Spermatogenese von *Janthina* (Prosobranchia, Ptenoglossa). *Z. Zellforsch. u. mikroskop. Anat.* **11**, 491–608.

Ankel, W. E. (1933). Untersuchungen über Keimzellbildung und Befruchtung bei *Bythinia tentaculata* L. II. Gibt es in der Spermatogenese von *Bythinia tentaculata* eine Polymegalie? *Z. Zellforsch. u. mikroskop. Anat.* **17**, 160–198.

Ankel, W. E. (1935). Das Gelege von *Lamellaria perspicua. Z. Morphol. Ökol. Tiere* **30**, 635–647.

Awati, P. R., and Rai, H. S. (1931). *Ostrea cucullata* (the Bombay oyster). *Indian Zool. Mem.* **3**, 1–107.

Bacci, G. (1947). L'inversione del sesso ed il ciclo stagionale della gonade in *Patella coerulea* L. *Pubbl. staz. zool. Napoli* **21**, 183–217.

Bacci, G. (1951). L'ermafroditismo di *Calyptraea chinensis* L. e di alni Calyptraeidae. *Pubbl. staz. zool. Napoli* **23**, 66–90.

Barraud, E. M. (1957). The copulatory behaviour of the freshwater snail (*Limnaea stagnalis* L.). *Brit. J. Animal Behaviour* **5**, 55–59.

Berry, A. J. (1956). Some factors affecting the distribution of *Littorina saxatilis* (Olivi). Ph.D. Thesis, University of London.

Blancquaert, T. (1925). L'origine et la formation des spermatophores chez les céphalopodes décapodes. *Cellule rec. cytol. histol.* **36**, 315–356.

Bloomer, H. H. (1939). A note on the sex of *Pseudanodonta* Bourguignat and *Anodonta* Lamarck. *Proc. Malacol. Soc. London* **23**, 285–297.

Boettger, C. R. (1944). Basommatophora. In "Die Tierwelt der Nord- und Ostsee" (G. Grimpe and E. Wagler, eds.), Part IXb₂, pp. 241–478. Akad. Verlagsges., Leipzig.

Bondesen, P. (1940). Preliminary investigations into the development of *Neritina fluviatilis* L. in brackish and fresh water. *Damsk Naturhist. Foren. Videnskab. Medd.* **104**, 283–318.

Bott, R. (1938). Kopula und Eiablage von *Sepia officinalis* L. *Z. Morphol. Ökol. Tiere* **34**, 150–160.

Bourne, G. C. (1908). Contribution to the morphology of the group Neritacea of aspidobranch gastropods. Part I. The Neritidae. *Proc. Zool. Soc. (London)* pp. 810–887.

Boycott, A. E. (1919). Parthenogenesis in *Paludestrina jenkinsi. J. Conchol.* **16**, 54.

Buresch, I. (1912). Untersuchungen über die Zwitterdrüse der Pulmonaten. I. Die Differenzierung der Keimzellen bei *Helix arbustorum. Arch. Zellforsch.* **7**, 314–343.

Burger, J. W., and Thornton, C. S. (1935). A correlation between the food eggs of

Fasciolaria tulipa and the apyrene spermatozoa of prosobranch molluscs. *Biol. Bull.* **68**, 253–257.

Callan, H. G. (1940). The absence of a sex-hormone controlling regeneration of the hectocotylus in *Octopus vulgaris* Lam. *Pubbl. staz. zool. Napoli* **18**, 15–19.

Charin, N. (1926). Über die Nahrung des Embryo von *Paludina vivipara*. *Bull. soc. naturalistes Voronèje* **1**, 60–66.

Coe, W. R. (1931). Sexual rhythm in the California oyster (*Ostrea lurida*). *Science* **74**, 247–249.

Coe, W. R. (1938a). Conditions influencing change of sex in mollusks of the genus *Crepidula*. *J. Exptl. Zool.* **77**, 401–424.

Coe, W. R. (1938b). Influence of association on the sexual phases of gastropods having protandric consecutive sexuality. *Biol. Bull.* **75**, 274–285.

Coe, W. R. (1942). The reproductive organs of the prosobranch mollusk *Crepidula onyx* and their transformation during the change from male to female phase. *J. Morphol.* **70**, 501–512.

Coe, W. R. (1943). Sexual differentiation in mollusks. I. Pelecypods. *Quart. Rev. Biol.* **18**, 154–164.

Coe, W. R. (1944). Sexual differentiation in mollusks. II. Gastropods, amphineurans, scaphopods, and cephalopods. *Quart. Rev. Biol.* **19**, 85–97.

Coe, W. R. (1948). Nutrition and sexuality in protandric gastropods of the genus *Crepidula*. *Biol. Bull.* **94**, 158–160.

Coe, W. R. (1953). Influences of association, isolation and nutrition on the sexuality of snails of the genus *Crepidula*. *J. Exptl. Zool.* **122**, 5–19.

Colton, H. S. (1918). Fertilization in the air-breathing pond snails. *Biol. Bull.* **35**, 48–49.

Conklin, E. G. (1897). The embryology of *Crepidula*. *J. Morphol.* **13**, 1–226.

Crabb, E. D. (1927). The fertilization process in the snail, *Lymnaea stagnalis appressa* Say. *Biol. Bull.* **53**, 67–108.

Creek, G. A. (1951). The reproductive system and embryology of the snail *Pomatias elegans* (Müller). *Proc. Zool. Soc. (London)* **121**, 599–640.

Dan, J. C., and Wada, S. K. (1955). Studies on the acrosome. IV. The acrosome reaction in some bivalve spermatozoa. *Biol. Bull.* **109**, 40–55.

de Larambergue, M. (1939). Etude de l'autofécondation chez les gastéropodes pulmonés. Recherches sur l'aphallie et la fécondation chez *Bulinus (Isidora) contortus* Michaud. *Bull. biol. France et Belg.* **73**, 21–231.

Drew, G. A. (1901). The life history of *Nucula delphinodonta* (Mighels). *Quart. J. Microscop. Sci.* **44**, 313–391.

Drew, G. A. (1911). Sexual activities of the squid, *Loligo pealeii* (Les.). *J. Morphol.* **22**, 327–360.

Drew, G. A. (1919). Sexual activities of the squid *Loligo pealeii*. II. The spermatophore; its structure, ejaculation and formation. *J. Morphol.* **32**, 379–435.

Field, I. A. (1922). Biology and economic value of the sea mussel *Mytilus edulis*. *Bull. U.S. Bur. Fisheries* **38**, 127–159.

Fort, G. (1937). Le spermatophore des céphalopodes. Etude du spermatophore d'*Eledone cirrhosa* (Lamarck, 1799). *Bull. biol. France et Belg.* **71**, 357–373.

Fort, G. (1941). Le spermatophore des céphalopodes. Etude du spermatophore d'*Eledone moschata* (Lamarck, 1799). *Bull. biol. France et Belg.* **75**, 249–256.

Franzén, A. (1955). Comparative morphological investigations into the spermiogenesis among Mollusca. *Zool. Bidrag Uppsala* **30**, 399–456.

Franzén, A. (1956). On spermiogenesis, morphology of the spermatozoon, and biology of fertilization among invertebrates. *Zool. Bidrag Uppsala* **31**, 356–482.

Fretter, V. (1941). The genital ducts of some British stenoglossan prosobranchs. *J. Marine Biol. Assoc. U.K.* **25**, 173–211.

Fretter, V. (1946). The genital ducts of *Theodoxus*, *Lamellaria* and *Trivia*, and a discussion on their evolution in the prosobranchs. *J. Marine Biol. Assoc. U.K.* **26**, 312–351.

Fretter, V. (1948). The structure and life history of some minute prosobranchs of rock pools: *Skeneopsis planorbis* (Fabricius), *Omalogyra atomus* (Philippi), *Rissoella diaphana* (Alder) and *Rissoella opalina* (Jeffreys). *J. Marine Biol. Assoc. U.K.* **27**, 597–632.

Fretter, V. (1951a). Some observations on the British cypraeids. *Proc. Malacol. Soc. London* **29**, 14–20.

Fretter, V. (1951b). Observations on the life history and functional morphology of *Cerithiopsis tubercularis* (Montagu) and *Triphora perversa* (L.). *J. Marine Biol. Assoc. U.K.* **29**, 567–586.

Fretter, V. (1951c). *Turbonilla elegantissima* (Montagu), a parasitic opisthobranch. *J. Marine Biol. Assoc. U.K.* **30**, 37–47.

Fretter, V. (1953). The transference of sperm from male to female prosobranch, with reference also to the pyramidellids. *Proc. Linnean Soc. London* **164**, 217–224.

Fretter, V., and Graham, A. (1949). The structure and mode of life of the Pyramidellidae, parasitic opisthobranchs. *J. Marine Biol. Assoc. U.K.* **28**, 493–532.

Fretter, V., and Graham, A. (1962). "British Prosobranch Molluscs," 755pp. Ray Society, London.

Galtsoff, P. S. (1930). The role of chemical stimulation in the spawning reactions of *Ostrea virginica* and *Ostrea gigas*. *Proc. Natl. Acad. Sci. U.S.* **16**, 555–559.

Galtsoff, P. S. (1938). Physiology of reproduction of *Ostrea virginica*. II. Stimulation of spawning in the female oyster. *Biol. Bull.* **75**, 286–307.

Galtsoff, P. S. (1940). Physiology of reproduction of *Ostrea virginica*. III. Stimulation of spawning in the male oyster. *Biol. Bull.* **78**, 117–135.

Gascoigne, T. (1956). Feeding and reproduction in the Limapontiidae. *Trans. Roy. Soc. Edinburgh* **63**, 129–151.

George, J. C., and Jura, C. (1958). A histochemical study of the capsule fluid of the egg of a land snail *Succinea putris* L. *Koninkl. Ned. Wetenschap., Proc.* **C61**, 598–603.

Gerhardt, U. (1933). Zur Kopulation der Limaciden. *Z. Morphol. Ökol. Tiere* **27**, 401–450.

Giese, M. (1915). Der Genitalapparat von *Calyptraea sinensis* Linn., *Crepidula unguiformis* Lam. und *Capulus hungaricus* Lam. *Z. wiss. Zool.* **114**, 169–231.

Glaser, O. C. (1906). Über den Kannibalismus bei *Fasciolaria tulipa* (var. *distans*) und deren larvale Excretionsorgane. *Z. wiss. Zool.* **80**, 80–121.

Glaser, O. C. (1921). Fertilization and egg-secretions. *Biol. Bull.* **41**, 63–72.

Goldschmidt, R. (1923). "The Mechanism and Physiology of Sex Determination," 259pp. Methuen, London.

Gould, H. N. (1919). Studies on sex in the hermaphrodite mollusc *Crepidula plana*. III. Transference of the male-producing stimulus through sea-water. *J. Exptl. Zool.* **29**, 113–120.

Gould, H. N. (1947). Conditions affecting the development of the male phase in *Crepidula plana*. *Biol. Bull.* **93**, 194.

Gould, H. N. (1952). Studies on sex in the hermaphrodite mollusk *Crepidula plana*. IV. Internal and external factors influencing growth and sex development. *J. Exptl. Zool.* **119**, 93–160.

Graham, A. (1954). Some observations on the reproductive tract of *Janthina janthina* (L.). *Proc. Malacol. Soc. London* **31**, 1–6.

Grave, B. H. (1922). An analysis of the spawning habits and spawning stimuli of *Chaetopleura apiculata* (Say). *Biol. Bull.* **42**, 234–256.

Grimpe, G. (1926). Biologische Beobachtungen an *Sepia officinalis. Verhandl. deut. zool. Ges.* **31**, 148–153.

Hamon, M. (1942). Recherches sur les spermatophores. Thesis, University of Algiers.

Hancock, D. A. (1956). The structure of the capsule and the hatching process in *Urosalpinx cinerea* (Say). *Proc. Zool. Soc. (London)* **127**, 565–571.

Hanson, J., Randall, J. T., and Bayley, S. T. (1952). The microstructure of the spermatozoa of the snail *Viviparus. Exptl. Cell Research* **3**, 65–78.

Heath, H. (1905). The breeding habits of chitons of the Californian coast. *Zool. Anz.* **29**, 390–393.

Horstmann, H. J. (1956). Der Galaktogengehalt der Eier von *Lymnaea stagnalis* L. während der Embryonalentwicklung. *Biochem. Z.* **328**, 342–347.

Hoyle, W. E. (1907). Presidential address to Section D. *Rept. Brit. Assoc. Advance. Sci.* pp. 520–539.

Hultin, T. (1947). On the question of sperm-antifertilizin. *Pubbl. staz. zool. Napoli* **21**, 153–163.

Hyman, O. W. (1923). Spermic dimorphism in *Fasciolaria tulipa. J. Morphol.* **37**, 307–383.

Inaba, F. (1936). Studies on the artificial parthenogenesis of *Ostrea gigas* Thunberg. *J. Sci. Hiroshima Univ.*, Ser. B1 **5**, 29–46.

Ishiki, H. (1936). Sex changes in Japanese slipper limpets *Crepidula aculeata* and *Crepidula walshi. J. Sci. Hiroshima Univ.*, Ser. B1 **3**, 91–99.

Iwata, K. S. (1949). Spawning of *Mytilus edulis.* II. Discharge by electrical stimulation. *Bull. Japan. Soc. Sci. Fisheries* **15**, 443–446.

Jacob, J. (1957). Cytological studies of Melaniidae (Mollusca) with special reference to parthenogenesis and polyploidy. I. Oögenesis of the parthenogenetic species of *Melanoides* (Prosobranchia-Gastropoda). *Trans. Roy. Soc. Edinburgh* **63**, 341–352.

Jacob, J. (1958). Cytological studies of Melaniidae (Mollusca) with special reference to parthenogenesis and polyploidy. II. A study of meiosis in the rare males of the polyploid race of *Melanoides tuberculatus* and *Melanoides lineatus. Trans. Roy. Soc. Edinburgh* **63**, 433–444.

Jenner, C. E., and Chamberlain, N. A. (1955). Seasonal resorption and restoration of the copulatory organ in the mud snail, *Nassa obsoleta. Biol. Bull.* **109**, 347.

Jura, C., and George, J. C. (1958). Observations on the jelly mass of the eggs of three molluscs, *Succinea putris, Limnaea stagnalis* and *Planorbis corneus* with special reference to metachromasia. *Koninkl. Ned. Akad. Wetenschap., Proc.* **C61**, 590–594.

Korringa, P. (1947). Relations between the moon and periodicity in the breeding of marine animals. *Ecol. Monographs* **17**, 347–381.

Korringa, P. (1957). Water temperature and breeding throughout the geographical range of *Ostrea edulis. Année biol.* [3] **33**, 109–116.

Künkel, K. (1910). Zuchtversuche mit *Campylaea cingulata* Studer. *Abhandl. senckenberg. naturforsch. Ges.* **32**, 253–267.

Lang, A. (1896). Kleine biologische Beobachtungen über die Weinbergschnecke (*Helix pomatia*). *Vierteljahresschr. naturforsch. Ges. Zürich* **41**, 488–495.

Laviolette, P. (1950). Rôle de la gonade dans la morphogenèse du tractus génital, chez quelques mollusques Limacidae et Arionidae. *Compt. rend. acad. sci.* **231**, 1567–1569.

Levy, F. (1912). Über die Copula von *Sepiola atlantica* D'Orb. *Zool. Anz.* **39**, 284–290.

Lilly, M. M. (1953). The mode of life and the structure and functioning of the reproductive ducts of *Bithynia tentaculata* (L.). *Proc. Malacol. Soc. London* **30**, 87–110.

Linke, O. (1933). Morphologie und Physiologie des Genitalapparates der Nordseelittorinen. *Wiss. Meeresuntersuch., Abt. Helgoland* **19**, No. 5, 3–52.

Linke, O. (1934a). Beiträge zur Sexualbiologie der Littorinen. *Z. Morphol. Ökol. Tiere* **28**, 170–177.

Linke, O. (1934b). Über die Beziehungen zwischen Keimdrüse und Soma bei Prosobranchiern. *Verhandl. deut. zool. Ges.* **36**, 164–175.

Lloyd, H. M. (1952). A study of the reproductive systems of some opisthobranchiate molluscs. Ph.D. thesis, University of London.

Loosanoff, V. L. (1960). Challenging problems in shellfish biology. *In* "Perspectives in Marine Biology" (A. A. Buzzati-Traverso, ed.), pp. 483–495. Univ. of California Press, Berkeley, California.

Loosanoff, V. L., and Davis, H. C. (1950). Spawning of oysters at low temperatures. *Science* **111**, 521–522.

Loosanoff, V. L., and Davis, H. C. (1952). Temperature requirements for maturation of gonads of northern oysters. *Biol. Bull.* **103**, 80–86.

Loosanoff, V. L., and Engle, J. B. (1940). Spawning and setting of oysters in Long Island Sound in 1937 and discussion of the method for predicting the intensity and time of oyster setting. *Bull. U.S. Bur. Fisheries* **49**, 217–255.

Loosanoff, V. L., and Engle, J. B. (1942). Accumulation and discharge of spawn by oysters living at different depths. *Biol. Bull.* **82**, 413–422.

Loosanoff, V. L., and Nomejko, C. A. (1951). Spawning and setting of the American oyster, *O. virginica*, in relation to lunar phases. *Ecology* **32**, 113–134.

Lubet, P. (1956). Effets d'ablation des centres nerveux sur l'émission des gamètes chez *Mytilus edulis* L. et *Chlamys varia* L. *Ann. sci. nat. Zool. et biol. animale* [11] **18**, 175–183.

Lubet, P. (1957). Cycle sexuel de *Mytilus edulis* L. et de *Mytilus galloprovincialis* Lmk. dans le bassin d'Arcachon (Gironde). *Année biol.* [3] **33**, 19–29.

Marchand, W. (1907). Studien über Cephalopoden. I. Der männliche Leitungsapparat der Dibranchiaten. *Z. wiss. Zool.* **86**, 311–415.

Marchand, W. (1913). Studien über Cephalopoden. II. Über die Spermatophoren. *Zoologica, Stuttgart* **26**, 171–200.

Meisenheimer, J. (1912). "Die Weinbergschnecke *Helix pomatia*," 140pp. Klinkhardt, Leipzig.

Montalenti, G. (1950). Recherches récentes sur la sexualité dans les crustacés et les mollusques. *Compt. rend. congr. intern. zool. 13 Congr. Paris 1948*, 162–163.

Montalenti, G. (1960). Perspectives of research on sex problems in marine animals. *In* "Perspectives in Marine Biology" (A. A. Buzzati-Traverso, ed.), pp. 589–602. Univ. of California Press, Berkeley, California.

Montalenti, G., and Bacci, G. (1951). Osservazioni e ipotesi sulla determinazione del sesso negli ermafroditi. *Sci. Genet.* **4**, 5–12.

Moquin-Tandon, A. (1855). "Histoire naturelle des mollusques terrestres et fluviatiles de France." Paris.

Morris, M. (1917). A cytological study of artificial parthenogenesis in *Cumingia*. *J. Exptl. Zool.* **22**, 1–35.

Myazaki, I. (1938). On the incubatory habits and shelled larvae of bivalves. *Botany and Zool. (Tokyo)* **6–7**, 1213–1218.

Nelson, T. C. (1936). Water filtration by the oyster and a new hormone effect upon the rate of flow. *Proc. Soc. Exptl. Biol. Med.* **34**, 189–190.

Nelson, T. C., and Allison, J. B. (1940). On the nature and action of diantlin; a new hormone-like substance carried by the spermatozoa of the oyster. *J. Exptl. Zool.* **85**, 299–338.

Noland, L. E., and Carriker, M. R. (1946). Observations on the biology of the snail *Lymnaea stagnalis appressa* during twenty generations in laboratory culture. *Am. Midland Naturalist* **36**, 467–493.

Oldfield, E. (1955). Observations on the anatomy and mode of life of *Lasaea rubra* (Montagu) and *Turtonia minuta* (Fabricius). *Proc. Malacol. Soc. London* **31**, 226–249.

Oldfield, E. (1959). The embryology of *Lasaea rubra* (Montagu), and the functional morphology of *Kellia suborbicularis* (Montagu), *Montacuta ferruginosa* (Montagu) and *M. substriata* (Montagu). Ph.D. thesis, University of London.

Orton, J. H. (1920). Sea temperature, breeding and distribution in marine animals. *J. Marine Biol. Assoc. U.K.* **12**, 339–366.

Orton, J. H. (1924). Sex change and breeding in the native oyster, *O. edulis. Nature* **114**, 191–192.

Orton, J. H. (1927a). Observations and experiments on sex-change in the European oyster (*O. edulis*). Part I. The change from female to male. *J. Marine Biol. Assoc. U.K.* **14**, 967–1045.

Orton, J. H. (1927b). A note on the physiology of sex and sex-determination. *J. Marine Biol. Assoc. U.K.* **14**, 1047–1055.

Orton, J. H., Southward, A. J., and Dodd, J. M. (1956). Studies on the biology of limpets. II. The breeding of *Patella vulgata* L. in Britain. *J. Marine Biol. Assoc. U.K.* **35**, 149–176.

Pasteels, J. (1938). Le rôle du calcium dans l'activation de l'oeuf de pholade. *Trav. sta. zool. Wimereux* **13**, 515–530.

Patil, A. M. (1958). The occurrence of a male of the prosobranch *Potamopyrgus jenkinsi* (Smith) var. *carinata* Marshall in the Thames at Sonning, Berkshire. *Ann. Mag. Nat. Hist.* [13] **1**, 232–240.

Pellegrini, O. (1948). Ricerche statistiche sulla sessualità di *Patella coerulea* L. *Boll. Zool.* **15**, 115–121.

Pellegrini, O. (1949). Ermafroditismo proterandrico in *Calyptraea chinensis* (L.) (Gasteropoda, Prosobranchiata). *Boll. Zool.* **16**, 49–59.

Pelseneer, P. (1894). Recherches sur divers opisthobranches. *Mém. cour. acad. roy. Belg.* **53**, 1–157.

Pelseneer, P. (1895). Hermaphroditism in Mollusca. *Quart. J. Microscop. Sci.* **37**, 19–46.

Pelseneer, P. (1911). Recherches sur l'embryologie des gastropodes. *Mém. acad. roy. Belg., Classe sci.* [2] **3**, 1–167.

Pelseneer, P. (1926). La proportion relative des sexes chez les animaux et particulièrement chez les mollusques. *Mém. acad. roy. Belg., Classe sci.* [2] **8**, 1–258.

Pelseneer, P. (1935). Essai d'éthologie zoologique d'après l'étude des mollusques. *Acad. roy. Belg. Classe sci. Publ. Fondation Agathon De Potter* **1**, 1–662.

Perrier, R., and Fischer, H. (1914). Sur l'existence de spermatophores chez quelques opisthobranches. *Compt. rend. acad. sci.* **158**, 1366–1369.

Phillips, R. A., and Watson, H. (1930). *Milax gracilis* (Leydig) in the British Isles. *J. Conchol.* **19**, 65–93.

Purchon, R. D. (1941). On the biology and relationships of the lamellibranch *Xylophaga dorsalis* (Turton). *J. Marine Biol. Assoc. U.K.* **25**, 1–39.

Quick, H. E. (1960). British slugs (Pulmonata; Testacellidae, Arionidae, Limacidae). *Brit. Museum Nat. Hist., Bull. Dept. Zool.* **6**, 105–226.

Racovitza, E. G. (1894). Notes de biologie. Accouplement et fécondation chez *Octopus vulgaris. Arch. zool. exptl. et gén.* [3] **2**, 23–49.

Rammelmeyer, H. (1925). Zur Morphologie der *Puncturella noachina. Zool. Anz.* **64**, 105–114.

Retzius, G. (1904). Zur Kenntnis der Spermien der Evertebraten. *Biol. Untersuch.* [N.F.] **11**, 1–32.

Retzius, G. (1906). Die Spermien der Gastropoden. *Biol. Untersuch.* [N.F.] **13**, 1–36.

Retzius, G. (1909). Spermien der Insekten, *Aurelia aurita* (L.), Nereiden, Cestoden, Trematoden, Chaetognathen, Bryozoen und *Nassa reticulata* (L.). *Biol. Untersuch.* [N.F.] **14**, 54–78.

Retzius, G. (1912). Weitere Beiträge zur Kenntnis der Spermien der Gastropoden und Vögel. *Biol. Untersuch.* [N.F.] **17**, 95–99.

Rhein, A. (1935). Diploide Parthenogenese bei *Hydrobia jenkinsi* Smith. *Naturwissenschaften* **23**, 100.

Richter, E. (1935). Der Bau der Zwitterdrüsen und der Entstehung der Geschlechtszellen bei *Agriolimax agrestris. Jena. Z. Naturwiss.* **69**, 507–544.

Riedel, A. (1955). O zaniku męskich narządów kopulacyjnych u ślimaków trzonkoocznych (Stylommatophora), ze szczególnym uęzglwdnieniem *Retinella nitens* Mich. *Ann. Mus. Zool. Polon.* **15**, 83–100.

Rigby, J. E. (1960). A study of the reproductive and alimentary systems of *Oxychilus cellarius* (Müller) and *Succinea putris* (L.). Ph.D. thesis, University of Reading.

Rohlack, S. (1959). Über das Vorkommen von Sexualhormonen bei der Meeresschnecke *Littorina littorea* L. *Z. vergleich. Physiol.* **42**, 164–180.

Rosenwald, K. (1926). Beeinflussung des Geschlechts von *Limax laevis. Z. Indukt. Abstammungs- u. Vererbungslehre* **43**, 238–251.

Rothschild, Lord (1956). "Fertilization," 170pp. Methuen, London.

Rothschild, Lord, and Tyler, A. (1955). Acrosomal filaments in spermatozoa. *Exptl Cell Research* Suppl. 3, 304–311.

Runnström, J., and Monné, L. (1945). On some properties of the surface-layers of immature and mature sea-urchin eggs, especially the changes accompanying nuclear and cytoplasmic maturation. *Arkiv Zool.* **36A**, No. 18, 1–26.

Sampson, M. M. (1922). Iso-agglutination and hetero-agglutination of spermatozoa. *Biol. Bull.* **43**, 267–283.

Sander, K. (1950). Beobachtungen zur Fortpflanzung von *Assiminea grayana* Leach. *Arch. Molluskenk.* **79**, 147–149.

Sander, K. (1952). Beobachtungen zur Fortpflanzung von *Assiminea grayana* Leach (2). *Arch. Molluskenk.* **81**, 133–134.

Sanderson, A. R. (1939). The cytology of parthenogenesis in the snail *Potamopyrgus jenkinsi* Smith. *Advance. of Sci.* **1**, 46.

Sanderson, A. R. (1940). Maturation in the parthenogenetic snail *Potamopyrgus jenkinsi* Smith and in the snail *Peringia ulvae* (Pennant). *Proc. Zool. Soc. (London)* **110**, 11–15.

Sereni, E. (1929). Correlazioni nei cefalopodi. *Am. J. Physiol.* **90**, 512.

Staiger, H. (1950). Zur Determination der Nähreier bei Prosobranchiern. *Rev. suisse zool.* **57**, 496–503.

Staiger, H. (1951). Cytologische und morphologische Untersuchungen zur Determination der Nähreier bei Prosobranchiern. *Z. Zellforsch. u. mikroskop. Anat.* **35**, 496–549.

Stauber, L. A. (1947). On the possible physiological species in the oyster *Ostrea virginica*. *Anat. Record* **99**, 614.

Stauber, L. A. (1950). The problem of physiological species with special reference to oysters and oyster drills. *Ecology* **31**, 109–118.

Tattersall, W. M. (1920). Notes on the breeding habits and life history of the periwinkle. *Sci. Invest. Fisheries Branch, Dept. Agr. Ireland* **1**, 1–11.

Taylor, J. W. (1900). "A Monograph of the Land and Freshwater Mollusca of the British Isles," pp. 1–454. Taylor Bros., Leeds.

Terao, A. (1926). On the fertilizing of the oyster, *Ostrea circumpincta*. *Sci. Repts. Tôhoku Imp. Univ. Fourth Ser.* **2**, 127–132.

Thorson, G. (1935). Studies on the egg-capsules and development of Arctic marine prosobranchs. *Medd. Grønland* **100**, 1–71.

Thorson, G. (1946). Reproduction and larval development of Danish marine bottom invertebrates. *Medd. Komm. Havundersøg. Kbh. (Plankton)* **4**, 1–523.

Thorson, G. (1950). Reproductive and larval ecology of marine bottom invertebrates. *Biol. Revs. Cambridge Phil. Soc.* **25**, 1–45.

Tinbergen, L. (1939). Zur Fortpflanzungsethologie von *Sepia officinalis* L. *Arch. néerl. zool.* **3**, 323–364.

Tuzet, O. (1928). Sur la spermatogenèse de *Theodoxia fluviatilis* (Sandberger), *Bythinia tentaculata* (L.) et *Cyclostoma elegans* (Müll.), mollusques prosobranches. *Compt. rend. soc. biol.* **99**, 124–125.

Tuzet, O. (1930). Recherches sur la spermatogenèse des prosobranches. *Arch. zool. exptl. et gén.* **70**, 95–229.

Tuzet, O. (1939). La spermiogenèse d'*Aplysia depilans* Linné. *Arch. zool. exptl. et gén.* **81**, 130–138.

Tuzet, O. (1940). Sur la spermatogenèse de l'*Oncidiella celtica*. Cuv. *Arch. zool. exptl. et gén.* **81**, 371–394.

Tuzet, O. (1950). Le spermatozoide dans la série animale. *Rev. suisse zool.* **57**, 433–451.

Tyler, A. (1939). Extraction of an egg membrane-lysin from sperm of the giant keyhole limpet (*Megathura crenulata*). *Proc. Natl. Acad. Sci. U.S.* **25**, 317–323.

Tyler, A. (1940a). Agglutination of sea-urchin eggs by means of a substance extracted from the eggs. *Proc. Natl. Acad. Sci. U.S.* **26**, 249–256.

Tyler, A. (1940b). Sperm agglutination in the keyhole limpet *Megathura crenulata*. *Biol. Bull.* **78**, 159–178.

Tyler, A., and Fox, S. W. (1940). Evidence for the protein nature of the sperm agglutinins of the keyhole limpet and the sea-urchin. *Biol. Bull.* **79**, 153–165.

Van Cleave, H. J., and Altringer, D. A. (1937). Studies on the life cycle of *Campeloma rufum*, a parthenogenetic snail. *Am. Naturalist* **71**, 167–184.

Van Oordt, G. J. (1938). The spermatheca of *Loligo vulgaris*. 1. Structure of the spermatheca and function of its unicellular glands. *Quart. J. Microscop. Sci.* **80**, 593–599.

von Medem, F. (1945). Untersuchungen über die Ei- und Spermwirkstoffe bei marinen Mollusken. *Zool. Jahrb. Abt. allgem. Zool. u. Physiol. Tiere* **61**, 1–44.

Wada, S. K. (1936). Thermal stimulation of spawning in the Japanese pearl oyster. *Suisan Gakkwai Ho* **7**, 131–133.

Wada, S. K. (1954). Spawning in the tridacnid clams. *Japan. J. Zoöl.* **11**, 273–285.

Webb, G. R. (1942). Comparative observations of the mating habits of three California landsnails. *Bull. S. Calif. Acad. Sci.* **41**, 102–108.

Webb, G. R. (1950). The sexology of *Polygyra septemvolva* Say, life history notes, possible utility and data on *Stenotrema* (Mollusca, Gastropoda, Pulmonata, Polygyridae). *Trans. Am. Microscop. Soc.* **69**, 387–393.

Weill, R. (1927). Recherches sur la structure, la valeur systématique et le fonction-nement du spermatophore de "*Sepiola atlantica*" d'Orb. *Bull. biol. France et Belg.* **61**, 59–92.

Wells, M. J., and Wells, J. (1959). Hormonal control of sexual maturity in *Octopus*. *J. Exptl. Biol.* **36**, 1–33.

Wiesensee, N. (1916). Die Geschlechtsverhältnisse und der Geschlechtsapparat bei *Anodonta*. *Z. wiss. Zool.* **115**, 262–335.

Wilczynski, J. Z. (1955). On sex behaviour and sex determination in *Crepidula fornicata*. *Biol. Bull.* **109**, 353–354.

Willcox, M. A. (1898). Zur Anatomie von *Acmaea fragilis*. *Jena. Z. Naturwiss.* **32**, 411–456.

Willcox, M. A. (1905). Biology of *Acmaea testudinalis* Müller. *Am. Naturalist* **39**, 325–333.

Wilson, D. P., and Wilson, M. A. (1956). A contribution to the biology of *Janthina janthina* (L.) *J. Marine Biol. Assoc. U.K.* **35**, 291–305.

Yonge, C. M. (1953). Observations on *Hipponix antiquatus* (Linnaeus). *Proc. Calif. Acad. Sci.* **28**, 1–24.

Yonge, C. M. (1962). On the biology of the mesogastropod *Trichotropis cancellata* Hinds, a benthic indicator species. *Biol. Bull.* **122**, 160–181.

Young, R. T. (1942). Spawning season of the Californian mussel *Mytilus califor-nianus*. *Ecology* **23**, 490–492.

Young, R. T. (1946). Stimulation of spawning in the mussel (*Mytilus californianus*). *Ecology* **26**, 58–69.

CHAPTER 5

Development

C. P. Raven

ZOOLOGICAL LABORATORY, UNIVERSITY OF UTRECHT, THE NETHERLANDS

This treatment of the physiology of development of molluscs will be subdivided according to the main periods of embryonic development: maturation and fertilization, cleavage, gastrulation, and embryogenesis. For reasons of space limitations only summary indications of normal development can be given. For a more extensive survey see Raven (1958a).

I. MATURATION AND FERTILIZATION

In most molluscs maturation of the egg may begin spontaneously, independent of fertilization. In other cases the fertilizing sperm normally enters at the germinal vesicle stage; and in at least some of these species maturation will not begin spontaneously.

A. Maturation

In some marine bivalves belonging to the last-mentioned category, breakdown of the germinal vesicle may be provoked in unfertilized eggs by salt solutions (Kostanecki, 1902; Dalcq, 1928) or irradiation with ultraviolet light (Pasteels, 1931; Tchakhotine, 1935). Further analysis in *Barnea* (Pasteels, 1938a,b) and *Spisula* (Allen, 1953) has led to the conclusion that calcium ions give the actual stimulus for maturation; other agents may have a sensitizing action in eggs that have previously been impregnated with a certain amount of calcium in the ovary. The calcium is probably bound to protein in the egg cortex and may be released by the action of certain stimuli. As long as the eggs are in the ovary, maturation is apparently prevented by the presence of certain polysaccharides in the body fluid and egg cortex (Sawada, 1952, 1954a,b).

When molluscan eggs are centrifuged some time before the extrusion of the polar bodies, the germinal vesicle or maturation spindle as a rule comes to lie in the zone of hyaloplasm. With the approach of maturation, the spindle rises to the surface. Sometimes it apparently returns to the original animal pole, pushing aside the egg substances accumulated in this region (Morgan, 1910; Raven, 1938). In other cases the polar bodies may be extruded at an arbitrary point of the surface (Conklin, 1910, 1917; Costello, 1939) (cf. Fig. 4). But even in these cases the original polarity of the egg has not been changed, as is shown by the further development of these eggs (only by very strong centrifugal forces may an actual change in polarity be effected; cf. Pease, 1940; Peltrera, 1940). It is evident that the polarity is bound to some component of the egg that is relatively immovable by centrifugal force; this is presumably the more or less rigid egg cortex. The polar migration of the maturation spindle in normal development is apparently controlled by factors residing in the cortex.

The inequality of the maturation divisions is not due to inherent properties of the maturation spindles but to their eccentric position. If the spindles are stretched (Conklin, 1917) or displaced toward the center of the egg by centrifuging (Clement, 1935; Morgan, 1936, 1937), giant polar bodies are formed, which may in extreme cases be as large as the rest of the egg (Fig. 1).

A similar displacement of the maturation spindles (depolarization) may also be effected by exposing the eggs to external agents (e.g., calcium or lithium ions) primarily affecting the egg cortex (Pasteels, 1930, 1931, 1938a; Raven and Mighorst, 1946; de Groot, 1948). This supports the assumption that the movements of the maturation spindles are controlled by cortical factors.

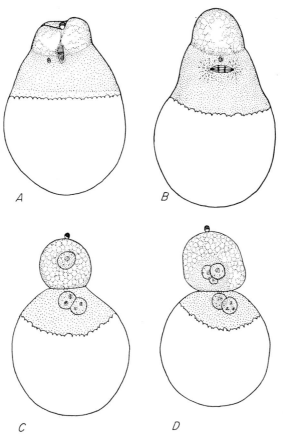

Fig. 1. Formation of giant polar bodies in centrifuged eggs of *Ilyanassa*. (*A*) Second maturation spindle is forced away from animal pole, but remains connected by strands of cytoplasm. Condensed sperm nucleus at border of oil and cytoplasmic zones. (*B*) Second maturation spindle lying free in cytoplasmic zone. Sperm nucleus between spindle and oil zone. First polar body lost. (*C* and *D*) Giant polar bodies in eggs centrifuged before second maturation division. After Clement (1935).

B. Fertilization

Interacting substances of eggs and sperm, playing a part in fertilization, have been found in various molluscs (Southwick, 1939; Tyler, 1939, 1940, 1949a,b; Tyler and Fox, 1939, 1940; von Medem, 1942, 1945; Metz and Donovan, 1949; Berg, 1950; Krauss, 1950; see also Chapter 4, Section III,A,3). The substances secreted by the eggs (fertilizin) activate the sperm and may cause their agglutination. The sperm contain antifertilizin, neutralizing the sperm agglutinins from eggs, and sometimes inactivating themselves and foreign sperm. Finally, egg membrane lysins have been demonstrated in various species. They are probably located in the acrosome of the sperm and are liberated when this breaks down on its contact with the vitelline membrane, giving rise to an acrosome filament which pierces the egg envelopes (Dan and Wada, 1955; Wada *et al.*, 1956).

Scarcely any observations have been made in molluscs on the nature and course of the cortical reaction following fertilization which causes the eggs to become refractory to the entrance of additional sperm. Sawada and Murakami (1959) observed that fertilization in *Mactra* causes the disappearance of cortical granules, although often not as completely as in sea urchins. In *Mytilus* the cortical granules are still present in fertilized and cleaving eggs (Reverberi and Mancuso, 1961). Experiments by Tyler and Scheer (1937) in *Dentalium*, and by Allen (1953) in *Spisula* have shown that the loss of fertilizability is reversible, when the eggs are transferred soon after fertilization to acidified or calcium-free sea water.

Experimental parthenogenesis has been induced in various bivalves (Kostanecki, 1902, 1904, 1908; Morris, 1917; Heilbrunn, 1925; Tchakhotine, 1935; Inaba, 1936; Pasteels, 1938a,b); Hollingsworth, 1941; Allen, 1953, Motomura, 1954). As usual, there is a great variety of activating agents. Pasteels assumed that calcium is the actual activating agent, whereas other treatments have only a sensitizing action, either by increasing the permeability of the egg membrane for the calcium ions of the outer medium, or by liberating bound calcium in the cortex, which is then free to diffuse into the inner cytoplasm.

As a rule, there is an inverse relation in parthenogenesis between polar body formation and cleavage: eggs which extrude both polar bodies do not usually cleave; those without polar bodies may cleave.

Changes in shape and volume of eggs after sperm penetration or activation have been observed in *Spisula* (Allen, 1953); and rhythmic changes in permeability of the egg surface leading to localized extrusions of substances have been described in *Mactra* and *Gryphaea* (Pasteels, 1950; Pasteels and Mulnard, 1957).

C. Metabolic Changes at Fertilization

Changes in respiratory activity of the egg occurring at the moment of fertilization have been observed in various species (Whitaker, 1933; Ballentine, 1940; Sclufer, 1955). There may be an increase, a decrease, or no change, depending upon the species (Cleland, 1950). The respiratory quotient does not change at fertilization in *Ostrea commercialis* and *Spisula*.

D. The Sequence of the Processes of Maturation and Fertilization

The various processes taking place in the uncleaved egg in normal development follow each other in a regular sequence characteristic of the species. When *Lymnaea* eggs are treated with hypertonic solutions, either development is retarded as a whole, the normal sequence remaining unchanged, or development is blocked at a certain stage, and all processes normally occurring after this stage are suppressed (Raven and Hupkens van der Elst, 1950). In normal development, the egg chromosomes of *Lymnaea* swell to karyomeres immediately after the extrusion of the second polar body; at the same time, the sperm nucleus also swells to the male pronucleus, and migrates toward the egg karyomeres at the animal pole. If the eggs are treated with lithium chloride, the swelling of the egg chromosomes and of the sperm nucleus, and the migration of the latter toward the animal pole, may occur immediately after the extrusion of the first polar body (de Groot, 1948; Raven and Roborgh, 1949). Moreover, in eggs so treated, the amoeboid motility after the extrusion of the second polar body is often greatly exaggerated and prolonged, and the sperm aster may remain visible long after its normal time of disappearance, while its center shows a strong vacuolization.

Elbers (1959) has shown by means of electron-microscopic observations that lithium chloride in subcytolytic concentrations has no visible influence on the structure of the cytoplasm of *Lymnaea* eggs. He concluded that the lithium ions do not penetrate into the interior of the egg, and that the effects of lithium treatment are due to its action on the egg cortex. If this is true, the above observations suggest that various processes in the uncleaved egg are dependent on the state of the cortex. It is possible that their normal sequence is due to a progressive change in the cortex, which successively switches on the various component processes, and provides the basic mechanism underlying their temporospatial order.

E. Oöplasmic Segregation

The various components of the cytoplasm of the ripe, unfertilized mollusc egg are more or less evenly distributed throughout the egg. From ovulation until first cleavage, however, a shifting of various substances occurs, through which they are accumulated or concentrated at certain places in the egg cell (Fig. 2). These processes may be summarized under the term oöplasmic segregation; they give rise to differences in chemical composition between various parts of the egg. In molluscs the oöplasmic segregation in the uncleaved eggs takes place almost entirely in relation to the original animal-vegetal polarity. A certain degree of localization along a radius of the egg may be involved. But, apart from certain cephalopods, no traces of a bilateral symmetry generally occur in the uncleaved stage.

The driving forces behind these displacements of egg substances are not known. The assumption that an intracellular electric field is involved (Spek, 1934; Costello, 1945) was not corroborated by the observation that *Lymnaea* eggs exposed to a strong external electric field showed no

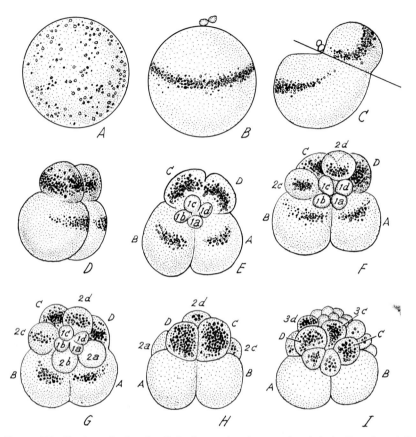

Fig. 2. Distribution of vitamin C during early cleavage in *Aplysia limacina*. (*A*) Immature egg shortly after laying. Vitamin C granules distributed in peripheral cytoplasm of whole egg. (*B*) Mature egg after completion of oöplasmic segregation, about 3 or 4 hours after oviposition. Annular arrangement of vitamin C granules. (*C*) Beginning first cleavage, viewed from one side. Plane of cleavage furrow indicated. (*D*) Four-cell stage, obliquely from one side. (*E*) The vitamin-free micromeres *1a–1d* are formed. Viewed from the animal pole. (*F*) C and D have formed the second micromeres *2c* and *2d,* which contain somewhat less vitamin granules than their macromeres. (*G*) Twelve-cell stage, viewed from the animal pole. A and B have formed, respectively, a vitamin-free micromere *2a* and *2b.* (*H*) The same stage from the other side. (*I*) Somewhat further advanced cleavage stage in the same orientation as (*H*). The cells C, D, *3c*, and *3d* are especially rich in vitamin C. After Ries (1937).

deviations of development, provided the egg cortex remained intact (Raven, 1948). It is possible, however, that an intracellular field is insulated from outward disturbance by the intact cortex.

In molluscan eggs centrifuged at the uncleaved stage, the stratification of substances brought about by centrifugal force disappears in a relatively short time, and a more or less normal distribution of substances is soon recovered (Morgan, 1933; Pasteels, 1934; Ries, 1938; Raven, 1938; Raven and Bretschneider, 1942) (see Fig. 4). Not only do the accumulated substances tend to a more nearly homogeneous distribution as soon as the

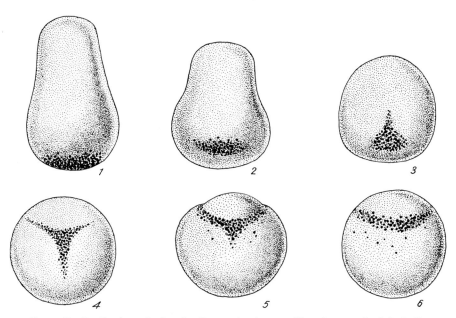

Fig. 3. Redistribution of vitamin C granules in centrifuged eggs of *Aplysia limacina*. (*1*) Immediately after centrifugation; granules accumulated at centrifugal pole. (*2–4*) Recovery of spherical shape. Granules migrate through center of egg. (*5–6*) Granules returned to their normal position in the egg (cf. Fig. 2). After Peltrera (1940).

centrifugal force ceases to act, but in addition the normal processes of oöplasmic segregation take place in relation to the original egg polarity (Raven, 1938, 1945; Raven and Brunnekreeft, 1951; Peltrera, 1940) (Fig. 3). This shows that the factors controlling oöplasmic segregation, like those directing the nuclei and spindles, are bound to some component which is not displaced by moderate centrifuging, presumably to the egg cortex. This view receives further support from cases in which the oöplasmic segregation is disturbed by external agencies primarily affecting the egg cortex, as has been pointed out for eggs of *Lymnaea* treated with lithium chloride (de Groot, 1948).

Electron-microscopic observations by Elbers (1959) indicate that the cortical layer involved is extremely thin. In centrifuged *Lymnaea* eggs the accumulated cytoplasmic inclusions extend to immediately beneath an outer plasma membrane, which is only about 100 Å thick. This appears as a double membrane, consisting of two dark layers separated by a clear zone. Presumably it is this membrane alone which is not displaced by centrifugal force, and must therefore be considered as the carrier of the directing factors of polarity and oöplasmic segregation.

II. CLEAVAGE

In all molluscs, except the cephalopods, cleavage is spiral. At the first two cleavages, the egg divides into the quadrants *A*, *B*, *C*, and *D* (see Fig. 2). In the next four cleavages four micromere quartettes are formed at the animal pole by alternating dexiotropic and laeotropic divisions. At early cleavages a polar lobe is often formed at the vegetal pole, the substance of which ultimately passes into the *D*-quadrant. The second and fourth micromeres of this quadrant, *2d* and *4d*, are especially important; *2d* gives rise to most of the shell gland and foot, *4d* to the primary mesoderm (for further details see Raven, 1958a).

A. *Polarity and Symmetry in Cleavage*

The direction of cleavage planes is dependent on the original animal-vegetal polarity of the egg. The first two cleavage furrows nearly always pass through the animal pole both in normal and in centrifuged eggs (Morgan, 1910; Conklin, 1910, 1917). In compressed eggs, at least the first furrow tends to pass through this pole (Browne, 1910; Tyler, 1930).

The second axis, the dorsoventral (often wrongly called anterioposterior) axis, does not become visible until cleavage. The question of whether this axis arises *de novo* at this stage, or was already preformed in the uncleaved egg, has not yet been answered. In *Cumingia* the *D*-blastomere is always situated opposite the point of sperm entrance (Morgan and Tyler, 1930, 1938). In those eggs where first cleavage is unequal, this inequality is probably due to cortical factors influencing the orientation of the cleavage spindle. The first cleavage may be equalized by various agents—salt solutions, detergents, and ultraviolet radiation—which presumably act primarily on the cortex (Pasteels, 1930, 1931, 1934; Fauré Fremiet and Mugard, 1948; Fauré Fremiet and Thaureaux, 1949).

In eggs possessing a polar lobe, the factors of bilateral symmetry lie within the lobe. If the lobe is removed at first cleavage, the four quadrants are of the same size, and no indications of bilateral symmetry appear at further cleavage (Crampton, 1896; Wilson, 1904a; Clement, 1952). Animal pole fragments of unfertilized or fertilized eggs show an equal cleavage without polar lobe as a rule; vegetal pole or meridional fragments, as far as they cleave at all, do so as a normal egg (Wilson, 1904a; Morgan, 1935a,b, 1936). If by certain treatments the first cleavage is equalized, the polar lobe substance being equally divided between the two blastomeres, then both blastomeres as a rule behave as *CD*-cells at further cleavage (Crampton, 1896; Tyler, 1930; Morgan, 1936, Yasugi, 1938). In dispermic *Dentalium* eggs, which show a simultaneous first division into three or four cells, the polar lobe fusing with one or more of the cells, any blastomere that has received all or part of the polar lobe substance behaves at further cleavage as a *CD*-cell (Schleip, 1925). Although these results are most easily explained by the assumption that the polar lobe in normal development fuses arbitrarily with one or the other of the two first blastomeres, in this way determining the dorsoventral axis of the embryo, the alternative supposition that dorsoventrality is already preformed in the uncleaved egg is not entirely disproved by them. Unfortunately, the crucial experiment attempted by Morgan (1936), namely, the removal of one of the blastomeres before the fusion of the polar lobe had taken place, did not bring about the expected result, so that the problem remains open.

B. *Determination of Cleavage Pattern*

The direction of cleavage planes and the relative sizes of blastomeres are dependent on the direction and place of the cleavage spindles, and on local activities of the egg cortex directly influencing the course of the cleavage furrows.

The orientation of the cleavage spindles may be altered by mechanical means, e.g., by compression (Browne, 1910; Conklin, 1912; Tyler, 1930; Morgan, 1936) or by centrifugation (Conklin, 1917; Pease, 1940). Abnormal positions of cleavage spindles may also occur after cold treatment (Conklin, 1938), probably by modification of protoplasmic currents orienting the spindles in normal development. Finally, deviations in direction of the cleavage spindles may be effected by agents influencing the egg cortex: abnormal ionic composition of the medium (Pasteels, 1930), lithium chloride (Raven and Roborgh, 1949), quinone derivatives (Abd-el-Wahab, 1957, 1958), and ultraviolet irradiation (Pasteels, 1931).

If the first two cleavages are abnormal owing to such treatments, the formation of micromeres may nevertheless begin at the right moment. On the other hand, it is not necessary that two mitotic divisions should have been completed for micromere formation to begin; divisions may be either skipped or intercalated in the mitotic cycle (Conklin, 1912, 1938).

The relative sizes of the micromeres and macromeres may be altered by mechanical displacement of the spindles (Conklin, 1917), but also by lithium (Raven *et al.*, 1952) and ultraviolet irradiation (Pasteels, 1931), which presumably act primarily on the cortex.

That local kinetic activities of the egg cortex play a part in cleavage is most obvious in the eggs forming a polar lobe. If these eggs are centrifuged at the uncleaved stage, a polar lobe forms at cleavage at the original vegetal pole, irrespective of the egg substances lying in this region (Morgan, 1933, 1935a) (Fig. 4). Vegetal fragments of fertilized eggs which do not cleave form a polar lobe synchronously with the divisions of the corresponding animal fragment (Wilson, 1904a; Morgan, 1935b, 1936). Isolated polar lobes exhibit rhythmic changes in shape more or less synchronously with the rest of the egg.

The observations may be explained by the assumption that there is some fundamental process in the egg which goes on more or less independently

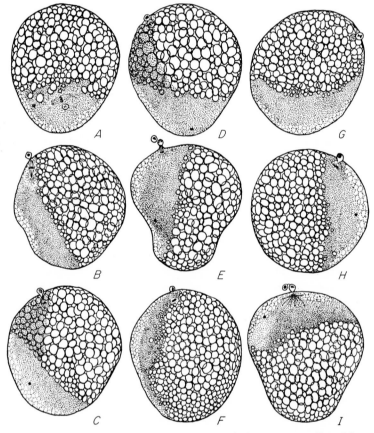

Fig. 4. The formation of the polar lobe in eggs of *Ilyanassa*, centrifuged in reverse orientation before the first polar body had been formed. The second polar lobe arose 70 minutes later. All 9 eggs [except (*A*) and (*I*)] show partial return of the cytoplasm toward the animal pole. The polar bodies were given off before the spindle reached the pole. The lobe formed at or near its normal field. When [as in (*A*)] the spindle did not return to the animal pole, the lobe formed at the vegetal pole and contained only cytoplasm and oil. In (*I*) the egg had probably not reversed or only partly so, and the polar bodies were given off at the animal pole. After Morgan (1933).

of nuclear and cellular divisions. This controls the direction and place of the cleavage spindles by setting up regular patterns of attractive and repulsive forces in the egg cortex, which by their interplay determine the spindle positions. The latter determine, in their turn, in conjunction with more or less autonomous kinetic activities of the cortex, the direction of the cleavage planes.

Isolated blastomeres generally give rise to the same sequence of cells as in normal development (Crampton, 1896; Wilson, 1904b; Conklin, 1912; Rattenbury and Berg, 1954; Hess, 1956a). The factors controlling the cleavage pattern are apparently bound more or less rigidly to the single cells. This is understandable from the mainly cortical localization of these factors, since the cortex is parceled out among the blastomeres during cleavage. Under certain circumstances transformations of a regulative nature may occur, however. In *Aplysia* eggs submitted to strong centrifugal force, a physical or "physiological" isolation of blastomeres may occur, which then have a tendency to cleave as a whole egg (Peltrera, 1940). The distortion of the cortex by the elongation of the eggs in such a case may have disrupted the normal pattern.

C. Normal and Reversed Cleavage

In those species of snails in which the shell is coiled in a left-handed spiral, cleavage is the mirror image of the ordinary pattern. The same holds for the sinistral form of the otherwise dextral species, *Lymnaea peregra* (Miss G. A. Ubbels, unpublished observations). The young produced by one individual of this snail are, in general, all either dextral or sinistral, irrespective of the direction of coiling of the parent (Boycott and Diver, 1923; Boycott *et al.*, 1931; Diver and Andersson-Kottö, 1938). The same relationships are found in another pulmonate, *Laciniaria biplicata* (Degner, 1952). The explanation has been given by Sturtevant (1923). Direction of coiling (and apparently of cleavage) is due to one pair of Mendelian alleles, dextral being dominant over sinistral (in *Lymnaea peregra*) or inversely (in *Laciniaria biplicata*). The direction of coiling of a certain specimen may not be dependent on its own genotype, however, but on that of its mother: the expression of the genotype is shifted one generation. Apparently, the asymmetry of egg structure, which determines the direction of cleavage and, thereby, that of coiling, is laid down in the immature egg during oögenesis, either under the influence of its own diploid oöcyte nucleus, or of the diploid nuclei of the surrounding maternal tissues.

D. Shape and Coherence of the Blastomeres

In normal cleavage, the more or less spherical blastomeres after each division flatten against each other, with the formation of a separating interblastomeric membrane. In a calcium-free medium this flattening does not occur, and at later stages the cells lose their coherence and fall apart (Raven and Klomp, 1946; Berg, 1950). It has been shown in *Lymnaea* that calcium is essential for preserving the normal properties of the egg cortex (Raven and Mighorst, 1946; Hudig, 1946; Stalfoort, 1952). The role of calcium may be taken over by magnesium, and, to a certain extent, by lithium, but not by sodium and potassium (de Groot, 1948; Grasveld, 1949). It has been suggested that a complex colloid system in which phosphatides take part is involved. Rounding up and loss of coherence of the blastomeres has also been obtained with sperm extracts (Berg, 1950), anionic detergents (Fauré Fremiet and Mugard, 1948; Fauré Fremiet and Thaureaux, 1949), and cysteine (Rugh, 1953).

E. *Chemodifferentiation*

The oöplasmic segregation, which begins at the uncleaved stage, continues during cleavage. The substances previously accumulated at certain places in the egg now come to lie in different cells, which consequently differ in their cytoplasmic composition (see Fig. 2).

The redistribution of egg substances displaced by centrifuging (cf. Section I,E) may continue during cleavage (Raven and Bretschneider, 1942; Raven, 1946b). Some of the substances may pass directly through the cell membranes; other cell inclusions (e.g., proteid yolk) must first be mobilized in order to pass. Presumably, cortical factors are still important for controlling these displacements. The first visible deviations in *Lymnaea* eggs treated with lithium chloride concern alterations in the distribution of cytoplasmic substances (Raven, 1952).

F. *Metabolism of the Developing Egg*

Respiration begins to rise with the onset of cleavage, and shows a gradual increase during its course (Cleland, 1950; Berg and Kutsky, 1951; Sclufer, 1955; Horstmann, 1958). Rhythmic fluctuations corresponding with the cleavage cycles have been observed in *Ostrea* (Cleland, 1950) and *Lymnaea* (Geilenkirchen, 1961). At later stages the rise in respiratory rate is not uniform, periods of rapid rise alternating with horizontal parts of the curve.

The respiratory quotient (R.Q.) during cleavage remains at a value of about 0.8–0.85 in *Ostrea* (Cleland, 1950) and *Aplysia* (Buglia, 1908). In *Spisula* it rises from about 0.7 after fertilization toward unity (Sclufer, 1955). On the other hand, the mean value of the R.Q. in *Lymnaea* is 1.05 during early stages (Baldwin, 1935). This is explained by the fact that in this species fat is synthesized at the expense of carbohydrate (Baldwin, 1935; Horstmann, 1956a,b, 1958).

At later cleavage stages all superficial cells of the eggs of various pulmonates begin to ingest the surrounding egg-capsule fluid, which is laid down in the cells in special albumen vacuoles (Meisenheimer, 1896; Holmes, 1900; Raven, 1946a). The uptake in *Lymnaea* takes place by pinocytosis (Elbers and Bluemink, 1960). The egg-capsule fluid consists in large part of carbohydrate, mainly galactogen. This is partly oxidized, but a great proportion is converted into fat (Horstmann, 1956a,b, 1958). Carbohydrate breakdown probably takes place along the Embden-Meyerhof pathway. In addition, the embryos contain all enzymes of the pentose-phosphate cycle (Horstmann, 1960a,b).

Interesting comparisons of the metabolic activity of various blasto-meres have been made in eggs possessing a polar lobe, especially in *Mytilus*. In view of the great morphogenetic significance of the polar lobe substance (cf. Section IV,B) one might expect its metabolic activity to be high. This appears by no means to be the case. The oxygen consumption per unit volume is lower in *CD* than in *AB*, and lower in the isolated polar lobe than in the whole egg (Berg and Kutsky, 1951). No differences in dipeptidase activity between different cells, or between polar lobe and egg, were observed either in *Mytilus* (Berg, 1954a) or in *Ilyanassa* (Collier, 1957). The uptake of radioactive phosphorus in the form of phosphate is lower in the isolated polar lobe and the *D*-blastomere than in *AB* and *C* (Berg, 1954b; Berg and Prescott, 1958). The incorporation of glycine-C^{14}, adenine-C^{14} and methionine-S^{35} in the isolated polar lobe is lower than in the rest of the egg; in the intact egg there is no difference between *AB* and *CD* (Abd-el-Wahab and Pantelouris, 1957). On the other hand, removal of the polar lobe in *Ilyanassa* leads to a retardation and reduction of protein synthesis in the lobeless embryo at later stages (Collier, 1961).

III. GASTRULATION

Gastrulation in molluscs may take place by invagination, or by epiboly, or by a combination of the two. The blastopore is originally situated in the center of the vegetal hemisphere, but is later displaced toward the ventral side. The stomodaeum is formed at a point corresponding with the final position of the blastopore. Only in *Viviparus* does the blastopore remain at the posterior end of the embryo where it becomes the anus. The mesoderm originates from two mesodermal teloblasts, which are derived from the daughter cells of 4*d*.

A. Gastrulation in Partial Embryos

Gastrulation may occur in partial embryos derived from isolated blasto-meres *AB, CD, A, B, C,* or *D* (Crampton, 1896; Wilson, 1904a,b; Clement, 1952, 1956; Rattenbury and Berg, 1954). Micromeres isolated at the eight-cell stage do not gastrulate, but macromeres do. Removal of the polar lobe at early cleavage does not prevent gastrulation. Both animal and vegetal fragments of unfertilized eggs of *Dentalium* give rise to gastrulating embryos.

On the other hand, the polar lobe substance is essential for mesoderm formation: while *CD*-embryos of *Dentalium*, *Ilyanassa*, and *Mytilus* possess mesoderm, *AB*-embryos do not. Removal of the polar lobe prevents the formation of the mesoderm bands.

Half-embryos from isolated blastomeres of *Bithynia* and *Lymnaea* may occasionally gastrulate, but mostly they exhibit exogastrulation (Hess, 1956a, 1957).

B. Exogastrulation

Exogastrulation in molluscs has been observed in *Lymnaea* eggs treated at early stages with lithium chloride (Raven, 1942). Invagination of the archenteron was suppressed, and vesicular or dumbbell-shaped embryos were formed. Some cellular differentiation takes place in these embryos, which then die (Raven, 1952). The production of exogastrulae by this means is restricted to an early period of cleavage, during which there are regular changes in sensitivity (Raven *et al.*, 1947; Raven and Rijven, 1948; Raven and Burgers, 1952; Geilenkirchen, 1952a; E. D. Nijenhuis, unpublished observations). Exogastrulation may also occur after treatment with other cations, but much less frequently and only at higher concentrations (Raven and Simons, 1948; Raven *et al.*, 1956). After treatment with various combinations of salts, positive and negative interactions between them become apparent (Elbers, 1952; de Vries, 1953; Haye and Raven, 1953; Raven *et al.*, 1956; Raven, 1957): in particular, calcium ions at certain concentrations entirely suppress the effect of lithium.

Exogastrulation may also occur after treatment with KCN or reduced oxygen pressure (Geilenkirchen, 1952b; Haye and Raven, 1953; Raven and Mooy, 1954). While these exogastrulae are similar to those produced by lithium (Raven and van Rijckevorsel, 1953), exogastrulae from eggs exposed to a heat shock (Visschedijk, 1953) are much more disturbed in their histological differentiation (Raven *et al.*, 1955).

Exogastrulation may occur after centrifugation of the eggs, especially when it takes place just before third cleavage (Raven and van Egmond, 1951; Raven and Koevoets, 1952; Paris, 1953; Raven and Tates, 1961).

Exogastrulation has also been produced in other snails by lithium or lack of oxygen (Hess, 1956b) and by sodium azide (Mancuso, 1955; Attardo, 1955).

The occurrence of exogastrulation in centrifuged eggs points to the importance of oöplasmic segregation for normal gastrulation. The fact that centrifugation is most effective when it takes place immediately prior to the formation of the first micromere quartette at a stage when very considerable cytoplasmic displacements occur in *Lymnaea*, speaks strongly in favor of this view. In Raven and Tates' experiments the percentage of exogastrulae rises regularly from 6% in eggs centrifuged 60 minutes before third cleavage, to 67% in eggs centrifuged immediately before the onset of this cleavage, dropping again to 16% as soon as the cleavage furrows have appeared. The differential distribution of substances between the animal and vegetal cells of the embryo effected by this cleavage apparently is a prerequisite for the normal course of gastrulation.

The effect of treatments which upset the normal course of respiration (anaerobiosis, cyanide, azide, perhaps also heat shock) and affect development may be explained by the assumption that the normal course of oöplasmic segregation is dependent on energy potentials generated by respiration. Moreover, as oöplasmic segregation is controlled by cortical factors (cf. Section I,E), agents influencing the properties of the egg cortex may produce exogastrulation. This holds for lithium and other ions, perhaps also for heat shock treatment (Raven and van Erkel, 1955). The peak of sensitivity of the *Lymnaea* egg for the production of exogastrulae by lithium is, at most, half an hour before the phase of intensive protoplasmic shifting. This argues strongly for a connection between the two. Whether lithium has, in addition, a direct harmful effect on the vegetal material of the egg (Raven, 1952; Geilenkirchen and Nijenhuis, 1959) is not yet entirely clear.

IV. EMBRYOGENESIS

In most groups of molluscs, development is indirect. The first larval stage is the trochophore, which may later transform into a veliger. This metamorphoses after some time, and acquires the adult structure. A divergent larval type, the glochidium, is found in the Unionidae among the Bivalvia. Moreover, the larval stages may be more or less suppressed when a part, or even the whole, period of development is passed within the egg capsules or in a brood pouch.

The trochophore is divided by a band of cilia, the prototroch, into a pretrochal and posttrochal region. The pretrochal part may bear a tuft of apical flagellae. Two small-celled cephalic plates give rise to the cerebral ganglia, eyes, and tentacles; they are separated by a median apical plate. In the posttrochal region, the dorsal side bears the shell gland, while the stomodaeum and foot are situated on its ventral side. The anus breaks through later at its posterior end. The paired mesoderm bands lie also in the posttrochal part of the body.

A. *The Theory of Mosaic Development*

Experiments on the development of isolated blastomeres—for example, those of Wilson (1904b) on *Patella*—led to the view that the eggs of molluscs belong to the "mosaic eggs," in which the fate of the various parts of the germ is definitely and irrevocably determined at an early stage. Isolated blastomeres on further development form just those parts which they would have produced in the normal embryo. This was explained by assuming that the cytoplasm of the uncleaved egg is a mosaic of "organ-forming substances," which are divided during cleavage in a passive way among the blastomeres.

When molluscan eggs are centrifuged at the uncleaved stage, the arrangement of egg substances is greatly modified. Nevertheless, a great percentage of normal embryos may develop, even from eggs in which the distribution of the egg substances among the cleavage cells is quite abnormal (Morgan, 1910; Conklin, 1910; Peltrera, 1940; Raven and Bretschneider, 1942). This was originally explained by the assumption that the visible inclusions of the egg are only indifferent building and food materials, while the "organ-forming substances" proper are not displaced by centrifugal force. However, this explanation could hardly be upheld when it was shown by cytochemical methods that various substances which are important for cell metabolism, like enzymes and vitamins, are also accumulated in layers during centrifuging (Ries, 1938; Peltrera, 1940; Raven and Bretschneider, 1942), and that this does not prevent a normal development of these eggs.

Still greater difficulties for the hypothesis of mosaic development arose from the fact that egg fragments, lacking part of the substances, may develop to more or less normal, harmoniously built dwarf larvae (Clement, 1938; Costello, 1939; Peltrera, 1940). Moreover, double monsters may sometimes develop from compressed or centrifuged eggs (Tyler, 1930; Peltrera, 1940).

It is clear from these experiments that the hypothesis of organ-forming substances in its original form is untenable. Cellular determination is not due merely to a passive distribution among the cells of a substance mosaic already present in the uncleaved egg. The substances which are important for the determination of the cells are not prelocalized in the uncleaved egg, but they are shunted into the right cells by a system of directed displacements in the course of development.

B. *Germinal Localization*

Both at the uncleaved stage and during cleavage regular displacements and local accumulations of cytoplasmic substances take place (cf. Sections

I,E and II,E). These processes are important for the determination of the cells.

Several authors (Crampton, 1896; Wilson, 1904a; Clement, 1952, 1956; Rattenbury and Berg, 1954) have experimented on eggs possessing a distinct polar lobe. When the larger blastomere *CD*, containing the whole of the polar lobe substance, is isolated at the 2-cell stage in such eggs, it may develop to a more or less normal larva. The smaller blastomere *AB*, on the other hand, which is devoid of polar lobe substance, becomes a defective larva; it lacks the apical tuft, and the posttrochal part of the body is either lacking entirely, or its main organs (shell gland, foot, stomodaeum) do not develop (Fig. 5). After isolation at the 4-cell stage the cells *A*, *B*, and

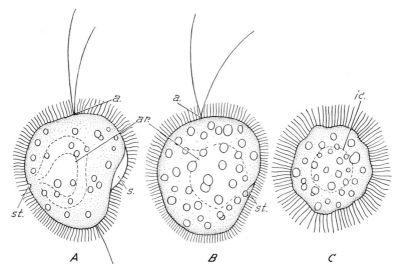

FIG. 5. Trochophore stages of *Mytilus edulis* at 24 hours. (*A*) From a whole egg. (*B*) From an isolated *CD*-blastomere. (*C*) From an isolated *AB*-blastomere. *a*, apical tuft; *ar*, archenteron; *ic*, internal cavity; *s*, shell; *st*, stomodaeum. After Rattenbury and Berg (1954).

C produce partial larvae resembling those from *AB; D* behaves more like *CD*, forming a more or less complete trochophore. Removal of the polar lobe from whole eggs at first cleavage results in larvae without apical tuft and with defective or undifferentiated posttrochal region. If the lobe is cut off at second cleavage, the results are nearly the same, but now the larva as a rule possesses an apical tuft.

It may be concluded from these experiments that the formation of the posttrochal body region (or, in other species, the differentiation of its main organs) is dependent on a substance, which is localized in the first polar lobe, passes with the latter into *CD*, is again present in the second lobe, and finally in *D*. The formation of the apical tuft is controlled by a substance present in the first polar lobe and *CD*, but not in the second lobe. For other organs, as the velum or stomodaeum, still other determining factors were found. Apparently, a number of different cytoplasmic substances, preformed in the uncleaved egg, are reshuffled during early development, partly by means of the mechanism of unequal cleavage with polar lobe formation, partly by displacements in the interval between cleavages.

We have seen above (Section IV,A) that eggs moderately centrifuged at the uncleaved stage usually give rise to normal embryos. Centrifugation at later stages is often more injurious, however; many abnormal embryos are produced in this way (Clement, 1938; Raven and van Egmond, 1951). This is probably due to increasing segregation and decreasing possibilities of readjustment of the egg substances. Centrifuging immediately prior to second or third cleavage is especially harmful. If batches of *Lymnaea* eggs are centrifuged at regular intervals during the last hour before third cleavage, the number of normal embryos per batch decreases from 74 to 9%, then rises sharply again to 73% as soon as the cleavage furrows have been formed (Raven and Tates, 1961). A characteristic effect was observed by Raven and Beenakkers (1955) in embryos from such eggs consisting in the formation of a supernumerary cephalic plate in an abnormal location. This result may be explained by the assumption that the differentiation of a cephalic plate depends on egg substances which are displaced by centrifugal force.

In summary, these experiments show that in many cases the differentiation of certain regions of the embryo is dependent on the presence and localization of cytoplasmic substances contained in the egg. Such substances may be called "morphogenetic substances." This does not mean that the presence of a single substance is in itself a sufficient cause for the differentiation of a certain organ. Apparently, as a rule quantitative relationships are involved, a certain proportion of various cytoplasmic substances being required for development of the cells in one direction, while another ratio of the amounts of the same substances gives rise to another type of differentiation. The importance of such "histochemical equilibria" is clearly indicated, for instance, by Peltrera's (1940) experiments on the development of egg fragments and isolated blastomeres of centrifuged *Aplysia* eggs.

C. The Cortical Field

The directed displacements of egg substances during early development must be controlled by a system of directing factors. Centrifugation experiments have shown that this system remains intact in moderately centrifuged eggs. We have concluded (Section I,E) that it is probably bound to the egg cortex.

By very strong ultracentrifugation, using centrifugal forces up to 100,000 times gravity or more, it is perhaps possible to deform the cortical field, in this way causing deviations in development (Costello, 1939; Pease, 1940; Peltrera, 1940).

Deformations of the cortical field have also been produced by chemical agents. Ranzi (1928a) treated *Loligo* eggs with lithium, and obtained malformations of various kinds, many of which belonged to the cyclocephalic series: synophthalmia, cyclopia, anophthalmia, acephaly. Similar cyclocephalic embryos were obtained from *Lymnaea* eggs treated with lithium (Raven, 1942). Such embryos show a characteristic syndrome of malformations. The cephalic plates are connected by small-celled ectoderm across the mid-line. In this unpaired field of small-celled ectoderm the eyes and tentacles approach each other or are fused in the mid-line. The left and right cerebral ganglia are often fused, and the cerebral commissure is shortened (Raven, 1949). The differentiation of the velum and head vesicle is often suppressed. No characteristic defects in the mesodermal and endodermal organs are found. It was concluded that the effect of the treatment consisted in a suppression of the differentiation of the ectoderm, being most pronounced at the animal pole, and decreasing with increasing distance from this pole.

This view was corroborated by a study of exogastrulae produced by lithium treatment (Raven, 1952). Three types of exogastrulae could be distinguished, possessing either two, one, or no small-celled cephalic plates in the ectodermal hemisphere. The study pointed to a progressive suppression of animal differentiation under the influence of lithium.

In exogastrulae produced by centrifugation this effect does not occur; they always possess two cephalic plates (Paris, 1953). Moreover, the pattern of head organs in embryos from centrifuged eggs is relatively undisturbed; cyclocephalic malformations do not occur (Raven and Beenakkers, 1955). A combination of centrifugation and lithium treatment gives a summation, not an interaction between the effects of the two treatments (Raven and Koevoets, 1952).

From these experiments the conclusion was drawn that lithium acts directly on the cortical field, and that this field has the character of a gradient field, a certain property having its maximum value at the animal pole, and decreasing gradually from this point. The pattern of differentiation is dependent on this field, each type of cellular differentiation corresponding to a certain range of values of the field factor. Lithium treatment leads to a weakening of the field, so that the pattern of differentiation is shifted toward the animal pole, while its median parts drop out.

This view received strong support when it was found that heat shock treatment of the eggs also gave rise to head malformations (Visschedijk, 1953), which in a way appeared to be the reverse of the lithium effect. The most characteristic effect of the treatment consists in the formation of a supernumerary median cephalic plate, bordered on either side by a row of apical plate cells; this plate may give rise to an eye or a tentacle (Raven et al., 1955). This was explained by the assumption that a strengthening of the animal gradient field had taken place, so that the pattern of head organs was drawn out toward the sides, while its median part was reduplicated by the formation of two new apices on either side of the midline.

The fact that $CaCl_2$ decreases the effect of a heat shock (Raven and van Erkel, 1955) supports the view that the latter acts primarily on the cortex.

The assumption that lithium and heat shock have more or less opposite effects on the cortical field was further corroborated by the fact that local organ reductions following lithium treatment at early cleavage stages occur preferentially on the left side (Raven, 1942, 1958b), while they are found mainly on the right side after a heat shock at the same stage (Raven et al., 1955). Moreover, when lithium and heat-shock treatment are combined, a statistically significant decrease in the frequency of the characteristic lithium effects occurs (S. C. M. Schouten, unpublished observations).

However, recent (unpublished) observations by N. H. Verdonk have thrown doubt on the correctness of the original interpretation. He has studied the cell-lineage of normal, lithium- and heat-shock-treated embryos of Lymnaea, and has found no indications of the presumed distortions of the head pattern. The connection between the cephalic plates of both sides by a bridge of small ectoderm cells in lithium-treated embryos seems rather to occur by exaggerated cell division in the region behind the animal pole normally occupied by the anterior part of the head vesicle. The formation of a supernumerary median cephalic plate, as previously found in heat-shock embryos, is apparently due to a similar, but somewhat differently located process. Eyes and tentacles may differentiate at various places within these areas of small ectoderm, either laterally or medially. Although a consistent interpretation of the results cannot yet be given, they seem to indicate that the determination of the head pattern cannot be explained simply by purely quantitative differences of a gradient character. Presumably, the structure of the cortical field is more complex.

In Loligo cyclopic embryos are produced only if the eggs are transferred to lithium solutions at or before the stage with 170 blastomeres; synophthalmic embryos may still be provoked at a somewhat later stage (Ranzi, 1928a). In Lymnaea cyclocephalic malformations may be caused by lithium treatment from the beginning of cleavage until the 54-cell stage (Raven *et al.*, 1947; Raven and Rijven, 1948; Raven, 1952; Verdonk, unpublished observations). The eggs are probably most susceptible in the middle of the 4-cell stage (Raven and Burgers, 1952). Susceptibility fluctuates rhythmically with the cleavage cycles (Raven *et al.*, 1947; E. D. Nijenhuis, unpublished observations).

Anaerobiosis may produce similar effects as lithium in *Lymnaea* (Raven and van Rijckevorsel, 1953). Mancuso (1955, 1956) obtained head malformations in *Physa* by treating eggs with sodium azide.

An extensive investigation on the action of various ions on the *Lymnaea* egg (Raven *et al.*, 1956) showed that the typical cyclocephalic malformations are almost specific lithium effects. Only sporadically can similar malformations be produced by CsCl and CaCl$_2$. Calcium (de Vries, 1953) and cyanide (Haye and Raven, 1953) at certain concentrations may entirely suppress the effect of lithium. Sodium and rubidium are strongly, cesium weakly antagonistic to lithium; potassium proved to be neutral or slightly synergistic (Elbers, 1952; Raven *et al.*, 1956). From the "action spectrum" of various cations it was concluded that head malformations are caused by an action on a phosphate colloid.

This conclusion was strongly corroborated by a further detailed study of the ionic interactions playing a part in these processes (Raven, 1957). This has led to the following view (Raven *et al.*, 1956; Geilenkirchen, 1961). The layer which carries the cortical field in the *Lymnaea* egg (and which, in the absence of evidence to the contrary, may perhaps be identified with the double plasma membrane observed by Elbers, cf. Section I,E) consists of a complex colloid composed of proteins, phosphatides, and, probably, ribonucleic acid (the latter has been demonstrated by histochemical methods). Calcium ions, adsorbed to this complex, are important for maintaining its stability and physiological properties. Electrolytes in the surrounding medium may act on this system in various ways. First, they may change the electrical charge on the membrane; this influences in its turn the mutual electrical attractions of the colloid particles, and thereby the mechanical and physiological properties of the membrane. Second, an exchange of calcium ions of the membrane with other cations in the medium may occur. Up to a certain point, the latter may replace the calcium ions without altering the physiological properties of the membrane. When a certain proportion of the calcium ions has been exchanged, however, further substitution may entail definite changes of the cortical membrane which may be incompatible with normal development, and lead, in increasing order of gravity, to malformations of the pattern of development, to exogastrulation, or to death.

If this superficial plasma membrane is to be the carrier of the cortical field, it must be assumed that it shows variations in its structure or composition in different egg regions, resulting in a more or less stable two-dimensional pattern of its physiological properties (cf. Elbers, 1959). These variations may be continuous, according to a gradient, but also discontinuous, in a mosaic fashion, or a combination of both. Moreover, in addition to variations in space along the surface of the egg, variations in time, in the course of early development, may be considered. Each point within the field is characterized at any moment of development by a certain constellation of properties and may influence the underlying cytoplasm in a variety of ways: either by differential permeability, by exerting local attractions or repulsions (e.g., of an electrostatic nature) upon certain cytoplasmic components, or by any other kind of "resonance relationship" between cortex and cytoplasm. If the ribonucleic acid demonstrated in the cortex is also bound to this layer, then even the possibility of differential protein synthesis along the surface should be considered. However this may be, it would seem that the structure of the plasma membrane presumed above could fulfill the demands to be made on an organelle having a general coordinating and integrating function in the development of the egg cell.

D. The Determination of Organ Development

Embryos of *Lymnaea* which have exogastrulated following lithium treatment (cf. Section III,B) exhibit a certain degree of cellular differentiation (Raven, 1952). In general, an ectodermal hemisphere, an endodermal hemisphere, and an intermediate "marginal zone" may be distinguished.

In the ectodermal hemisphere as a rule a large-celled and a small-celled part can be observed. The large-celled ectoderm represents the velum, head vesicle, and apical plate of normal embryos. These cells often show a good differentiation, partly into ciliary cells corresponding to those found in the velum and apical plate of normal embryos. The small-celled ectoderm represents the cephalic plates; its cells remain more or less undifferentiated.

In the endodermal hemisphere, as well, large- and small-celled regions are found. The large-celled endoderm corresponds to the "albumen cells," forming the larval livers of the embryo. They attain a fair degree of differentiation, showing apocrine secretion and uptake of egg-capsule fluid which is laid down in the cells in large "albumen vacuoles." The small-celled endoderm, representing the primordium of mid-gut and hind-gut, remains undifferentiated.

The marginal zone develops from an equatorial girdle of cells surrounding the blastopore in normal embryos. It contains the primordia of the posttrochal ectoderm and the mesoderm. Most of this part remains undifferentiated. Sometimes a stomodaeal invagination may be formed, at the bottom of which the esophagus anlage shows a beginning differentiation. In the mesoderm in some instances a more or less atypical protonephridium may be formed.

It is clear, therefore, that a certain degree of histological differentiation has taken place in exogastrulae, but it has stopped at an early stage. Moreover, it is mainly restricted to larval differentiations (ciliary cells, albumen cells, protonephridium). The adult types of tissue differentiation do not occur, and such adult organs as gut, radular sac, shell anlage, nervous system, and sense organs have never been found in exogastrulae.

We may conclude that the primary chemodifferentiation under the control of the cortical field occurring at early stages of development, besides laying down the general pattern of the embryo in broad outline, forms a sufficient cause for larval differentiations. Both organogenesis and histogenesis of adult organs require the intervention of new causal factors which are lacking when gastrulation does not occur. Presumably, these factors make their appearance during gastrulation, probably in consequence of the displacements of cells taking place at this time. On the other hand, it could be concluded from a study of abnormal *Lymnaea* embryos produced by various treatments that the determination of the organs of the head is about completed at an early trochophore stage (Raven, 1958b).

Occasionally, in *Lymnaea* eggs treated with lithium, the invagination of the archenteron does occur in a more or less abnormal way, part of the presumptive endoderm remaining at the surface. In such embryos protonephridia are formed much more frequently than in true exogastrulae; sometimes paired protonephridia develop. Moreover, in a great number of cases a shell gland is formed. It is always situated at a place where the tip of the archenteron touches the inner side of the ectoderm. In those cases where the archenteron has grown inward in an abnormal direction, its tip may come into contact with the inner side of the pretrochal part of the ectoderm; then a shell gland may even develop in this abnormal location (Fig. 6). It has been concluded that the formation of the shell gland is due to an inductive action exerted by the tip of the archenteron on the ectoderm with which it makes contact (Raven, 1952). Observations by Hess (1957) indicate that perhaps even a few endoderm cells suffice for induction.

The supposition that the formation of the shell gland in gastropods generally is due to contact induction by the invaginated endoderm has been corroborated by observations of Hess (1956a,b) in *Bithynia*. In exogastrulae of this species a delayed invagination of part of the endoderm takes place, apparently corresponding to the formation of the larval liver in normal embryos. Then a shell gland may be formed at the place of contact between endoderm and ectoderm. In normal embryos of

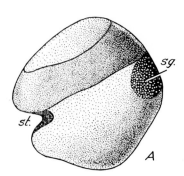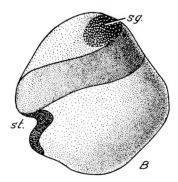

Fig. 6. Diagram of the position of the shell gland, induced by the invaginated archenteron in abnormal embryos of *Lymnaea stagnalis*. (*A*) Posttrochal. (*B*) Pretrochal. *sg*, shell gland; *st*, stomodaeum.

Bithynia a shell gland appears after 3 days, but in exogastrulae only after 6–7 days, when the endodermal invagination has occurred. While the shell gland in normal development is a derivative of the *D*-quadrant, after isolation at the 2-cell stage both *AB*- and *CD*-embryos are able to form a shell gland. It may be concluded that shell gland formation in *Bithynia* is also due to contact induction.

We may conjecture that induction phenomena play an important part in the processes of organogenesis. Unfortunately, the experimental evidence in this field is extremely scanty. Some observations by Ranzi (1928a,b) may be mentioned. He found that the development of the optic ganglion in cephalopods is dependent on the presence of the eye and that the statocyst influences the pedal ganglion in a similar way.

References

Abd-el-Wahab, A. (1957). Influence of the antimitotic naphthoquinone on the cleavage of the eggs of the mollusc, *Mytilus edulis* L. *Wilhelm Roux' Arch. Entwicklungsmech. Organ.* **149**, 613.

Abd-el-Wahab, A. (1958). Influence of the antimitotic phenanthrenequinone on the cleavage of the eggs of the mollusc, *Mytilus edulis* L. *Wilhelm Roux' Arch. Entwicklungsmech. Organ.* **150**, 481.

Abd-el-Wahab, A., and Pantelouris, E. M. (1957). Synthetic processes in nucleated and non-nucleated parts of *Mytilus* eggs. *Exptl. Cell Research* **13**, 78.

Allen, R. D. (1953). Fertilization and artificial activation in the egg of the surf-clam, *Spisula solidissima*. *Biol. Bull.* **105**, 213.

Attardo, C. (1955). Effetti dell' azide sodico sulle uova di *Bithynia codiella*. *Atti accad. nazl. Lincei, Rend. Classe sci. fis. mat. e nat.* [8] **19**, 83.

Baldwin, E. (1935). The energy sources in ontogenesis. VIII. The respiratory quotient of developing gastropod eggs. *J. Exptl. Biol.* **12**, 27.

Ballentine, R. (1940). Analysis of the changes in respiratory activity accompanying the fertilization of marine eggs. *J. Cellular Comp. Physiol.* **15**, 217.

Berg, W. E. (1950). Lytic effects of sperm extracts on the eggs of *Mytilus edulis*. *Biol. Bull.* **98**, 128.

Berg, W. E. (1954a). Peptidases in isolated blastomeres of *Mytilus edulis*. *Proc. Soc. Exptl. Biol. Med.* **85**, 606.

Berg, W. E. (1954b). Investigations of cytoplasmic determination in mosaic eggs. Cellular biology. *Proc. 15th Ann. Biol. Colloquium Corvallis, Oregon, 1954*, p. 30.

Berg, W. E., and Kutsky, P. B. (1951). Physiological studies of differentiation in *Mytilus edulis*. I. The oxygen consumption of isolated blastomeres and polar lobes. *Biol. Bull.* **101**, 47.

Berg, W. E., and Prescott, D. M. (1958). Physiological studies of differentiation in *Mytilus edulis*. II. Accumulation of phosphate in isolated blastomeres and polar lobes. *Exptl. Cell Research* **14**, 402.

Boycott, A. E., and Diver, C. (1923). On the inheritance of sinistrality in *Limnaea peregra*. *Proc. Roy. Soc.* **B95**, 207.

Boycott, A. E., Diver, C., Garstang, S. L., and Turner, F. M. (1931). The inheritance of sinistrality in *Limnaea peregra* (Mollusca, Pulmonata). *Phil. Trans. Roy. Soc.* **B219**, 51.

Browne, E. N. (1910). Effects of pressure on *Cumingia* eggs. *Wilhelm Roux' Arch. Entwicklungsmech. Organ*, **29**, 243.

Buglia, G. (1908). Sullo scambio gassoso delle uova di *Aplysia limacina* nei vari periodi dello sviluppo. *Arch. fisiol.* **5**, 455.

Cleland, K. W. (1950). Respiration and cell division in developing oyster eggs. *Proc. Linnean Soc. N. S. Wales* **75**, 282.

Clement, A. C. (1935). The formation of giant polar bodies in centrifuged eggs of *Ilyanassa*. *Biol. Bull.* **69**, 403.

Clement, A. C. (1938). The structure and development of centrifuged eggs and egg fragments of *Physa heterostropha*. *J. Exptl. Zool.* **79**, 435.

Clement, A. C. (1952). Experimental studies on germinal localization in *Ilyanassa*. I. The role of the polar lobe in determination of the cleavage pattern and its influence in later development. *J. Exptl. Zool.* **121**, 593.

Clement, A. C. (1956). Experimental studies on germinal localization in *Ilyanassa*. II. The development of isolated blastomeres. *J. Exptl. Zool.* **132**, 427.

Collier, J. R. (1957). A study of the alanylglycine dipeptidase activity during the development of *Ilyanassa obsoleta*. *Embryologia* **3**, 243.

Collier, J. R. (1961). The effect of removing the polar lobe on the protein synthesis of the embryo of *Ilyanassa obsoleta*. *Acta Embryol. Morphol. Exptl.* **4**, 70.

Conklin, E. G. (1910). The effects of centrifugal force upon the organization and development of the eggs of fresh water pulmonates. *J. Exptl. Zool.* **9**, 417.

Conklin, E. G. (1912). Experimental studies in nuclear and cell division in the eggs of *Crepidula plana*. *J. Acad. Nat. Sci. Philadelphia* **15**, 501.

Conklin, E. G. (1917). Effects of centrifugal force on the structure and development of the eggs of *Crepidula*. *J. Exptl. Zool.* **22**, 311.

Conklin, E. G. (1938). Disorientations of development in *Crepidula plana* produced by low temperatures. *Proc. Am. Phil. Soc.* **79**, 179.

Costello, D. P. (1939). Some effects of centrifuging the eggs of nudibranchs. *J. Exptl. Zool.* **80**, 473.

Costello, D. P. (1945). Segregation of oöplasmic constituents. *J. Elisha Mitchell Sci. Soc.* **61**, 277.

Crampton, H. E. (1896). Experimental studies on gastropod development. *Wilhelm Roux' Arch. Entwicklungsmech. Organ.* **3**, 1.

Dalcq, A. (1928). Le rôle du calcium et du potassium dans l'entrée en maturation de l'oeuf de pholade (*Barnea candida*). *Protoplasma* **4**, 18.

Dan, J. C., and Wada, S. K. (1955). Studies on the acrosome. IV. The acrosome reaction in some bivalve spermatozoa. *Biol. Bull.* **109**, 40.

Degner, E. (1952). Der Erbgang der Inversion bei *Laciniaria biplicata* MTG (Gastr. Pulm.). *Mitt. Hamburg. zool. Mus.* **51**, 3.

de Groot, A. P. (1948). The influence of higher concentrations of lithium chloride on maturation and first cleavages of the egg of *Limnaea stagnalis*. *Proc. Koninkl. Ned. Akad. Wetenschap.* **51**, 588.

de Vries, L. G. (1953). The antagonistic action of calcium with respect to the effects of lithium on the development of *Limnaea stagnalis*. *Proc. Koninkl. Ned. Akad. Wetenschap.* **C56**, 584.

Diver, C., and Andersson-Kottö, I. (1938). Sinistrality in *Limnaea peregra* (Mollusca, Pulmonata). The problem of mixed broods. *J. Genet.* **35**, 447.

Elbers, P. F. (1952). On the influence of potassium ions on the lithium effect in *Limnaea stagnalis*. *Proc. Koninkl. Ned. Akad. Wetenschap.* **C55**, 74.

Elbers, P. F. (1959). "Over de beginoorzaak van het Li-effect in de morphogenese. Een electronenmicroscopisch onderzoek aan eieren van *Limnaea stagnalis* en *Paracentrotus lividus*," 59 pp. Thesis, Utrecht.

Elbers, P. F., and Bluemink, J. G. (1960). Pinocytosis in the developing egg of *Limnaea stagnalis* L. *Exptl. Cell Research* **21**, 619.

Fauré Fremiet, E., and Mugard, H. (1948). Ségrégation d'un matériel cortical au cours de la segmentation chez l'oeuf de *Teredo norvegica*. *Compt. rend. acad. sci.* **227**, 1409.

Fauré Fremiet, E., and Thaureaux, J. (1949). Effet de quelques détergents sur l'oeuf de *Teredo norvegica*. *Biochim. et Biophys. Acta* **3**, 536.

Geilenkirchen, W. L. M. (1952a). Differences in lithium effects in *Limnaea* after treatment of whole egg-masses and isolated egg capsules. *Proc. Koninkl. Ned. Akad. Wetenschap.* **C55**, 192.

Geilenkirchen, W. L. M. (1952b). The action of lithium chloride on the eggs of *Limnaea stagnalis* at different oxygen pressures. *Proc. Koninkl. Ned. Akad. Wetenschap.* **C55**, 311.

Geilenkirchen, W. L. M. (1961). "Effects of mono- and divalent cations on viability and oxygen uptake of eggs of *Limnaea stagnalis*," 96pp. Thesis, Utrecht.

Geilenkirchen, W. L. M., and Nijenhuis, E. D. (1959). The influence of lithium chloride on the development of embryos of *Limnaea stagnalis* treated during and after the gastrula stage. *Proc. Koninkl. Ned. Akad. Wetenschap.* **C62**, 214.

Grasveld, M. S. (1949). On the influence of various chlorides on maturation and cleavage of the egg of *Limnaea stagnalis* L. *Proc. Koninkl. Ned. Akad. Wetenschap.* **52**, 284.

Haye, S. C. A., and Raven, C. P. (1953). The influence of cyanide on the lithium effect in the development of *Limnaea stagnalis*. *Proc. Koninkl. Ned. Akad. Wetenschap.* **C56**, 326.

Heilbrunn, L. V. (1925). Studies in artificial parthenogenesis. IV. Heat parthenogenesis. *J. Exptl. Zool.* **41**, 243.

Hess, O. (1956a). Die Entwicklung von Halbkeimen bei dem Süsswasser-Prosobranchier *Bithynia tentaculata* L. *Wilhelm Roux' Arch. Entwicklungsmech. Organ.* **148**, 336.

Hess, O. (1956b). Die Entwicklung von Exogastrulakeimen bei dem Süsswasser-Prosobranchier *Bithynia tentaculata* L. *Wilhelm Roux' Arch. Entwicklungsmech. Organ.* **148**, 474.

Hess, O. (1957). Die Entwicklung von Halbkeimen bei dem Süsswasser-Pulmonaten *Limnaea stagnalis*. *Wilhelm Roux' Arch. Entwicklungsmech. Organ.* **150**, 124.

Hollingsworth, J. (1941). Activation of *Cumingia* and *Arbacia* eggs by bivalent cations. *Biol. Bull.* **81**, 261.

Holmes, S. J. (1900). The early development of *Planorbis*. *J. Morphol.* **16**, 369.

Horstmann, H. J. (1956a). Der Galaktogengehalt der Eier von *Lymnaea stagnalis* L. während der Embryonalentwicklung. *Biochem. Z.* **328**, 342.

Horstmann, H. J. (1956b). Der Lipidgehalt der Embryonen von *Lymnaea stagnalis* L. während ihrer Entwicklung. *Biochem. Z.* **328**, 348.

Horstmann, H. J. (1958). Sauerstoffverbrauch und Trockengewicht der Embryonen von *Limnaea stagnalis* L. *Z. vergleich. Physiol.* **41**, 390.

Horstmann, H. J. (1960a). Untersuchungen zum Stoffwechsel der Lungenschnecken. I. Glykolyse bei den Embryonen von *Lymnaea stagnalis* L. *Z. physiol. Chem.* **319**, 110.

Horstmann, H. J. (1960b). Untersuchungen zum Stoffwechsel der Lungenschnecken. II. Die Enzyme des Pentosephosphat-Cyclus bei den Embryonen von *Lymnaea stagnalis*. *Z. physiol. Chem.* **319**, 120.

Hudig, O. (1946). The vitelline membrane of *Limnaea stagnalis*. *Proc. Koninkl. Ned. Akad. Wetenschap.* **49**, 554.

Inaba, F. (1936). Studies on the artificial parthenogenesis of *Ostrea gigas* Thunberg. *J. Sci. Hirosima Univ., Ser. B1* **5**, 29.

Kostanecki, K. (1902). Ueber künstliche Befruchtung und künstliche parthenogenetische Furchung bei *Mactra*. *Bull. intern. acad. sci. Cracovie, Classe sci.* p. 363.

Kostanecki, K. (1904). Cytologische Studien an künstlich parthenogenetisch sich entwickelnden Eiern von *Mactra*. *Arch. mikroskop. Anat.* **64**, 1.

Kostanecki, K. (1908). Zur Morphologie der künstlichen parthenogenetischen Entwicklung bei *Mactra*. Zugleich ein Beitrag zur Kenntnis der vielpoligen Mitose. *Arch. mikroskop. Anat.* **72**, 327.

Krauss, M. (1950). Lytic agents of the sperm of some marine animals. I. The egg membrane lysin from sperm of the giant keyhole limpet *Megathura crenulata*. *J. Exptl. Zool.* **114**, 239.

Mancuso, V. (1955). L'azione dell'azide sodico sullo sviluppo dell'uovo di *Physa rivularis* Ph. *Riv. biol. (Perugia)* **47**, 203.

Mancuso, V. (1956). Anomalie cefaliche di *Physa rivularis* Ph. per azione dell'azide sodico. *Rend. ist. super. sanità* **19**, 247.

Meisenheimer, J. (1896). Entwicklungsgeschichte von *Limax maximus* L. I. Furchung und Keimblätterbildung. *Z. wiss. Zool.* **62**, 415.

Metz, C. B., and Donovan, J. E. (1949). Fertilizin from the eggs of the clam, *Mactra solidissima*. *Biol. Bull.* **97**, 257.

Morgan, T. H. (1910). Cytological studies of centrifuged eggs. *J. Exptl. Zool.* **9**, 593.

Morgan, T. H. (1933). The formation of the antipolar lobe in *Ilyanassa*. *J. Exptl. Zool.* **64**, 433.

Morgan, T. H. (1935a). Centrifuging the eggs of *Ilyanassa* in reverse. *Biol. Bull.* **68**, 268.

Morgan, T. H. (1935b). The separation of the egg of *Ilyanassa* into two parts by centrifuging. *Biol. Bull.* **68**, 280.

Morgan, T. H. (1936). Further experiments on the formation of the antipolar lobe of *Ilyanassa*. *J. Exptl. Zool.* **74**, 381.

Morgan, T. H. (1937). The behavior of the maturation spindles in polar fragments of *Ilyanassa* obtained by centrifuging. *Biol. Bull.* **72**, 88.

Morgan, T. H., and Tyler, A. (1930). The point of entrance of the spermatozoon in relation to the orientation of the embryo in eggs with spiral cleavage. *Biol. Bull.* **58**, 59.

Morgan, T. H., and Tyler, A. (1938). The relation between entrance point of the spermatozoon and bilaterality of the egg of *Chaetopterus*. *Biol. Bull.* **74**, 401.

Morris, M. (1917). A cytological study of artificial parthenogenesis in *Cumingia*. *J. Exptl. Zool.* **22**, 1.

Motomura, I. (1954). Parthenogenetic activation with potassium permanganate in the eggs of the bivalve and the sea urchin. *Sci. Repts. Tôhoku Univ., Fourth Ser.* **20**, 213.

Paris, A. J. (1953). Histological investigations on exogastrulae of *Limnaea stagnalis* obtained by centrifuging the eggs. *Proc. Koninkl. Ned. Akad. Wetenschap.* **C56**, 406.

Pasteels, J. (1930). Les effets de la rupture de la balance des chlorures de l'eau de mer sur l'oeuf de Pholade, *Barnea candida*. *Arch. biol. (Liège)* **40**, 247.

Pasteels, J. (1931). Recherches sur le déterminisme du mode de segmentation des Mollusques Lamellibranches (actions des rayons ultraviolets sur l'oeuf de *Barnea cand.*). *Arch. biol. (Liège)* **42**, 389.

Pasteels, J. (1934). Recherches sur la morphogénèse et le déterminisme des segmentations inégales chez les Spiralia. *Arch. anat. microscop. morphol. exptl.* **30**, 161.

Pasteels, J. (1938a). Le rôle du calcium dans l'activation de l'oeuf de pholade. *Trav. sta. zool. Wimereux* **13**, 515.

Pasteels, J. (1938b). Sensibilisateurs et réalisateur dans l'activation de l'oeuf de *Barnea candida*. *Bull. acad. roy. Belg., Classe sci.* [5] **24**, 721.

Pasteels, J. (1950). Mouvements localisés et rhythmiques de la membrane de fécondation chez des oeufs fécondés ou activés (*Chaetopterus, Mactra, Nereis*). *Arch. biol. (Liège)* **61**, 197.

Pasteels, J., and Mulnard, J. (1957). La métachromasie in vivo au bleu de toluidine et son analyse cytochimique dans les oeufs de *Barnea candida, Gryphaea angulata* (Lamellibranches) et de *Psammechinus miliaris*. *Arch. biol. (Liège)* **68**, 115.

Pease, D. C. (1940). The influence of centrifugal force on the bilateral determination and the polar axis of *Cumingia* and *Chaetopterus* eggs. *J. Exptl. Zool.* **84**, 387.

Peltrera, A. (1940). La capacità regolative dell'uovo di *Aplysia limacina* L. studiate con la centrifugazione e con le reazioni vitali. *Pubbl. staz. zool. Napoli* **18**, 20.

Ranzi, S. (1928a). Suscettibilità differenziale nello sviluppo dei Cefalopodi (Analisi sperimentale dell'embriogenesi). *Pubbl. staz. zool. Napoli* **9**, 81.

Ranzi, S. (1928b). Correlazioni tra organi di senso e centri nervosi in via di sviluppo (Ricerche di morfologia sperimentale nei Cefalopodi). *Wilhelm Roux' Arch. Entwicklungsmech. Organ.* **114**, 364.

Rattenbury, J. C., and Berg, W. E. (1954). Embryonic segregation during early development of *Mytilus edulis*. *J. Morphol.* **95**, 393.

Raven, C. P. (1938). Experimentelle Untersuchungen über die "bipolare Differenzierung" des Polychaeten- und Molluskeneies. *Acta Neerl. Morphol.* **1**, 337.

Raven, C. P. (1942). The influence of lithium upon the development of the pond snail, *Limnaea stagnalis* L. *Proc. Koninkl. Ned. Akad. Wetenschap.* **45**, 856.

Raven, C. P. (1945). The development of the egg of *Limnaea stagnalis* L. from oviposition till first cleavage. *Arch. néerl. zool.* **7**, 91.

Raven, C. P. (1946a). The development of the egg of *Limnaea stagnalis* L. from the first cleavage till the trochophore stage, with special reference to its "chemical embryology." *Arch. néerl. zool.* **7**, 353.

Raven, C. P. (1946b). The distribution of substances in eggs of *Limnaea stagnalis* L. centrifuged immediately before cleavage. *Arch. néerl. zool.* **7**, 496.

Raven, C. P. (1948). The influence of an electric field on the eggs of *Limnaea stagnalis* L. *Proc. Koninkl. Ned. Akad. Wetenschap.* **51**, 1077.

Raven, C. P. (1949). On the structure of cyclopic, synophthalmic and anophthalmic embryos, obtained by the action of lithium in *Limnaea stagnalis. Arch. néerl. Zool.* **8**, 323.

Raven, C. P. (1952). Morphogenesis in *Limnaea stagnalis* and its disturbance by lithium. *J. Exptl. Zool.* **121**, 1.

Raven, C. P. (1957). Wisselwerkingen van ionen met betrekking tot het ei van de poelslak. *Verslag Gewone Vergader. Afdel. Natuurk., Koninkl. Ned. Akad. Wetenschap.* **66**, 76.

Raven, C. P. (1958a). "Morphogenesis. The Analysis of Molluscan Development," 310pp. Pergamon Press, New York.

Raven, C. P. (1958b). Abnormal development of the foregut in *Limnaea stagnalis. J. Exptl. Zool.* **139**, 189.

Raven, C. P., and Beenakkers, A. M. T. (1955). On the nature of head malformations obtained by centrifuging the eggs of *Limnaea stagnalis. J. Embryol. Exptl. Morphol.* **3**, 286.

Raven, C. P., and Bretschneider, L. H. (1942). The effect of centrifugal force upon the eggs of *Limnaea stagnalis* L. *Arch. néerl. zool.* **6**, 255.

Raven, C. P., and Brunnekreeft, F. (1951). The formation of the animal pole plasm in centrifuged eggs of *Limnaea stagnalis* L. *Proc. Koninkl. Ned. Akad. Wetenschap.* **C54**, 440.

Raven, C. P., and Burgers, A. C. J. (1952). The influence of temperature on the lithium effect in *Limnaea stagnalis. Proc. Koninkl. Ned. Akad. Wetenschap.* **C55**, 554.

Raven, C. P., and van Egmond, M. T. C. (1951). Centrifuging the eggs of *Limnaea* round about the third cleavage. *Proc. Koninkl. Ned. Akad. Wetenschap.* **C54**, 325.

Raven, C. P., and van Erkel, G. A. (1955). The influence of calcium on the effects of a heat shock in *Limnaea stagnalis. Exptl. Cell Research, Suppl.* **3**, 294.

Raven, C. P., and Hupkens van der Elst, W. (1950). The influence of hypertonicity on the eggs of *Limnaea stagnalis. Proc. Koninkl. Ned. Akad. Wetenschap.* **53**, 1005.

Raven, C. P., and Klomp, H. (1946). The osmotic properties of the egg of *Limnaea stagnalis* L. *Proc. Koninkl. Ned. Akad. Wetenschap.* **49**, 101.

Raven, C. P., and Koevoets, T. C. M. (1952). Combined effects of lithium and centrifuging on the eggs of *Limnaea. Proc. Koninkl. Ned. Akad. Wetenschap.* **C55**, 697.

Raven, C. P., and Mighorst, J. C. A. (1946). The influence of high concentrations of $CaCl_2$ on maturation in the egg of *Limnaea stagnalis. Proc. Koninkl. Ned. Akad. Wetenschap.* **49**, 1003.

Raven, C. P., and Mooy, H. W. (1954). The influence of calcium and cyanide on the morphogenetic effects of reduced partial oxygen pressure in the development of *Limnaea stagnalis. Proc. Koninkl. Ned. Akad. Wetenschap.* **C57**, 424.

Raven, C. P., and van Rijckevorsel, F. (1953). The influence of anaerobiosis on the eggs of *Limnaea stagnalis. Proc. Koninkl. Ned. Akad. Wetenschap.* **C56**, 1.

Raven, C. P., and Rijven, A. H. G. C. (1948). Induction of head malformations in *Limnaea stagnalis* L. by lithium treatment in advanced cleavage stages. *Proc. Koninkl. Ned. Akad. Wetenschap.* **51**, 427.

Raven, C. P., and Roborgh, J. R. (1949). Direct effects of isotonic and hypotonic lithium chloride solutions on unsegmented eggs of *Limnaea stagnalis. Proc. Koninkl. Ned. Akad. Wetenschap.* **52**, 614, 773.

Raven, C. P., and Simons, M. A. (1948). On the specificity of the lithium effect on the development of *Limnaea stagnalis*. *Proc. Koninkl. Ned. Akad. Wetenschap.* **51**, 1232.

Raven, C. P., and Tates, A. D. (1961). Centrifugation of *Limnaea* eggs at stages immediately preceding third cleavage. *Proc. Koninkl. Ned. Akad. Wetenschap.* **C64**, 129.

Raven, C. P., Kloek, J. C., Kuiper, E. J., and de Jong, D. J. (1947). The influence of concentration, duration of treatment and stage of development in the lithium-effect upon the development of *Limnaea stagnalis*. *Proc. Koninkl. Ned. Akad. Wetenschap.* **50**, 584.

Raven, C. P., Bezem, J. J., and Isings, J. (1952). Changes in the size relations between macromeres and micromeres of *Limnaea stagnalis* under the influence of lithium. *Proc. Koninkl. Ned. Akad. Wetenschap.* **C55**, 248.

Raven, C. P., de Roon, A. C., and Stadhouders, A. M. (1955). Morphogenetic effects of a heat shock on the eggs of *Limnaea stagnalis*. *J. Embryol. Exptl. Morphol.* **3**, 142.

Raven, C. P. (in collaboration with Drinkwaard, A. C., Haeck, J., Verdonk, N. H., and Verhoeven, L. A.) (1956). Effects of monovalent cations on the eggs of *Limnaea*. *Pubbl. staz. zool. Napoli* **28**, 136.

Reverberi, G., and Mancuso, V. (1961). The constituents of the egg of *Mytilus* as seen at the electron microscope. *Acta Embryol. Morphol. Exptl.* **4**, 102.

Ries, E. (1937). Die Verteilung von Vitamin C, Glutathion, Benzidin-Peroxydase, Phenolase (Indophenolblauoxydase) und Leukomethylenblau-Oxydoredukase während der frühen Embryonalentwicklung verschiedener wirbelloser Tiere. *Pubbl. Staz. Zool. Napoli* **16**, 363.

Ries, E. (1938). Histochemische Untersuchungen über früh-embryonale Sonderungs-prozesse in zentrifugierten Eiern von *Aplysia*. *Biodynamica* **40**, 1.

Rugh, R. (1953). The X-irradiation of marine gametes. A study of the effects of X-irradiation at different levels on the germ cells of the clam, *Spisula* (formerly *Mactra*). *Biol. Bull.* **104**, 197.

Sawada, N. (1952). Experimental studies on the maturation division of eggs in *Mactra veneriformis*. I. Inhibitory effect of the body fluid. *Mem. Ehime Univ., Sect. II* **1**, 231.

Sawada, N. (1954a). Experimental studies on the maturation division of eggs in *Mactra veneriformis*. IV. On the effect of certain polysaccharides. *Mem. Ehime Univ., Sect. II* **B2**, 89.

Sawada, N. (1954b). Experimental studies on the maturation division of eggs in *Mactra veneriformis*. V. On the activation by periodate. *Mem. Ehime Univ., Sect. II* **B2**, 93.

Sawada, N., and Murakami, T. H. (1959). Experimental studies on the maturation division of eggs in *Mactra veneriformis*. VI. Histochemical study on eggs. *Mem. Ehime Univ., Sect. II* **3**, 235.

Schleip, W. (1925). Die Furchung dispermer Dentalium-Eier. *Wilhelm Roux' Arch. Entwicklungsmech. Organ.* **106**, 86.

Sclufer, E. (1955). The respiration of *Spisula* eggs. *Biol. Bull.* **109**, 113.

Southwick, W. E. (1939). The "agglutination" phenomenon with spermatozoa of *Chiton tuberculatus*. *Biol. Bull.* **77**, 157.

Spek, J. (1934). Die bipolare Differenzierung des Cephalopoden- und des Proso-branchiereies. *Wilhelm Roux' Arch. Entwicklungsmech. Organ.* **131**, 362.

Stalfoort, T. G. J. (1952). On the influence of Na-oxalate and Na-citrate on matura-tion and cleavage of the egg of *Limnaea stagnalis* L. *Proc. Koninkl. Ned. Akad. Wetenschap.* **C55**, 184.

Sturtevant, A. H. (1923). Inheritance of direction of coiling in *Limnaea*. *Science* **58**, 269.

Tchakhotine, S. (1935). La parthénogénèse artificielle de l'oeuf de la pholade, par micropuncture ultraviolette. *Compt. rend. soc. biol.* **119**, 1394.

Tyler, A. (1930). Experimental production of double embryos in annelids and molluscs. *J. Exptl. Zool.* **57**, 347.

Tyler, A. (1939). Extraction of an egg membrane-lysin from sperm of the giant keyhole limpet (*Megathura crenulata*). *Proc. Natl. Acad. Sci. U.S.* **25**, 317.

Tyler, A. (1940). Sperm agglutination in the keyhole limpet, *Megathura crenulata*. *Biol. Bull.* **78**, 159.

Tyler, A. (1949a). Fertilization and immunity. *Physiol. Revs.* **28**, 180.

Tyler, A. (1949b). Properties of fertilizin and related substances of eggs and sperm of marine animals. *Am. Naturalist* **83**, 195.

Tyler, A., and Fox, S. W. (1939). Sperm agglutination in the keyhole limpet and the sea urchin. *Science* **90**, 516.

Tyler, A., and Fox, S. W. (1940). Evidence for the protein nature of the sperm agglutinins of the keyhole limpet and the sea-urchin. *Biol. Bull.* **79**, 153.

Tyler, A., and Scheer, B. T. (1937). Inhibition of fertilization in eggs of marine animals by means of acid. *J. Exptl. Zool.* **75**, 179.

Visschedijk, A. H. J. (1953). The effect of a heat shock on morphogenesis in *Limnaea stagnalis*. *Proc. Koninkl. Ned. Akad. Wetenschap.* **C56**, 590.

von Medem, F. (1942). Beiträge zur Frage der Befruchtungsstoffe bei marinen Mollusken. *Biol. Zentr.* **62**, 431.

von Medem, F. (1945). Untersuchungen über die Ei- und Spermawirkstoffe bei marinen Mollusken. *Zool. Jahrb., Abt. allgem. Zool. u. Physiol. Tiere* **61**, 1.

Wada, S. K., Collier, J. R., and Dan, J. C. (1956). Studies on the acrosome. V. An egg-membrane lysin from the acrosomes of *Mytilus edulis* spermatozoa. *Exptl. Cell Research* **10**, 168.

Whitaker, D. M. (1933). On the rate of oxygen consumption by fertilised and un-fertilised eggs. *J. Gen. Physiol.* **16**, 475, 497.

Wilson, E. B. (1904a). Experimental studies on germinal localization. I. The germ-regions in the egg of *Dentalium*. *J. Exptl. Zool.* **1**, 1.

Wilson, E. B. (1904b). Experimental studies on germinal localization. II. Experiments on the cleavage-mosaic in *Patella* and *Dentalium*. *J. Exptl. Zool.* **1**, 197.

Yasugi, R. (1938). On the mode of cleavage of the eggs of the oysters *Ostrea spinosa* and *O. gigas* under experimental conditions (a preliminary note). *Annotationes Zool. Japon.* **17**, 295.

CHAPTER 6

The Culture of Marine Bivalve Larvae

P. R. WALNE

FISHERIES EXPERIMENT STATION, CONWAY, NORTH WALES

I. INTRODUCTION

The culture of the larvae of some bivalve species, all marine, has received considerable detailed attention because of their commercial value. For many years *Ostrea* and *Crassostrea* have been studied, while more recently the investigations have been widened to include other species, in particular *Venus mercenaria*. Since these investigations have been confined to commercially important species from shallow waters in the temperate zone, the cultural requirements of tropical, arctic, or offshore forms remain unknown.

Culture experiments fall into two main types: (*1*) those which are made in outdoor tanks or seminatural ponds and particularly directed toward commercial exploitation, and (*2*) those made under laboratory or hatchery conditions with more precise control. These latter experiments are suitable for elucidating the food and physical requirements of the larvae.

II. CULTURE IN PONDS AND OUTDOOR TANKS

Natural ponds 200–300 meters in diameter have been used for many years in Norway for the commercial production of *Ostrea edulis*. Their entrances to the sea are closed in the early spring and a layer of fresh water 0.5–1.0 meter deep accumulates on the surface from local streams.

As a result the lower layer of salt water reaches a higher temperature than it would otherwise. The method of operation of these ponds is described in detail by Gaarder and Bjerkan (1934). Flooded slate quarries have been used successfully in Scotland, but, due to the absence of an adequate fresh-water supply, water temperatures have been usually unsuitable (Millar, 1951). Carriker (1959) reviews previous work and presents the results of a detailed study over 3 years of a pond on Long Island Sound. Although *Venus* and *Crassostrea* grew well, the rate of exchange with the outside sea was so high that few larvae were retained throughout their development. Unlike the previous examples this pond was enclosed by mud and sand and not by rock, and undesirable conditions would soon develop if the entrance was closed.

Concrete tanks have received considerable attention as they offer greater possibility of controlling the conditions, and a moderate quantity of spawning stock will give much higher densities of larvae than are obtainable in seminatural ponds. A further advantage is that they are not affected by the release of dissolved substances from the surrounding soil.

Tanks at Conway, North Wales, have been used for 40 years for experiments in rearing the larvae of *Ostrea edulis*, and a technique has evolved which is reasonably reliable (Cole, 1938) and sometimes very successful. Two tanks, each holding 380,000 liters of water, have been used; smaller tanks have not given good results. The tanks are filled in May and each is stocked with 300–600 adult oysters, which invariably has yielded a high density of larvae (over 50 per liter) at intervals during July and August. Direct observation supplemented by laboratory studies indicated that, apart from temperature, the most important variable was the abundance of nannoplankton—pelagic algae measuring not more than 10μ in diameter. Unless adequate densities of suitable species were present as food for the larvae, satisfactory growth was not obtained. The addition of finely ground crab meat stimulated the development of nannoplankton, whereas enrichment with inorganic fertilizers produced blooms of unsuitable and larger forms. Over a period of years (Walne, 1956b) this technique did not always ensure a substantial increase in spatfall, perhaps because the species of nannoplankton which grew were unsuitable as food organisms. The variable nature of the results of tank or pond culture has been the general experience elsewhere, where the experiments have been repeated over a period of years (Dannevig, 1951; Korringa, 1951). Korringa found that nannoplankton densities as high as 50–100 per cubic millimeter gave poor results; he suggests that accumulation of toxic metabolites from the algae and possibly oxygen supersaturation were important factors.

All large tanks and ponds suffer from the great disadvantage that detailed control over the conditions is difficult. Greater control has been obtained in tanks of 2,500 to 19,000 liter capacity at Onagawa in Japan, where the water, after filtration through sand and charcoal, was enriched with a food organism. The organism used (Imai, *et al.*, 1950a,b, 1954) was a holozoic, colorless flagellate, *Monas* sp., which fed on bacteria. It grew readily in dense culture in a sea-water medium enriched with phosphate and nitrate and with glucose as a carbon source for the dense growth of bacteria on which the *Monas* fed. A few days after inoculation, the nutrients would be exhausted and small quantities could be added to the tanks without a dense bloom of bacteria appearing. When the *Monas* culture was added the tanks were also enriched with 0.5 to 1.0 gm of starch per 10,000 liters, which gave sufficient growth of bacteria to maintain the flagellate population at about 0.1 to 10.0 cells per cubic millimeter. These densities of *Monas* are very low compared with the densities of colored flagellates used in Europe and America and this may account for the rather slow rates of growth recorded. Larvae from artificial fertilizations were introduced to give up to 100 per liter. This technique has been used successfully to rear the larvae of members of the genera *Ostrea, Crassostrea, Mactra, Meretrix, Venerupis, Chlamys,* and *Teredo* at Onagawa, but has not been repeated elsewhere.

In view of the recent discoveries on the importance of controlling the development of bacteria in larval cultures (Walne, 1958; Guillard, 1959), it is obviously a difficult technique to control precisely.

III. CULTURE UNDER LABORATORY CONDITIONS

The culture of larvae in the laboratory[1] may be divided into two phases: the obtaining of healthy embryos and their culture. At present there is little experimental evidence on the influence of the physiological or genetic condition of the parent on the subsequent growth and survival of the larvae, but it is the general experience of workers in this field that there are considerable differences in the performance of different batches of larvae grown under identical conditions. Cole (1939) noted that oysters which had been overwintered in unfavorable conditions produced a meager quantity of larvae which he describes as "inherently non-viable," while Loosanoff and Davis (1950) state that not all batches of eggs discharged by one *Venus* possessed the same vitality. Studies made with *Crassostrea* and *Venus* (Loosanoff *et al.*, 1953) have shown no greater variation in the survival and growth of larvae between young and old parents than between different members of the same age group. An interesting study by Chanley (1955) on the growth rate of *Venus* larvae from the same female crossed with two different males and from

[1] See also the exhaustive review by Loosanoff & Davis (1963).

two females crossed with the same male showed significant differences, suggesting that inherited factors from either parent were responsible. This is an important field that needs further investigation.

A. Preparation for Spawning

The gonads of most adult bivalves undergo an annual cycle of activity divisible into three phases: (1) a resting phase of little activity, when resorption of unspawned material from the previous spawning may take place, followed by (2) a phase of active gametogenesis leading to the presence of ripe oöcytes or spermatozoa in the gonads. At this stage a stimulus is required to initiate (3) the liberation of the sexual products.

In a number of temperate water species active gametogenesis can be stimulated (referred to as "conditioning" by Loosanoff and his collaborators) out of season by raising the water temperature, and a number of techniques have been developed to induce subsequent spawning. The resting period after spawning is often a period of rapid body growth and replenishment of food reserves, and until this has taken place it is useless to attempt to condition molluscs in preparation for artificial spawning. Once sufficient reserves have been accumulated, it has been shown in *Crassostrea virginica* (Loosanoff and Davis, 1952) that the period required for the development of mature gametocytes is a function of temperature; the higher the temperature in the range 15°–30°C the more rapid the maturation of the gonad. Raising the water temperature to 20°–22°C over 2–3 weeks was satisfactory for *Venus mercenaria* (Loosanoff and Davis, 1950), although its behavior is less predictable than that of *Crassostrea* (Davis and Chanley, 1956a). A similar technique is satisfactory with *Ostrea edulis* (Dannevig, 1951; Aboul-Ela, 1960). It is generally better to raise the temperature gradually, rather than to transfer the animals from the winter temperatures to 20°C, as this may lead to some deaths (Loosanoff, 1954). The conditioning of tropical species has not been attempted.

It is the usual practice to maintain the breeding stock in running sea water enriched with algal culture. Glass tanks are used at Conway and the arrangement used is illustrated in Walne (1956b). Extensive use is made of enamel trays at Milford and the arrangement illustrated in Loosanoff (1954) allows large numbers to be kept in a small area.

B. Induction of Spawning

In general it is better for experimental work to use gametes which have been shed by the parent. Teasing out gonadal tissue is liable to give material which is not fully ripe. A number of methods have been used to stimulate the release of the gametes from animals which are ripe.

1. TEMPERATURE

During the breeding season, or at the end of the conditioning period, raising the temperature a few degrees induces spawning within a few hours in a number of species. Loosanoff and Davis (1950) state that after a conditioning period the following species have been induced to spawn by this method: *Crassostrea virginica*, *C. gigas*, *Ostrea lurida*, *O. edulis*, *Venus mercenaria*, *Mya arenaria*, *Mactra solidissima*, *Anomia aculeata*, *Ensis directus*, and *Petricola pholadiformis*.

2. GONAD EXTRACT

Mass spawnings of some bivalves are not uncommon in nature and experiment has shown that the presence of eggs or sperm in the water will often induce ripe animals to spawn; ripe male *Crassostrea* can be induced to spawn in a few seconds if a suspension of eggs is added to the water, while relying on a temperature shock alone takes up to several hours (Galtsoff, 1940). *Venus mercenaria* is more resistant to stimulation by the presence of egg or sperm (Loosanoff, 1937).

3. CHEMICAL AND ELECTRICAL STIMULATION

Iwata (1948a,b, 1950, 1951) has developed techniques which induce spawning in ripe animals, apparently by stimulating the muscles of the gonad to contract. The injection of 0.5 to 2.0 ml of a 0.5 M solution of KCl or other neutral potassium salts into the mantle cavity of *Mytilus*, *Venerupis*, *Meretrix*, and *Mactra* or a stimulation of 20 volts at 50 cycles for 5 seconds induces a copious discharge of eggs or sperm, which are mature and may be used for artificial fertilization. Aboul-Ela (1960) found that a stimulus of 20 volts induced many male *Mytilus edulis* to spawn, but only a few *Ostrea edulis*; he presents some evidence that a sperm suspension stimulated female *O. edulis* to spawn. He was unsuccessful with potassium, ammonium, and barium salts.

C. Cultural Techniques

Because of the corrosive nature of sea water and the great sensitivity of larvae to traces of dissolved substances, the majority of larval culture experiments have been made in vessels of glass or glazed earthenware. The recent rapid development of cheap plastic containers has widened the range of materials available; polythene vessels are used extensively in the Milford laboratory in Connecticut and fiber-glass tanks, which are available in large sizes, have been used at Conway. Care should be taken that all pumps, distribution pipes, and storage tanks are made of nontoxic materials.

The sea water should either be freshly pumped or else stored in large tanks of 10,000 to 20,000 gallons to avoid the changes which take place during storage in small vessels (ZoBell and Anderson, 1936). The water is filtered before use to remove silt and competing organisms, especially protozoa. Earlier workers (Cole, 1937; Bruce *et al.*, 1940) used ceramic filter candles with a small pore diameter and this remains a satisfactory method where only small quantities are required. It is better to force the water through the filter rather than to suck it through as the latter method tends to draw gases out of solution, which then have to be restored before the water can be used. More recently it has become the practice to strain the water through a coarse filter and then sterilize with ultraviolet light. Lamps can be obtained in which the discharge tube is in a quartz jacket and the water flows between this and an outer glass jacket. The coarse filter can be of ceramic, sand, cotton, or glass wool.

Some workers have stirred the water in the larval cultures to ensure that the larvae remain suspended, although work at Milford has shown that this is not necessary if the water is changed frequently. Rotary stirring tends to throw the larvae to the bottom; a reciprocating motion is better. Glass plunger plates moving slowly up and down through the water give excellent results (Bruce *et al.*, 1940); in smaller vessels a stream of air bubbles is easy to arrange and quite satisfactory (Walne, 1956a).

Most larval cultures are maintained in either a darkened room or in opaque vessels to reduce the photosynthetic activity of the food organisms, and neither stirring nor aeration is needed to control any changes in pH due to CO_2. The respiratory activity of the larvae does not have any apparent effect on the gas content of the water.

There is considerable variety in the amount of water change given to larval cultures by different workers. Walne (1956a) has shown that *Ostrea edulis* larvae can be successfully reared to metamorphosis without any change of water, but densities are limited to 500–1000 larvae per liter. With higher larval concentrations, the accumulation of feces and dead larvae leads to unhealthy conditions. Bruce *et al.* (1940) made extensive use of slow continuous water changes which protect the larvae from the sudden changes and mechanical shocks involved in complete water changes. Slow changes are, however, difficult and laborious to maintain. The work of Loosanoff and his colleagues has shown that the larvae of many species are well able to withstand the shocks involved in complete changes. Complete water changes have the advantage that they allow the vessels to be cleaned thoroughly and the sediment removed. The technique at Milford is to pour or siphon the larval culture through a stainless steel test sieve of suitable mesh. The larvae remain on the sieve where they can be well washed with clean water to remove fecal masses. At this stage quantitative samples of the larvae can readily be obtained if the contents of the sieve are washed into a graduated cylinder and made up to a known volume. An even dispersion is ensured by brisk agitation with a perforated plastic plunger and samples can then be taken with an automatic pipette.

Bacteria readily develop in small bodies of sea water where the area of solid surface is high compared with the volume of water and their control is important for successful larval culture (Walne, 1958; Guillard, 1959). Passing the water under an ultraviolet lamp before use reduces the bacteria to very low numbers and frequent changes of water during the experiment keep the population down. The writer (Walne, 1958) found that the addition of 50 units of penicillin G and 0.05 mg of streptomycin sulfate per milliliter to cultures where the water was unchanged suppressed the development of bacteria for 9 days and many more O. edulis larvae developed into spat compared with the controls.

Apart from the obvious necessity of maintaining the temperature and salinity of the water at a suitable level for the species concerned, it is probable that not all batches of water are equally suitable for larval rearing. It has been shown at Plymouth (reviewed in Wilson, 1958) that the larvae of *Echinus esculentus* would not develop into normal plutei in some waters, while samples from the same artificial fertilization developed normally in water obtained elsewhere. Davis and Chanley (1956b) have noticed on several occasions that during dinoflagellate blooms at Milford their bivalve cultures failed to grow normally. Such experiments may imply the presence of toxic extracellular metabolites or the absence from time to time of required substances from the sea water which, although they may be of great importance to successful larval growth, are extremely difficult to investigate.

D. Feeding the Larvae

It is now generally accepted that bivalve larvae must feed during their planktonic phase; hence the provision of an adequate food supply is of the utmost importance. Larvae thrive on a diet of unicellular algae which must be sufficiently small to be swallowed—generally either the length or the breadth must be less than 10μ—and of a suitable nutritive value. A number of species are of little or no food value and some are probably toxic. A practical point is that if the culture is not stirred, it is an advantage to use species which are motile, or else readily float; some species soon sink to the bottom and are not available to the larvae.

Rich cultures of mixed algal species can be obtained by adding nutrient salts or commercially compounded agricultural fertilizers to sea water (Loosanoff and Engle, 1942). Such cultures, consisting mainly of *Chlorella*, have been used to rear an impressive array of bivalve larvae. Loosanoff and Marak (1951) and Loosanoff and Davis (1950) have successfully reared larvae of species of *Ostrea, Crassostrea, Venus, Mya, Mactra, Mytilus, Petricola, Pitar,* and *Ensis* on such a diet. A mixed culture is, however, in an unstable state and a bloom of one algal species is usually succeeded by another species, and so on. Thus, not only will composition change over a period of time, but it is not necessarily reproducible in different places. This is important because different algal species differ widely in their food value to bivalve larvae: unialgal cultures give more reliable results. Many species are now in culture in laboratories throughout the world and the food value and cultural requirements of many are known.

Algae differ considerably in their nutritional requirements and the selection of a suitable medium for their culture may present some difficulty. If only small quantities are required, the so-called "Erd-schreiber" medium (Gross, 1937) is very satisfactory. Its preparation is straightforward and it will grow a much larger variety of organisms than any other. Its composition is shown in Table I.

TABLE I

Composition of Erd-schreiber Medium

Ingredient	Amount
$NaNO_3$	0.10 gm
Na_2HPO_4	0.02 gm
Soil extract	50 ml
Sea water	1000 ml

The soil extract is prepared by autoclaving together a rich loam soil and distilled water in the proportion of 1 liter of water to 1 kg of soil. After standing, the supernatant liquid is decanted, sterilized, and allowed to stand for a further period of a week or so before again decanting, and adding to the medium. Although not a chemically specified medium, it supports the growth of many algae and, because of the properties of the soil extract, the algae grow and remain active in it for a long period. If large quantities of medium are required the preparation of soil extract becomes laborious and synthetic media are more suitable. Various types have been developed to suit different algal species and their formulas may be found in papers by Droop (1955, 1957), McLaughlin (1958) and Provasoli *et al.* (1956). More rapid growth of the algae can be promoted by continuous illumination, the supply of air enriched with carbon dioxide, stirring, and temperature control. If the conditions are suitably controlled, about ⅓ of an algal culture of 10–20 liters can be harvested daily and replaced with fresh medium. It is not usually practicable to maintain such cultures in a bacteria-free condition, but it is important

(Guillard, 1958) to keep the cultures rapidly growing and bacterial contamination as low as possible. Cultures with a dense bacterial flora can become toxic to larvae.

For large-scale work the apparatus for the provision of substantial quantities of unialgal culture is fairly elaborate; that in use at Conway is illustrated in Yonge (1960). That used at Milford is described by Davis and Ukeles (1961).

Critical feeding experiments using a number of species in unialgal culture have been reported by Davis (1953), Walne (1956a), Loosanoff et al. (1955), and Davis and Guillard (1958), and it is on these papers, which also review the earlier literature, that the following remarks are based. The comments are arranged under the appropriate algal classes, and it should be remembered that we are only concerned with the unicellular planktonic forms.

1. CHLOROPHYCEAE

These are green organisms and include both motile and nonmotile forms. The genus *Chlorella*, which is nonmotile and has a well-defined cell wall, is widely distributed and often abundant in nature; many species thrive well in culture. For the larvae of *Ostrea* and *Crassostrea* it is an indifferent food, particularly when the larvae are small, and it is generally held that the larvae of these genera require species in which rigid cell walls are absent. Other species of bivalves, for example, *Venus mercenaria* and *Mytilus edulis,* are more tolerant and apparently will "thrive on most micro-organisms provided they are small enough to be ingested" (Loosanoff et al., 1955), although subsequent work (Davis and Guillard, 1958) has shown that not all species of *Chlorella* give good growth. Furthermore, *Chlorella* cultures are liable to contain toxic metabolites and overfeeding the larvae will result in death.

The motile forms without a cell wall of the genera *Dunaliella* and *Pyramimonas* give good growth; motile forms with a cell wall (*Chlamydomonas*) do not. *Pyramimonas* (as flagellate H) gave excellent results in early work (Bruce et al., 1940), but it is rather more difficult to culture than *Dunaliella*, most species of which grow very vigorously. Species of *Dunaliella* known as *Chlamydomonas* I and III and now described as *D. primolecta* and *D. tertiolecta*, respectively (Butcher, 1959), have been widely used as food organisms in marine biological research and are of considerable value.

2. CHRYSOPHYCEAE

This group of yellow-brown flagellates includes the most generally valuable larval foods. Three species, *Isochrysis galbana, Monochrysis lutheri,* and *Chromulina pleiades* have been found to give excellent growth of the larvae of *Ostrea edulis, Crassostrea virginica,* and *Venus mercenaria.* The cultures rarely become toxic and their cultural requirements have been the subject of considerable study (Provasoli *et al.,* 1956; McLaughlin, 1958; Kain and Fogg, 1958). Any one of these three species will probably serve as a satisfactory food for most, if not all, bivalve larvae.

The genus *Prymesium,* which belongs to this group, gives very little growth and is probably toxic.

3. BACILLAROPHYCEAE

Few diatoms are small enough to be eaten by bivalve larvae, and feeding experiments have been reported only with *Phaeodactylum tricornutum,* an aberrant form with a number of cell types, only one of which develops a typical diatom valve (Lewin, 1958). It has also been classified among the *Chrysophyceae* (Hendey, 1954). It has been used as a general purpose food organism in many marine laboratories, and has a moderate food value for bivalve larvae, but as it is nonmotile, the cultures probably require stirring for the best results.

4. CRYPTOPHYCEAE

The unicellular flagellates in this group are without a readily visible cell wall, and tend to be difficult to maintain in consistently dense culture. The results from the *Cryptophyceae* are variable; some experiments have been successful but, generally, results have been indifferent.

Other foods which have been tried without success include detritus for *Crassostrea* and *Venus,* bacteria for *Crassostrea* and *Ostrea,* and the blue-green alga *Synechococcus* for *Ostrea.*

It is perhaps surprising that using a single algal species as food gives a growth rate comparable with that occurring in the field. Some experiments have been reported (Davis and Guillard, 1958) in which *Crassostrea* and *Venus* were fed with a mixture of four species; rather better growth was obtained with them than with equivalent amounts of the single food, although in an earlier paper (Davis, 1953) a number of combinations of species did not give a more rapid growth than equivalent quantities of a single food. The enhanced value of mixed cultures over unialgal cultures may have contributed to the excellent results obtained at the Milford Laboratory with the mixed *Chlorella* culture.

The relation between the quantity of culture fed to the larvae and the density of the larvae is important. Good growth and spatfall of *Ostrea edulis* is obtained when 500 to 1000 larvae per liter are maintained with 20 to 60 cells of *Isochrysis galbana* per cubic millimeter (Bruce *et al.,* 1940; Walne, 1956a). Much higher densities of larvae have been used at Milford ranging from 5,000 to 15,000 per liter and fed with 100 to 400 *I. galbana* cells per cubic millimeter per day. Experiments on the effect of different feeding rates showed that the rates given in Table II were required to give the maximum larval growth.

TABLE II

CULTURE FEEDING RATES NECESSARY FOR MAXIMUM LARVAL GROWTH[a]

		Daily cell increment per mm³	
Organism	Larvae per ml	Isochrysis galbana	Monochrysis lutheri
Crassostrea virginica	9	400	250
Venus mercenaria	10	200	250

[a] Davis and Guillard (1958).

The writer, using a radioactive tracer technique (Walne, 1959), has shown that maximum assimilation by O. edulis larvae is obtained at a constant food concentration of 100 I. galbana cells per cubic millimeter. Observations on the decrease in the number of cells in the culture of O. edulis suggests that each larva ate about 20,000 to 40,000 cells per day.

E. Pests and Diseases

Despite the provision of suitable conditions, insofar as they are known, varying proportions of larvae die before reaching metamorphosis. Davis et al. (1954) have described how a fungus occasionally can acquire epidemic proportions in some larval cultures, killing most of the larvae in 2–4 days. In this case the causative organism has been isolated and described as Sirolpidium zoophthorum (Vishniac, 1955), but, in general, little is known of the causes of larval mortality in experiments with apparently ideal conditions. As dead larvae are of a similar size to the rest of the population they cannot readily be separated and will, therefore, tend to accumulate on the bottom of the culture vessel. Among the dead and moribund larvae a mixed population of bacteria, colorless flagellates, and ciliates develops. It is possible that some of these organisms may be pathogens, but rigorous infection experiments are required to prove that they are not simply invading moribund larvae.

REFERENCES

Aboul-Ela, I. A. (1960). Conditioning Ostrea edulis L. from the Limfjord for reproduction out of season. Medd. Komm. Havundersøg., Kbh. (Ny Ser.) 2, No. 25.

Bruce, J. R., Knight, M., and Parke, M. W. (1940). The rearing of oyster larvae on an algal diet. J. Marine Biol. Assoc. U.K. 24, 337–374.

Butcher, R. W. (1959). An introductory account of the smaller algae of British coastal waters. Part I: Introduction and Chlorophyceae. Gt. Brit. Fishery Invest., Ser. IV.

Carriker, M. R. (1959). The role of physical and biological factors in the culture of *Crassostrea* and *Mercenaria* in a salt-water pond. *Ecol. Monographs* **29**, 219–266.

Chanley, P. E. (1955). Possible causes of growth variation in clam larvae. *Proc. Natl. Shellfish. Assoc.* **45**, 84–94.

Cole, H. A. (1937). Experiments in the breeding of oysters (*Ostrea edulis*) in tanks, with special reference to the food of the larva and spat. *Gt. Brit. Fishery Invest. Ser. II* **15**, No. 4.

Cole, H. A. (1938). A system of oyster culture. *J. Conseil permanent intern. exploration mer* **13**, 221–235.

Cole, H. A. (1939). Further experiments in the breeding of oysters (*Ostrea edulis*) in tanks. *Gt. Brit. Fishery Invest., Ser. II* **16**, No. 4.

Dannevig, A. (1951). Lobster and oyster in Norway. *Rapp. et proc. Conseil permanent intern. exploration mer* **128**, Pt. 2, 92–96.

Davis, H. C. (1953). On food and feeding of larvae of the American oyster, *C. virginica. Biol. Bull.* **104**, 334–350.

Davis, H. C., and Chanley, P. E. (1956a). Spawning and egg production of oysters and clams. *Proc. Natl. Shellfish. Assoc.* **46**, 40–58.

Davis, H. C., and Chanley, P. E. (1956b). Effects of some dissolved substances on bivalve larvae. *Proc. Natl. Shellfish. Assoc.* **46**, 59–74.

Davis, H. C., and Guillard, R. R. (1958). Relative value of ten genera of microorganisms as foods for oyster and clam larvae. *U.S. Fish Wildlife Serv., Fishery Bull.* **58**, 293–304.

Davis, H. C., and Ukeles, R. (1961). Mass culture of phytoplankton as food for metazoans. *Science* **134**, 562–563.

Davis, H. C., Loosanoff, V. L., Weston, W. H., and Martin, G. (1954). A fungus disease in clam and oyster larvae. *Science* **120**, 36–38.

Droop, M. (1955). Some new supra-littoral Protista. *J. Marine Biol. Assoc. U.K.* **34**, 233–245.

Droop, M. R. (1957). Auxotrophy and organic compounds in the nutrition of marine phytoplankton. *J. Gen. Microbiol.* **16**, 286–293.

Gaarder, T., and Bjerkan, P. (1934). "Østers og osterskultur i Norge," 96pp. Griegs Boktrykkeri, Bergen; see J. C. Medcof (ed.), Oysters and oyster culture in Norway. *Fisheries Research Board Can., Transl. Ser.* **217**.

Galtsoff, P. S. (1940). Physiology of reproduction of *O. virginica*, Part II. Stimulation of spawning in the male oyster. *Biol. Bull.* **78**, 117–135.

Gross, F. (1937). Notes on the culture of some marine plankton organisms. *J. Marine Biol. Assoc. U.K.* **21**, 753–768.

Guillard, R. R. (1958). Some factors in the use of nannoplankton cultures as food for larval and juvenile bivalves. *Proc. Natl. Shellfish Assoc.* **48**, 134–141.

Guillard, R. R. (1959). Further evidence of the destruction of bivalve larvae by bacteria. *Biol. Bull.* **117**, 258–266.

Hendey, N. I. (1954). Notes on the Plymouth "Nitzschia" culture. *J. Marine Biol. Assoc. U.K.* **33**, 335–339.

Imai, T., Hatanaka, M., Sato, R., Sakai, S., and Yuki, R. (1950a). Artificial breeding of oysters in tanks. *Tôhoku J. Agr. Research* **1**, 69–86.

Imai, T., Hatanaka, M., and Sato, R. (1950b). Breeding of marine timber-borer, *Teredo navalis* L., in tanks and its use for anti-boring test. *Tôhoku J. Agr. Research* **1**, 199–208.

Imai, T., Sakai, S., Okada, H., and Yoshida, T. (1954). Breeding of the Olympia oyster in tanks and culture experiments in Japanese waters. *Tôhoku J. Agr. Research* **5**, 13–25.

Iwata, K. S. (1948a). Artificial discharge of reproductive substances by potassium salts injection in *Venerupis philippinarum, Meretrix lusoria* and *Mactra sulcataria* (Bivalves). *Bull. Japan. Soc. Sci. Fisheries* **13**, 237–240.

Iwata, K. S. (1948b). Artificial discharge of reproductive substances by K-salts injection in *Mactra veneriformis* (Bivalves). *Bull. Japan. Soc. Sci. Fisheries* **13**, 188–192.

Iwata, K. S. (1950). Spawning of *Mytilus edulis*. (2). Discharge by electrical stimulation. *Bull. Japan. Soc. Sci. Fisheries* **15**, 443–446.

Iwata, K. S. (1951). Spawning of *Mytilus edulis*. (4). Discharge by KCl injection, *Bull. Japan. Soc. Sci. Fisheries* **16**, 393–394.

Kain, J. M., and Fogg, G. E. (1958). Studies on the growth of marine phytoplankton. II. *Isochrysis galbana* Parke. *J. Marine Biol. Assoc. U.K.* **37**, 781–788.

Korringa, P. (1951). Difficulties encountered in tank-breeding of oysters (*Ostrea edulis*). *Rapp. et proc. Conseil permanent intern. exploration mer* **128**, Pt. 2, 35–38.

Lewin, J. C. (1958). The taxonomic position of *Phaeodactylum tricornutum*. *J. Gen. Microbiol.* **18**, 427–432.

Loosanoff, V. L. (1937). Spawning of *Venus mercenaria* (L.) *Ecology* **18**, 506–515.

Loosanoff, V. L. (1954). New advances in the study of bivalve larvae. *Am. Scientist* **42**, 607–624.

Loosanoff, V. L., and Davis, H. C. (1950). Conditioning *V. mercenaria* for spawning in winter and breeding its larvae in the laboratory. *Biol. Bull.* **98**, 60–65.

Loosanoff, V. L., and Davis, H. C. (1952). Temperature requirements for maturation of gonads of northern oysters. *Biol. Bull.* **103**, 80–96.

Loosanoff, V. L., and Davis, H. C. (1963). Rearing of bivalve mollusks. *Advances in Marine Biology*, **1**, 1–136.

Loosanoff, V. L., and Engle, J. B. (1942). Use of complete fertilisers in cultivation of micro-organisms. *Science* **95**, 487–488.

Loosanoff, V. L., and Marak, R. R. (1951). Culturing lamellibranch larvae. *Anat. Record* **111**, 129–130.

Loosanoff, V. L., Davis, H. C., and Chanley, P. E. (1953). No relationship found between age of oyster and quality of spawn. *Atlantic Fisherman* **34**, 22–23.

Loosanoff, V. L., Davis, H. C., and Chanley, P. E. (1955). Food requirements of some bivalve larvae. *Proc. Natl. Shellfish. Assoc.* **45**, 66–83.

McLaughlin, J. J. A. (1958). Euryhaline chrysomonads: nutrition and toxigenesis in *Prymnesium parvum*, with notes on *Isochrysis galbana* and *Monochrysis lutheri*. *J. Protozool.* **5**, 75–81.

Millar, R. H. (1951). Scottish research on oyster fisheries. *Rapp. et proc. Conseil permanent intern. exploration mer* **128**, Pt. 2, 18.

Provasoli, L., McLaughlin, J. J. A., and Droop, M. R. (1956). Development of artificial media for marine algae. *Arch. Mikrobiol.* **25**, 392–428.

Vishniac, H. S. (1955). The morphology and nutrition of a new species of *Sirolpidium. Mycologia* **47**, 633–645.

Walne, P. R. (1956a). Experimental rearing of the larvae of *Ostrea edulis* L. in the laboratory. *Gt. Brit. Fishery Invest., Ser. II* **20**, No. 9.

Walne, P. R. (1956b). Observations on the oyster (*Ostrea edulis*) breeding experiments at Conway, 1939–1953. *Rapp. et proc. Conseil permanent intern. exploration mer* **140**, Pt. 3, 10–13.

Walne, P. R. (1958). The importance of bacteria in laboratory experiments on rearing the larvae of *Ostrea edulis* (L.). *J. Marine Biol. Assoc. U.K.* **37**, 415–425.

Walne, P. R. (1959). Some observations on the feeding behaviour of oyster (*Ostrea edulis*) larvae and their relation to rearing problems. *Proc. 15th Intern. Congr. Zool., London* pp. 234–236.

Wilson, D. P. (1958). Some problems in larval ecology related to the localized distribution of bottom animals. *In* "Perspectives in Marine Biology" (A. A. Buzzati-Traverso, ed.), pp. 87–103. Univ. of California Press, Berkeley, California.

Yonge, C. M. (1960). "Oysters," 209pp. Collins, London.

ZoBell, C. E., and Anderson, D. Q. (1936). Observations on the multiplication of bacteria in different volumes of stored seawater, and the influence of oxygen tension and solid surfaces. *Biol. Bull.* **71**, 324–342.

CHAPTER 7

Growth

Karl M. Wilbur

DEPARTMENT OF ZOOLOGY, DUKE UNIVERSITY, DURHAM, NORTH CAROLINA

Gareth Owen

DEPARTMENT OF ZOOLOGY, UNIVERSITY OF GLASGOW, SCOTLAND

I. REPRESENTATION OF GROWTH DATA

Perhaps the outstanding feature of growth in molluscs is its variation in rate. Variations with developmental stage, age, and environmental conditions have been described. The study of growth should properly consist of an analysis of these rates, and, ultimately, of the rates of chemical reactions which govern body composition and dimensions. But the analysis in the case of most multicellular organisms, including molluscs, is still in the stage of examining the less detailed aspects of growth: alterations in body dimensions, increase in mass, changes in chemical constituents of tissues, and others.

Changes during growth can be represented in two ways: in one, a parameter of growth of the whole organism is related to age; in the other, the rate of growth of one part or dimension is related to that of another part or to the whole body. We shall consider both approaches.

A. Absolute and Relative Growth

From successive weighings of individual molluscs of short life span (Baily, 1931; Abeloos, 1942) or from linear measurements on individuals of known age as indicated by annual growth rings (Weymouth and McMillin, 1930; Weymouth *et al.*, 1931; Quayle, 1951–1952; Stevenson and Dickie, 1954) one can plot a series of connected points as a function

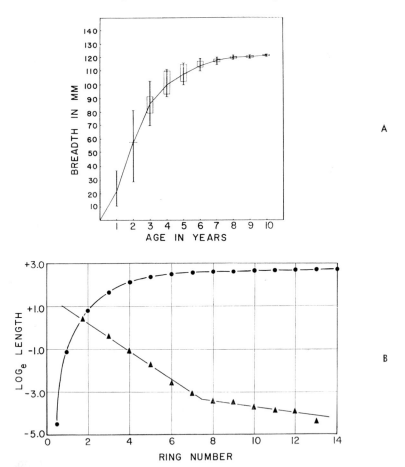

Fig. 1.A. Growth curve for the scallop *Pecten maximus* (Gibson, 1956). Vertical lines represent size ranges within each age group. The rectangles show the relative numbers of individuals in the age groups. B. Growth of the razor clam *Siliqua patula* (after Weymouth *et al.*, 1931). Upper curve (●): The logarithm of shell length ($\log_e L$) is plotted against age in years as indicated by ring number. Lower curve (▲): The logarithm of the relative growth rate, $\log_e (\triangle \log_e L)$.

of age. The cumulative increase with time represented by such a curve is termed *absolute growth* (See Fig. 1A). The growth increment per unit mass or per unit length per unit time is termed *relative growth*. If length (L) is used as a measure of growth, then the absolute growth rate can be represented as dL/dt where t is time. The relative growth rate is dL/Ldt. The course of relative growth can be conveniently shown graphically by plotting the growth increments for successive intervals on a scale of natural logarithms on which equal percental changes are represented by equal vertical distances. Figure 1B (upper curve) illustrates this method of presenting growth data. The relative growth rate would be the change in slope of the curve of $d\log L/dt$. On differentiation this becomes dL/Ldt which is the expression for relative growth rate given above (see Fig. 1B, lower curve). It should be borne in mind that averaged growth curves of the types illustrated in Fig. 1 have been derived from data on many individuals and are an approximation in most instances. Accordingly, they fail to bring out the detailed growth pattern of the individual specimens (Sholl, 1954).

The rate of growth during short intervals may be expressed as the *instantaneous relative growth rate* according to the relation

$$k = \frac{dL/dt}{L} \tag{1}$$

where k is the instantaneous relative growth rate, L is length, and t is time (Brody, 1945; Dehnel, 1955). On integration this becomes $\ln L = \ln A + kt$, where A is the natural logarithm of L when $t = 0$. For computation of the growth rate, this expression can be converted to

$$k = \frac{2.303}{t} \log \frac{L_n}{L_0} \tag{2}$$

where L_n and L_0 are lengths at two times. This mode of expression has been used for the growth of veliger larvae measured at intervals of one day (Dehnel, 1955, 1956).

B. Allometry

1. GENERAL

In molluscs, as in other animals, the growth rate of the various parts of the body may not be uniform, with the result that the relative proportions of the body change with increase in size. The difference in growth rate between one part and the whole organism or between one part and another part considered as a standard is termed *allometry of growth* (Huxley and Teissier, 1936). The relations between a part and the whole body or between two parts of the growing animal can usually be described by the general equation

$$y = bx^\alpha \tag{3}$$

where y is some measure of a part, x is a measure of the whole body or another part, and b and α are constants. The constant b is equal to y when $x = 1$ and is called the initial growth index. Its value will depend upon the units of measurement employed. The more meaningful constant is the equilibrium constant, α, which indicates the ratio of the two growth rates under examination. Expressed in logarithms, Eq. (3) becomes

$$\log y = \alpha \log x + \log b \tag{4}$$

In applying Eq. (4) we may expect to find that a logarithmic plot of one parameter (x) against another (y) results in a straight line of slope α. When Eq. (4) holds and α has a value other than 1, the relation is said to be *allometric*. If the relationship between two parts or dimensions remains constant as the animal grows, then α is unity and the general equation (3) becomes

$$y = bx \tag{5}$$

This relation is said to be *isometric*. For discussions of allometry, literature sources, and interesting examples, the reader is referred to works by Huxley (1932), Needham (1942), and Teissier (1960).

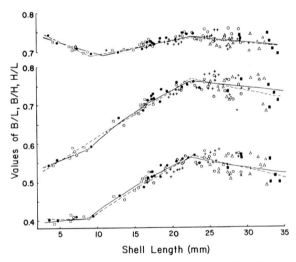

Fig. 2. Alteration of relations between parameters of shell with increase in size of *Tapes japonica* (after Ohba, 1959). H is height, B is breadth, and L is length. The changes in slope illustrate that a single allometric relation does not hold for the entire growth range. Solid lines are calculated from allometric formulas. Broken lines represent actual growth values.

In describing allometric relations in molluscs, investigators have employed a number of measures including linear measurements, total weight, gonad weight, and total volume. Growth may be advantageously represented by simple linear plots rather than the double logarithmic relation (see Sholl, 1954). The use of the allometric formulation may, in fact, obscure features evident from a linear plot. Within a limited period the growth pattern will follow a single allometric relation. However, over a more extended period, multiple relations frequently become evident and are expressed as changes in slope (Fig. 2). The alteration in pattern occurs at definite stages of growth and is well illustrated by the change in ratio of shell dimensions in the clams *Mya arenaria* (Swan, 1952), *Tapes japonica*, and *Meretrix meretrix* (Hamai, 1937; Ohba, 1959) (see also Kristensen, 1957, on *Cardium edule*.) Other phyla also show this growth behavior (Teissier, 1960). The clams *Mya arenaria* (Newcombe and Kessler, 1936) and *Donax cuneatus* (Nayar, 1955) follow a simpler course of growth; in these species the length-breadth and the length-thickness parameters are each described by a single allometric relation (Fig. 3). (See also Mason (1957) on *Pecten maximus*.)

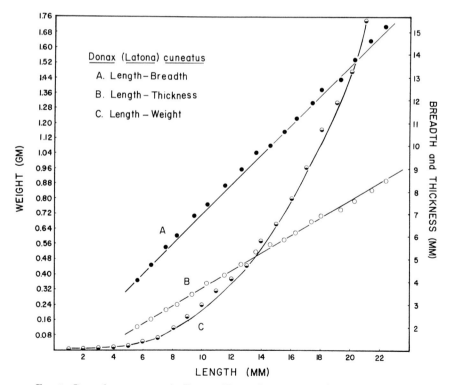

Fig. 3. Growth parameters in *Donax (Latona) cuneatus* (after Nayar, 1955).

Values for Eq. (4) have been provided for various parameters of a number of species (Nomura, 1928; Nomura and Sasaki, 1928; Hamai, 1936; Newcombe and Kessler, 1936; Fox and Coe, 1943; Hanoaka and Shimadzu, 1949; Isham et al., 1951; Swan, 1952; Nayar, 1955; Ohba, 1959; Leighton and Boolootian, 1963). When length is the reference parameter x, and y is weight (total weight, shell weight, tissue dry weight), the values for α lie between 2.5 and 4.5 with the exception of the worm-like *Teredo* (Isham et al., 1951) in which a more nearly linear relation ($\alpha =$ 1.37) is found. The values of α represent the relative growth in weight as compared with length. The allometric relation between weight and length also holds for *Octopus* in which length is measured from the posterior edge of the mantle to the end of the longest arm (M. Tauchi, quoted by Tanaka, 1958). In certain bivalves (*Tapes philippinarum, Meretrix meretrix*) and gastropods (*Haliotis gigantea* var. *discus, Littorina sitchana*) several parameters of growth can be expressed by the general equation

$$W = K_1 a^x bc = K_2 ab^x c = K_3 abc^x \qquad (6)$$

where W is weight; a, b, and c are shell dimensions such as height, width, and thickness; and K_1, K_2, and K_3 are constants (Nomura, 1928; Nomura and Sasaki, 1928). The same equation will serve for *Meretrix meretrix* where W represents volume (Hamai, 1934).

2. MANTLE AND SHELL SHAPE

The growth and form of the molluscan shell is frequently considered solely in terms of "length," "breadth," and "height," but these characters alone do not enable shell form in different genera to be satisfactorily related. Typically, the relation between the mantle and shell is such that the latter increases in area only by the addition of marginal increments. A consequence of this accretionary mode of growth is that the form of the shell can, in principle, be fully described in terms of the growth rates operating at different points on the margin during the formation of the shell. Thus, mantle growth and shell shape have been treated quantitatively by use of allometric equations of the form $y = bL^\alpha$, where y is a linear measure of the shell (such as is designated by UA, UM, UP, or UB, in Fig. 4); L is length (AP) and α is the relative rate of growth of y. The growth rate of y is determined by measurement of shells of increasing size. The ratio of the growth rates then provides a quantitative picture of the shell as it becomes larger. Figure 4 illustrates this for *Cyclina sinensis* (Hamai, 1936). The heavy lines in the larger diagram show the alterations in the shape when the relative growth rates of UA, UM, UP, and UB are in the ratio of $1.08 : 1.07 : 0.99 : 1.23$. The light lines indicate the theoretical form of the shell at different sizes assuming that it grew uniformly. Sexual dimorphism in the form of the shell can be analyzed similarly by expressing differences between male and female shells in terms of growth gradients at various points along the lines *UA*, *UM*, etc. (Hamai, 1938).

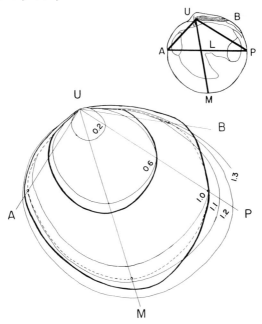

FIG. 4. Growth gradients in *Cyclina sinensis* (Hamai, 1936). Upper diagram shows axes of shell measurement. Lower diagram shows relative growth of shell margins and gradients of relative growth. Heavy lines show heterogonic growth of shell. Dotted line shows the relative growth gradients along axes *UB*, *UP*, *UM*, and *UA*, taking 1.0 on *UP* as a reference. Slender lines show shell margins expressed as isogonic growth, taking 1.0 on *UP* as a reference.

A limitation of the allometric method is that it compares only two portions of the shell at a time. Moreover, it is important that any quantitative treatment of growth and form of the mantle-shell relation be founded on, and preceded by, a thorough qualitative study of the shell. This may be achieved by resolving the rate of growth at each point on the growing edge (i.e., the generating curve represented by the mantle-shell margin), at each moment of growth, into component rates acting in different directions. This has been attempted for the Bivalvia by Lison (1949) and by Owen (1953a). A fundamental error in the extensive analysis undertaken by Lison, however, is the statement that the growth forces of the mantle are parallel to one another. This is certainly not so. The lines of growth of the mantle-shell *radiate* from a region of minimum growth situated near the umbones, and it is for this reason that radial coordinates can be used in comparing shell, although not body, form in the Bivalvia (Yonge, 1952). In many bivalves, the direction of growth at any region of the mantle edge may be resolved into: (*a*) a radial component radiating from the umbones and acting in the plane of the generating curve (Fig. 5 A and B; *R*), (*b*) a transverse component acting

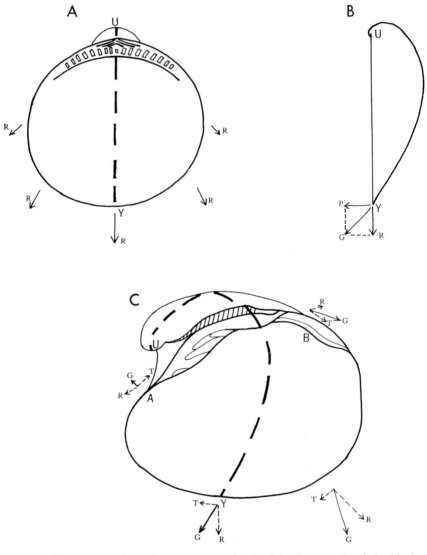

Fig. 5. Diagrams to show the components involved in the growth of the bivalve shell (after Owen, 1953a). A. The left valve of *Glycymeris*. B. A section of A through *UY*. C. The left valve of *Glossus*. G, the direction of growth at the mantle-shell margin; P, transverse component; R, radial component; T, tangential component; *UY*, demarcation line.

at right angles to the plane of the generating curve (P) (Owen, 1953a). The form of the shell valves is the resultant of these two components (G), while their ratio determines the spiral angle and so the concavity of the valves. In *Glycymeris* (Fig. 5 A), a convenient starting point for any discussion of shell form in the Bivalvia, marginal increment of each valve is greatest mid-ventrally (Y), least mid-dorsally (U), and intermediately graded around both sides of the valve margins. As a result, each valve would, if a complete whorl were produced, describe a planospiral about the umbo. Moreover, assuming the ratio of the radial and transverse components remained more or less constant throughout, the spiral would exhibit the properties of a logarithmic spiral (Thompson, 1942).

A similar analysis may be applied to the planospiral shells of gastropods and cephalopods. The shells of most gastropods, however, and of many bivalves, have the form of a turbinate or screw spiral. Huxley (1932) has explained such a shell form as the resultant of two differential growth ratios (median and lateral), inclined at an angle to one another. This is represented diagrammatically in Fig. 6, 2 and 5 (*Note:* the effect of the radial component is not represented in *1*, *2*, and *3*). The median differential growth ratio (UX) is similar to that of planospiral shells (Fig. 6, *1* and *4*), where growth out of the plane of the generating curve is greatest at X and least at U. But, whereas in a planospiral shell, growth is symmetrically graded around both sides of the mantle-shell edge, in the turbinate spiral shell (Fig. 6, 2) it is asymmetrical on either side of UX, thus giving rise to a second or lateral differential growth ratio between A and B. These two differential growth ratios could result solely from variations in the radial and transverse components of growth around the mantle-shell margin and such a turbinate spiral shell may be considered as the resultant of two systems of planospirals inclined at an angle to one another and both perpendicular to the plane of the generating curve.

In the Bivalvia, growth of a turbinate spiral shell is complicated by the existence of two shell valves and a connecting ligament, and here a turbinate spiral shell results from the existence of a third component of growth acting tangentially to, and in the plane of, the generating curve (Owen, 1953a). The effect of this third component is well shown in the shell of *Glossus humanus* (Fig. 5 C; T). In the majority of bivalves in which growth is affected by a tangential component, the radial and tangential components oppose one another anterior to the umbones (at A in Fig. 5 C) while posterior to the umbones they augment one another (at B). Consequently, a lateral differential growth ratio is produced between A and B (Fig. 6, 6). Thus, as in gastropods, growth of a turbinate spiral shell in the Bivalvia is the resultant of two differential growth ratios; but whereas one, the median ratio (UX), acts perpendicularly to the plane of the generating curve, the other, the lateral ratio *(AB)*, acts in the same plane as the generating curve. Only in this way can a turbinate spiral shell be produced in the Bivalvia while at the same time retaining the identity of the mantle isthmus which connects the two mantle lobes.

Lison (1949), when considering growth and form in these animals, concluded that a significant sector of the bivalve shell is represented by the "directive spiral." Unfortunately he did not consider the effect of a

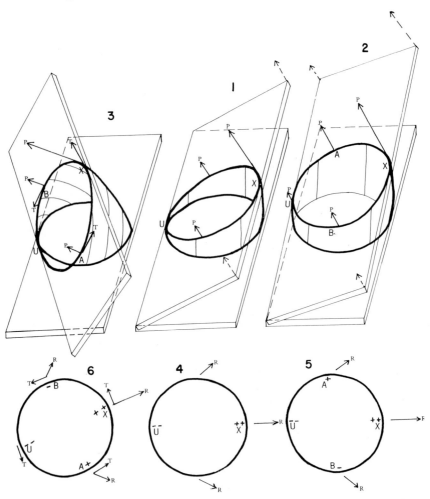

Fɪɢ. 6. Diagrams to illustrate the formation of *1*, a planospiral shell; *2*, a turbinate spiral shell in the gastropods (Huxley, 1932); *3*, a turbinate spiral shell in the Bivalvia (Owen, 1953a); *4*, *5*, and *6* are projections of the growing edge of the mantle of *1*, *2*, and *3*, respectively. *P*, transverse component; *R*, radial component; *T*, tangential component; *UX* and *AB*, median and lateral differential growth ratios, respectively. The effect of the radial component is not shown in *1*, *2*, and *3*.

tangential component on the growth of the shell; consequently, the directive spiral has little value either in the analysis of shell form or the comparison of shell form in different bivalves. In this connection Owen (1953a) has suggested that the significant sector of the bivalve shell is that represented by the demarcation line (Yonge, 1955; or "normal axis," Owen 1953a), which starts at the umbo and follows the region of greatest inflation of each valve. It is that sector of the shell produced by the region of the mantle margin where the ratio of the transverse to the radial component is greatest and divides the mantle-shell into anterior and posterior territories. In those shells where growth is not affected by a tangential component, the demarcation line of each valve has the form of a planospiral (Fig. 6, 1), but where growth is affected by a tangential component the demarcation line has the form of a turbinate spiral (Fig. 6, 3). The use of the demarcation line for comparing shell form in different bivalves and for analyzing qualitatively the interrelationships of the form of the mantle-shell with that of the body is illustrated in various papers by Yonge (1953a,b, 1955) and Owen (1953b, 1958, 1959).

3. Ecological Influences

Allometric relationships are altered by a variety of environmental influences, both seasonal (Hamai, 1935a) and regional (Hamai, 1935b, 1937; Walne, 1956). For example, the length:width ratio of oysters (*Crassostrea virginica*) growing on a soft bottom is considerably greater than it is for oysters growing on a hard bottom in the same general area (Orton, 1936; Gunter, 1938). The ratio has been shown to decrease with crowding in the pearl oyster, *Pinctada martensii* (Tanita and Kikuchi, 1957). In the bivalve *Venerupis rhomboides* the height:length ratio was found to decrease with depth (Holme, 1961). The relative height of the shell of the limpet *Patelloida conulus* (Hamai, 1937) and the shell angles of *Purpura lapillus* (Moore, 1936) vary according to environment. Specimens of *Mytilus californianus* living near or below low-water level were observed to have narrower and thinner shells than those exposed between tides (Fox and Coe, 1943).

Ecological influences can be expressed quantitatively by Eq. (4), the numerical values for which will be different for different localities and environments (Hamai, 1934, 1935a,b; Newcombe and Kessler, 1936; Fox and Coe, 1943; Swan, 1952). On the other hand, differences in shell parameters of a species growing in different localities are not necessarily of ecological origin as shown in a study in which two groups of young pearl oysters of differing shell shape were transplanted to the locale of a third distinct group. After a season of growth, two of the groups were similar in shell shape but the third remained distinct (Hasuo, 1958).

II. METHODS OF GROWTH MEASUREMENT

Growth measurements have had as their most frequent objective a determination of the influence of season, habitat, or age and thus have been usually concerned with a considerable time span. A few studies have been directed toward estimates of growth occurring in shorter periods, even as brief as a few hours. We present here a brief summary of methods used in these various studies.

A. Growth Rings

Variations in growth rate often result in shell markings called rings or checks. These growth rings when formed annually permit a measure of growth increments and accordingly growth rates. Rings are formed when, with increasing shell size, the fine striae of normal growth alternate with

Fig. 7. X-ray photograph of single valve of *Placopecten magellanicus*. Umbo region is not included. Note growth rings and circular area of muscle attachment. The sensitivity of the method is indicated by the appearance of the square of masking tape at right center. Operating characteristics of soft X-ray machine: 160 primary volts; 10 ma.; exposure 7 seconds; Panatomic-X film. A photograph of this same shell taken with visible light is shown in Stevenson and Dickie, 1954.

more closely spaced markings of changed contour or there is increased deposition of conchiolin at the shell periphery. Inter-ring distances can be measured directly on the outer shell surface with the aid of transmitted light (Saldau, 1939), or from X-ray photographs (Fig. 7). Physiologically, rings are of interest in that they indicate changes in mantle secretory activity and particularly alterations in the ratio of matrix to crystalline deposition.

A number of conditions bring about ring formation. They may be formed during the winter (*winter rings* or annuli) and one or more may be seen at the border of the new spring growth (Orton, 1923; Quayle, 1951–1952; Stevenson and Dickie, 1954). The counterpart of winter rings in the pearl is an increased deposition of conchiolin (Watabe, 1952b). A *summer ring* resulting from inhibition of growth at high temperatures may occur in species with a low temperature growth optimum (J. A. Posgay, cited by Haskin, 1954). Physical disturbances no greater than the handling required to make a shell measurement may be sufficient to induce ring formation (*disturbance ring* or check) (Orton, 1926–1927; Coe, 1947). Following interruption of shell growth, the new shell formed by the clam *Tivela stultorum* extends from underneath the shell edge, forming a slightly raised ring. The color of the shell may be quite different in the region of the ring (Coe, 1947). Violent wave action probably induces checks since they have been produced in *Mya* in the laboratory by stirring of the water containing silt (Shuster, 1951). A study of young stages of nine species of marine bivalves has shown that a ring is laid down between prodissoconch and spat stages and another ring is formed at the time that the spat detaches from the substratum (Yoshida, 1953). Larvae of bivalves such as the ark shell *Anadara subcrenata* form several rings within a few days (Kusakabe, 1959) and for this reason may very well be favorable experimental organisms for studies of mantle secretion.

Clearly, the use of rings as an indicator of age requires their establishment as annual marks for the species under study. Other natural markers which have been used as age indicators are ligament scars in the oyster *Crassostrea virginica* (T. C. Nelson, 1942, cited by Haskin, 1954); opercular rings in the marine gastropod *Babylonia japonica* (Kubo, 1953); and lines on the plates of the amphineuron *Chiton tuberculatus* (Crozier, 1918).

B. Marked or Segregated Individuals: Linear and Weight Measurements

Linear or weight measurements of segregated or marked individuals are commonly employed for following growth responses to particular experimental or environmental conditions and to provide information on growth over the complete life span of individuals of annual and biennial species (Baily, 1931; Abeloos, 1942). Marking and measuring may in themselves bring about temporary interruption of growth, as in all cases in which molluscs are handled. Disturbance can be minimized by weighing in water which provides a sensitive measure of growth changes and gives good reproducibility. Because of the difference in specific gravity between shell and tissue, shell growth is emphasized by this method (Havinga, 1928).

The growth of embryos and larvae has been followed under controlled laboratory conditions by successive measurements on samples from a single clutch or spawning (Dehnel, 1955; Loosanoff, 1954).

C. X-Ray Measurements

The increase in length and volume of marine borers growing in wood panels can be followed without interfering with growth by making X-ray photographs at intervals (Crisp et al., 1953; Trussel et al., 1956; Quayle, 1959). By means of soft X-rays one should be able to follow changes in form and thickness of growing shell in living molluscs. Estimates of thickness could be made from densitometric measurements of X-ray photographs.

D. Radioisotope Measurements

Molluscs placed in solutions to which Ca^{45} or C^{14}-bicarbonate have been added will incorporate these isotopes into their shell. The weight of mineral deposition can then be calculated from a direct measurement of the radioactivity of the inner shell surface according to the following relation:

$$D = \frac{A_s}{A_w} \times C \tag{7}$$

where D is milligrams of calcium or carbonate deposited per square centimeter; A_s is counts per minute per square centimeter of shell; A_w is counts per minute per liter of medium; and C is milligrams of calcium or bicarbonate per liter of medium (Wilbur and Jodrey, 1952). The application of the method requires: (1) that the shell-depositing mantle tissue be in approximate equilibrium with the surrounding solution; (2) that the period of growth measurement be brief enough and shell deposition small enough that self-absorption is unimportant; and (3) that exchange between shell and solution be of a low order of magnitude. The most serious limitation is probably the disturbance to normal growth resulting from handling.

E. Tetracycline as a Marker

Tetracycline HCl (Achromycin) (2 mg/0.1 ml) injected into the adductor muscle of the pearl oyster *Pinctada martensii* is incorporated into newly formed nacre and can be identified as a fluorescent line in sections of shell and pearls observed with ultraviolet light (Nakahara, 1961). The fluorescence can be observed after 1 day and is present after more than 2 years. By injecting tetracycline at intervals throughout the year a series of fluorescent lines is laid down, and from the distances between lines a measure of seasonal growth can be obtained. Tetracycline at a dose of 4 mg per oyster was found to be toxic.

F. Population Sampling

By plotting the frequency distribution of shell length or another growth parameter of a population sample, we obtain a series of modes representing individual year classes (Fig. 8). From the shift in mean values of year

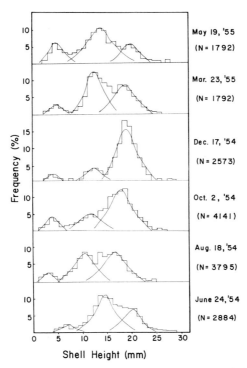

FIG. 8. Shell height frequency distributions showing growth of the clam *Corbicula japonica* (after Fuji, 1957). The different size groups at a given date are presumed to correspond to different age classes. The growth rates of these year classes as the season advances are estimated from the shift to the right in mean values of fitted normal curves.

classes the growth rate can be calculated. The method is adequate only under those conditions of seasonal growth such that each year class consists of a well-defined size group (Quayle, 1951–1952). Other limitations are (1) the possible error in age estimation due to poor representation of a particular year class; (2) difficulty in estimating the age of the youngest year class in the absence of additional information (Haskin, 1954); and (3) continuous hatching over several months, giving an increased size range. The frequency distribution method is frequently used in conjunction with another method. The cultivated Japanese pearl oyster has a special advantage here in that populations of known age from various localities are available for study.

III. AGE AND GROWTH

A. Molluscs as Experimental Material for Studies of Aging

Molluscs have a number of characteristics which make it likely that this group will prove advantageous for the study of aging processes, as Comfort (1957) has suggested in his review of longevity and aging. Species are available for study with life spans of less than 1 year (certain marine prosobranchs; Fretter, 1948); 1 year (certain opisthobranchs and pulmonates; Comfort, 1957); 1 to 2 years (Comfort, 1957); and several species are known to live 10 to 20 years or longer (Weymouth and McMillin, 1930; Weymouth et al., 1931; Hamai, 1937). For comparative studies populations with large numbers of individuals of many age groups covering a span of years are accessible. Studies could be carried through an entire life span on individuals from a single spawning raised under controlled conditions by utilizing culture methods now available (see Chapter 6). As an example of one type of study, Comfort (1957) found that the mortality rate in the snail *Planorbis* was decreased by lowering the temperature of culture. In the Mollusca as in other phyla, the sexes may show a difference in longevity with the female surviving longer. But in spite of the excellent experimental opportunities, information on aging is sparse; there is need for physiological, biochemical, and pathological investigations.

B. Absolute and Relative Growth

A measure of absolute growth for most of the life span of some species can be obtained from the spacing of annual rings, or in the case of short-lived species raised in the laboratory, from linear or weight measurements. The curve of growth as a function of age is commonly, though not invariably, sigmoid (Fig. 1A). Equations describing growth curves have been developed for *Siliqua patula* (Weymouth and McMillin, 1930; Baker, 1943), *Cardium corbis* (Weymouth and Thompson, 1930), *Limnaea columella* (Baily, 1931), *Patelloida grata, P. conulus,* and *Patella vulgata* (Hamai, 1937).

A number of conditions are known to alter the sigmoid shape of the growth curve. Seasonal changes in growth rate may give a sigmoid curve for each year, and these annual cycles will then be superimposed on the more general changes with age. The plateau toward the end of the life span indicating a decreased growth rate has been said to be absent in wild populations of annual and biennial species (Comfort, 1957); however, this phase is present in certain species grown in the laboratory (Abeloos, 1944). The absence of a plateau may be due to death from various causes, and under conditions favoring survival, the plateau might well be present. Abeloos followed the weight changes of molluscs of the genus *Arion* through development and found distinct phases related to the state of development of the gonad (Fig. 9). Interestingly, there were

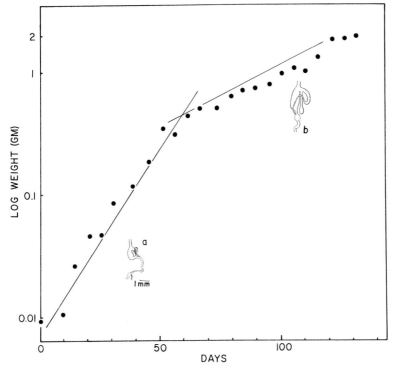

Fig. 9. Growth of *Arion subfuscus* (after Abeloos, 1944). The mean weight of 6 to 10 individuals is shown on a logarithmic scale. Note two main phases of growth which are related to gonad development.

two or three phases depending upon the species. Two cycles of shell growth have been described for the developmental stages of *Lymnaea japonica* prior to hatching (Imai, 1937). Ecological conditions may also influence the shape of the growth curve as shown for the razor clam *Siliqua patula* (see Chapter 2).

The course of relative growth can be followed by measuring the relative increase in some growth parameter during a limited period for individuals of different ages or of different sizes. From a physiological viewpoint, relative growth rather than absolute growth is the more useful mode of representation in that the growth increments are expressed in terms of the unit of tissue which produced them (Murray, 1925). Figure 10 illustrates changes in relative growth with age and size. In this example

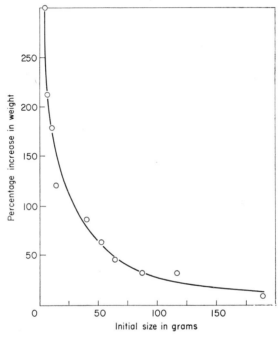

Fig. 10. Relative growth of the clam *Mercenaria mercenaria* (Haskin, 1954). The points give the average percentage increase in total weight in one year for marked clams of differing initial weight. Weight rather than age is used as reference because of the uncertainty of age determination. However, increase in weight would represent an increase in age.

and in Fig. 1B it is evident that relative growth decreases with age. The growth rate, highest in the youngest individuals, commonly declines rapidly with age; then in the older individuals there may be an extended period during which a slow growth continues at a rate which does not change greatly with time. This latter phase is evident from the sigmoid curves of absolute growth (Fig. 1A). From the curve of relative growth (Fig. 1B, lower curve) it can be seen that the growth rate during this period is greater than would be anticipated from an extrapolation of the curve for younger individuals. The decrease in growth rate with age, characteristic of organisms generally, has been described for a number of species of molluscs. The following provide examples: *Cardium edule* (Orton, 1926–1927; Kristensen, 1957); *Paphia stamina* (Fraser and Smith, 1928); *Siliqua patula* (Weymouth *et al.*, 1931); *Meretrix meretrix* (Hamai, 1935a); *Patelloida grata* (Hamai, 1937); *Crassostrea virginica* (Ingle and Dawson, 1952); *Crepidula fornicata* (Walne, 1956); *Pecten maximus* (Mason, 1957); *Tapes japonica* (Ohba, 1959); and *Siphonaria pectinata* (Voss, 1959). D'A. Thompson (1942), in discussing spiral shells, said it was reasonable to assume that the times required to deposit areas of shell subtended by equal angles is the same; that is, an inner whorl will be formed in the same period as an outer whorl. In view of the decrease in growth rate with age, this manner of growth is not to be expected. Growth of the minute cyclophorid snail *Opisthostoma* (*Plectostoma*) *retrovertens* is pertinent in this respect in that it forms rather evenly spaced ribs at a rate of about one per day except for the last few ribs which are more closely spaced. Shell growth ceased after about 124 days in the laboratory although the snails survived considerably longer (Berry, 1962).

Walne (1958) has measured the weight increments during a single season for oysters (*Ostrea edulis*) of the same age but of different initial weights. When the relative increments are calculated from his data (Fig. 11) one obtains the interesting result that the larger individuals grew less rapidly. Here is an instance in which individuals of the same age exhibit a decreased growth efficiency as their size increases. Kristensen (1957) has pointed out a similar relationship in *Cardium edule*. These findings suggest the possibility that the decreased growth rate in older individuals may be an effect of size as well as age. One result of a relatively slower growth rate with increase in size will be the reduction of the size spread in the population as growth continues. Such a decrease in variability has been described in the clam *Siliqua patula* (Weymouth *et al.*, 1931).

The rate of linear shell growth with age seen in various species provides a general index of the growth of the whole organism and of the mantle which is responsible for shell deposition. Yet one may not infer that rate of increase in shell mass necessarily corresponds to rate of increase in area since the shell continues to thicken after its increase in area becomes negligible (Fox and Coe, 1943). However, from weight measurements on pearl oysters of known age it was found that the rate of shell deposition decreased with age (Kobayashi and Watabe, 1959). The same was true of *Cardium edule* in which a more or less linear relationship held between shell length and the cube root of the shell weight but with variations due to age, season, and habitat (Kristensen, 1957). The growth of pearl, a process closely related to shell deposition, is affected by the age of the pearl oyster. To produce a pearl of a given size, a 1-year-old oyster may require 1 year whereas a 3-year-old oyster may require 2 years. (Watabe, 1963; see also Yamaguchi, 1958). The results on shell and pearl indicate a decrease in mantle efficiency with age in the deposition of $CaCO_3$. But other parts of the organism, less directly concerned but

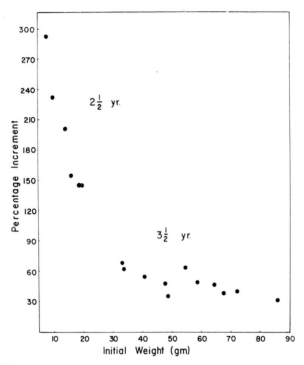

Fig. 11. Weight increments of one season as a function of initial weight in the oyster *Ostrea edulis* (data of Walne, 1958). Each point represents a single animal. The change in percentage increment with initial weight is greater and growth is more rapid for the 2½ year group.

nevertheless contributing to shell and pearl formation, may be involved as well. That mantle efficiency and a less favorable *milieu interieur* are both concerned in aging appears likely from studies on cultured pearls. The pearl is produced by inserting into the gonad a sphere of calcium carbonate shell and a piece of mantle from another oyster. The rate of pearl growth depends upon both the age of the host oyster and the age of the inserted piece of mantle which forms it (Yamaguchi, 1958).

C. Metabolic Studies

Since the growth rate decreases as the individual becomes larger and older, one may expect to find metabolic correlations with size and age.

The few metabolic studies of aging in molluscs which have been carried out indicate that progressive changes do occur.

Metabolic rate per unit weight has been found to decrease with increasing size in *Mytilus* (Zeuthen, 1947), *Teredo pedicellata* (Lane and Tierney, 1951), and in several arctic bivalves (Thorson, 1936). A comparison of the oxygen consumption of veliger larvae and adults of the prosobranch snails *Nassa reticulata* and *Littorina littorea* has shown that the respiration in the adults drops to one fourth or one fifth that in the larvae on a unit nitrogen basis (Zeuthen, 1947). From respiratory data and growth rates, Jørgensen (1952) has calculated the efficiency of growth for various size ranges of *Mytilus*, using combined data for *M. edulis* and *M. californianus*. The growth efficiency based on unit oxygen consumption decreased from 84% in animals of 0.35–6.0 mm in length to 11% in animals of about 90 mm in length.

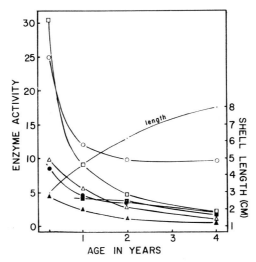

Fig. 12. Relations between carbonic anhydrase activity, age, and shell length in the pearl oyster *Pinctada martensii* (after Kawai, 1955). □, mantle edge; O, gill; ●, outer epidermis of mantle; △, digestive diverticula; ■, gonad; ▲, adductor muscle.

The efficiency of feeding in bivalves decreases as the individual becomes larger. Measurements using suspended material or radioactively-labeled microorganisms have shown that the rate of filtration by *Mytilus californianus*, *Pecten irradians*, and *Venus mercenaria* expressed in terms of unit weight or unit tissue is reduced with increase in size (Fox *et al.*, 1937; Jørgensen, 1949; Chipman and Hopkins, 1954; Rice and Smith, 1958). But we do not know the cause, whether from a decrease in efficiency of the filtration mechanism or from entrapment of particulates by mucus. In any case, the result is a reduced intake of food per unit tissue.

To what degree the observed decrease in relative growth rate with increase in size and age is due to this factor is also unknown.

The activity of the enzyme carbonic anhydrase in certain tissues of the pearl oyster *Pinctada martensii* has been observed to decrease sharply during the first year and to continue to decrease, though less markedly, during the second and third years (Kawai, 1955) (Fig. 12). Also, it has been found that in the mantle of *Crassostrea virginica* the activity of carbonic anhydrase is in general inversely proportional to shell length (Wilbur and Anderson, 1950). Carbonic anhydrase is associated with shell deposition (Wilbur and Jodrey, 1955; Freeman, 1960), and the decrease in enzyme activity with age in *Pinctada* has been related to the decreased rate of shell formation (Kawai, 1955). A causal relationship has not been established, however, and indeed this would present difficult experimental problems in view of the several factors concerned in shell formation (see Chapter 8).

Needham (1942) has cited data indicating that there is relatively little change in the dry weight/wet weight ratio with growth during the post-larval life of the snail *Littorina irrorata* and with embryonic development of *Sepia officinalis*, but that total ash as a function of dry weight decreases with growth in *Sepia* embryos ($\alpha = 0.86$; see p. 214).

IV. ENVIRONMENTAL CONDITIONS

A. Nutrients

Nutritional aspects of growth have been but little studied in molluscs. In fact, we do not know the organisms or materials serving as major nutritional sources for most species.

Leighton and Boolootian (1963) determined the food value of individual species of marine plants for growth of the abalone *Haliotis cracherodii*. Differences in food value were found and some species of plants failed to support growth (Table I). Also, in *H. discus hannai* two species of algae were reported to support growth whereas a third did not (Kinoshita, 1934, cited by Ino, 1953). Ino found a range of values for the brown alga *Eisenia* similar to those in Table I. In another study Ino (1958) fed various seaweeds to the gastropod *Turbo cornutus* for a 13-month period and found the relative effectiveness in promoting growth to be: *Eisenia bicyclis* > *Gelidium amansii* > *Sargassum ringgoldianum*. The cause of the differences between dietary sources will have to await information on the chief constituents of the plants and the extent of their digestion by the mollusc. *Haliotis* subjected to experimental starvation died in 2 or 3 months as the weight loss increased sharply and reached 14–27% (Leighton and Boolootian, 1963). The snail *Australorbis glabratus*, starved at 96% humidity, died after a weight loss of 30–35% or less during which as much as 50–60% of its organic material had been metabolized (von Brand *et al.*, 1957).

Coe (1948) found some correlation between the mean monthly increase in growth of the three bivalves *Mytilus californianus, M. edulis diegensis,* and *Tivela stultorum* and the abundance of dinoflagellates and diatoms. Similarly, Matthiessen (1960) observed that the growth of the clam *Mya arenaria* during a 50-day period was correlated with the average number of flagellates, and Pratt and Campbell (1956) found that the growth rate of *Venus (Mercenaria) mercenaria* was a function of the

TABLE I

Weight-Promoting Capacity of Marine Plants for
Haliotis cracherodii[a]

Species	Range of algal value quotients[b]
Macrocystis pyrifera	2.43– 8.80
Gigartina canaliculata	5.20– 9.80
Pelvetia fastigiata	6.20– 8.40
Gigartina spinosa	7.00–12.90
Eisenia arborea	9.80–18.80
Egregia laevigata	10.50–21.50
Dictyota flabellata	13.00–18.00
Pterocladia pyramidale	−1.2
Gelidium purpurascens	−1.1
Phyllospadix sp.	−0.9

[a] Leighton and Boolootian, (1963)

[b] The algal value quotient indicates the number of grams of a plant required to produce a weight gain of 1 gm in an experimental abalone. A negative value indicates a weight loss.

abundance of small diatoms in the environment. However, as Coe pointed out, correlations of this type are not necessarily meaningful and may indicate only that conditions favorable to the production of large populations of microorganisms also favor the growth of molluscs. There is the additional consideration that the number of microorganisms ingested is not necessarily a measure of nutritional intake since they may not be digested (Coe, 1947, 1948; Leighton and Boolootian, 1963). Also, detritus may well be an important nutritional source (Coe, 1948). By employing radioactively-labeled microorganisms, both living and dead, it should be possible to determine what fraction of the material filtered by the mollusc is absorbed (see Chipman and Hopkins, 1954).

The nutritional requirements of larvae may be different from those of the adult as suggested by the observation of Ino (1953) that larvae of *Haliotis* grow well on calcareous algae and microalgae but are retarded in growth on reaching a certain stage. Nutrition and feeding of mollusc larvae are discussed in Chapter 6.

B. Temperature

The effects of temperature on growth rate in molluscs have been examined in natural populations and under controlled laboratory conditions.

Field studies of temperature effects face the obvious complexity of the influence of multiple factors. Food quality and intake (Loosanoff *et al.*, 1953; Davis and Guillard, 1958), age (Hamai, 1935a), and latitude (Bullock, 1955) all may have concomitant effects in addition to the direct effects of temperature on metabolic and active transport reactions. Below a given temperature, feeding ceases, the digestive tract becomes empty, and growth is very slow or absent. The animal is said to be in hibernation although equivalence to hibernation in vertebrates is not implied by this term. Cessation of feeding occurs at the relatively high temperature of 13°C in the Japanese pearl oyster *Pinctada martensii* (Kobayashi and Watabe, 1959), at about 5°C in the oyster drill *Urosalpinx cinerea* (Hanks, 1957), and below 5°C in *Crassostrea virginica* (Loosanoff, 1958) and *Mytilus edulis* (Loosanoff, 1942). Growth of *Venus* (*Mercenaria*) *mercenaria* was found to be negligible below 10°C (Pratt and Campbell, 1956). The influence of factors other than temperature can be shown by plotting continuous growth rates as a function of temperature over an

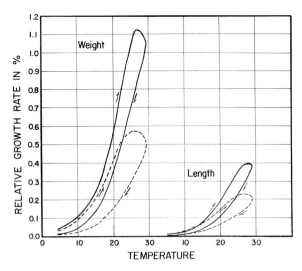

FIG. 13. Relative rates of shell growth of *Meretrix meretrix* as a function of temperature (Hamai, 1935a). Solid line, second year of growth; broken line, third year of growth. Note that the relative growth rate during the second year is greater than that during the third year at a given temperature. Also, the relative growth rate is higher with ascending than with descending temperature.

extended period (Hamai, 1935a). In *Meretrix meretrix*, for example, the growth rate for a given temperature decreases with the advance of the season (Fig. 13; note direction of arrows).

The quantitative aspects of temperature and growth rate are simple in some species and of considerable complexity in others. Equations relating growth rate to environmental temperatures have been given for a few species. Watabe (1952a) found that the weight of the nacreous layer of the growing pearl increased directly as the summation of the average daily temperature when the daily average was above 13°C, which was the lower limit for growth (Fig. 14). The break in the curve at June oc-

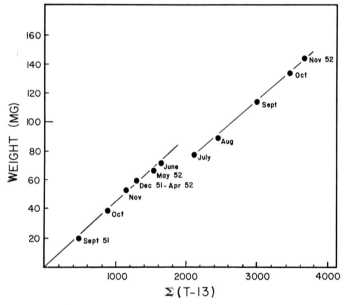

FIG. 14. Growth of pearl as a function of temperature (Watabe, 1952). Ordinate: mean weight of nacreous layer. Each ponit represents 80 pearls.

curred at a time of spawning and low salinity. Taking into account food supply as well as temperature, Yuki (1953) developed an equation which described the growth of young pearl oysters growing at different rates in two localities. In this equation

$$W = \frac{a \log (T - 13)}{t} - b$$

W is weight, T is average daily temperature, t is the average daily water transparency used as a measure of food supply, and a and b are constants (Yuki, 1953). Taylor (1959), using air temperatures as an index of environmental temperature, has calculated a regression equation for growth rate as a function of temperature for the clam *Siliqua* growing at various latitudes. Although a correlation coefficient of 0.911 was found for temperature and growth, evidence of several kinds indicates that physiological rates at different latitudes involve more than temperature differences.

One may expect that temperature will affect different parameters of growth differently. This was found to be the case in marine gastropod embryos and larvae in which the Q_{10} values for body growth were different from those for shell growth (Dehnel, 1955). Moreover, for shell the temperature effect on increase in weight is different from its effect on increase in length, as Hamai (1935a) (Fig. 13) has demonstrated in *Meretrix meretrix*. That there should be a difference is not surprising since the increase in weight is primarily a function of moving ions across the mantle, whereas the increase in length is determined by the extent of mantle growth. The growth response to temperature is probably age-dependent as indicated by the difference in response of second- and third-year specimens of *Meretrix meretrix* (Fig. 13). It is also suggestive that the oxygen consumption of arctic bivalves rises more steeply with temperature in young individuals than in adults (Thorson, 1936).

The temperature and growth relationships in larval stages are complex. Even larvae of the same age, raised under identical conditions, show variations in their growth responses. Usually the rate of growth increases with temperature, and Loosanoff (1959) found an approximately rectilinear relation for *Mercenaria mercenaria* larvae between 18° and 30°C. On the other hand, in individual experiments the rate decreased with a temperature increase of a few degrees within the viable range (Loosanoff *et al.* 1951) or showed relatively little change (Dehnel, 1955; see also Imai, 1937).

The effect of temperature on the growth rate of the embryos and larvae of a given species from different latitudes may be quite different, as Dehnel (1955) has shown for intertidal gastropods. Growth rates of northern populations (lat. 57° 03′ N.) were found to be 2 to 9 times that of southern populations (lat. 34° 00′ N.) of the same species at a given comparable temperature (see Chapter 2, IVA).

V. VARIABILITY AND ABNORMALITIES OF GROWTH

Variability in growth in a population of molluscs living in a restricted locality may be very considerable. This is perhaps to be expected in stock of unknown genetic constitution and with differences in micro-environments such as might occur in the field. In one case in which individuals from a single clutch of eggs of the snail *Lymnaea columella* were measured throughout their life span under laboratory conditions, the growth rates were similar (Baily, 1931). The same was found in *Arion*, but not in all cases (Abeloos, 1944). An extreme case of a variant was seen in stunted oysters (Cole and Waugh, 1959) which exhibited minimal linear growth when other oysters in the same population were growing normally. The interesting point is that the growth inhibition appeared to be permanent in that relocation in a favorable environment usually did not bring about resumption of growth (see Chestnut, 1952). Physiological studies of these individuals, and others placed temporarily in environmental situations in which stunting occurs, might contribute information for the general understanding of growth.

Individual snails of the genera *Hydrobia* (*Peringia*) and *Bulimus* attain an unusually large size. A high percentage of the giant forms are infected with larval trematodes which may bring about partial or complete destruction of the gonads (Rothschild, 1936; Boettger, 1952). Infected snails grew at a rate which was faster than normal (Rothschild and Rothschild, 1939). The cause of the unusual growth, whether from gonad destruction or compounds from the parasite, is unknown. However, a hormonal deficiency is an obvious possibility, particularly in view of the decreased growth rate occurring at the time of gonad ripening in some gastropods (Boettger, 1952).

REFERENCES

Abeloos, M. (1942). Les étapes de la croissance chez la Limace rouge (*Arion rufus* L.). *Compt. rend. acad. sci.* **215**, 38–39.

Abeloos, M. (1944). Recherches expérimentales sur la croissance. La croissance des mollusques arionidés. *Bull. biol. France et Belg.* **78**, 215–256.

Baily, J. L. (1931). Some data on growth, longevity, and fecundity in *Lymnaea columella* Say. *Biol. Generalis* **7**, 407–428.

Baker, G. A. (1943). Length-growth curves for the razor clam *Siliqua patula. Growth* **7**, 439–443.

Berry, A. J. (1962). The growth of *Opisthostoma* (*Plectostoma*) *retrovertens* Tomlin, a minute cyclophorid from a Malayan limestone hill. *Proc. Malacol. Soc. London* **35**, 46–49.

Boettger, C. R. (1952). Grössenwachstum und Geschlechsreife bei Schnecken und pathologíscher Riesenwuchs als Folge einer gestörten Wechselwirkung beider Faktoren. *Zool. Anz.* Suppl. No. 17, 468–487.

Brody, S. (1945). "Bioenergetics and Growth." Reinhold, New York.

Bullock, T. H. (1955). Compensation for temperature in the metabolism and activity of poikilotherms. *Biol. Revs. Cambridge Phil. Soc.* **30**, 311–342.

Chestnut, A. F. (1952). Growth rates and movements of hard clams, *Venus mercenaria. Proc. Gulf Caribbean Fisheries Inst.*, 49–59.

Chipman, W. A., and Hopkins, J. G. (1954). Water filtration by the bay scallop, *Pecten irradians,* as observed with the use of radioactive plankton. *Biol. Bull.* **107**, 80–91.

Coe, W. R. (1947). Nutrition, growth and sexuality in the pismo clam (*Tivela stultorum*). *J. Exptl. Zool.* **104**, 1–24.

Coe, W. R. (1948). Nutrition, environmental conditions, and growth of marine bivalve molluscs. *J. Marine Res. (Sears Foundation)* **7**, 586–601.

Cole, H. A., and Waugh, G. D. (1959). The problem of stunted growth in oysters. *J. conseil perm. intern. exploration Mer* **24**, 355–365.

Comfort, A. (1957). The duration of life in molluscs. *Proc. Malacol. Soc. London* **52**, 219–241.

Crisp, D. J., Jones, L. W. G., and Watson, W. (1953). Use of x-ray stereoscopy for examining shipworm infestation in vivo. *Nature* **172**, 408–409.

Crozier, W. J. (1918). Growth and duration of life in *Chiton tuberculatus. Proc. Natl. Acad. Sci. U.S.* **4**, 322–325.

Davis, H. C., and Guillard, R. R. (1958). Relative value of ten genera of microorganisms as foods for oyster and clam larvae. *U.S. Fish Wildlife Serv., Fishery Bull.* **136**, 293–304.

Dehnel, P. A. (1955). Rates of growth of gastropods as a function of latitude. *Physiol. Zoöl.* **28**, 115–144.

Dehnel, P. A. (1956). Growth rates in latitudinally and vertically separated populations of *Mytilus californianus. Biol. Bull.* **110**, 43–53.

Fox, D. L., and Coe, W. R. (1943). Biology of the California sea-mussel (*Mytilus californianus*). II. Nutrition, metabolism, growth and calcium deposition. *J. Exptl. Zool.* **93**, 205–249.

Fox, D. L., Sverdrup, H. U., and Cunningham, J. P. (1937). The rate of water propulsion by the California mussel. *Biol. Bull.* **72**, 417–438.

Fraser, C. M., and Smith, G. M. (1928). Notes on the ecology of the butter clam, *Saxidomus giganteus* Deshayes. *Proc. & Trans. Roy. Soc. Canada* [3] **22**, 271–286.

Freeman, J. A. (1960). Influence of carbonic anhydrase inhibitors on shell growth of a fresh water snail, *Physa heterostropha. Biol. Bull.* **118**, 412–418.

Fretter, V. (1948). The structure and life history of some minute prosobranchs of rock pools: *Skeneopsis planorbis* (Fabricius), *Omalogyra atomus* (Philippi), *Risseola diaphana* (Alder), and *Risseola opalina* (Jeffreys). *J. Marine Biol. Assoc. U.K.* **27**, 597–632.

Fuji, A. (1957). Growth and breeding season of the brackish-water bivalve, *Corbicula japonica* in Zyusan-Gata Inlet. *Bull. Fac. Fisheries, Hokkaido Univ.* **8**, 178–184.

Gibson, F. A. (1956). Escallops (*Pecten maximum* L.) in Irish waters. *Sci. Proc. Roy. Dublin Soc.* **27**, 253–270.

Gunter, G. (1938). Comments on the shape, growth and quality of the American oyster. *Science* **88**, 546–547.

Hamai, I. (1934). Relation between the weight, volume and linear dimensions in *Meretrix meretrix* (L.). *Sci. Repts. Tôhoku Univ., Fourth Ser.* **9**, 205–212.

Hamai, I. (1935a). On the growth of the shell of *Meretrix meretrix*, especially with regard to periodicity of growth relatively to the seasonal variations in the environment. *Sci. Repts. Tôhoku Univ., Fourth Ser.* **9**, 339–371.

Hamai, I. (1935b). A study of one case in which different environmental conditions produce different types of *Meretrix meretrix. Sci. Repts. Tôhoku Univ., Fourth Ser.* **10**, 485–498.

Hamai, I. (1936). Relative growth in some bivalves. *Sci. Repts. Tôhoku Univ., Fourth Ser.* **10**, 753–765.

Hamai, I. (1937). Some notes on relative growth, with special reference to the growth of limpets. *Sci. Repts. Tôhoku Univ., Fourth Ser.* **12**, 71–95.

Hamai, I. (1938). Relative growth of *Meretrix meretrix* and its local variation, as shown by experiments in rearing. *Sci. Repts. Tôhoku Univ. Fourth Ser.* **13**, 205–220.

Hanaoka, T., and Shimadzu, T. (1949). Studies on the morphometry and rate of growth in the clam *Mactra sulcataria* Reeve, in Tokyo Bay. *Bull. Japan. Soc. Sci. Fisheries* **15**, 311–317.

Hanks, J. E. (1957). The rate of feeding of the common oyster drill, *Urosalpinx cinerea* (Say), at controlled water temperatures. *Biol. Bull.* **112**, 330–335.

Haskin, H. H. (1954). Age determination in molluscs. *Trans. N. Y. Acad. Sci.* [2] **16**, 300–304.

Hasuo, M. (1958). The shell variation during growth in the Mie pearl-oysters and those transplanted from Nagasaki Prefecture. *Bull. Natl. Pearl Research Lab.* **4**, 318–324.

Havinga, B. (1928). The daily rate of growth of oysters during summer. *J. Conseil permanent intern. exploration mer.* **3**, 231–245.

Holme, N. A. (1961). Shell form in *Venerupis rhomboides*. *J. Marine Biol. Assoc. U.K.* **41**, 705–722.

Huxley, J. S. (1932). "Problems of Relative Growth." Dial Press, New York.

Huxley, J. S., and Teissier, G. (1936). Terminology of relative growth. *Nature* **137**, 780–781.

Imai, T. (1937). The larval shell growth of *Lymnaea japonica* Jay. In special reference to the influence of temperature. *Sci. Repts. Tôhoku Univ., Fourth Ser.* **11**, 419–432.

Ingle, R. M., and Dawson, C. E. (1952). Growth of the American oyster *Crassostrea virginica* (Gmelin) in Florida waters. *Bull. Marine Sci. Gulf and Caribbean* **2**, 393–404.

Ino, T. (1953). Biological studies on propagation of Japanese abalone (genus *Haliotis*). *Bull. Tokai Regional Fisheries Research Lab.* **5**.

Ino, T. (1958). Ecological studies of the topshell, *Turbo cornutus* (Solander). II. Relation between diet and coloration of the shell. *Bull. Tokai Regional Fisheries Res. Lab.* **22**, 33–36.

Isham, L. D., Moore, H. B., and Smith, F. G. W. (1951). Growth rate measurement of shipworms. *Bull. Marine Sci. Gulf and Caribbean* **1**, 136–147.

Jørgensen, C. B. (1949). The rate of feeding by Mytilus of different kinds of suspension. *J. Marine Biol. Assoc. U.K.* **28**, 333–344.

Jørgensen, C. B. (1952). Efficiency of growth in *Mytilus edulis* and two gastropod veligers. *Nature* **170**, 714.

Kawai, D. K. (1955). Carbonic anhydrase in pearl oyster. II. Changes of the enzyme activity in relation to growth and seasons. *Publs. Seto Marine Biol. Lab. (Kyoto Univ.)* **5**, 89–94.

Kinoshita, T. (1934). On the growth of ezoawabi (*H. ramtschatkana*). *Rakusuikai shi* **29**, 1–7.

Kobayashi, S., and Watabe, N. (1959). "The Study of Pearls." Gihodo Press, Tokyo.

Kristensen, I. (1957). Differences in density and growth in a cockle population in the Dutch Wadden Sea. *Arch. neerl. zool.* **12**, 351–453.

Kubo, I. (1953). Age determination of the *Babylonica japonica* (Reeve) an edible marine gastropod, basing on the operculum. *J. Tokyo Univ. Fisheries* **34**, 199.

Kusakabe, D. (1959). Studies on the culture of the artificial seeds of the ark shell *Anadara subcrenata* (Lischke). *J. Fac. Fisheries Animal Husb. Hiroshima Univ.* **2**, 183–239.

Lane, C. E., and Tierney, J. Q. (1951). Hydrodynamics and respiration in *Teredo*. *Bull. Marine Sci. Gulf and Caribbean* **1**, 104–110.

Leighton, D., and Boolootian, R. A. (1963). *Ecology*, in press.

Lison, L. (1949). Recherches sur la forme et la mechanique de developpement des coquilles de Lamellibranches. *Mem. inst. roy. sci. nat. Belg.* **34**, 1–87.

Loosanoff, V. L. (1942). Shell movements of the edible mussel *Mytilus edulis* (L.) in relation to temperature. *Ecology* **23**, 231–234.

Loosanoff, V. L. (1954). New advances in the study of bivalve larvae. *Am. Scientist* **42**, 607–624.

Loosanoff, V. L. (1958). Some aspects of behavior of oysters at different temperatures. *Biol. Bull.* **114**, 57–70.

Loosanoff, V. L. (1959). The size and shape of metamorphosing larvae of *Venus* (*Mercenaria*) *mercenaria* grown at different temperatures. *Biol. Bull.* **117**, 308–318.

Loosanoff, V. L., Miller, W. S., and Smith, P. B. (1951). Growth and setting of larvae of *Venus mercenaria* in relation to temperature. *J. Marine Research* (Sears Foundation) **10**, 59–81.

Loosanoff, V. L., Davis, H. C., and Chanley, P. E. (1953). Behavior of clam larvae in different concentrations of food organisms. *Anat. Record* **117**, 586–587.

Mason, J. (1957). The age and growth of the scallop, *Pecten maximus* (L.), in Manx waters. *J. Marine Biol. Assoc. U.K.* **36**, 473–492.

Matthiessen, G. C. (1960). Observations on the ecology of the soft clam, *Mya arenaria*, in a salt pond. *Limnol. Oceanog.* **5**, 291–300.

Moore, H. B. (1936). The biology of *Purpura lapillus*. I. Shell variation in relation to environment. *J. Marine Biol. Assoc. U.K.* **21**, 61–89.

Murray, H. A. (1925). Physiological ontogeny. *J. Gen. Physiol.* **9**, 39–48.

Nakahara, H. (1961). Determination of growth rates of nacreous layer by the administration of tetracycline. *Bull. Natl. Pearl Research Lab.* **6**, 607–614.

Nayar, K. N. (1955). Studies on the growth of the wedge clam *Donax* (*Latona*) *cuneatus* Linnaeus. *Indian J. Fisheries* **2**, 325–348.

Needham, J. (1942). "Biochemistry and Morphogenesis." Cambridge Univ. Press, London and New York.

Newcombe, C. L., and Kessler, H. (1936). Variations in growth indices of *Mya arenaria* L. on the Atlantic Coast of North America. *Ecology* **17**, 429–443.

Nomura, E. (1928). On the relation between weight and dimensions in the bivalves *Tapes philippinarum* and *Cythera meretrix* Linn. *Sci. Repts. Tôhoku Univ., Fourth Ser.* **3**, 113–124.

Nomura, E., and Sasaki, K. (1928). On the relation between weight and dimensions in the gastropods, *Haliotis gigantea* var. *discus* and *Littorina sitchana*. *Sci. Repts. Tôhoku Univ., Fourth Ser.* **3**, 125–131.

Ohba, S. (1959). Ecological studies in the natural population of a clam, *Tapes japonica*, with special reference to seasonal variations in the size and structure of the population and to individual growth. *Biol. J. Okayama Univ.* **5**, 13–42.

Orton, J. H. (1923). On the significance of "rings" on the shells of *Cardium* and other molluscs. *Nature* **112**, 10.

Orton, J. H. (1926–1927). On the rate of growth of *Cardium edule*, Part I, Experimental observations. *J. Marine Biol. Assoc. U.K.* **14**, 239–279.

Orton, J. H. (1936). Habit and shell-shape in the Portuguese oyster, *Ostrea angulata*. *Nature* **138**, 466–467.

Owen, G. (1953a). On the biology of *Glossus humanus* (L.) (*Isocardia cor* Lam.) *J. Marine Biol. Assoc. U.K.* **32**, 85–106.

Owen, G. (1953b). The shell in the Lamellibranchia. *Quart. J. Microscop. Sci.* **94**, 57–70.

Owen, G. (1958). Shell form, pallial attachment and the ligament in Bivalvia. *Proc. Zool. Soc.* (*London*) **131**, 637–648.

Owen, G. (1959). Observations on the Solenacea with reasons for excluding the family Glaucomyidae. *Phil. Trans. Roy. Soc.* **B242**, 59–96.

Pratt, D. M., and Campbell, D. A. (1956). Environmental factors affecting growth in *Venus mercenaria*. *Limnol. Oceanog.* **1**, 2–17.

Quayle, D. B. (1951–1952). The rate of growth of *Venerupis pullastra* (Montagu) at Millport, Scotland. *Proc. Roy. Sci. Edinburgh* **B64**, 384–406.

Quayle, D. B. (1959). The growth rate of *Bankia setacea* Tryon. *In* "Marine Boring and Fouling Organisms" (D. L. Ray, ed.), pp. 175–183. Univ. of Washington Press, Seattle, Washington.

Rice, T. R., and Smith, R. J. (1958). Filtering rates of the hard clam (*Venus mercenaria*) determined with radioactive phytoplankton. *Fisheries Bull. Fish and Wildlife Serv.* **58**, 73–82.

Rothschild, A., and Rothschild, M. (1939). Some observations on the growth of *Peringia ulvae* (Pennant) 1777 in the laboratory. *Novitates Zool.* **41**, 240–247.

Rothschild, M. (1936). Gigantism and variation in *Peringia ulvae* Pennant 1777, caused by larval trematodes. *J. Marine Biol. Assoc. U.K.* **20**, 537–546.

Saldau, M. P. (1939). Rate of growth of commercially valuable molluscs in the European part of U.S.S.R. in relation to ecologic conditions. *Bull. Inst. Fresh-water Fish.* **22**, 244–269.

Sholl, D. A. (1954). Regularities in growth curves including rhythms and allometry. *In* "Dynamics of Growth Processes" (E. J. Boell, ed.), pp. 224–241. Princeton Univ. Press, Princeton, New Jersey.

Shuster, C. N. (1951). On the formation of mid-season checks in the shell of *Mya*. *Anat. Record* **111**, 543.

Stevenson, J. A., and Dickie, L. M. (1954). Annual growth rings and rate of growth of the giant scallop *Placopecten magellanicus* (Gmelin) in the Digby area of the Bay of Fundy. *J. Fisheries Research Board Can.* **11**, 660–671.

Swan, E. F. (1952). Growth indices of the clam *Mya arenaria*. *Ecology* **33**, 365–374.

Tanaka, J. (1958). On the stock of *Octopus (Octopus) vulgaris* Lamarck, on the east coast of Boso Peninsula, Japan. *Bull. Japan. Soc. Sci. Fisheries* **24**, 601–607.

Tanita, S., and Kikuchi, S. (1957). On the density-effect of the raft cultured oysters. I. The density effect within one plate. *Bull. Tôhoku Reg. Fisheries Research Lab.* **9**, 133–142.

Taylor, C. C. (1959). Temperature and growth—The Pacific razor clam. *J. Conseil permanent intern. exploration mer.* **25**, 93–101.

Teissier, G. (1960). Relative growth. *In* "The Physiology of Crustacea" (T. H. Waterman, ed.), Vol. I. pp. 537–560. Academic Press, New York.

Thompson, D'A. W. (1942). "On Growth and Form." Cambridge Univ. Press, London and New York.

Thorson, G. (1936). The larval development, growth, and metabolism of arctic marine bottom invertebrates. *Medd. Grønland* **100**, No. 6.

Trussell, P. C., Greer, B. A., and LeBrasseur, R. J. (1956). Storage ground study. *Pulp. & Paper Mag. Can.* **57**, 77–80.

von Brand, T., McMahon, P., and Nolan, M. O. (1957). Physiological observations on starvation and desiccation of the snail *Australorbis glabratus*. *Biol. Bull.* **113**, 89–102.

Voss, N. A. (1959). Studies on the pulmonate gastropod *Siphonaria pectinata* (Linnaeus) from the southeast coast of Florida. *Bull. Marine Sci. Gulf and Caribbean* **9**, 84–99.

Walne, P. R. (1956). The biology and distribution of the slipper limpet *Crepidula fornicata* in Essex rivers. *Ministry Agr. Fish and Food, Fisheries Invest.* [2] **20**, 1–50.

Walne, P. R. (1958). Growth of oysters (*Ostrea edulis L.*). *J. Marine Biol. Assoc. U.K.* **37**, 591–602.

Watabe, N. (1952a). Relation between water temperature and nacre-secreting activity of the pearl-oyster *Pinctada martensii*. *J. Fuji Pearl Inst.* **2**, 21–34.

Watabe, N. (1952b.) On the abnormal lamellae of cultured pearls and the environmental conditions under which these lamellae are formed. *J. Fuji Pearl Inst.* **2**, 27–34.

Watabe, N. (1963). Personal communication.

Weymouth, F. W., and McMillin, H. C. (1930). Relative growth and mortality of Pacific razor clam (*Siliqua patula* Dixon) and their bearing on the commercial fishery. *Bull. U.S. Bur. Fisheries* **46**, 543–567.

Weymouth, F. W., McMillin, H. C., and Rich, W. H. (1931). Latitude and relative growth of the razor clam, *Siliqua patula* Dixon. *J. Exptl. Biol.* **8**, 228–249.

Weymouth, F. W., and Thompson, S. H. (1930). The age and growth of the Pacific cockle (*Cardium corbis* Martyn). *Bull. U.S. Bur. Fisheries* **46**, 633–641.

Wilbur, K. M., and Anderson, N. G. (1950). Carbonic anhydrase and growth in the oyster and *Busycon*. *Biol. Bull.* **98**, 19–24.

Wilbur, K. M., and Jodrey, L. H. (1952). Studies on shell formation. I. Measurement of the rate of shell formation using Ca^{45}. *Biol. Bull.* **103**, 269–276.

Wilbur, K. M., and Jodrey, L. H. (1955). Studies on shell formation. V. The inhibition of shell formation by carbonic anhydrase inhibitors. *Biol. Bull.* **108**, 359–365.

Yamaguchi, K. (1958). On the difference of color and thickness of pearl layer of cultured pearls caused by the disparity in age of mother oysters. *Bull. Natl. Pearl Res. Lab.* **4**, 325–328.

Yonge, C. M. (1952). Studies on Pacific coast molluscs. IV. Observations on *Siliqua patula* Dixon and on evolution within the Solenidae. *Univ. Calif. (Berkeley) Publs. Zool.* **55**, 421–438.

Yonge, C. M. (1953a). The monomyarian condition in the Lamellibranchia. *Trans. Roy. Soc. Edinb.* **62**, 421–478.

Yonge, C. M. (1953b). Form and habit in *Pinna carnea* Gmelin. *Phil. Trans. B.* **237**, 335–374.

Yonge, C. M. (1955). Adaptation to rock-boring in *Botula* and *Lithophaga* (Lamellibranchia, Mytilidae). *Quart. J. Microscop. Sci.* **96**, 383–410.

Yoshida, H. (1953). Studies on larvae and young shells of industrial bivalves in Japan. *Shimonoseki Coll. Fisheries* **3**, 1–105.

Yuki, R. (1953). Personal communication.

Zeuthen, E. (1947). Body size and metabolic rate in the animal kingdom with special regard to the marine micro-fauna. *Compt. rend. trav. lab. Carlsberg, Sér. chim.* **26**, 17–161.

CHAPTER 8

Shell Formation and Regeneration

KARL M. WILBUR

DEPARTMENT OF ZOOLOGY, DUKE UNIVERSITY, DURHAM, NORTH CAROLINA

I. SHELL FORMATION

Studies of the shell have contributed perhaps the largest fraction of the literature on the Mollusca—and understandably so. Important investigational aspects have included taxonomy, growth and form, microscopic crystalline structure, and the capacity of the mollusc to replace portions lost through injury. Another area of investigation—recent, promising, and relatively little studied—has implications beyond mollusc shell as such and relates to all those biological systems which form crystals. This is the study of calcification. Here one encounters the problems of analysis of crystal formation, the building of complex crystalline structures, and the synthesis of the organic matrix of the shell. The methods are those of crystallography, molecular biology, biochemistry, and cellular physiology. Our discussion will emphasize these more recent aspects of shell study from which only the major features have begun to be evident.

A. Structural Relations

The mollusc in depositing its shell accomplishes the formation of a structure external to its tissues and yet highly ordered in the arrangement of its mineral and organic components. Essentially, the process consists in the deposition of crystals of calcium carbonate on an organic matrix which is largely protein and is called conchiolin. The tissue responsible for forming the shell is the mantle, which covers the inner growing surface of the shell and in some species is reflected over the outer surface as well. The rate of increase in shell area is thus a function of the increase in mantle area, whereas the rate of increase in thickness and weight is a function of the rate of secretion of the calcium carbonate and the organic matrix. The calcium carbonate is deposited in three crystalline forms— calcite, aragonite, and vaterite—which differ in the arrangement of the crystal lattice. Chalky deposits in shell have been said to be amorphous calcium carbonate, but in the oyster *Crassostrea virginica*, X-ray diffraction analysis shows this material to be calcite (Watabe and Simkiss, 1963).

The structural organization of shell is enormously varied depending upon the species, and no brief account can provide an adequate summary of the crystalline structures. Three commonly occurring crystal arrangements may be mentioned: (1) *prismatic structure* consisting of a columnar arrangement of crystals surrounded by matrix; (2) *foliate or laminar structure* in which a layer comprises parallel crystalline sheets one crystal in thickness; and (3) *crossed lamellar structure* characterized by large lamellae made up of numerous small cross lamellae and arranged in such a way that the small lamellae of adjoining large lamellae are inclined in opposite directions and at definite angles to each other. Detailed discussions of shell structure are given by Bøggild (1930) and Haas (1935).

As a reference model for our discussions of shell formation it will be convenient to consider a bivalve mollusc with a shell consisting of three layers (Fig. 1). In vertical section one would see an outer organic layer

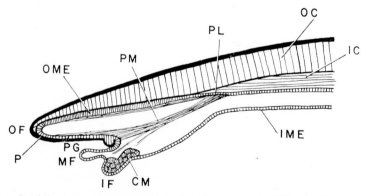

Fig. 1. Semidiagrammatic cross section of shell and mantle. CM, circular muscle; IC, inner crystalline layer; IF, inner mantle fold; IME, inner mantle epithelium; MF, middle mantle fold; OC, outer crystalline layer; OF, outer mantle fold; OME, outer mantle epithelium; P, periostracum; PG, periostracal groove; PL, pallial line; PM, pallial muscle.

called the periostracum and two crystalline layers. The columnar crystalline layer adjacent to the periostracum is the prismatic layer. The inner layer, laminate in arrangement, is known as the nacreous layer if the crystals are aragonite, or calcitostracum if the crystals are calcite. Viewed from the inner surface of the shell, the large central portion would be the nacreous layer or calcitostracum, with the prismatic layer as a narrow border at the periphery. Each of the three layers of the shell is deposited by a specialized portion of the mantle (Beedham, 1958a).

There are three major aspects involved in the formation of shell: (1) metabolic reactions associated with calcium carbonate formation and the synthesis of the organic matrix; (2) the secretion of components of the shell by the mantle; and (3) crystal growth and the formation of the crystalline layers. We shall consider details of these.

B. Metabolic Aspects of Shell Formation

1. CALCIUM

a. *Uptake of Calcium.* The metabolic features of shell formation may be viewed in terms of a multicompartmented system (see Fig. 2): the cells of the mantle are bathed on one side by body fluids or external medium and secrete, into the extrapallial fluid in contact with the inner shell surface on the other side, the inorganic and organic components of shell. The components of the extrapallial fluid separate out as a solid phase compartment which is the shell itself.

The amount of calcium deposited as shell will be a function of the calcium concentration of the medium and the amount entering the body. From ecological studies it is known that in land and fresh-water environments in which calcium is not readily available, shells are often thin (e.g., Boycott, 1934). In marine molluscs a marked reduction of the calcium concentration of sea water may reduce or prevent calification (Bevelander and Benzer, 1948; Koczy and Titze, 1958; Kado, 1960). Kado found that as the calcium content of sea water was increased from about 125 mg/liter to the normal concentration of about 400 mg/liter the rate of calcium deposition in *Crassostrea gigas* was increased but that there was no further increase at higher concentrations. The limiting factor determining the maximum rate is not known.

The calcium utilized in shell formation may enter the mantle directly, as well as through other parts of the mollusc with transfer to the mantle by the blood (Schoffeniels, 1951a,b; Jodrey, 1953b; Rao and Goldberg, 1954; Horiguchi, 1958; Kado, 1960). As an interesting environmental adaptation, the land snail *Euhadra nipponensis* is able to take in calcium through the epithelium of the foot by active transport (Kado, 1960).

b. *Calcium Turnover Rate.* Calcium can move across the mantle in both directions, as can be shown by arranging a mantle as a membrane separating two fluid chambers and following the movement of Ca^{45} (Jodrey,

1953a; Kirschner, 1963). The rate of movement of calcium is approximately ten times that of sodium (Kirschner, 1963). The turnover rate of calcium, although not a measure of unidirectional transport, provides an index of the capacity of the mantle to move calcium outward across its epithelium to the site of deposition. Table I gives the turnover rates and

TABLE I

COMPARISON OF CALCIUM METABOLISM IN MARINE AND FRESH-WATER BIVALVES[a]

Species	Turnover rate (mg/gm wet wt/hr)	Time to establish equilibrium (hr)	Per cent of calcium renewed at equilibrium
Marine			
Crassostrea virginica[b]			
Mantle edge	0.06	1.5	2.4
Pinctada martensii[c]			
Mantle	—	5	—
Ostrea (Crassostrea) gigas[d]			
Mantle edge	—	1–2	12.7
Fresh-Water			
Anodonta lauta[e]			
Mantle edge	0.0008	8	1.1
Mantle interior	0.0011	24	1.8
Hyriopsis schlegelii[f]			
Mantle	0.0012	40	2.6

[a] After Kado, 1960.
[b] Jodrey, 1953b. Mantle-shell preparation.
[c] Tanaka and Hatano, 1955.
[d] Kado, 1960.
[e] Asano *et al.*, 1956.
[f] Horiguchi, 1957.

other data on calcium metabolism for five species, both marine and fresh-water. Because of the nonuniformity of the experimental conditions, comparisons between species must be made with caution. However, it is evident that equilibrium between the medium and tissue calcium is reached more rapidly in marine than in fresh-water species (see also Rao and Goldberg, 1954). Two factors enter into this difference: a much greater tissue calcium content (Kobayashi and Watabe, 1959; Kado, 1960) and a slower turnover rate in the fresh-water species. In all five species, most of the calcium is inert and only a small fraction turns over.

2. CARBON DIOXIDE

a. The Conversion of CO_2 to Carbonate. The carbonate of shell derives from the CO_2-bicarbonate pool within the mantle which is a part of the larger pool of the body as a whole. Perhaps an additional source for some bivalve species may be the bicarbonate and the carbonate of sea water which may have access to the site of crystallization through apertures in the pallial attachment (and via the periostracum). The CO_2 and bicarbonate pools of the body may originate from three sources: (1) from the medium (Hammen and Wilbur, 1959); (2) from urea through urease activity in some marine species (Florkin, 1945; Ishida, 1954); and (3) from decarboxylation of Krebs cycle compounds (see Martin, 1961). Oxaloacetate may provide one source of CO_2 through decarboxylation by oxaloacetic decarboxylase which is present in mantle tissue (Wilbur and Jodrey, 1955). For the continuing operation of the Krebs cycle the replenishment of oxaloacetate would of course be required. This compound could be supplied through CO_2 fixation in which succinate and other cycle intermediates are synthesized (see Section I,B,2,b). One can calculate that the normal respiratory activity of the mantle alone could supply the carbonate of shell in *Crassostrea virginica* even though only a small fraction of the CO_2 were to be converted to carbonate.

The rate of conversion of CO_2 to bicarbonate and carbonate may be an important aspect of carbonate formation in shell. Interrelations between these compounds may be represented in the following way:

$$\underset{(a)}{CO_2 + H_2O} \overset{(a)}{\rightleftharpoons} \underset{(b)}{H_2CO_3} \overset{(b)}{\rightleftharpoons} HCO_3^- + H^+ \underset{-OH^-}{\overset{\overset{(d)}{+OH^-}}{\rightleftharpoons}} CO_3^= + H_2O$$

$$(c) \Updownarrow$$

$$CO_3^= + CO_2 + H_2O$$

It will be seen that carbonate may be formed by way of bicarbonate in the presence of hydroxyl ions (reaction d) or through removal of CO_2 (reaction c). The reactions

$$CO_2 + H_2O \rightarrow H_2CO_3 \quad \text{and} \quad CO_2 + OH^- \rightarrow HCO_3^-$$

are catalyzed by carbonic anhydrase (Meldrum and Roughton, 1933). This enzyme has been found in the mantle of many, but not all, species (see Freeman and Wilbur, 1948; Stolkowski, 1951; Tsujii and Machii, 1953; Kawai, 1954, 1955; Clark, 1957). Carbonic anhydrase appears to play a part in the rate of calcification, as indicated by the finding that sulfonamide compounds which inhibit carbonic anhydrase also inhibit calcification in molluscs (Stolkowski, 1951; Wilbur and Jodrey, 1955; Freeman, 1960). Some of the carbonic anhydrase inhibitors have other effects as well and their retardation of shell formation may not be limited to their action on carbonic anhydrase in all cases.

We have seen that carbonic anhydrase can accelerate bicarbonate formation. If bicarbonate is not in short supply, the rate of carbonate formation may be determined by the rate of conversion of bicarbonate to carbonate. The removal of CO_2 will favor this conversion (reaction c); and as Simkiss (1963) has pointed out, the removal would be aided by CO_2 fixation which takes place in the mantle.

b. Carbon Dioxide Fixation. In addition to its conversion to shell carbonate, CO_2 is fixed into organic compounds. By the use of C^{14}-labeled compounds added to the isolated mantle for very brief periods, it has been demonstrated that CO_2 combines with propionate to form succinate. Succinate, in turn, is converted to other Krebs cycle intermediates (Hammen and Wilbur, 1959). The keto acids of the cycle are apparently transaminated since the label of the fixed CO_2 is also found in the free amino acids, aspartic and glutamic acids and alanine. At least one of these, together with other amino acids, is synthesized into the shell matrix as indicated by the presence of the label in the matrix when C^{14}-bicarbonate was administered in the sea water medium. Details of the synthesis have not been studied.

Figure 2 brings together pathways of CO_2 and bicarbonate related to shell formation.

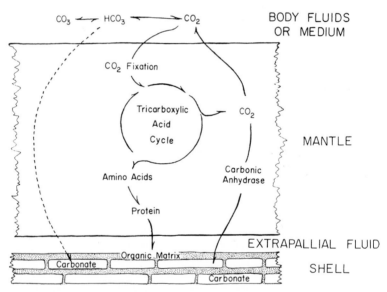

Fig. 2. Diagram showing relations of CO_2 to calcium carbonate and the organic matrix of shell. Not all of the pathways shown have been firmly established.

C. *The Environment of Shell Formation: The Extrapallial Fluid*

1. General

Shell is formed within a thin layer of fluid termed the extrapallial fluid, enclosed between the mantle and the inner shell surface. This fluid is the medium from which two solid phases form: the organic matrix and the crystalline components of shell. Its composition determines the chemical nature and the submicroscopic pattern of the matrix, the rate and character of crystal growth, and directly or indirectly, the polymorphic type of the calcium carbonate crystals.

The extrapallial fluid space of certain bivalves (e.g., *Crassostrea virginica, Pinctada martensii, Chlamys nipponensis*) has access to the external medium, whereas in other species (e.g., *Mercenaria mercenaria*) there is no external communication as judged by the absence of passage of India ink (Kobayashi, 1961; Watabe, 1961). But even with openings present, the extrapallial fluid may differ in composition from the external medium so long as the mantle maintains close contact with the shell at its periphery.

Knowledge of the composition of the extrapallial fluid is fragmentary. Moreover, all analyses of the extrapallial fluid face the problem of changing composition resulting from (*1*) a varying rate of secretion by the mantle, and (*2*) the decrease in concentration of constituents during the deposition of organic matrix and the crystallization of $CaCO_3$. The fluid volume obtainable from a single specimen may be very small (a fraction of a milliliter) as in *Crassostrea virginica* or reasonably copious (a few milliliters) as in *Anodonta lauta* and *Modiolus demissus*.

2. pH AND INORGANIC IONS

The pH of the extrapallial fluid reported for several species spans the range pH 7 to pH 8.35 (Table II). The pH values are frequently similar to those for blood of the same individual, although marked differences in pH between extrapallial fluid and blood (Kobayashi, 1961) and extrapallial fluid and body fluid (Wada, 1961) have been reported. The values given by Watabe and Kobayashi (1961) are undoubtedly the best yet obtained, since the measurements were made within the first minutes after careful removal of the fluid by a hypodermic needle inserted through the pallial attachment. These investigators found that in *Mercenaria mercenaria* exposure of the fluid to the air for 2 minutes resulted in a decrease of a few tenths of a pH unit in summer or a slight increase in winter, presumably due to the uptake or loss, respectively, of CO_2. The pH of the extrapallial fluid *in situ* may accordingly be somewhat higher than the values in Table II (summer animals). Earlier published values on the pH of extrapallial fluid and blood are difficult to evaluate in that the measurements were not carried out under the same conditions (Wada, 1961) or information on loss or gain of CO_2 has not been indicated. From values obtained by Watabe and Kobayashi it appears that in some species, at least, $CaCO_3$ may be precipitated to form shell from extrapallial fluid which is not especially alkaline. Metabolic acids are undoubtedly responsible for the

TABLE II

pH of Extrapallial Fluid[a]

Species	Extrapallial fluid	Blood	Reference
Bivalvia			
Crassostrea virginica	7.46 ± 0.06	7.43 ± 0.10	Watabe and Kobayashi, 1961
Aequipecten irradians concentricus	7.43 ± 0.08	7.53 ± 0.14	Watabe and Kobayashi, 1961
Mercenaria mercenaria	7.37 ± 0.02	7.52 ± 0.11	Watabe and Kobayashi, 1961
Modiolus demissus	7.34 ± 0.05	7.31 ± 0.09	Watabe and Kobayashi, 1961
Pinctada martensii	7.2–8.2[b]		Wada, 1961
Chlamys nipponensis	7.1–7.2	7.3–7.7	Kobayashi, 1961
Anodonta cygnea	8.3		Stolkowski, 1951
Unio pictorum	8.25		Stolkowski, 1951
Gastropoda			
Paludina vivipara	7.9		Stolkowski, 1951
Busycon carica	7.50–7.87		Watabe and Kobayashi, 1961
Planorbis corneus	7.8–8, 8.35		Stolkowski, 1951
Sphaerium corneum	8		Stolkowski, 1951
Lymnaea stagnalis	7.7–7.8		Stolkowski, 1951

[a] The figures for *Crassostrea, Aequipecten, Mercenaria*, and *Modiolus* give confidence limits at the 95% level. Measurements were carried out on 17 to 23 individuals of each of these four species in winter at water temperature of approximately 9°C. Measurements made during the summer at a water temperature of approximately 27°C gave values which were not significantly different statistically except in *Mercenaria* in which the summer values were approximately 0.4 pH unit higher than those obtained in winter. An accuracy of measurement of only 0.2 pH unit is claimed by Stolkowski (1951).

[b] The range includes seasonal changes.

fact that the extrapallial fluid is not more alkaline even though it is in intimate contact with the carbonate of the inner shell surface. Under conditions leading to acid accumulation, particularly when the valves are closed, the $CaCO_3$ of the shell will act as a buffer (Dugal, 1939). The result is an etching or erosion of the inner shell surface.

It has been found that the extrapallial fluid of *Anodonta cygnea* contained the same ions as the blood and in essentially the same proportions (de Waele, 1930). The following ions were present: sodium, potassium, calcium, magnesium, manganese, chloride, sulfate, and phosphate. Similar concentrations of calcium in extrapallial fluid and blood have also been found in *Chlamys nipponensis* (Kobayashi, 1961).

The concentration of trace elements in shell is an interesting unsolved physiological and crystallographic problem. Compared with sea water, shells of marine molluscs generally have an extremely low magnesium content (but see Section I,F,1), a slight enrichment of barium, and a decreased strontium content (Turekian and Armstrong, 1960). (See Koczy

and Titze, 1958, for radium/calcium ratio of sea water and shells.) But
the pertinent comparison is not between shell and sea water but rather
between the shell and the extrapallial fluid in which shell is being deposited. The amount of trace element incorporated in the shell will
presumably depend upon the concentration of the element in the extrapallial fluid which will influence the amount deposited with calcium carbonate and the amount bound by the organic portions of the shell. Further
study of the trace element problem awaits the analysis of the extrapallial
fluid in various species.

3. ORGANIC COMPOUNDS

Electrophoretic studies of the extrapallial fluid of bivalves and gastropods, using cellulose acetate strips, have indicated the presence of one to
three or more proteins and a migration pattern which is characteristic of
the genus (Kobayashi, 1962). Of 11 species examined those with a calcite
shell (*Aequipecten irradians concentricus*, *Chlamys nipponensis*, *Crassostrea virginica*, and *Crassostrea gigas*) had a single protein fraction in the
extrapallial fluid, while species with an aragonite shell (*Busycon carica*,
Elliptio complanatus, *Viviparus intertextus*, *Mercenaria mercenaria*, and
Cristaria) or a shell of both aragonite and calcite (*Modiolus demissus*)
had three or more protein fractions. The number of protein fractions cor-
responded to that in the blood of the same species, although the migration
velocities were not always the same for the two fluids. The difference in
protein fractions in calcitic and aragonitic species is suggestive of a possible
relation between protein and crystal type but further evidence using other
methods of analysis is needed.

The presence of mucopolysaccharides in extrapallial fluid has been
shown directly for several species by paper strip electrophoresis
(Kobayashi, 1962) and indirectly by positive histochemical tests for
polysaccharides in both shell matrix and spherulites of regenerating shell
(Bevelander and Benzer, 1948; Tsujii, 1955; Durning, 1957; Abolins-
Krogis, 1958). Other organic compounds of the extrapallial fluid remain
to be examined.

D. The Organic Matrix of Shell

The organic matrix of shell is secreted into the extrapallial fluid in
soluble form by the mantle and is deposited as a layer on the inner shell
surface. In the electron microscope the matrix is seen as a continuous sheet
or as a fenestrated sheet with a pattern of holes characteristic of the
taxonomic group (Grégoire *et al.*, 1955; Grégoire, 1957, 1960). X-ray
diffraction analysis of matrix indicates an α- or β-type keratin structure,
depending upon the species (see also Section II,D). The study of the
stages from the soluble to the final form is an interesting subject for
polymer research and is yet to be explored.

Chemical analysis of the matrix of decalcified shell has shown the presence of three fractions: a protein, a scleroprotein, and a polypeptide (Grégoire et al., 1955). Some 19 amino acids have been found on acid hydrolysis of the matrix of various species. Of these asparagine, glutamine, cysteine, hydroxyproline, and hydroxylysine do not appear to be of general occurrence (Roche et al., 1951; Beedham, 1954; Grégoire et al., 1955; Tanaka et al., 1960; Hare, 1963). Hydroxylysine, which is present in collagen, has been identified in the matrix of the regenerating shell of *Australorbis glabratus* (Piez, 1961) and oxyproline is present in the normal matrix of *Pinctada martensii* (Tanaka and Hatano, 1953).

Differences in amino acid composition occur between matrix of the calcitic and matrix of the aragonitic regions of shell of a single species (Roche et al., 1951; Tanaka et al., 1960; Hare, 1963) and between the periostracum and the shell matrix (Hare, 1963). Such differences indicate the specificity of regions of the mantle epithelium in their synthesis of particular proteins. The cells of the mantle responsible for depositing the various shell regions also exhibit morphological differences (Beedham, 1958a). Similarly, in the pearl sac epithelium which lays down the substance of pearl, the cells have an appearance related to the type of pearl being formed, that is, whether a normal, prismatic, or a periostracal pearl (Nakahara, 1957).

Mucopolysaccharides secreted by the mantle (Durning, 1957; Horiguchi, 1959a; Tsujii, 1960; Abolins-Krogis, 1963) and present in the extrapallial fluid and shell are probably associated with the organic matrix. Mucopolysaccharide extracted from the normal shell of the oyster *C. virginica* has been shown by infrared analysis to be acid mucopolysaccharide (Simkiss, 1963).

It has been suggested that the periostracum covering the outer shell surface is a quinone-tanned protein (Brown, 1952) which undergoes tanning through the action of a phenolic compound oxidized by dopa oxidase present in epithelial cells of the mantle (Hillman, 1961).

E. The Formation of Crystalline Layers

The microscopic structure of shell has been carefully studied in many species, but our understanding of calcification of the organic matrix and of crystal growth on the submicroscopic level is only at its beginning. Nonetheless, it is on this level as studied by the techniques of electron microscopy and crystallography that we shall consider the formation of crystalline layers. Most of the information comes from electron microscope studies of replicas of the growing surface or fracture surfaces of the shells of *Crassostrea virginica*, *Pinctada martensii*, and a few other species, and the surface of pearls (Watabe, 1954, 1955; Wada, 1957a,b, 1960a,b, 1961; Tsujii et al., 1958; Watabe et al., 1958; Watabe and Wilbur, 1961). Until electron microscope studies are carried out on more species, generalizations concerning mechanisms of layer formation will not be possible.

1. NACRE AND CALCITOSTRACUM

The structure of the more centrally located nacre and calcitostracum, as seen in the light microscope, differs strikingly from that of the prismatic region at the shell periphery. Whereas the latter is commonly built on a plan of closely fitting vertical or oblique columns, the nacre and calcitostracum usually consist of neatly packed horizontal or oblique layers of crystals of tabular form (Fig. 3). However, electron microscope

FIG. 3. Vertical section of the nacre of *Hyriopsis schegelii*. (Wada, 1961.) ×7200.

studies have shown that a feature common to both areas is the intimate association of the organic matrix and the $CaCO_3$ crystals (Figs. 4, 10, and 12). Wada (1961) examined the nacre and calcitostracum of seven species, including bivalves and gastropods, and found that the thickness of the crystal lamellae varied within a single shell, and ranged from 0.3 to 2.3 μ. The organic matrix present between the layers was commonly less than 0.05 μ in thickness.

Briefly, the crystalline layers are formed from small crystals which, through growth, come into side-to-side contact and in some species then overlap. The initial step in the deposition of a layer is the formation of crystal nuclei in solution, on the organic matrix, or on previously formed crystals.

Fig. 4. Nacreous layer of the bivalve *Elliptio complanatus* (Watabe, unpublished). Vertical section partially decalcified in phosphotungstic acid to show relation of crystals (white, *left*) to the organic matrix. Matrix between rows of crystals is seen as prominent horizontal white lines. Matrix forms a wall around each crystal and is also present within crystals. ×17,500.

a. Crystal Nucleation. Crystals develop from submicroscopic nuclei which form by a process known as nucleation. That the organic matrix provides nucleation sites for crystal formation is indicated by its influence on the type of crystals which form on its surface (see Section I,F,2). The induction of nucleation may result from an arrangement of binding sites of appropriate chemical groups of the matrix such that the bound ions have a configuration and spacing, or a multiple of the spacing, of the planes of the calcium carbonate lattice. The bound calcium or carbonate could then initiate the formation of the crystal phase (see Neuman and Neuman, 1958; Glimcher, 1960; Glimcher and Krane, 1962). Crystal growth would occur through the addition of other ions to the plane established by the bound ions.

No evidence is yet available as to the role of any particular compound in nucleation of the matrix. The possible involvement of mucopolysaccharide in calcification is suggested by its binding of calcium (Horiguchi *et al.*, 1954; Rao and Goldberg, 1954; Tanaka and Hatano, 1955; Horiguchi, 1956) and the displacement of calcium from spherulites of regenerating shell by toluidine blue which combines with mucopolysaccharide (Abolins-Krogis, 1958). However, the ability to bind calcium does not imply nucleation sites; in mammalian tissue mucopolysaccharide has been considered to have an inhibitory influence on calcification by tying up calcium (Glimcher, 1960).

b. Crystal Growth. In the electron microscope, crystals are first seen as round or elongate crystal seeds on the matrix or on the surface of crystals (Fig. 5). As the seeds increase in size, the larger ones grow at the

Fig. 5. The first stage of nacreous layer formation in *Crassostrea virginica* showing deposition of rounded crystal seeds, about 200 to 3000 A in diameter, in or on thick organic matrix which covers crystals. Edges of the underlying crystals are seen in the lower half of the figure. The seeds are randomly distributed. The two light circular areas are artifacts. (Watabe, unpublished.) ×17,500.

expense of the smaller ones which undergo dissolution. This is termed recrystallization. Further growth of the crystals occurs through the formation of extensions called dendrites (Buckley, 1951; Watabe, 1954; Wada, 1961; Watabe and Wilbur, 1961).

The next phase in crystal growth is layer formation. The most complete analyses of the sequence of events involved have been made on *Crassostrea virginica* (Tsujii *et al.*, 1958; Watabe *et al.*, 1958; Watabe and Wilbur, 1961) and *Pinctada martensii* (Wada, 1961). In *C. virginica* the stem of the crystal develops side branches (Fig. 6 (2), P_1) at right angles

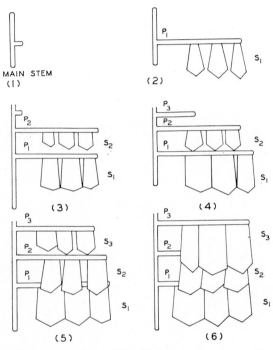

MAIN STEM
(1)

(2)

(3)

(4)

(5)

(6)

Fig. 6. Schematic representation of dendritic growth of crystals. (Watabe and Wilbur, 1961.)

to its main axis (see also Wada, 1961, Fig. 119). The side branches in turn form secondary branchings (Fig. 6 (2), S_1). By a repetition of this process and through dendritic growth of the side branches, overlapping rows of crystals are formed (Figs. 6 (5) and 7). Overlapping rows may also originate from imperfections, called geometric faults, in the lattice of the crystal surface from which daughter crystals develop through dendritic growth. By this means multiple layers from daughter crystals may be formed at one time, as Gorodetsky and Saratovkin (1958) have demonstrated in the growth of cadmium iodide crystals and as appears to be the case in *C. virginica* (Watabe and Wilbur, 1961). When matrix is abundant, these processes may be inhibited with the result that the individual crystals stop growing when they come into juxtaposition. A single layer of crystals, each surrounded by matrix, then results.

Crystal growth may take a spiral pattern in limited areas of the more slowly growing central portions of the nacre of bivalves with a pearly luster (Wada, 1961). The spirals are made up of crystallites which in some but not all cases appear to have their center of origin in one or more crystals showing screw dislocation. From this center a lamella of

FIG. 7. Well developed calcite crystals of tabular form arranged in roughly parallel overlapping rows in the nacreous region of *Crassostrea virginica*. The corresponding free edges of the crystals and the corresponding axes are parallel. (Watabe, unpublished.) ×15,000.

crystallites is laid down in spiral form, each turn of the spiral having an increased diameter and each turn forming a step which is the thickness of the lamella. In this manner a spiral growth pyramid is built up. The spirals may be distorted horizontally as local conditions bring about directional growth. Spiral growth has not been seen in calcitic shells.

c. Factors Influencing Crystal Form. Crystals of calcium carbonate are laid down in a variety of forms during shell formation, depending upon the environmental conditions (Wada, 1957a, 1961), the species (Haas, 1935), and the region of the shell (Tsujii *et al.*, 1958; Schmidt, 1924; Watabe and Wilbur, 1961; Wada, 1961). Conditions at the site of crystal formation are those that will determine the rate and form of crystal growth, of course. Crystals undergoing slow growth are likely to be large with straight faces and well-defined angles (Fig. 8), whereas crystals that

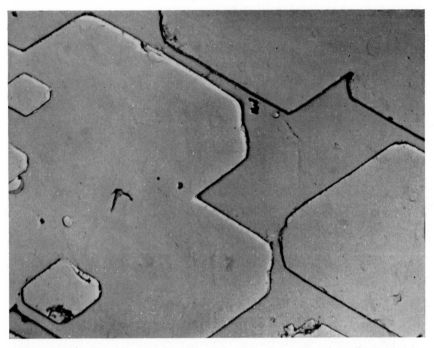

Fig. 8. Aragonite crystals of well developed form from the nacre of a pearl oyster (*Pinctada martensii*) collected in December. The crystals are of tabular shape and develop by parallel growth. (Wada, 1961.) ×13,000.

are growing rapidly may be smaller and perhaps more rounded (Fig. 9). For example, crystals from the more slowly growing central part of the nacre of *Pinctada martensii* are larger on the average than those at the more rapidly growing margin (Wada, 1961). In other instances the relation between crystal size and growth rate may be more complex.

Through dendritic growth the crystals of a particular area of nacre or calcitostracum may have an elongate tabular form with a common orientation of their optic axes. Such growth is characteristic of crystals developing in a thin layer of supersaturated solution in which the degree of supersaturation is not uniform but becomes metastable in one place and labile in another. This results in strong concentration gradients and preferential growth from the metastable areas toward the labile ones. Such localized differences in concentration might well develop in the thin layer of extrapallial fluid between the mantle and the shell as a result of unequal secretion by different parts of the mantle (Watabe *et al.*, 1958). The orientation of crystal axes deposited by transplanted mantle epithelium has been found to correspond to the direction of cell growth (Wada, 1961). After

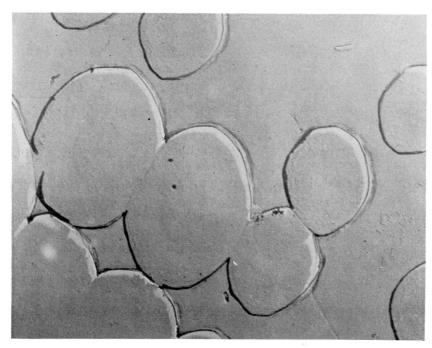

FIG. 9. Aragonite crystals from the nacre of a pearl oyster (*Pinctada martensii*) collected at a time of rapid shell growth. Note the rounded form of the crystals as compared with crystal form in Fig. 8. (Wada, 1961.) ×9600.

an examination of crystal arrangement in the shell of representatives of different classes of molluscs, Wada has suggested that the crystallographic axis is controlled by the direction of elongation and the tension of the growing mantle, factors which bring about an orientation of the organic matrix on which the crystals develop. Movement of extrapallial fluid as a result of these forces is also thought to play a part in the orientation of the matrix. By means of electron microscope studies of undecalcified sections of shell it may be possible to determine whether or not the orientation of the crystals coincides with the orientation of the organic matrix.

Dissolution of crystals, either partial or complete, is probably of common occurrence and can be brought about by a pH decrease. During hibernation and during periods of shell deposition crystal dissolution frequently occurs, as shown by electron micrographs of the inner shell surface (Watabe *et al.*, 1958; Wada, 1961).

d. Secretion of Matrix and Multiple Layer Formation. A vertical section of shell commonly shows crystalline layers alternating with layers of organic matrix. In pearl formation an alternation of crystalline and matrix layers also occurs; and from the known age of the pearl it can be calculated that two to eight double layers form each day (Watabe, 1952). This layering arrangement indicates that the organic matrix has been secreted periodically rather than continuously, and such a periodic secretion has been described for the snail *Viviparus* (Kessel, 1933). Whether the calcium carbonate has also been secreted periodically in these cases we cannot say, since the presence of the matrix would bring about an interruption in any case.

The mechanism by which the mantle cells are caused to secrete periodically is an especially interesting situation which has not been examined experimentally. The mantle and its immediate environment apparently constitute a self-regulating system in which the periodic secretion of matrix is determined by stimuli received by the shell side of the mantle. The stimuli may be physical, presented to the mantle cells by a crystalline or a matrix surface; or the chemical environment provided by the extrapallial fluid (see Section I,C,2 and 3) may be the determining factor. Insight into the nature of the stimuli might be gained perhaps by applying various physical and chemical stimuli to the mantle and analyzing the extrapallial fluid for secreted organic compounds, calcium, and carbonate.

A potential of 2 to 10 mv is present across the isolated mantle of freshwater clams, the shell side being positive (Kirschner, 1963). Mantles of *Crassostrea virginica* and *Mercenaria mercenaria* have potentials of only 0.5 to 2.0 mv in a sea-water medium (Sterns, 1961; Kirschner, 1963). It was demonstrated that the potential in a fresh-water clam is the sum of two potentials, presumably produced by the layer of epithelium on the two sides of the mantle. After an initial decrease with time, the potential could be increased by addition of calcium on the body side and then decreased and reversed by addition of calcium on the shell side. Magnesium, potassium, and sodium were essentially without effect. With CO_2 added to the shell side, the potential was increased (Kirschner, 1963). We have no information on the relationship of these potentials to secretory processes.

From the structure of crystalline layers it is clear that individual crystals attain a thickness which lies within relatively narrow limits (see Section I,E,1). Crystal growth is then interrupted, and a layer of matrix or a new crystalline layer is added. At least three factors could serve to interrupt crystallization: (*1*) intermittent secretion of matrix over the crystal surfaces inhibiting crystal growth (Section I,E,1,b); (*2*) decrease in the calcium or carbonate of the extrapallial fluid below the saturation concentration as a result of alteration of physiological activity of the mantle;

and (3) the unavailability of nucleation sites, for the initiation of crystallization, due to the presence of inhibitors. In the last case, the later initiation of a layer would require a mechanism for removal of the inhibitor (see Glimcher, 1960, for a discussion of this factor). The secretion of matrix is almost certainly the usual method of terminating growth of the individual layer.

2. PRISMATIC REGION

The development of the prismatic layer can be pictured as the growth of small crystals scattered in a shallow sea of organic matrix. Individual crystals grow and unite with others forming larger crystals (Fig. 10).

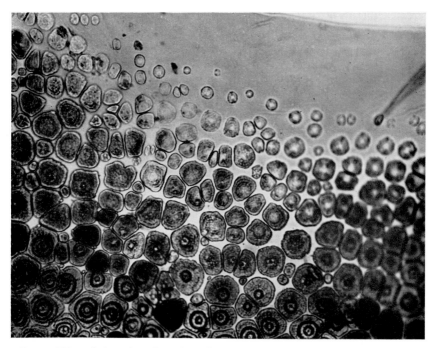

FIG. 10. Edge of the prismatic region of a pearl oyster (*Pinctada martensii*) showing crystals in the organic matrix. The most recently formed crystals at the periphery (*top*) are smaller than the older crystals (*bottom*). Polarized light. (Wada, 1961.) ×300.

These increase still further in size until a complete crystalline layer is formed. As the growing crystals make contact with neighboring crystals, they assume a polygonal form (Fig. 11, *left*). The organic matrix, displaced by the growing crystals, surrounds and separates the individual crystals as they grow together. The matrix finally hardens (de Waele, 1930; Tsujii *et al.*, 1958; Grégoire, 1961a). Sections or replicas of the crystals or prisms of *C. virginica* and *P. martensii* (Watabe and Wada, 1956; Wada, 1961) show them to be composed of small crystals which may be similarly oriented (Fig. 11, *right*) and embedded in matrix. These small crystals within a prism may well be dendrites of a larger crystal. However, a prism may include more than one large crystal, as indicated by extinction patterns in polarized light.

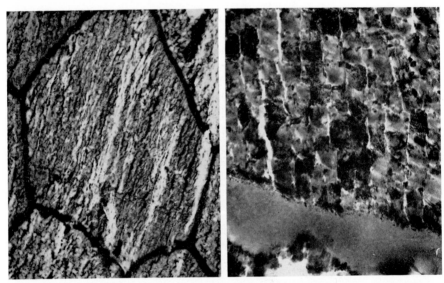

Fig. 11. Prismatic layer of the oyster *Crassostrea virginica* (Watabe, Unpublished). *Left.* Horizontal section showing one prism and parts of neighboring prisms. The broad lines are matrix. ×9,120. *Right.* Prismatic region showing detail of a portion of one prism. Note parallel crystals. The broad band at the bottom is the matrix boundary of the prism. ×26,325.

With continued growth on the free surface, the crystalline prisms take the form of columns. Partial decalcification of the prismatic layer of *Atrina nigra* reveals that the columns are made up of discs, indicating that calcification has not proceeded continuously (Fig. 12). The columns in *Pinctada martensii* show an alternation of very thin layers of mineral and organic material (Wada, 1961; see also Grégoire, 1961b). The matrix surrounding the individual columns takes the form of tubular sheaths which together form a network. In some species, as the columns add crystalline material to their free inner ends some of them increase in width, with the result that neighboring columns decrease in width. At the same time the mantle is growing in area and depositing crystals at the periphery of the shell from which new columns originate. The prisms on the shell surface thus represent a sequence of increasing age—and often increasing size—progressing centrally from the shell periphery.

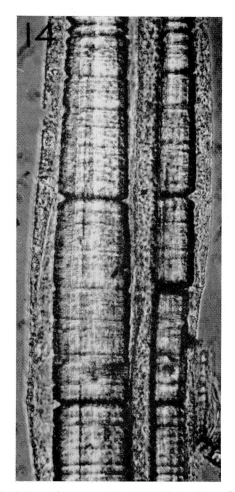

Fig. 12. Longitudinal view of two partially decalcified prisms of *Atrina nigra*. Note horizontal lines in prisms indicating non-uniform growth rate. Organic material is shown around prisms. (Grégoire, 1961b.)

A transitional zone joins the prismatic and nacreous regions. It is distinct in structure but has certain features of both regions. The microscopic and submicroscopic structure of this zone have been described by Schmidt (1924), Tsujii *et al.* (1958), and Watabe and Wilbur (1961).

F. Factors Influencing Calcium Carbonate Crystal Type

The calcium carbonate of mollusc shells occurs as calcite in some groups (e.g., Ostreidae, Anomiidae; Octopoda) and as aragonite in others (e.g., fresh-water Unionidae). Still others (Neritidae, Patellidae; some Haliotidae) have one layer of calcite and one or more layers of aragonite

(Bøggild, 1930; Lutts *et al.*, 1960; Wada, 1961). Vaterite, a third polymorph of calcium carbonate, has been reported in the regenerating shell of *Helix* (Mayer, 1931; Mayer and Weineck, 1932; Stolkowski, 1951). Interestingly, the calcium carbonate of the shell ligament is present as aragonite in species in which the shell is entirely calcite (Wada, 1961; Stenzel, 1962). Magnesium carbonate is also found in shells as a solid solution between calcite and dolomite, which is $CaMg(CO_3)_2$ (Chave, 1952; Kitano and Furutsu, 1959).

Calcite is the most stable form of the three polymorphic types of $CaCO_3$. The problem of the formation of aragonite and vaterite in biological systems is an old one (see Prenant, 1927) and several explanations for their occurrence have been advanced. The factors include: (*1*) certain inorganic ions; also CO_2; (*2*) organic matrix of shell (Roche *et al.*, 1951; Ranson, 1952; Watabe and Wilbur, 1960; Wilbur and Watabe, 1963) and dissolved organic materials (Takagi and Tanaka, 1955; Kitano, 1961); (*3*) temperature (Lowenstam, 1954a,b); (*4*) salinity (Bøggild, 1930); (*5*) carbonic anhydrase (Stolkowski, 1951; see also Wilbur, 1960); and (*6*) transformation of one crystal type to another. Our discussion will be limited to the first three.

If the mechanism of $CaCO_3$ formation in the mollusc is similar to that *in vitro*, then we can say that aragonite formation will probably be determined by the following conditions: (*1*) that the solution in which the crystals are forming is supersaturated with respect to both aragonite and calcite; (*2*) that nucleation and crystal growth proceed more rapidly for aragonite than for calcite. Agents favoring aragonite formation presumably may act not only through acceleration of aragonite crystal growth but by inhibiting the nucleation and growth of calcite crystals or by inhibiting the dissolution of aragonite and its recrystallization as calcite (see Curl, 1962).

1. Inorganic Ions

Bøggild in 1930 stated as a rule without exception that all aragonite shells are low in magnesium. Calcitic shells are more complicated: some species have little magnesium; others have much. Transitional forms are uncommon. More recently a large number of species have been examined to see whether aragonite formation might be correlated with the magnesium and strontium content of the shell. For the bivalves and gastropods the magnesium content was usually found to be greater as the proportion of calcite increased (Chave, 1954). On the other hand, the strontium content of aragonitic shell was generally higher than for calcitic shells, while shells having both calcite and aragonite had an intermediate strontium content (Thompson and Chow, 1955). But there are exceptions (see Turekian and Armstrong, 1960). *Pinctada martensii* is an interesting case in point in that the magnesium content of the calcitic prismatic region of three species is lower than that of the aragonitic nacreous region (Horiguchi, 1959b; Wada, 1961). As more species have been analyzed, it has become clear that taxonomic relationships have an important bearing on the magnesium and strontium content of the shell (Thompson and Chow, 1955; Turekian and Armstrong, 1960).

The material just mentioned provides no basis, however, for questioning the possible influence of magnesium and other salts on the formation of calcite and aragonite. In fact, *in vitro* experiments have shown that aragonite formation can be induced by the appropriate concentration of Mg^{++}, Sr^{++}, Cs^+, Rb^+, SO_4^{--}, HCO_3^-, or CO_3^{--} when $CaCO_3$ is precipitated from a solution of $Ca(HCO_3)_2$ (Kitano, 1961, 1962; see also Curl, 1962). Calcite formation can be induced by the appropriate concentration of NH_4^+, Li^+, Na^+, K^+, Rb^+, Cs^+, Ba^{++}, Cl^-, or CO_2. Magnesium inhibited vaterite formation very strongly (Kitano, 1961; Kitano *et al.*, 1962). A primary consideration with respect to the influence of ions on shell crystal type is their concentration in the extrapallial fluid in which the crystals are being formed. Unfortunately, pertinent data on the composition of this fluid are lacking. Moreover, it is precarious to attribute aragonite and calcite formation to the influence of certain ions on the basis of the shell content of these ions. In the first place, ions which influence crystal type may not be included in the calcium carbonate crystals, as Kitano (1961) has shown in *in vitro* experiments with Mg^{++}, Li^+, Na^+, K^+, Rb^+, Cs^+, NH_4^+, Cl^-, and SO_4^{--}. Also, the organic components of shell may account for a part of the trace elements of shell by providing binding sites.

2. ORGANIC MATRIX AND DISSOLVED ORGANIC COMPOUNDS

The finding of a difference in the amino acid composition of the calcitic and aragonitic regions of shell (Roche *et al.*, 1951; see also Tanaka *et al.*, 1960; Hare, 1963) suggested that the organic matrix may influence crystal type. A study of the chemical composition of matrix of calcitic shells (*Gryphaea (Crassostrea) angulata, Ostrea edulis, Pecten maximus*) and of an aragonitic shell (*Turbo marmoratus*), however, indicated no general relationship between matrix composition and crystal type (Roche *et al.*, 1951). Further, Grégoire (1961b) found no characteristic difference in matrix structure between calcitic and aragonitic shells in an electron microscope study of 22 species. While data of the nature cited might provide interesting correlations, they could be no more than suggestive. The influence of the matrix on crystal type has been studied more directly by determining the capacity of decalcified matrix from aragonitic shell to induce aragonite formation (*1*) when inserted into a mollusc which normally forms only calcite, and (*2*) when calcium carbonate was precipitated on this matrix *in vitro* under conditions in which calcite is normally formed (Watabe and Wilbur, 1960; Wilbur and Watabe, 1963). The insertion of matrix from aragonitic shell of *Elliptio complanatus* at the site of shell formation in the oyster *Crassostrea virginica* resulted in the deposition of aragonite crystals along with calcite crystals which are normally deposited. On other inserted substrata (glass coverslip, plastics) only calcite was formed. Similarly, when calcium carbonate was precipitated from weakly alkaline solutions *in vitro*, aragonite crystals were formed in contact with aragonite matrix of *E. complanatus, Pinctada martensii,* and *Viviparus intertextus,* but not on other materials. These experiments indicate that the organic matrix is a factor in the determination of crystal type.

The mechanism whereby the matrix influences crystal type is presumably one of nucleation in which reactive groups on the matrix bring about a positioning of calcium and carbonate ions corresponding to that of the crystal lattice (see also Section I,E,1,a). No information is available as to compounds or groups providing binding sites on the matrix; nor do we have X-ray diffraction data on the organic matrix which permit a comparison of spacings of the matrix and aragonite.

Dissolved organic substances influence the crystal type on precipitation of calcium carbonate *in vitro* (Kitano and Hood, 1961). Substances that favor the formation of each of the crystal types are given below.

Aragonite: taurine, glutamate, glycine, serine.
Calcite: citrate, malate, pyruvate, succinate, lactate, arginine, glycyl-glycine, glycogen, chondroitin sulfate, glycoprotein.
Vaterite: glutamate, glycine, serine, glycoprotein.

The ability of organic compounds to influence crystal type appears to be correlated with their action in reducing the rate of $CaCO_3$ precipitation.

It has been suggested that organic anions present in molluscs may suppress the growth of calcite crystal nuclei through adsorption and so favor aragonite formation (Saylor, 1928). Studies using extrapallial fluid from which high-molecular-weight compounds have been removed are needed to determine whether substances other than shell matrix, both organic and inorganic, can influence crystal type.

3. TEMPERATURE

When $CaCO_3$ is precipitated from solutions of $Ca(HCO_3)_2$ at temperatures within the biological range, calcite is the usual crystal type; but if the temperature is raised, aragonite and vaterite may be formed. This effect of temperature on crystal type *in vitro* and the observed inconstancy of the ratio of calcite to aragonite in certain species have raised the question of a possible correlation of environmental temperature and crystal type in molluscs. In species which deposit both calcite and aragonite Lowenstam (1954a,b) found that the proportion of aragonite is higher in animals living at higher environmental temperatures. An increased aragonite content with increasing temperature was also described by Dodd (1963) in large specimens of *Mytilus californianus* although small specimens did not show the effect. In two subspecies the temperature effect was not clearcut. Since calcite and aragonite are found in different layers,

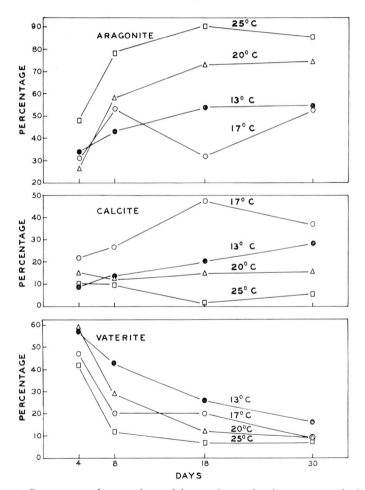

Fig. 13. Percentage of aragonite, calcite, and vaterite in regenerated shell of *Viviparus intertextus*. The percentage of each polymorph is plotted as a function of the temperature and period of regeneration. Each point represents a pooled sample of regenerated shell covering a small hole bored in each of 20 specimens. Samples were collected from the same specimens after the period of regeneration indicated on the abscissa. Animals maintained at 17° laid eggs during the course of the experiment. (Wilbur and Watabe, 1963.)

a differential growth response to temperature by these layers might serve to alter the calcite-aragonite ratio (Dodd, 1962).

The complication of the two shell regions is not encountered in studies of temperature effects on crystal type in the snail *Viviparus intertextus,* for this animal normally deposits only aragonite but on regeneration forms calcite, aragonite, and vaterite. The proportion of the three poly-morphs has been determined in the regenerating shell of snails maintained at different temperatures for various periods of regeneration (Fig. 13). The proportion of aragonite increased with increasing temperatures and the period of regeneration; vaterite, the predominant polymorph first deposited, decreased. A decrease in vaterite with time is probably associ-ated with its conversion to the more stable forms, aragonite and calcite, through recrystallization. This will continue at a measurable rate so long as the vaterite crystals are in contact with solution. In addition, conditions at the site of crystal formation may well be altered in a manner favoring aragonite as regeneration proceeds.

Although the proportion of aragonite increased with temperature both in *in vitro* crystallization and in shell formation, the influence of temperature on crystal type within the biological range is probably mediated through alterations in the secretory activity of the mantle. As a consequence, changes occur in the inorganic and/or organic constitu-ents of the extrapallial fluid and secondarily in the organic matrix. The crystal type will then be determined by the ionic and molecular environ-ment of the nucleation sites.

G. *Conditions Affecting the Rate of Shell Formation*

The rate of shell formation may be expected to be governed by the following factors: (*1*) the supply of calcium furnished to the mantle by the blood or external medium (see Section I,B,1,a); (*2*) the rate of con-version of CO_2 and bicarbonate to carbonate (see Section I,B,2,a); (*3*) the rate of synthesis of components of the organic matrix; (*4*) the rate of secretion of calcium and components of the matrix by the mantle; and (*5*) a sufficiently alkaline pH of extrapallial fluid to permit deposition of $CaCO_3$. Any one of these factors may be limiting. Other factors pertaining to growth of the whole organism including shell are considered in Chap-ter 7. The effect of a particular experimental condition on the rate of shell formation can be ascertained by placing a mollusc in a medium con-taining labeled calcium or bicarbonate or organic compounds and measur-ing the amount of radioactivity incorporated into the crystals or organic matrix (p. 224). Also, the mantle-shell preparation (Hirata, 1953), which deposits both the crystalline and organic portion of shell, can be used with labeled substances for studying the action of agents on the mantle tissue.

TABLE III

EFFECT OF CHEMICAL AGENTS ON CALCIUM DEPOSITION[a]

Compound	Per cent of normal deposition	Per cent of normal uptake by mantle	Presumed action	Species	Reference
Beryllium nitrate					
$10^{-4} M$	13.9	98.5	Inhibits alkaline phosphatase	Crassostrea gigas	Kado, 1960
$10^{-4} M^b$	7.6	101.1	Inhibits alkaline phosphatase	C. gigas	Kado, 1960
Monoiodoacetate					
$10^{-3} M$	19.6	96.2	Reacts with SH groups	C. gigas	Kado, 1960
Sodium fluoride					
$10^{-2} M$	45.2	93.0	Inhibits glycolysis	C. gigas	Kado, 1960
$10^{-3} M$	116.0	111.5	Inhibits glycolysis	C. gigas	Kado, 1960
2,4-Dinitrophenol					
$10^{-3} M^b$	10.8	—	Reduces high-energy phosphate concentration	C. virginica	Maroney et al., 1957
2-Acetylamino-1,3,4-thiadiazole-5-sulfonamide					
0.5–15.0 mg/liter	65	—	Inhibits carbonic anhydrase	Physa. heterostropha	Freeman, 1960
10 mg/liter	52	—	Inhibits carbonic anhydrase	C. virginica	Wilbur and Jodrey, 1955
Benzenesulfonamide					
50 mg/liter	63	—	Inhibits carbonic anhydrase	P. heterostropha	Freeman, 1960
p-Toluenesulfonamide					
50 mg/liter	63	—	Inhibits carbonic anhydrase	P. heterostropha	Freeman, 1960
Sulfanilamide					
10–50 mg/liter	68	—	Inhibits carbonic anhydrase	P. heterostropha	Freeman, 1960
Sodium succinate					
0.01 M	110	—	Respiratory substrate	C. virginica	Wilbur and Jodrey, 1955
Sodium malate					
0.01 M	120	—	Respiratory substrate	C. virginica	Wilbur and Jodrey, 1955
Sodium oxaloacetate					
0.01 M	420	—	Respiratory substrate	C. virginica	Wilbur and Jodrey, 1955

[a] The references give effects of concentration in addition to those listed.
[b] Mantle-shell preparation.

1. Ionic Concentration

The rate of calcium deposition varies greatly during the course of the year in temperate climates and is very low during the colder months. Wada (1961) in following calcium deposition over a period of 13 months found a rather surprising inverse relation between the total calcium concentration of the extrapallial fluid and the deposition rate. Relative to crystal formation and growth, one would also wish to know the concentrations and activity of calcium and carbonate ions and the extent of saturation during periods when calcium carbonate deposition is occurring. These data are unfortunately lacking.

2. Inhibitors

Table III summarizes effects of a number of agents on calcium deposition. Beryllium nitrate, iodoacetate, and fluoride are all inhibitory. Since the uptake of calcium by the mantle remains essentially normal in their presence, a later step in the sequence of processes leading to shell deposition appears to be involved in their action. Iodoacetate and fluoride would decrease the production of respiratory intermediates which provide CO_2 for carbonate and would also interfere with the formation of high-energy phosphate which may be required for the secretion of calcium carbonate and protein synthesis. Kado (1960) has suggested that both beryllium and iodoacetate inhibit protein synthesis and that the subsequent failure of the secretion of the shell matrix would interfere with calcification.

Dinitrophenol may also be expected to decrease the high-energy phosphate compounds present in mantle. Besides affecting the synthesis and secretion of compounds which make up shell, dinitrophenol by inhibiting transport may alter the composition of the extrapallial fluid in other ways as well.

Of the Krebs cycle compounds studied, oxaloacetate is outstanding in its marked stimulation of calcium deposition in the mantle-shell preparation (Wilbur and Jodrey, 1955). The effect may be related to the provision of CO_2 through decarboxylation by oxaloacetic decarboxylase, and this should be tested by examining the effect of adding CO_2, since other effects of oxaloacetate may also be involved. The inhibitory action of carbonic anhydrase inhibitors on calcification has been pointed out in an earler section (Section I,B,2,a).

II. SHELL REGENERATION

A. General Considerations

Studies of regeneration in molluscs have concerned the foot, tentacles, eyes, Oberkiefer (jaws), operculum, and the shell, but chiefly the shell

(Bierbauer, 1957). Investigations of shell regeneration have been of two kinds: descriptive studies of repair of shells which have undergone accidental injury in nature, and experimental studies of the replacement of portions of shell which have been removed. Our discussion will consider the more recent analytical approaches to shell regeneration.

The removal of a marginal portion of the shell will usually be followed by its restoration. A priori, one might suppose that the replacement of the damaged area would lie within the normal shell-depositing activities of the mantle but, in fact, regeneration of the shell encompasses more than this and presents a number of additional and largely unexplored physiological aspects of considerable interest. Briefly stated, regeneration involves: (1) a stimulus or stimuli resulting from removal of a portion of the shell; (2) the mobilization of calcium from different regions of the organism; (3) calcium transport to the area of repair; and (4) the localized deposition of organic matrix and calcium carbonate (Sioli, 1935). In the regenerated area both the ultrastructure of the organic matrix and the crystal type may differ from the normal.

The rate of regeneration depends upon the region of the shell and the species. Wagge and Mittler (1953) found that land snails (18 species) readily repaired a hole cut in the central area of the shell, whereas marine Prosobranchia (28 species), Opisthobranchia (3 species), and Bivalvia (6 species) could not regenerate the shell unless the hole was first covered by placing material over it. Even then regeneration took place more slowly than in the land forms (see also Techow, 1910). The fresh-water snails *Viviparus*, *Limnaea*, and *Planorbis* behave like the marine forms in that a hole not at the shell edge fails to regenerate, or does so slowly unless it is covered (Kessel, 1933).

Regeneration of the shell edge of the oyster *Crassostrea virginica* has been considered by Loosanoff and Nomejko (1955) to occur at a rate exceeding that of normal shell deposition, since the portion removed was restored in area more rapidly than an equivalent area of normal shell was laid down. To establish an increased rate, however, would require measurements of the weight of the crystalline and matrix portions of regenerated shell as compared with normal deposition in a corresponding area.

B. Stimuli for Regeneration

The stimuli caused by injury to the shell first result in a contraction of the muscles of the mantle; in snails, the oyster *Crassostrea virginica*, and the pearl oyster *Pinctada martensii*, where attachment of the mantle is not firm, marked retraction occurs. Unless the mantle relaxes to the extent of covering the injured area, regeneration will obviously fail.

Of the possible stimuli initiating the sequence of regenerative changes, mechanical irritation of mantle cells in the region of the shell defect is perhaps the most obvious. Sioli (1935) considered the altered chemical relation between mantle cells and the shell surface a more probable stimulus. But almost certainly any material, even if chemically inert, lodging between the mantle and the shell will serve as a stimulus, and probably does so quite commonly in certain species, as indicated by the frequent occurrence of areas of regeneration on the inner shell surface. A localized stimulus, such as that produced by the most careful drilling of a tiny hole in a bivalve shell with a high-speed dental drill, may produce regeneration in an area involving a large part of the valve (see also Wagge, 1952). This result suggests (1) that a small region of the mantle can be stimulated to secrete sufficient material to provide for a large area of regeneration, or (2) that a portion of the mantle considerably larger than the immediate area in contact with the shell defect has been stimulated. The latter alternative leads to the question of whether localized stimulation may result in the formation of substances inducing secretory responses in more distant cells of the mantle. Evidence on this appears to be lacking.

The stimulus of the shell defect brings about the release of calcium in the digestive gland and kidney (see Section II, C) but the method of transmission from the mantle to these areas, whether neural or hormonal, is unknown. Cytological changes in the digestive gland involving a disintegration of the calcium spherules normally present there are under way within 1 hour and are at their peak within 3 hours after the defect occurs (Abolins-Krogis, 1961). Conceivably, enzyme activation with consequent alteration of organic constituents associated with the spherules could be involved (Sioli, 1935). It is known that alkaline phosphatase activity of the digestive gland does increase at the time of regeneration of the shell of *Helix aspersa* (Wagge, 1951).

C. Calcium Sources

Sources of calcium for regeneration are present in the mantle (Durning, 1957; Guardabassi and Piacenza, 1958; Tsujii, 1960; Abolins-Krogis, 1963); the digestive glands (Sioli, 1935; Wagge, 1951; Abolins-Krogis, 1961); the kidney (Sioli, 1935); and, of course, the blood and the medium. In the mantle calcium is found as spherules of calcium carbonate. In the digestive gland of *Helix* the calcium carbonate is associated with organic compounds including acid mucopolysaccharide and protein. Both protein and calcium are dietary requirements for the formation of the calcium deposits, since calcium is not laid down in the absence of either (Wagge, 1951). Phosphorus has also been thought to be present (Sioli, 1935; Manigault, 1939; Fretter, 1952), although the crystalline material has been said to be carbonate rather than phosphate (Wagge, 1951). A definite answer as to the crystalline state of the spherules could be given easily by electron diffraction studies.

Chemical analyses during regeneration have shown a decrease in the total ash of the digestive gland and kidney, a decrease in the calcium of the digestive gland (Sioli, 1935), and an increase in blood calcium (Holtz and von Brand, 1940; but see Sioli, 1935). Sioli calculated that the tissue calcium was not adequate to account for the calcium of the regenerated part of the shell of the nonfeeding snail and that a portion of the calcium must have been derived from the remainder of the shell. The movement of calcium from shell to tissue appears probable. Wagge (1952) obtained evidence for this; the partial dissolution of shell crystals commonly seen in electron micrographs of the inner surface is a further indication. An initial and temporary production of acid resulting from injury might bring about dissolution of the shell. If the dissolved calcium were then absorbed through the mantle, it might later contribute to shell repair.

The transfer of calcium from the digestive gland and the supplying of the shell matrix material have been attributed to amoebocytes (Wagge, 1951), but the importance of their role has been questioned (Durning, 1957). Even though amoebocytes may participate in repair processes, it would seem probable that the mantle contributes, directly and indirectly, the major share both of the calcium and the protein.

Calcium supply may reasonably be expected to limit the rate and amount of shell regeneration, especially with reduced calcium intake. Bierbauer (1957) has reported that shell repair in *Helix pomatia* is more rapid following the injection of calcium. A decrease in rate of regeneration found in winter snails was attributed to decreased availability of calcium. In view of the possibility that other factors may also be concerned, it would be interesting to determine whether the regeneration rate in winter animals could be brought to the maximal level by calcium injection. *Helix aspersa* rapidly lost the capacity to repair its shell in the absence of food. However, this was attributed to reduced digestive activity rather than to lack of calcium ingestion since feeding on cellulose restored the ability to repair the shell (Wagge, 1951). However, the amount of calcium deposited was dependent upon the calcium intake and was increased by the addition of cholesterol and ergosterol to the food (Wagge, 1952). Calcification of the regenerating shell margin of the marine bivalve *Isognomon* (*Pedalion*) *alatum* was inhibited when the calcium content of the sea water was reduced to one-eighth or magnesium was withdrawn. The organic matrix continued to be formed under these conditions, however (Bevelander and Benzer, 1948).

D. *The Organic Matrix of Regenerating Shell*

The first observed event in shell regeneration in the land snail *Helix* is the collection of fluid in the region from which the shell has been removed. From the fluid there is formed a thin organic membrane which gradually becomes calcified with spherulites. The latter increase in size and form calcified layers (see also Andrews, 1934a). The initial covering of the defect is frequently accomplished within a very few hours (Durning, 1957; Abolins-Krogis, 1958; Wagge, 1951), although complete repair requires a much longer period (Holtz and von Brand, 1940). Cellular changes in the mantle associated with shell repair in *Helix pomatia* during the first 24 hours have been described by Abolins-Krogis (1963). Constituents of various mantle cells, including calcium spherites, disintegrate and the cells of the outer epithelium release large amounts of acid mucopolysaccharide and protein granules, probably originating in part in other portions of the mantle. Protein and polysaccharide, probably acid mucopolysaccharide, are present in the organic matrix material (Durning, 1957) and within the spherulites (Abolins-Krogis, 1958). In other species the calcium carbonate of the regenerating shell occurs in other crystal forms as well as spherulites (see Section II,E).

X-ray diffraction studies have shown that the structure of the organic matrix of regenerated shell differs from that of normal shell in *Crassostrea virginica* and *Elliptio complanatus*, but not in *Mercenaria mercenaria* (see Table IV, columns 2 and 3). The measurements also give some

TABLE IV

X-RAY DIFFRACTION STUDIES OF SHELL MATRIX[a]

Species	Normal	Regenerated	Substances indicated	Crystal type in regenerated shell
Crassostrea virginica (calcitic)	α-keratin	β-keratin	Two substances in both normal and regenerated	Calcite and aragonite
Elliptio complanatus (aragonitic)	β-keratin	β- and α-keratin	New substance in regenerated	Calcite, aragonite, and vaterite
Mercenaria mercenaria (aragonitic)	β-keratin	β-keratin	No change	Aragonite

[a] Wilbur and Watabe, 1963.

general information about the compounds contributing to the diffraction patterns (column 4). The difference between regenerated and normal matrix points to an alteration in the material synthesized during regeneration, but further details await chemical studies of the two kinds of matrix.

E. *Crystallization*

The regenerated shell may be (*1*) normal in its crystal pattern and crystal type, especially if the mantle edge rather than the central portion has repaired the shell; (*2*) normal but consisting of the inner shell layer only; or (*3*) aberrant in crystal pattern and crystal type (Techow, 1910; Kessel, 1933; Andrews, 1934a,b; Korschelt, 1937; Watabe and Wilbur, 1962).

The first crystals deposited in regeneration have been said to be calcium phosphate which are later converted to carbonate (Biedermann, 1902; Bevelander and Benzer, 1948). However, analyses of newly deposited crystals by X-ray diffraction and electron diffraction (Mayer, 1931; von Levetzow, 1932; Kessel, 1933; Watabe, 1961) have provided strong evidence that the first deposition is carbonate rather than phosphate.

Mayer (1931) and von Levetzow (1932) made the interesting observation that *Helix*, which normally lays down aragonite, forms both aragonite and vaterite on regeneration. Calcite may also be deposited in the regenerating shell (Stolkowski, 1948). Recently these studies have been extended by inducing regeneration in several species in various ways and

TABLE V

CRYSTAL TYPES IN REGENERATING SHELL[a,b]

Test system	Calcite	Aragonite	Vaterite
Nassarius obsoletus (aragonitic)			
Edge removed	0	12	0
Mercenaria mercenaria (aragonitic)			
Hole bored	0	8	0
Viviparus intertextus[c] (aragonitic)			
Hole bored	+	+	+
Elliptio complanatus (aragonitic)			
Hole bored	3	3	1
Edge removed	5	5	2
Crassostrea virginica (calcitic)			
Hole bored	5	5	0
Edge removed	10	10	0
Coverslip fragments, Formvar and			
Saran plastics inserted	31	31	0

[a] Wilbur and Watabe, 1963.

[b] Regeneration was induced by removing a portion of the shell edge, by boring a hole 2–5 mm in diameter in the central part of the shell with a high-speed dental drill, or by inserting materials between the mantle and the shell after breaking the shell edge. The number of specimens is indicated. Analysis was by polarized light and X-ray diffraction.

[c] Regenerated fragments from 80 specimens ground up together and analyzed by X-ray diffraction. All three crystal types were present.

determining the crystal type in the regenerating shell (Table V; Wilbur and Watabe, 1963). Two species, *Mercenaria mercenaria* and *Nassarius obsoletus*, did not alter their crystal type during shell regeneration. *Elliptio complanatus* and *Viviparus intertextus*, on the other hand, deposited all three crystal types of CaCO$_3$; Fig. 14 illustrates two of these

Fig. 14. Aragonite (A) and vaterite (V) crystals of regenerating shell of *Elliptio complanatus*. Polarized light. (Wilbur and Watabe, 1963.) ×675.

crystal types. Vaterite, induced by the special conditions of the regenerating system, may, because of its instability, undergo recrystallization as aragonite and calcite. Calcite and aragonite may also be formed directly (see p. 268). *Crassostrea virginica*, which is calcitic, laid down both calcite and aragonite during regeneration.

Divergence from the normal crystal type may be due to the matrix which in regenerating shell may be structurally different from normal matrix (Section II,D). That the matrix can influence crystal type has been pointed out. It may be noted that *M. mercenaria*, which does not have an altered matrix structure, does not have an altered crystal type (Table IV, column 5). Soluble materials of the extrapallial fluid, both inorganic and organic, may also have an influence. Both possibilities can be examined experimentally by precipitating calcium carbonate *in vitro* on normal and on regenerated matrix from decalcified shells, in the presence of extra-pallial fluid from normal and from regenerating individuals.

A diphasic change in the secretion of matrix and crystalline material by the mantle during the course of regeneration in the snail *Triodopsis albolabris* is suggested by percentage changes in shell CaCO$_3$ (Peightel, 1962). On the second day the percentage in the regenerated portion was 69% of normal, indicating increased matrix secretion. This was followed by a relative increase in CaCO$_3$ to 127% of normal on the 8th day and then a return toward the value of normal shell.

REFERENCES

Abolins-Krogis, A. (1958). The morphological and chemical characteristics of organic crystals in the regenerating shell of *Helix pomatia*. *Acta Zool.* (*Stockholm*) **39**, 19–38.

Abolins-Krogis, A. (1961). The histochemistry of the hepatopancreas of *Helix pomatia* (L.) in relation to the regeneration of the shell. *Arkiv Zool.* [2] **13**, 159–202.

Abolins-Krogis, A. (1963). The histochemistry of the mantle of *Helix pomatia* (L.) in relation to the repair of the damaged shell. *Arkiv. Zool.* **15**, 461–474.

Andrews, E. A. (1934a). Restoration of shell parts by the painted snail, *Polymita picta* Born. *Nautilus* **48**, 37–43.

Andrews, E. A. (1934b). Shell repair by the snail *Pleurodonta rostrata* Pfr. *Biol. Bull.* **67**, 294–299.

Asano, M., Ito, M., and Kumagai, T. (1956). Comparative biochemical studies on aquatic animals. I. Calcium turnover of the fresh-water fish and shell fish. *Tôhoku J. Agr. Res.* **6**, 341–360.

Beedham, G. E. (1954). Properties of the non-calcareous material in the shell of *Anodonta cygnea*. *Nature* **174**, 750.

Beedham, G. E. (1958a). Observations on the mantle of the Lamellibranchia. *Quart. J. Microscop. Sci.* **99**, 181–197.

Beedham, G. E. (1958b). Observations on the non-calcareous component of the shell of the Lamellibranchia. *Quart. J. Microscop. Sci.* **99**, 341–357.

Bevelander, G., and Benzer, P. (1948). Calcification in marine molluscs. *Biol. Bull.* **94**, 176–183.

Biedermann, W. (1902). Ueber die Bedeutung von Krystallisationsprozessen bei der Bildung der Skelett wirbelloser Tiere, namentlich, der Molluskenschalen. *Z. allgem. Physiol.* **1**, 154–208.

Bierbauer, J. (1957). Untersuchungen über die Regeneration und Histologie von *Helix pomatia. Acta Biol. Acad. Sci. Hung.* **7**, 419–431.

Bøggild, O. B. (1930). The shell structure of the mollusks. *Kgl. Danske Videnskab. Selskabs, Skrifter Naturvidenskab. math. Afdel.* **2**, 232–325.

Boycott, A. E. (1934). The habitats of land mollusca in Britain. *J. Ecol.* **22**, 1–38.

Brown, C. H. (1952). Some structural proteins of *Mytilus edulis*. *Quart. J. Microscop. Sci.* **93**, 487–502.

Buckley, H. E. (1951). "Crystal Growth," pp. 479–480. Wiley, New York.

Chave, K. E. (1952). A solid solution between calcite and dolomite. *J. Geol.* **60**, 190–192.

Chave, K. E. (1954). Aspects of the biogeochemistry of magnesium: (1) Calcareous marine organisms. *J. Geol.* **62**, 266–283.

Clark, A. M. (1957). The distribution of carbonic anhydrase in the earthworm and snail. *Australian J. Sci.* **19**, 205–207.

Curl, R. L. (1962). The aragonite-calcite problem. *Bull. Natl. Speleol. Soc.* **24**, 57–73.

de Waele, A. (1930). Le sang d'Anodonta cygnea et la formation de la coquille. *Mem. acad. roy. Belg. Classe sci.* [2] **10**, fasc. 3, 1–51.

Dodd, J. R. (1962). Personal communication.

Dodd, J. R. (1963). Paleoecological implications of shell mineralogy in two pelecypod species. *J. Geol.* **71**, 1–11.

Dugal, L. P. (1939). The use of calcareous shell to buffer the product of anaerobic glycolysis in *Venus mercenaria*. *J. Cellular Comp. Physiol.* **13**, 235–251.

Durning, W. C. (1957). Repair of a defect in the shell of the snail *Helix aspersa*. *J. Bone and Joint Surg.* **39A**, 377–393.

Florkin, M. (1945). L'evolution du metabolisme des substances azotées chez les animaux. *Actualités biochim.* **3**.

Freeman, J. A. (1960). Influence of carbonic anhydrase inhibitors on shell growth of a fresh-water snail, *Physa heterostropha*. *Biol. Bull.* **118**, 412–418.

Freeman, J. A., and Wilbur, K. M. (1948). Carbonic anhydrase in molluscs. *Biol. Bull.* **94**, 55–59.

Fretter, V. (1952). Experiments with P^{32} and I^{131} on species of *Helix*, *Arion* and *Agriolimax*. *Quart. J. Microscop. Sci.* **93**, 133–146.

Glimcher, M. J. (1960). Specificity of the molecular structure of organic matrices in mineralization. *In* "Calcification in Biological Systems" (R. F. Sognnaes, ed.), pp. 421–487. Am. Assoc. Advance. Sci., Washington, D.C.

Glimcher, M. J., and Krane, S. M. (1962). Studies of the interactions of collagen and phosphate I. The nature of inorganic orthophosphate binding. *In* "Radioisotopes and Bone" (L. P. Lacroix and A. Budy, eds.), pp. 393–418. Blackwell, Oxford.

Gorodetsky, A. F., and Saratovkin, D. D. (1958). Dendritic form of crystals produced in antiskeletal growth. Rostu Kristallov (Crystal Growth). *Repts. 1st Conf. on Crystal Growth, U.S.S.R. (Engl. Transl.)*, pp. 151–158 (Consultants Bureau, New York).

Grégoire, C. (1957). Topography of the organic components in mother-of-pearl. *J. Biophys. Biochem. Cytol.* **3**, 797–808.

Grégoire, C. (1960). Further studies on structure of the organic components in mother-of-pearl, especially in pelecypods (Part 1). *Bull. inst. roy. sci. nat. Belg.* **36**, No. 23, 1–22.

Grégoire, C. (1961a). Structure of the chonchiolin cases of the prisms in *Mytilus edulis Linné*. *J. Biophys. Biochem. Cytol.* **9**, 395–400.

Grégoire, C. (1961b). Sur la structure submicroscopique de la conchioline associée aux prismes de coquilles de mollusques. *Bull. inst. roy. sci. nat. Belg.* **37**, No. 3, 1–34.

Grégoire, C., Duchâteau, G., and Florkin, M. (1955). La trame protidique des nacres et des perles. *Ann. inst. océanogr. (Paris)* [N.S.] **31**, 1–36.

Guardabassi, A., and Piacenza, M. L. (1958). Le manteau de l'escargot *Helix pomatia*. Étude cytologique et histochimique. *Arch. Anat. microscop. et morphol. exptl.* **47**, 25–46.

Haas, F. (1935). *In* "Klassen und Ordnungen des Tier-Reichs (H. G. Bronn, ed.), Vol. 3, Sect. III, Part I, fasc. 7, pp. 865–984. Akad. Verlagsges., Leipzig.

Hammen, C. S., and Wilbur, K. M. (1959). Carbon dioxide fixation in marine invertebrates. I. The main pathway in the oyster. *J. Biol. Chem.* **234**, 1268–1271.

Hare, P. E. (1963). Amino acids in the proteins from aragonite and calcite in the shells of *Mytilus californianus*. *Science* **139**, 216–217.

Hillman, R. E. (1961). Formation of the periostracum in *Mercenaria mercenaria*. *Science* **134**, 1754–1755.

Hirata, A. A. (1953). Studies on shell formation. II. A mantle-shell preparation for *in vitro* studies. *Biol. Bull.* **104**, 394–397.

Holtz, F., and von Brand, T. (1940). Quantitative studies upon some blood constituents of *Helix pomatia*. *Biol. Bull.* **79**, 423–431.

Horiguchi, Y. (1956). Biochemical studies on *Pteria (Pinctada) martensii* (Dunker) and *Hyriopsis schlegelii* (v. Martens). II. Separation of crude sulfomucopolysaccharides from various tissues of *Pteria (Pinctada) martensii* (Dunker) and *Hyriopsis schlegelii* (v. Martens). *Bull. Japan. Soc. Sci. Fisheries* **22**, 463–466.

Horiguchi, Y. (1957). Biochemical studies on *Pteria (Pinctada) martensii* (Dunker) and *Hyriopsis schlegelii* (Martens). III. Accumulation and disappearance of Ca^{45} in various organs of *Hyriopsis schlegelii* (Martens). *Bull. Japan. Soc. Sci. Fish.* **22**, 747–751.

Horiguchi, Y. (1958). Biochemical studies on *Pteria* (*Pinctada*) *martensii* and *Hyriopsis schlegelii*. IV. Absorption and transference of Ca[45] in *Hyriopsis schlegelii*. *Bull. Japan. Soc. Sci. Fisheries* **23**, 710–715.

Horiguchi, Y. (1959a). Biochemical studies on *Pteria* (*Pinctada*) *martensii* (Dunker) and *Hyriopsis schlegelii* (v. Martens). VII. On the separation and purification of sulfomucopolysaccharide and detection of its component sugars. *Rept. Fac. Fisheries Prefect. Univ. Mie* **3**, 399–406.

Horiguchi, Y. (1959b). Biochemical studies on *Pteria* (*Pinctada*) *martensii* (Dunker) and *Hyriopsis schlegelii* (v. Martens). VIII. Trace components in the shells of shellfish. Part 1. *Bull. Japan. Soc. Sci. Fisheries* **25**, 392–396.

Horiguchi, Y., Miyaka, M., Yoshii, G., Okada, Y., Inoue, Y., and Miyamura, M. (1954). Biochemical studies with radioactive isotopes on *Pteria* (*Pinctada*) *martensii* (Dunker) and *Hyriopsis schlegelii* (v. Martens). I. Ca metabolism by Ca[45] tracer in *Hyriopsis schlegelii* (v. Martens). *Bull. Japan. Soc. Sci. Fisheries* **20**, 101–106.

Ishida, S. (1954). Metabolic patterns in bivalves. II. Distribution of the activity to deaminate urea in the soft parts of the clam, *Meretrix meretrix lusoria*. *Sci. Repts. Tôhoku Univ., Fourth Ser.* **20**, 256–259.

Jodrey, L. H. (1953a). Personal communication.

Jodrey, L. H. (1953b). Studies on shell formation. III. Measurement of calcium deposition in shell and calcium turnover in mantle tissue using the mantle-shell preparation and Ca[45]. *Biol. Bull.* **104**, 398–407.

Kado, Y. (1960). Studies on shell formation in Mollusca *J. Sci. Hiroshima Univ., Ser. B1* **19**, No. 4, 163–210.

Kawai, D. K. (1954). The metabolism of the pearl-oyster *Pinctada martensii*. II. Variations of the carbonic anhydrase of various tissues in relation to age and season, with special reference to the deposition of calcium carbonate. *Physiol. Ecol.* (*Japan*) **6**, 23–27.

Kawai, D. K. (1955). Carbonic anhydrase in pearl oyster. II. Changes of the enzyme activity in relation to growth and seasons. *Publs. Seto Marine Biol. Lab.* (*Kyoto Univ.*) **5**, 89–94.

Kawakami, I. K. (1952). Studies on pearl-sac formation. I. On the regeneration and transplantation of the mantle piece in the pearl oyster. *Mem. Fac. Sci. Kyushu Univ. Ser. E* **1**, 83–88.

Kessel, E. (1933). Über die Schale von *Viviparus viviparus* L. und *Viviparus fasciatus* Müll. Ein Beitrag zum Strukturproblem der Gastrapodenschale. *Z. Morphol. Ökol. Tiere* **27**, 129–198.

Kirschner, L. B. (1963). Personal communication.

Kirschner, L. B., Sorenson, A. L., and Kriebel, M. (1960). Calcium and electric potential across the clam mantle. *Science* **131**, 735.

Kitano, Y. (1961). Personal communication.

Kitano, Y. (1962). The behavior of various inorganic ions in the separation of calcium carbonate from a bicarbonate solution. *Bull. Chem. Soc. Japan* **35**, 1973–1980.

Kitano, Y., and Furutsu, T. (1959). The state of a small amount of magnesium contained in calcareous shells. *Bull. Chem. Soc. Japan* **33**, 1–4.

Kitano, Y., and Hood, D. W. (1961). Personal communication.

Kitano, Y., Park, K., and Hood, D. W. (1962). Pure aragonite synthesis. *J. Geophys. Res.* **67**, 4873–4874.

Kobayashi, S. (1961). Personal communication.

Kobayashi, S. (1962). Personal communication.

Kobayashi, S., and Watabe, N. (1959). "Studies of Pearls," 280pp. Gihodo Press, Tokyo.

Koczy, F. F., and Titze, H. (1958). Radium content of carbonate shells. *J. Marine Research (Sears Foundation)* **17**, 302–311.

Korschelt, E. (1937). Zum Schalenersatz bei den Weichtieren. *Zool. Jahrb., Abt. System Ökol. u. Geogr. Tiere* **69**, 417–468.

Loosanoff, V. L., and Nomejko, C. A. (1955). Growth of oysters with damaged shell-edges. *Biol. Bull.* **108**, 151–159.

Lowenstam, H. A. (1954a). Environmental relations of modification compositions of certain carbonate-secreting marine invertebrates. *Proc. Natl. Acad. Sci. U.S.* **40**, 39–48.

Lowenstam, H. A. (1954b). Factors affecting the aragonite : calcite ratios in carbonate-secreting marine organisms. *J. Geol.* **62**, 284–322.

Lutts, A., Grandjean, J., and Grégoire, C. (1960). X-ray diffraction patterns from the prisms of mollusk shells. *Arch. intern. physiol. et biochim.* **68**, 829–831.

Manigault, P. (1939). Recherches sur le calcaire chez les mollusques. Phosphatase et precipitation calcique. Histochimie du calcium. *Ann. inst. océanogr. (Paris)* [N.S.] **18**, 331–346.

Maroney, S. P., Barber, A. A., and Wilbur, K. M. (1957). Studies on shell formation. VI. The effect of dinitrophenol on mantle respiration and shell formation. *Biol. Bull.* **112**, 92–96.

Martin, A. W. (1961). The carbohydrate metabolism of the Mollusca. *In* "Comparative Physiology of Carbohydrate Metabolism in Heterothermic Animals" (A. W. Martin, ed.), pp. 35–64. Univ. of Washington Press, Seattle, Washington.

Mayer, F. K. (1931). Röntgenographische Untersuchungen an Gastropoden Schalen. *Jena. Z. Naturwiss.* **65**, 487–512.

Mayer, F. K., and Weineck, E. (1932). Die Verbreitung des Kalziumkarbonates im Tierreich unter besonderer Berücksichtigung der Wirbellosen. *Jena Z. Naturwiss.* **66**, 199–222.

Meldrum, N. U., and Roughton, F. J. W. (1933). Carbonic anhydrase. Its preparation and properties. *J. Physiol.* **80**, 113–170.

Nakahara, H. (1957). Some morphological features of pearl-sac tissues in relation to the normal and abnormal pearl production in the pearl-oyster. (*Pinctada martensii*). *J. Fac. Sci. Hokkaido Univ.*, Ser. VI, **13**, 268–270.

Neuman, W. F., and Neuman, M. W. (1958). "The Chemical Dynamics of Bone Mineral," 209 pp. Univ. of Chicago Press, Chicago, Illinois.

Peightel, W. (1962). Personal communication.

Piez, K. A. (1961). Amino acid composition of some calcified proteins. *Science* **134**, 841–842.

Prenant, M. (1927). Les formes minérologiques du calcaire chez les êtres vivants et le problème de leur détermination. *Biol. Revs. Cambridge Phil. Soc.* **2**, 365–393.

Ranson, G. (1952). Les huîtres et le calcaire. Calcaire et substratum organique chez les mollusques et quelques autres invertébrès marins. *Compt. rend. acad. sci.* **234**, 1485–1487.

Rao, K. P., and Goldberg, E. D. (1954). Utilization of dissolved calcium by a pelecypod. *J. Cellular Comp. Physiol.* **43**, 283–292.

Roche, J., Ranson, G., and Eysseric-Lafon, M. (1951). Sur la composition des scléroprotéines des coquilles des mollusques (conchiolines). *Compt. rend. soc. biol.* **145**, 1474–1477.

Saylor, C. H. (1928). Calcite and aragonite. *J. Phys. Chem.* **32**, 1441–1460.

Schmidt, W. J. (1924). Bau und Bildung der Perlmuttermasse. *Zool. Jahrb., Abt. Anat. u. Ontog. Tiere* **45**, 1–148.

Schoffeniels, E. (1951a). Mise en évidence par l'utilisation de radiocalcium d'un mécanisme d'absorption du calcium a partir du milieu extérieur chez l'anodonte. *Arch. intern. Physiol.* **58**, 467–468.

Schoffeniels, E. (1951b). Utilisation du radiocalcium pour l'étude de la diffusion et du remplacement du calcium au niveau des tissus de l'anodonte. *Arch. intern. physiol.* **58**, 469–472.

Simkiss, K. (1963). Personal communication.

Sioli, H. (1935). Ueber den Chemismus der Reparatur von Schalendefekten bei *Helix pomatia*. *Zool. Jahrb., Abt. allgem. Zool. u. Physiol. Tiere* **54**, 507–534.

Stenzel, H. B. (1962). Aragonite in the resilium of oysters. *Science* **136**, 1121–1122.

Sterns, C. (1961). Personal communication.

Stolkowski, J. (1948). Quelques precisions sur l'analyse quantitative par les rayons X de mélanges binaires et ternaires de carbonate de calcium anhydre. *Compt. rend. acad. sci.* **226**, 933–934.

Stolkowski, J. (1951). Essai sur le déterminisme des formes minérologique du calcaire chez les êtres vivants (calcaires coquilliers). *Ann. inst. océanogr.* (*Paris*) [N.S.] **26**, 1–113.

Takagi, Y., and Tanaka, S. (1955). On the pigment of the pearl oysters with special reference to porphyrin. *J. Chem. Soc. Japan, Pure Chem. Sect.* **76**, 406–409.

Tanaka, S., and Hatano, H. (1953). Analysis of amino acids in conchiolin of pearls and the Japanese pearl oyster. *J. Chem. Soc. Japan, Pure Chem. Sect.* **74**, 193–197.

Tanaka, S., and Hatano, H. (1955). Biochemical studies on the pearl oyster, *Pinctada martensii*. IV. On the uptake of radioactive calcium by pearl oyster and its deposition on the pearl and the shell. *J. Chem. Soc. Japan, Pure Chem. Sect.* **72**, 602–605.

Tanaka, S., Hatano, H., and Itasaka, O. (1960). Biochemical studies on pearl. IX. Amino acid composition of conchiolin in pearl and shell. *Bull. Chem. Soc. Japan* **33**, 543–545.

Techow, G. (1910). Zur Kenntnis der Schalenregeneration bei den Gastropoden. *Wilhelm Roux' Arch. Entwicklungsmech. Organ.* **31**, 258–288.

Thompson, T. G., and Chow, T. J. (1955). The strontium-calcium ratio in carbonate secreting marine organisms. *Deep Sea Research* **3**, Suppl., 20–39.

Tsujii, T. (1955). Histochemical studies of nucleic acids on shell and culture pearl formation. *Bull. Biogeog. Soc. Japan* **16–19**, 88–93. (Recent conceptions of Japanese fauna).

Tsujii, T. (1960). Studies on the mechanism of shell- and pearl-formation in Mollusca. *J. Fac. Fisheries Prefect. Univ. Mie* **5**, 2–70.

Tsujii, T., and Machii, A. (1953). Histochemical observation of carbonic anhydrase on shell and pearl-formation. *Kagaku* **23**, 148.

Tsujii, T., Sharp, D. G., and Wilbur, K. M. (1958). Studies on shell formation. VII. The submicroscopic structure of the shell of the oyster *Crassostrea virginica J. Biophys. Biochem. Cytol.* **4**, 275–279.

Turekian, K. K., and Armstrong, R. L. (1960). Magnesium, strontium, and barium concentrations and calcite-aragonite ratios of some recent molluscan shells. *J. Marine Research* (*Sears Foundation*) **18**, 133–151.

von Levetzow, K. G. (1932). Die Struktur einiger Schneckenschalen und ihre Entstehung durch typisches und atypisches Wachstum. *Jena Z. Naturwiss.* **66**, 41–108.

Wada, K. (1957a). Electron microscope observations on the shell structures of pearl oyster (*Pinctada martensii*). II. Observations of the aragonite crystals on the surface of the nacreous layers. *Bull. Natl. Pearl Research Lab.* **2**, 74–85.

Wada, K. (1957b). Electron-microscopic observations on the shell structures of pearl oyster (*Pinctada martensii*). III. On the laminary structure of shell. *Bull. Natl. Pearl. Research Lab.* **2**, 86–93.

Wada, K. (1960a). The relation between the crystalline structure of the cultured pearls and the elongation of the transplanted mantle tissue in the process of pearl-sac formation. *Bull. Japan Soc. Sci. Fisheries* **26**, 549–553.

Wada, K. (1960b). Crystal growth on the inner shell surface of *Pinctada martensii* (Dunker). I. *J. Electron microscopy* (*Chiba*) **9**, 21–23.

Wada, K. (1961). Crystal growth of molluscan shells. *Bull. Natl. Pearl Research Lab* **7**, 703–828.

Wagge, L. E. (1951). Amoebocytic activity and alkaline phosphatases during the regeneration of the shell in the snail *Helix aspersa*. *Quart. J. Microscop. Sci.* **92**, 307–321.

Wagge, L. E. (1952). Quantitative studies of calcium metabolism in *Helix aspersa*. *J. Exptl. Zool.* **120**, 311–342.

Wagge, L. E., and Mittler, T. (1953). Shell regenetration in some British molluscs. *Nature* **171**, 528–529.

Watabe, N. (1952). Relation between water temperature and nacre-secreting activity of pearl-oyster *Pinctada martensii*. *J. Fuji Pearl Inst.* **2**, 21–26.

Watabe, N. (1954). Electron microscopic observations of the aragonite crystals on the surface of the cultured pearls. I. *Rept. Fac. Fisheries Prefect. Univ Mie* **1**, 449–454.

Watabe, N. (1955). The observation of the surface structure of the cultured pearls relating to color and luster. *Rept. Fac. Fisheries Prefect. Univ. Mie* **2**, 18–26.

Watabe, N. (1961). Personal communication.

Watabe, N., and Kobayashi, S. (1961). Personal communication.

Watabe, N., and Simkiss, K. (1963). Personal communication.

Watabe, N., and Wada, K. (1956). On the shell structure of the Japanese pearl-oyster, *Pinctada martensii*. I. Prismatic layer. I. *Rept. Fac. Fisheries Prefect Univ. Mie* **2**, 227–232.

Watabe, N., and Wilbur, K. M. (1960). Influence of the organic matrix on crystal type in molluscs. *Nature* **188**, 334.

Watabe, N., and Wilbur, K. M. (1961). Studies on shell formation. IX. An electron microscope study of crystal layer formation in the oyster. *J. Biophys. Biochem. Cytol.* **9**, 761–772.

Watabe, N., and Wilbur, K. M. (1962). Unpublished data.

Watabe, N., Sharp, D. G., and Wilbur, K. M. (1958). Studies on shell formation. VIII. Electron microscopy of crystal growth of the nacreous layer of the oyster *Crassostrea virginica*. *J. Biophys. Biochem. Cytol.* **4**, 281–286.

Wilbur, K. M. (1960). Shell structure and mineralization in molluscs. *In* "Calcification in Biological Systems" (R. F. Sognnaes, ed.), pp. 15–40. Am. Assoc. Advance. Sci., Washington, D.C.

Wilbur, K. M., and Jodrey, L. (1955). Studies on shell formation. V. The inhibition of shell formation by carbonic anhydrase inhibitors. *Biol. Bull.* **108**, 359–365.

Wilbur, K. M., and Watabe, N. (1963). Experimental studies on calcification in molluscs and the alga *Coccolithus huxleyi*. *Ann. N.Y. Acad. Sci.* **109**, 82–112.

CHAPTER 9

Osmotic and Ionic Regulation

James D. Robertson

DEPARTMENT OF ZOOLOGY, THE UNIVERSITY OF GLASGOW, SCOTLAND

I. INTRODUCTION

This chapter is concerned with the influence of the aquatic medium, marine, brackish, or fresh-water, on the concentration and ionic composition of molluscan body fluids and tissues, and also with the mechanisms that molluscs have evolved for controlling salt and water balance. General surveys of osmotic and ionic regulation have been made by Krogh (1939), Prosser and Brown (1961), Beadle (1957), and Shaw (1960); these include some material from the molluscan phylum.

Molluscs, like most other aquatic animals, are much more abundant in the sea than in fresh water. Wide differences in composition exist between sea water and fresh water, and between different types of fresh water (Table I). The low salt content of the latter, between 1/100 and 1/1000 that of sea water, and its more variable composition, including a wide range of calcium and hydrogen ions, would seem to be among the principal factors responsible for the relative paucity of fresh-water species.

Sea water itself varies in strength at different places, depending on the

TABLE I

Composition of Some Natural Waters[a]

	Gm/liter								
	Na	K	Ca	Mg	Cl	SO$_4$	HCO$_3$	Total salts	pH
Sea water	10.543	0.382	0.403	1.272	19.000	2.652	0.141	34.4	8.1–8.3
Hard fresh water	0.021	0.016	0.064	0.014	0.041	0.024	0.242	0.42	7.7–7.8
Soft fresh water	0.003	—	0.002	0.001	0.005	0.005	0.004	0.02	6.7–6.8

[a] Data from Robertson (1941).

influx of fresh water and the amount of evaporation. A range of salinity to include most Atlantic and Pacific coastal waters and the Mediterranean would be 32–38‰ (gm per kg). This is equivalent to a chloride content of 18.1–21.6 gm per liter at 20°C, a freezing-point depression of Δ1.74°– 2.08°C and a vapor pressure equal to that of 0.517–0.620 molal NaCl.

At the outset it should be pointed out that most of the following data pertain to common, large European and American species; complete gaps exist for whole classes, such as the Amphineura and Scaphopoda.

II. OSMOTIC EQUILIBRIUM

A. Occurrence in Various Groups

Freezing-point measurements and chemical estimations have shown that the blood of marine molluscs of the major classes has the same total concentration of ions and other osmotically active particles as sea water. Thus the blood plasma is in osmotic equilibrium with sea water across the animal's permeable membranes, such as the gills, at least within 1–2%. Table II shows most of the freezing-point data. To the representatives of the seven orders it includes can be added all the species of Table III (see below), including members from five other orders, Neogastropoda (*Buccinum, Neptunea*), Notaspidea (*Pleurobranchus*), Acoela (*Archidoris*), Adapedonta (*Ensis, Mya*), and Decapoda (*Sepia, Loligo*); these have ionic concentrations 99–100% of those in sea water (98% in the case of *Sepia*). Isosmoticity within 1% for *Venus mercenaria*, *Mya arenaria* (Bivalvia), and *Busycon canaliculatum* (Neogastropoda) has been found at Woods Hole (Garrey, 1905).

A few marine species, particularly among the bivalves, are euryhaline, withstanding a broad range of external salinities. Thus in the Gulf of Finland *Mya arenaria*, *Cardium edule*, and *Mytilus edulis* can be found at salinities of 4–5‰, although much reduced in size (Segerstråle, 1957).

TABLE II

THE FREEZING-POINT DEPRESSION (Δ) OF THE BLOOD PLASMA OF MARINE MOLLUSCS IN RELATION TO THAT OF THE EXTERNAL MEDIUM

Species	Blood (Δ °C)	Sea water (Δ °C)	Equilibration period	Authority
Gastropoda				
Prosobranchia				
Archaeogastropoda				
Tugalia gigas	1.96	1.99	24 hr	Yazaki (1929)
Mesogastropoda				
Dolium galea	2.24	2.27	—	Bottazzi (1908)
Littorina littorea	1.99	1.97	2–21 days	Todd (1962)
L. littorea	1.42	1.42	4–7 days	
L. littorea	0.97	0.97	3–7 days	
L. littorea	1.06	0.48	3–7 days	
Opisthobranchia				
Anaspidea				
Aplysia fasciata	2.32	2.27	—	Bottazzi (1908)
Bivalvia				
Lamellibranchia				
Taxodonta				
Anadara inflata	1.95	1.95	24 hr	Yazaki (1929)
Anisomyaria				
Mytilus edulis	2.09	2.09	—	Potts (1954a)
M. edulis	1.54	1.54	—	
M. edulis	0.98	0.98	—	
M. edulis	0.58	0.58	4–5 days[a]	
M. dunkeri	1.93	1.98	24 hr	Yazaki (1929)
Modiolus capax	1.95	1.96	24 hr	Yazaki (1929)
Pecten maximus	1.91	1.91	—	Dakin (1909)
Ostrea circumpicta	1.95	1.98	—	Yazaki (1929)
O. circumpicta	0.92	0.85	21 days	
Heterodonta				
Venus mercenaria	1.76	1.76	—	Cole (1940)
V. mercenaria	1.39	1.34	—	
Scrobicularia plana	1.89	1.90	2 days	Freeman and
S. plana	1.60	1.55	2 days	Rigler (1957)
S. plana	1.05	1.05	$4\frac{1}{2}$ days	
S. plana	0.74	0.59	$4\frac{1}{2}$ days	
Cephalopoda				
Coleoidea				
Octopoda				
Octopus vulgaris	2.30	2.27	—	Bottazzi (1908)
O. macropus	2.32	2.27	—	Bottazzi (1908)

[a] Valves propped open.

There is no evidence that these species are other than isosmotic with the dilute environment. Bivalves often close their valves tightly when placed in dilute sea water or fresh water, and prolong their period of disequilibrium. *Ostrea circumpicta* placed in 50% sea water (Δ0.85°C) had not come into equilibrium completely even after 3 weeks (Table II). But *Mytilus* in water of Δ0.58°C becomes isosmotic within 4–5 days when the valves are propped open; equilibrium is rapid, and is virtually complete in 4 hr in animals transferred from water of Δ2.08°C to water of Δ1.36°C (Potts, 1961). The slight hypertonicity of *Venus mercenaria* in slightly diluted sea water, blood Δ1.39°C against sea water Δ1.34°C (Table II), is possibly only apparent as no details are given of the equilibration period; surface salinities may be lower than those of the water in contact with burrowing animals.

The intertidal limpet *Acmaea limatula* (Archaeogastropoda) cannot regulate osmotically; its blood becomes isosmotic to the medium at low or high salinities over the range S 17–50‰. Desiccation experiments in which limpets were placed on rock above the high tide level show that the extravisceral water of the animal probably acts as a temperature and an osmotic buffer, the latter function slowing down changes in blood concentration which, nevertheless, sometimes increased to 150% of the normal in 6 hr (Segal and Dehnel, 1962).

B. *Permeability to Water and Salts*

In diluted sea water, increases in weight due to osmotic uptake of water occur in soft-bodied gastropods such as the opisthobranchs *Aplysia fasciata* (= *limacina*) and *A. juliana*, and the marine pulmonate *Onchidium chamaeleon* (Bethe, 1930, 1934; van Weel, 1957; Dakin and Edmonds, 1931), and in bivalves such as *Mytilus*, if the valves are forcibly kept apart (Maloeuf, 1937). But the gills and the outer integument are far from being semipermeable: not only is the calculated theoretical weight not attained (say in 50 or 75% sea water), but the final weight usually falls, sometimes to below the value the animal had originally in full-strength sea water (*Aplysia fasciata*). The explanation of the imperfect semipermeability of the molluscs' integument and gills is that, after the initial transfer of water, salts begin to be lost to the dilute medium, as has been shown in *Aplysia* by chloride analyses of the blood and external medium (Bethe, 1930). The final drop in weight of *Aplysia* and *Onchidium* is probably due to muscular contraction with consequent forcing out of water through the tissues (Dakin and Edmonds, 1931).

In concentrated sea water, *Aplysia* loses weight as water is abstracted by the hyperosmotic solution, but the theoretical values are not attained.

Further confirmation of permeability to ions is given by experiments with *Aplysia*, the nudibranch *Archidoris*, and *Onchidium* in various mixtures of sea water and nonelectrolytes, including urea, sucrose, and glycerin, and in sea water plus a solution of magnesium sulfate, all mixtures being isosmotic with sea water. In all these artificial solutions, the gastropods lose weight, the blood becoming viscous, although the loss is only slight in the urea–sea water solution in the *Onchidium* experiments. Bethe's interpretation of the loss in weight is outward diffusion of ions, particularly sodium and chloride, thus lowering the osmotic pressure of the blood from which water is then abstracted by the bathing solution, the two processes continuing since equilibrium cannot be achieved. The more rapidly penetrating urea reduces the imbalance, and the weight loss is smaller.

This explanation is further supported by work on the bivalve *Scrobicularia plana*, kept in a mixture of sea water and isosmotic sucrose (Freeman and Rigler, 1957). Each of three specimens showing signs of very considerable dehydration had a blood Δ of 1.83°C, slightly less than the values from two specimens which did not open their valves ($\Delta1.91°$ and 1.92°C).

A physiologically more satisfactory demonstration of ionic permeability in *Aplysia* is obtained by keeping the animals in artificial sea waters of the same osmotic concentration but with different levels of ions. Thus in water with 0.48 mg Ca/ml, samples of blood from different *Aplysia punctata* gave values between 0.49 and 0.58 mg/ml, while in calcium-free water values of 0.15 and 0.16 were obtained after a stay of 6 and 24 hr, the animals themselves losing tonus; in calcium-rich water, 1.68 mg/ml, the blood of another specimen had a value of 0.70 after 5 hr, the animal showing increased tonus (Bethe, 1929).

In artificial sea water with 1.40 mg Mg/ml two animals had values of 1.22 and 1.54 mg/ml; but in magnesium-rich water, 2.82 mg/ml, a specimen had a concentration of 2.70 mg in 5 hr, and showed signs of narcosis. In 6 hr of potassium-free sea water, a value of 0.12 mg in the blood was obtained, compared with normal values of 0.45 and 0.49 mg/ml in water with 0.43 mg K/ml. Reducing the chloride to 11.2 mg Cl/ml by substituting sulfate caused wrinkling and contraction of a specimen, whose blood chloride became 16.2 mg/ml in 5 hr, compared to values of 21.4 and 21.6 in specimens in normal artificial sea water of Cl 22.0.

Similar experiments on *Aplysia fasciata*, in which the mouth was ligatured to prevent any possible ion transfer through the gut, showed that the body surface was permeable to calcium, magnesium, chloride, and sulfate ions (Bethe, 1934).

Data on three genera of gastropods and one bivalve might be considered rather meager for a generalization that some degree of permeability to ions is probable in the whole phylum, but this receives support from the fact that all marine invertebrates which have been tested have shown some measure of permeability [e.g., decapod crustaceans, echinoderms; Bethe (1929); Berger and Bethe (1931)].

C. Ionic Regulation of the Blood and Its Mechanism

Despite a presumed measure of permeability to ions, most molluscs have blood differing from sea water in the relative proportions of potassium, calcium, and sulfate. Ionic regulation may be defined as the maintenance in a body fluid of concentrations of ions differing from those of a passive equilibrium with the external medium. A measure of ionic regulation is obtained by comparing an analysis of one blood sample with another which has been dialyzed against sea water across a collodion membrane which is permeable to water and salts but not to protein. In such a passive equilibrium the concentrations (on a water content basis) of ions in the dialyzed blood differ slightly from those of the sea water, the differences depending on the concentration of the plasma proteins; the mean Donnan ratio, r, for univalent and divalent ions (except Ca^{++}) is, however, only 1.01–1.02 in prosobranchs and cephalopods where

$$r = \frac{Na_i}{Na_o} = \frac{\sqrt{Mg_i}}{\sqrt{Mg_o}} = \frac{Cl_o}{Cl_i}, \text{ etc. } (i = \text{blood}, o = \text{sea water})$$

The calcium value is higher owing to the presence of a nondiffusible calcium-protein complex (e.g., Ca_i/Ca_o is 1.05 in *Buccinum*, 1.19 in *Sepia*).

Such experiments and analyses show that some or all of the ions of the blood are regulated in every mollusc tested (Table III). In the gastropods and bivalves regulation consists chiefly in raised values of potassium and calcium, and lowered values of sulfate; sodium and chloride are virtually in equilibrium across the boundary membranes of these animals. Magnesium remains at the equilibrium value in practically all, being higher in the blood only in *Archidoris*. *Mytilus edulis* and *Ostrea edulis* show perhaps the least regulation. The Mediterranean *M. galloprovincialis* surprisingly accumulates sulfate.

In contrast, marked ionic regulation extending to all ions is shown by the three cephalopods. Noteworthy are the high potassium contents of the plasma, the slightly raised chloride, and the lower sodium and sulfate figures.

A progressive lowering of sodium in the series *Eledone, Loligo,* and *Sepia* is associated with a fall in sulfate and a rise in chloride, but the plasma remains isosmotic. These features have been interpreted in relation to the ideal laws of solutions (Robertson, 1949, 1953). If sea water and body fluids are considered hypothetically as mixtures of isosmotic solutions of various salts, then the replacement of some of the Na_2SO_4 solution by the same volume of NaCl solution results in a lowering of SO_4^{--} and Na^+ ions, and an increase of Cl^- ions, while the whole solu-

TABLE III

IONIC REGULATION IN BLOOD PLASMA OF MARINE MOLLUSCS[a]

Species	Concentrations in plasma as % concentrations in dialyzed plasma (prosobranchs and cephalopods) or in sea water (other groups) (water content basis)						Plasma protein (gm/liter)	Total ionic concentrations as % of that in sea water
	Na	K	Ca	Mg	Cl	SO$_4$		
Gastropoda								
Prosobranchia								
Neogastropoda								
Buccinum undatum	97	142	104	103	100	90	25.3	99
Neptunea antiqua	101	114	102	101	101	98	24.1	100
Opisthobranchia								
Notaspidea								
Pleurobranchus								
membranaceus	100	117	112	99	100	102	0.3	100
Acoela								
Archidoris								
pseudoargus	99	128	132	107	100	96	0.4	100
Bivalvia								
Lamellibranchia								
Anisomyaria								
Mytilus edulis	100	135	100	100	101	98	0.3	100
M. galloprovincialis	101	121	107	97	99	120	0.8	99
Pecten maximus	100	130	103	97	100	97	—	100
Ostrea edulis	100	129	101	102	100	100	0.2	100
Adapedonta								
Ensis ensis	99	155	108	99	99	87	—	99
Mya arenaria	101	107	107	99	100	101	—	100
Cephalopoda								
Coleoidea								
Decapoda								
Sepia officinalis	93	205	91	98	105	22	109	98
Loligo forbesi	95	219	102	102	104	29	150	99
Octopoda								
Eledone cirrosa	97	152	107	103	102	77	105	100

[a] Data from Robertson (1949, 1953).

tion retains the same osmotic concentration. Sodium ions are lowered because their activity is greater in association with Cl$^-$ ions than with SO$_4^{--}$ ions. Granted a marked decrease in sulfate as the result of active ionic regulation, then the chloride ions would rise to balance the cations, and the cations themselves decrease slightly. It can be calculated that in a synthetic sea water in which the sulfate is reduced to a fifth and the potassium doubled, the chloride would be 104.7% and the sodium 93.8% of the values in an isosmotic sea water of normal composition. As seen in Table III, these values are approached in the analysis of *Sepia* plasma. With reduced sulfate but normal potassium, the sodium figure would be higher, 95.9% (Robertson, 1953).

The mechanism of ionic regulation of the blood seems to be twofold: the elimination of a fluid which differs from an ultrafiltrate of the plasma in that its ions have been differentially excreted, and the replacement of this fluid by controlled absorption of ions and water in such a way that the blood remains isosmotic and approximately constant in ionic composition.

1. DIFFERENTIAL EXCRETION BY RENAL ORGANS

In marine molluscs the fluid excreted by the renal tubules has been analyzed in cephalopods. This fluid of low protein content (1/100 or less that of the plasma) is practically isosmotic with the blood in *Sepia* and *Eledone* (Table IV), and also in *Octopus vulgaris* (blood Δ2.30°C,

TABLE IV

PLASMA AND RENAL SAC FLUIDS OF CEPHALOPODS[a]

| | Mg/gm water | | | | | | Total |
	Na	K	Ca	Mg	Cl	SO₄	mg-ions/kg water
Sepia officinalis							
Plasma	10.58	0.931	0.434	1.383	20.87	0.47	1145
Renal sac fluid[b]	8.35	0.465	0.302	0.936	20.85	1.01	1166
Sea water	11.31	0.409	0.432	1.364	20.38	2.845	1174
Fluid as % plasma	79	50	70	68	100	215	102
Plasma ultrafiltrate as % plasma	98	98	84	96	102	105	100
Eledone cirrosa							
Plasma	10.26	0.581	0.466	1.318	18.92	1.983	1081
Renal sac fluid	10.41	0.522	0.405	1.218	18.35	2.705	1073
Sea water	10.43	0.378	0.399	1.258	18.80	2.624	1082
Fluid as % plasma	101	90	87	92	97	136	99
Plasma ultrafiltrate as % plasma	99	99	92	98	101	102	100

[a] Data from Robertson (1949, 1953).

[b] Also 2.64 mg NH₄/gm water.

urine Δ2.24°C; Bottazzi, 1908). Wide differences from the plasma or a plasma ultrafiltrate are found with respect to the concentrations of almost all the ions. In *Eledone* there occurs a reabsorption of potassium, calcium, magnesium, and chloride and secretion of sulfate and sodium, tending to raise the level in the blood of the former ions and lower that of the latter; in fact, relative to sea water the blood does show higher levels of potassium, calcium, magnesium, and chloride, and lower levels of sodium and sulfate.

While the differences between the values in urine and plasma ultra-filtrate of potassium, chloride, and sulfate are in step with the composition of the blood in *Sepia,* that between the sodium concentrations is not: the low sodium content of the renal sac fluid, far below that of a blood ultrafiltrate, would tend to increase the sodium content of the blood, which, however, is only 93% of the value in sea water. This anomaly is apparently the result of the large concentration of ammonium ions excreted in the fluid. Requirements of cation-anion balance and total osmotic concentration are met by reduction in sodium, the cation of greatest concentration. Ammonium forms 146 meq of the total cations, 613 meq/kg water, the chloride and sulfate anions coming to 609.

For an estimate of the water and ion turnover in cephalopods, estimates of the amount of urine produced and the volume of blood and other extracellular fluids are necessary. Figures are available for *Octopus hong-kongensis.* Expressed in terms of volume as per cent wet weight, a mean value of 28.0% has been found for the extracellular fluid, based on the distribution of injected inulin (Martin *et al.,* 1958). Of this, blood accounts for 5.8%, as measured by the dye T-1824 and colloidal mercuric sulfide (HgS). Urine output per 24 hr varies between 6.2 and 10.0% of the body weight, the lower value being obtained by tying off the renal sacs and measuring the increase in weight, the higher figure from catheterized animals (Martin, 1957). Thus the renal organs in this animal have a daily output equivalent to about 138% of the blood volume or 29% of the extracellular fluid volume.

In *Sepia* a minimal value for daily output of urine of 13% of the volume of extracellular fluid has been given (Robertson, 1953).

2. Controlled Uptake of Water and Ions

Loss of water and ions through excretory tubules must be balanced by uptake of water and ions from sea water, through the gills and any other permeable portions of the integument, or via the gut. This uptake is indicated by the increases in weight of cephalopods such as the octopus when the ureters are ligated. Absorption of pure water would alter the osmotic pressure of the body fluids. There is no evidence of this, and therefore ions must be absorbed with the water in concentrations sufficient to make it isosmotic with the fluid it is replacing.

Unfortunately, there is no information on the absorption of ions such as has been obtained in "balance" experiments with the crab *Carcinus*

(Robertson, 1960b), nor has any investigation been made with indicators, such as phenol red, of possible absorption of sea water via the gut.

An inference from the data of Table III that potassium, chloride, and possibly calcium are taken up against concentration gradients in the cephalopods may be correct, but a continuous loss of potassium in the excretory fluid without corresponding uptake, as in *Carcinus*, has not been excluded; sodium and sulfate may enter wholly or partly by diffusion, as their concentration gradients are favorable. In *Carcinus* the negative balance for potassium after 1 or 2 weeks' starvation may indicate that the crab normally obtains most of its potassium from food, not from ions absorbed from sea water. Its blood level of potassium rises after feeding.

D. *Ionic Regulation of Other Fluids*

Fluids from the eyes and statocysts of cephalopods differ from blood in being colorless, cell-free, and almost protein-free. The eye fluids of *Sepia*, *Loligo* and *Eledone* have a total ionic concentration within 1% or so of the plasma, but show very considerable divergencies from it in composition; they are far from being dialyzates or ultrafiltrates of the blood, but their mode of origin is obscure. Chief among the differences between the vitreous fluid (from the posterior eye chamber) and the plasma are consistently lower magnesium concentrations (9–19% on a water content basis) and higher sodium concentrations (112–115%). The aqueous humor of *Sepia* (from in front of the lens) differs considerably from the vitreous fluid; in most respects it is intermediate in composition between the vitreous fluid and sea water, a finding consistent with the potential channel of communication with the exterior, the corneal pore (Robertson, 1953).

The statocyst of *Octopus* has both an inner and outer sac, so that as in the vertebrate labyrinth one can distinguish endolymph and perilymph. Whereas mammalian endolymph has a very low Na/K molar ratio (<0.6), *Octopus* endolymph has a high ratio of 30, intermediate between that of the blood (17) and sea water (47). Perilymph has lower sodium and potassium concentrations than endolymph, but its ratio (33) is not markedly different (Amoore *et al.*, 1959).

Oceanic squid belonging to the family Cranchiidae have large coelomic spaces filled with slightly acid fluid (pH 5.2) containing a concentration of about 480 mg-ions ammonium, and 80 mg-ions sodium. Presumably these ammonium ions accumulate in the animals by secretion from the kidneys and perhaps other parts of the coelomic epithelium. The anions are almost exclusively chloride. This large volume of coelomic fluid, practically isosmotic with sea water and containing chiefly a solution of ammonium chloride, has a density lower than that of sea water and the heavier parts of the squid, thus bringing about buoyancy equilibrium in the animal (Denton *et al.*, 1958; see also Chapter 13).

III. OSMOTIC REGULATION

A. Definition

Osmotic regulation may be defined as the maintenance of the total particle concentration of body fluids at levels different from those of the external medium. The definition may be extended to terrestrial animals which control the concentration of their body fluids, although the source of ions and water is the more variable medium of ingested food and fluid.

All fresh-water molluscs and probably a few brackish-water species show hyperosmotic regulation, maintaining higher concentrations of ions in the blood than those of the medium. This type of regulation is a steady state in which energy is expended.

B. Brackish-Water Forms

Brackish water, that is, water of salinity 0.5–17‰, may contain two groups of molluscs as in the Baltic Sea: marine immigrants such as the bivalves *Mytilus edulis*, *Cardium edule*, *Macoma balthica*, and *Mya arenaria;* and fresh-water immigrants such as the pulmonate *Lymnaea peregra*, the prosobranchs *Bithynia tentaculata* and *Theodoxus fluviatilis*, and the bivalves *Anodonta cygnea* and *Dreissena polymorpha* (Segerstråle, 1957).

In British waters the bivalves *Scrobicularia plana* (Heterodonta) and the hydrobiids *Potamopyrgus jenkinsi* and *Hydrobia ulvae* (Mesogastropoda) are typically brackish-water species, living in estuaries.

Little work has been done on those gastropods which might be expected to show regulation. The periwinkle *Littorina littorea*, collected intertidally at Millport, Scotland, is isosmotic in salinities of S 17–36‰, but regulates when placed in dilute sea water (S 8.8‰), maintaining a mean blood Δ of 1.06°C (range 0.63°–1.50°) as against Δ0.48°C for the medium, after 3–7 days (Todd, 1962; Table II). This species extends into the southern part of the Baltic, withstanding there a salinity of about 7–8‰.

There is little information on the blood concentrations of the various Baltic pulmonates and prosobranchs of lacustrine origin which can tolerate low salinities, *Lymnaea peregra* tolerating 10–11‰, *Bithynia tentaculata* and *Physa fontinalis* 6‰ and *Theodoxus fluviatilis* up to 14‰ (Segerstråle, 1957). *Lymnaea* is probably isosmotic with the medium at these salinities. Only *Theodoxus* has been studied experimentally (Neumann, 1960). Snails from a brackish-water population (from the Kiel Canal) withstood a rise in salinity to 15‰ better than those from fresh water, and survived in 20‰ if previously acclimatized to 6.5‰. Another group kept at salinities of 3–25‰ (about $\Delta 0.15°$–$1.35°C$) were slightly hyperosmotic to the medium over this range. In fresh water ($\Delta 0.01°C$) the blood of *Theodoxus* is hyperosmotic, $\Delta 0.12°$–$0.18°$, mean $0.15°C$, the values being somewhat higher, $\Delta 0.20°$–$0.21°C$, in well-fed animals.

Unequivocal evidence of osmotic control in brackish-water bivalves is absent. *Mytilus edulis* seems to adjust to the medium; in the experiments of Conklin and Krogh (1938) the blood passively followed changes in salinity down to the lowest compatible with life. They worked with animals from Stockholm (salinity 5.5‰) among others. Beudant (1816) claimed to have acclimatized *M. edulis* and 15 other marine molluscs to fresh water, after slow dilution of the medium over a period of 5–8 months. A stage must come in this dilution process when the blood of the molluscs remains higher than the medium, since all fresh-water animals have mechanisms of active regulation. The salinity of the medium at this point may be quite low, since fresh-water lamellibranchs with large surfaces in contact with the external medium, and low metabolism, seem unable to maintain a high osmotic gradient between blood and water. The fresh-water mussel *Anodonta cygnea* comes into equilibrium with dilute sea water of $\Delta 0.12°C$, about S 2.3‰ (Florkin, 1938). Thus in specimens of this species inhabiting Baltic coastal water of S 3–4‰, the blood must be isosmotic with the medium.

The mussel *Dreissena polymorpha* is a fresh-water species found also in the Baltic [S 4.7‰, Segerstråle (1957)] and in suitable salinities in the Black and Caspian Seas (about 10‰ or less) where its blood must be isosmotic with the medium. Like *Anodonta*, it comes into equilibrium with a medium of about 2.3‰ (Rotthauwe, 1958).

Scrobicularia plana, an estuarine bivalve, cannot maintain an osmotic difference between blood and external medium in dilutions of sea water down to $\Delta 1.05°C$, if equilibrated for 48–110 hr (Table II). Animals observed to remain open come rapidly into equilibrium, usually in 6–7 hr. But after a period of equilibration of 110 hr the blood of specimens in dilute sea water of $\Delta 0.59°C$ had a mean Δ of $0.74°C$. It is not clear whether in the latter case the animals are showing active control of the blood concentration or whether they have resisted final dilution to the outside level by keeping the valves closed (Freeman and Rigler, 1957).

C. Fresh-Water Forms

Fresh-water molluscs are faced with a continuous osmotic inflow of water which they have to excrete, and with the problem of active absorption of ions from a dilute medium to replace those lost by outward diffusion and excretion. The level of blood concentration which they can maintain is low, and *Anodonta* has the distinction of having the lowest

TABLE V

CONCENTRATION AND IONIC COMPOSITION OF BLOOD AND URINE OF FRESH-WATER MOLLUSCS

Species	Osmotic concentration		Mg-ions/kg water						Authority
	Δ °C	As mM NaCl	Na	K	Ca	Mg	Cl	SO$_4$	
Bivalvia									
Lamellibranchia									
Anodonta cygnea									
Blood[a]	0.078	21.8	15.6	0.49	8.4	0.19	11.7	0.76	Potts (1954a)
Urine	0.042	11.8	—	—	—	—	—	—	Picken (1937)
Medium	0.01	3.4	—	—	—	—	—	—	
Hyridella australis									
Blood	0.16	46.0	—	—	—	—	16.1[b]	—	Hiscock (1953a)
Urine	—	—	—	—	—	—	9.4[b]	—	
Medium	—	—	—	—	—	—	3.4[b]	—	
Dreissena polymorpha									
Blood	0.09	26	—	—	—	—	—	—	Rotthauwe (1958)
Gastropoda									
Pulmonata									
Lymnaea peregra									
Blood	0.25	71.5	—	—	—	—	—	—	Picken (1937)
Urine	0.19	54.3	—	—	—	—	—	—	
Medium	0.01	3.4	—	—	—	—	—	—	
Lymnaea stagnalis									
Blood[b]	—	—	47.4	2.8	3.0	4.8	42.6	—	Huf (1934)
Blood[b]	—	—	31.2	1.2	7.1	2.1	27.2	—	Duchâteau and Florkin (1954)
Planorbarius corneus									
Blood[b]	—	—	85.9	2.3	6.0	1.1	21.0	0.31	Florkin (1943)
Prosobranchia									
Theodoxus fluviatilis									
Blood	0.15	43	—	—	—	—	—	—	Neumann (1960)
Viviparus fasciatus									
Blood	0.21	60	—	—	—	—	—	—	Obuchowicz (1958)
Potamopyrgus jenkinsi									
Blood	0.18	51	—	—	—	—	—	—	Todd (1962)
Urine	0.15	43	—	—	—	—	—	—	

[a] Other anions, etc.: HCO$_3^-$, 13.6; CO$_3^{--}$, 0.056; CO$_2$, 0.92; HPO$_4^{--}$, 0.17; H$_2$PO$_4^-$, 0.03 (all values at pH 7.52).
[b] Mg-ions/liter.

value recorded for any animal, $\Delta 0.08°C$, a concentration equivalent to about 4–5% sea water. *Dreissena's* value is only a little higher, and those of the pulmonates and prosobranchs investigated are about 2 to 3 times as high (Table V).

Noteworthy in the analysis of *Anodonta* blood are the relatively high concentrations of calcium and bicarbonate ions. The internal concentration alters with experimental changes in the external medium (Section III,B), and different levels are sustained in hard and soft fresh waters [equivalent to 0.103 and 0.080% NaCl, respectively (Picken, 1937)].

When *Anodonta*, *Hyridella*, and *Lymnaea stagnalis* are narcotized with ether or barbiturates, the animals increase in weight owing to osmotic uptake of water (Huf, 1934; Florkin and Duchâteau, 1948; Hiscock, 1953b). In *Anodonta* and *Lymnaea* corresponding reductions in the concentrations of the principal ions in the blood occur, except for potassium which increases. During narcosis all the blood ions apparently begin to diffuse out into the medium, but cellular release of potassium more than counteracts the loss of this ion (Florkin and Duchâteau, 1948). Urine formation also stops, as fluid practically ceases to filter across the heart wall into the pericardial cavity.

Mechanism of Osmotic Regulation

The production of urine by initial filtration of fluid through the heart wall and partial reabsorption of ions from this filtrate by the excretory tubule(s) (see Volume II, Chapter 9) inevitably leads to the loss of salts from the body. By producing urine hypo-osmotic to the blood (Table V), this loss is cut down to approximately 54–83% of what it would be if the urine contained salts equivalent to those in a blood filtrate. If nitrogenous substances of low molecular weight were secreted into the filtrate as Florkin and Duchâteau (1948) found in *Anodonta*, the loss of salts would be less than that calculated proportionally from the osmotic concentration values.

The loss of salts, however, remains considerable in view of the large amount of urine produced, about 24% of the body weight (including shell) per day in *Anodonta* (Potts, 1954b). The daily output of urine is equivalent in volume to 65% of the extracellular fluid.

Picken in 1937 suggested that ion absorption in *Anodonta* must take place at some part of the body surface, basing his proposal on the inadequacy of an estimate of the salt contribution from the food, and the knowledge that specimens remain alive for months in running tap water without serious fall in osmotic concentration. Florkin (1938) kept mussels in running tap water for 22 months, and most specimens had normal freezing points until the twenty-second month, when blood values were about half that of normal.

Proof of ion absorption was supplied by Krogh (1939), who found, after depleting the salts of various molluscs by treatment with distilled water, that active uptake of chloride and sometimes sodium ions could be demonstrated in *Anodonta, Unio, Dreissena,* and the gastropods *Lymnaea stagnalis* and *Paludina.* Most of these could reduce the chloride of 0.01 Ringer solution or 0.7–1.1 mM NaCl solution to 0.1–0.15 mM chloride. Krogh believed that the renal organs of these molluscs must produce an almost salt-free urine when the animals are in distilled water; otherwise the process of depleting their salts would be much more rapid. (*Anodonta* was able to withstand the washing-out process for a month.) Undoubtedly, tight closure of the valves must reduce any osmotic uptake of water through the soft tissues, and consequently cut down excretion.

Shell closure in *Hyridella australis* enables this bivalve to resist desiccation when river margins dry out. Experimentally, it can survive at least 3 months in dried up mud; in two specimens the chlorinity of the blood was 27 and 34 mg-ions/liter, compared with a mean value of 18.7 (range 10–26) in tank specimens. Rise in weight of 11% and 13% in two other specimens from the dried mud when they were placed in tank water indicated considerable dehydration during the enforced drought (Hiscock, 1953a).

Differences in the size of the kidneys have been found in *Lymnaea peregra* from fresh and from brackish waters (S 6.5–7.0‰). These differences can be correlated with excretory activity: specimens from fresh water have larger kidneys in line with their presumed greater turnover of water (Hubendick, 1948).

D. *Terrestrial Forms*

Terrestrial snails and slugs have somewhat higher osmotic concentrations and levels of ions in the blood than fresh-water species (cf. Tables V and VI). With their soft, moist, water-permeable skins, they are particularly subject to water losses under conditions of reduced relative humidity, and most of them are active only when the humidity of their immediate environment is high (see Chapter 3, Section IV).

Hibernating and estivating *Helix pomatia* have lower water contents and larger freezing-point depressions than active specimens. During both natural and artificial hibernation, the blood of this species becomes concentrated, and the protein content almost doubles (Meyer and Thibaudet, 1937). A suggestion by Lustig *et al.* (1937) that the raised magnesium level in hibernating *H. pomatia* (Table VI) is probably the cause of hibernation because of its narcotic action seems fanciful, quite apart from the fact that their magnesium values in active snails are less than a tenth

TABLE VI

CONCENTRATION AND IONIC COMPOSITION OF BLOOD OF TERRESTRIAL MOLLUSCS (PULMONATA)

Species	Δ °C	Na	K	Ca	Mg	Cl	HCO₃	Authority
				Mg-ions/liter				
Helix pomatia								
Active	0.30–0.40	—	—	—	—	62–84	21–27	Duval (1930)
Active	0.30[a]	—	—	—	—	—	—	Kamada (1933)
Active	—	60	4.7	4.1	[0.78][b]	56	—	Lustig et al. (1937)
Active	—	63	4.2	10.3	13.2	82–89	21–24	Duchâteau and Florkin (1954)
Hibernating	0.37–0.43	—	—	—	—	82–89	21–24	Duval (1930)
Hibernating	0.41[a]	—	—	—	—	—	—	Kamada (1933)
Hibernating	—	69	4.7	6.5	[2.01][b]	79	—	Lustig et al. (1937)
Estivating	0.40–0.50	—	—	—	—	84–103	20–22	Duval (1930)
H. aspersa								
Active	0.26–0.37	—	—	—	—	—	—	Arvanitaki and Cardot (1932)
Arion rufus								
Active	0.31–0.33	67	2.8	6.7	—	58	—	Duval (1930)
Archachatina marginata	—	—	—	—	—	64	23	Michon and Alaphilippe (1958)
Achatina achatina	0.33	59	9.7	9.7	[2.0][b]	40	20–27	Drilhon and Florence (1942)
Achatina fulica								
Blood	0.46	—	—	—	—	—	—	Martin (1957)
Urine	0.29	—	—	—	—	—	—	

[a] Mean values calculated from vapor pressure measurements.
[b] Doubtful values.

of those found by Duchâteau and Florkin (1954) and the author (unpublished).

Even under conditions of constant temperature, humidity, food and water supply, this species shows periodic weight fluctuations which are lessened only if food is withheld (Wells, 1944).

Arvanitaki and Cardot (1932) have found characteristically different values for the Δ of 4 species of *Helix* collected from a garden at the same time, correlating them with the conditions of their preferred microhabitats, particularly the degree of exposure to sun and dryness. Measurements of freezing point and conductivity showed that the mean value for groups of individuals rose or fell after period of drought and rain. Thus after a very wet period *H. aspersa* and *H. pisana* had Δ's of 0.26° and 0.35°C, respectively; after 7 rainless days, the Δ's found were 0.33° and 0.41°C. These investigators found that the dilution of the blood after rain was due to absorption of water from ingested food.

It would seem that snails and slugs tolerate quite large changes in water and salt content, undergoing alternate phases of hydration and dehydration which in nature are chiefly due to periods of feeding and fasting.

Little is known about conservation of salts in the urine of terrestrial molluscs. In the giant African snail *Achatina fulica* the urine is hypoosmotic to the blood (Table VI), but the amount passed to the exterior is probably small owing to reabsorption of water in the renal tubule.

IV. OSMOTIC AND IONIC RELATIONS IN TISSUES

An osmotic steady state seems to exist between cells and the internal medium in molluscs. Potts (1952) found the freezing point of isolated muscle fibers of *Mytilus* to be within 1.5% of that of the blood, confirming previous vapor pressure determinations by Krogh (1939) on the juice expressed from muscle. The ash content of invertebrate tissue has long been known to be much less than that of the blood, but only in recent years has any quantitative study been made on the organic compounds which make up the total osmotic concentration in the cells. These compounds include free amino acids, trimethylamine oxide, and betaine in cephalopod muscles, and free amino acids and isethionic acid in squid nerve. Whereas over 99% of the osmotic concentration of the blood of the squid *Loligo forbesi* is made up of the inorganic ions— sodium, potassium, calcium, magnesium, chloride, and sulfate (Robertson, 1953)—these ions constitute only about 49% of the total concentration in the axoplasm of the giant nerve fibers of the related species *L. pealeii*

(Deffner and Hafter, 1960). The remaining 51% is made up chiefly of free amino acids, glycine-betaine, glycerol, and isethionic acid.

TABLE VII

CATION-ANION BALANCE IN SQUID (*Loligo pealeii*) NERVE AXOPLASM (DIALYZABLE CONSTITUENTS)[a]

Cations (meq/kg water)		Anions (meq/kg water)	
Sodium	78.3	Chloride	168.6
Potassium	414.2	Phosphate	32.0
Calcium	8.4	Isethionic acid	183.0
Magnesium	24.1	Aspartic acid	87.9
Arginine	3.9	Glutamic acid	23.6
Lysine	2.9		495.1
Ornithine	2.2		
	534.0		

[a] Data from Deffner and Hafter (1960).

Cation-anion balance is given in Table VII. The dicarboxylic amino acids, aspartic and glutamic, are important anions; most important of all, forming over a third of the total anions, is isethionic acid, a hydroxy analog of the amino acid taurine, which is abundant in squid nerve and muscle.

Table VIII contains data for intracellular concentrations of muscle cells, obtained by correcting whole muscle analyses for their content of extracellular fluid (blood and interstitial fluid) as measured by the distribution of injected inulin. The fresh-water mussel, *Anodonta*, with a low osmolar content in the blood, also has low concentrations of ions in the muscle cells. Summation of the osmotic constituents of the muscle cells gives a figure considerably higher than that of the blood. This probably means that part or all of several of the constituents of the former are bound with organic molecules in unionized complexes of high molecular weight and low osmolar concentration; presumably some of the organic phosphate and many of the divalent ions are in this state.

Both *Sepia* and *Mytilus*, which are marine animals, have higher osmolar concentrations in the blood than has *Anodonta*, and correspondingly higher concentrations of ions in the muscle cells. *Sepia* mantle muscle differs from the fast adductor of *Mytilus* in having (1) higher concentrations of potassium, phosphate compounds, and free amino acids, and (2) lower concentrations of sodium, calcium, magnesium, chloride, and sulfate.

Comparisons by Potts (1958) of the levels of the major ions in some

TABLE VIII

COMPOSITION OF MOLLUSC MUSCLE[a]

	Anodonta fast adductor[b]			Mytilus fast adductor[b]			Sepia mantle muscle[c]		
	Whole muscle	Muscle cells	Blood plasma	Whole muscle	Muscle cells	Blood plasma	Whole muscle	Muscle cells	Blood plasma
Sodium	6.6	5.3	14.7	158	79	490	67.7	31	465
Potassium	18.4	21.3	0.5	125	152	12.5	174.7	189	21.9
Calcium	11.5	12.0	8.4	8.6	7.3	12.6	2.7	1.9	11.6
Magnesium	3.9	4.5	0.2	38	34	56	22.3	19	57.7
Chloride	3.9	2.4	10.7	187	94	573	91.4	45	591
Bicarbonate	—	—	13.6	—	—	5.0	—	—	—
Sulfate	—	—	0.8	13.0	8.8	30.7	2.4	2.0	6.3
Acid-soluble P	17.0	19.8	0.2	31.6	39.0	0.5	129.5	141.4	1.2
Free amino acids	9.5	11.0	0.5	238	295	2.5	442	483	3.9
Trimethylamine oxide	—	—	—	—	—	—	80.3	87.8	0
Betaine	—	—	—	—	—	—	99.0	108.2	—
Total ions + molecules	70.8	76.3	49.6	799.2	709.1	1183	1112	1108	1159

[a] Concentrations in mg-ions or millimoles per kilogram water.

[b] Data from Potts (1958).

[c] Data from Robertson (1953, 1963).

molluscan muscles have shown that the fastest muscles have the most potassium and the least sodium and chloride; the series starting with the muscle of the slowest speed is byssus retractor, slow adductor and fast adductor of *Mytilus*, slow and fast adductors of *Pecten maximus*.

When *Mytilus edulis* is kept in 50% sea water, the water content of the muscles increases (e.g., from 75 to 78% in the fast adductor) and the inulin space is reduced, but the fibers themselves are not acting as simple osmometers, since the water absorbed by them represents only 20–25% of the theoretical 100%. *Anodonta* muscles from animals in 18% sea water have a decreased water content compared with those in fresh water: for example, in the fast adductor, 76 instead of 84% (in fresh water) (Potts, 1958). While potassium changes in the muscle cells of the two species in the 50 and the 18% sea waters roughly correspond with the endosmosis and exosmosis of water, sodium and chloride ions show reductions and increases much greater than those expected from the altered water content. For example, *Anodonta* fast adductor has intracellular values of 44 mg-ions K, 50 mg-ions Na, and 29 mg-ions Cl when the animal is in 18% sea water, as against the values given in Table VIII from animals in their fresh-water environment; intracellular water concentrations per 100 gm dry matter were 440 gm in fresh-water animals, 187 gm in those acclimatized to 18% sea water.

Amino acids fall from the 295 millimoles value in *Mytilus* from 100% sea water (Table VIII) to 183 millimoles in 50% sea water; the concentration expected from the uptake of water is 234 millimoles per kg water. Amino acids increase in the fast adductor of *Anodonta* from 11 millimoles inside the cells (Table VIII) to 48 millimoles in animals from 18% sea water.

TABLE IX

RELATIVE PROPORTIONS (%) OF SOME OSMOTIC CONSTITUENTS IN *Mytilus* AND *Anodonta* MUSCLES[a]

	Mytilus fast adductor		*Anodonta* fast adductor	
	Sea water (%)	Sea water (50%) (%)	Fresh water (%)	Sea water (15%) (%)
Na + Cl	27.9	14.7	19.3	46.2
K	24.5	31.3	53.2	25.7
Amino acids	47.6	54.0	27.5	28.1
Total mg-ions/kg water	620	339	40.0	171

[a] Calculated from intracellular values of Potts (1958).

Thus, in adaptation to changed osmolar concentration not only are the water changes less than would be expected if the cells were acting as osmometers, but the relative proportions of the osmotic concentration due to sodium and chloride, and to potassium, change also, only the amino acid proportion remaining relatively stable (Table IX).

Studies on the total chloride of the tissues of *Mytilus californianus* kept in different concentrations of sea water show a linear relationship between the chloride concentrations of the animals (expressed on a tissue water basis) and the chlorinity of the sea water, an average ratio of 1:1.60 being obtained (Fox, 1941). This species withstands experimental changes between one-third and twice the normal chlorinity (6.2–35.0 gm chloride ‰) if gradual alteration of the medium is made. In nature the species is rarely found in bays and estuaries where the water is much less diluted than the solutions tolerated indefinitely in the laboratory. This is probably connected with the fact that eggs, sperm, and larvae of this species cannot withstand dilutions below about 75% sea water.

The brackish-water clam *Rangia cuneata* shows a decrease in the water content of the body (minus shell) with increased salinity of its medium, from 81% in 3‰ to 74% in 25‰. Both the salt content of the body (measured as ash) and the concentration of certain amino acids, especially alanine, show progressive increases in animals kept at five rising salinities between 3 and 20‰ (Allen, 1961).

Somewhat surprisingly, *Sepia officinalis* has a tissue fluid which is not isosmotic with the blood. The cuttlebones of this animal have variable densities, depending on the proportion of liquid they contain; they have also air spaces. This liquid, which is chiefly a solution of sodium chloride, is considerably hypo-osmotic to the blood, about three-quarters of the osmotic concentration, and the cuttlefish can make itself more or less dense by pumping liquid in or out of the rigid cuttlebone. Simple osmotic forces play a role in keeping water out of the cuttlebone, presumably balancing the hydrostatic pressure of the sea (Denton and Gilpin-Brown, 1959). The osmotic concentration of the liquid in the cuttlebone changes in about 6 hours from 75 to 97% of that of sea water in animals hauled from depths of about 70 meters to the surface (Denton *et al.*, 1961; also see Chapter 13).

V. GENERAL AND COMPARATIVE CONSIDERATIONS

Most marine invertebrates are in osmotic equilibrium with sea water. This equilibrium is probably more strictly an osmotic steady state in most cases, energy being required to bring in against the blood pressure an isosmotic fluid to replace that lost through excretory tubules.[1] All marine invertebrates show ionic regulation despite the fact that boundary membranes such as gills and integument are permeable in some degree to the ions of sea water. Marine gastropods and lamellibranchs can be grouped with coelenterates, echinoderms, polychaetes, and tunicates as simply organized animals which show only slight regulation (Robertson, 1949, 1953, 1954). In the more highly organized cephalopods and decapod crustaceans, ionic regulation extends to every ion. The basic mechanism of ionic regulation seems to be the same in these two groups, consisting of continuous selective excretion of ions in the excretory fluids and controlled uptake of ions by the permeable surfaces. Marked differences exist in the pattern of regulation, especially with regard to magnesium: decapod crustaceans show a wide range of Mg^{++} in the blood, from 14 to 99% of the equilibrium values; cephalopods maintain high levels of Mg^{++} ions like the other marine molluscs, but show considerable accumulation of K^+, up to twice that characteristic of a passive equilibrium with sea water (Table III).

Hyperosmotic regulation is shown by all fresh-water animals and by many crustaceans living in brackish water (Robertson, 1960a). In brackish-water molluscs this type of regulation is found in the periwinkle *Littorina littorea* and doubtfully in a bivalve (*Scrobicularia plana*). Most bivalves simply adjust to the diluted medium, remaining isosmotic down to the lowest salinities they can tolerate.

Active absorption of ions, particularly Na^+ and Cl^-, has been shown to occur in many fresh-water groups: annelids, bivalves, gastropods, insects, crustaceans, teleost fishes, and amphibians (Krogh, 1939). It must also occur in regulating *Littorina*, but has not been proved in molluscs living in full-strength sea water, although the chemical data on the blood suggest it in some cases (Table III and Section II,C,2). Careful analysis of known volumes of sea water into which molluscs are excreting calcium and potassium would show whether they were balancing the loss wholly or partly by absorbing these ions from the medium against their concentration gradients.

A lessening of the osmotic work of fresh-water animals is brought about by the production of a hypo-osmotic urine. This is found in crustaceans, teleost fishes, and amphibians (Prosser and Brown, 1961), as well as in lamellibranchs and gastropods (Table V). Potts (1954c) has considered the whole question of the energetics of osmotic regulation in brackish- and fresh-water animals. By evaluating the minimum thermodynamic work performed by an animal in terms of its surface area, permeability, and the concentration of blood, urine, and external medium,

---

[1] Where the protein of the blood is significant, the pressure against which fluid is absorbed is the hydrostatic pressure of the blood minus the colloid osmotic pressure.

he has shown that reduction in the concentration of the blood in an animal entering brackish water from the sea is the chief means of easing the strain on osmoregulatory mechanisms. Production of a hypo-osmotic urine has only a small effect on the osmotic work until the concentration of sea water falls below 50%. In a fresh-water animal, however, it can reduce the work of osmoregulation by 80–90%; even a moderate fall in the urine concentration can greatly reduce the osmotic work.

Potts has applied his equations to various crustaceans and to *Anodonta*. In the latter he calculates that the total osmotic work of a 60-gm mussel is 0.0145 cal per hr, about 1.2% of the total metabolic energy (1.2 cal per hr); of the total, 0.0131 is done at the body surface and 0.0014 (or about 10%) at the excretory organ. He calculates that the total osmotic work would have been almost double, 0.0245 cal per hr, if urine had been produced isosmotic with the blood. Comparable figures for an *Astacus* of the same weight are: total osmotic work 0.0367 cal per hr, at body surface 0.0288, at antennal glands 0.0079 (about 22% of the total), total metabolic energy 10.0 cal per hr; thus the osmotic work is about 0.4% of the metabolic energy.

Energy is also required for the active extrusion of sodium ions which seems necessary to explain the low level of this ion in most cells compared to the high value in the blood (e.g., Table VIII). It is probable that the energy required for sodium extrusion is much larger in marine species like *Mytilus* than in *Anodonta*. Potts (1959) has calculated from measurements of sodium fluxes with Na^{24} that in *Mytilus* muscle the apparent energy requirement for sodium extrusion is about half of the metabolic energy available in the muscle.

Oxygen consumption of aquatic animals is usually found to be influenced by the salinity of the medium, and a few cases are known among molluscs. The fresh-water mussel *Hyridella* shows a progressive decrease in uptake of oxygen when kept in media of increasing salinity (Hiscock, 1953b). On the other hand the marine *Mytilus edulis* and *M. galloprovincialis* show decreases in oxygen consumption both in concentrated and dilute sea water (Maloeuf, 1937; Bouxin, 1931). The curious finding that isolated gills of *M. edulis* have a higher oxygen consumption in brackish water than in full-strength sea water cannot be taken as evidence of increased osmoregulation, since the mussel possesses no control over its body fluid concentration in diluted sea water; the finding is correlated, however, with increased hydration of the gill tissues (Pieh, 1936; Schlieper, 1957). Isolated gills of the mussel *Dreissena polymorpha* show a slight increase in oxygen consumption from tap water up to S 7.2‰, but over 10.0‰ there is a decrease. The maximum salinity this animal can stand in the Caspian Sea is S 10‰ (Bielawski, 1961).

Muscles of *Mytilus* also show an increased water content in animals kept in 50% sea water (Potts, 1958), and it is probable that this tissue shows a lower oxygen consumption in this medium, since whole animals do so. *Venus mercenaria* tissues also show anomalous reactions to decreased salinity, the gills and mantle showing an increase and the muscles a decrease in oxygen consumption (Hopkins, 1949).

Continuous records of oxygen consumption of the gastropod *Aplysia juliana* during transfer for 5 hours to 95% and return to 100% sea water show an increase of nearly 10% in the less saline water, but also large temporary increases, due apparently to increased movement at first in 95% sea water and active swallowing of water in 100% sea water (van Weel, 1957).

In ionic composition and in the relative importance of free amino acids, trimethylamine oxide, and betaine in the osmotic balance of its cells, *Sepia* muscle (Table VIII) is like that of other active invertebrates such as the decapod crustaceans *Carcinus* (Shaw, 1958) and *Nephrops* (Robertson, 1961). Compared with mammalian muscle (Conway, 1957), it shows higher concentrations of all ions and of acid-soluble phosphorus compounds, and has over twenty times the amount of amino acids; its total osmotic concentration is, however, only three times that of rat muscle.

Changes in the relative proportions of intracellular ions and nonprotein nitrogenous compounds when animals are kept in water of reduced salinity have been studied in *Carcinus* (Shaw, 1958). In contrast to *Mytilus*, the blood and tissues remain hyperosmotic to the medium. Nitrogenous compounds, especially amino acids, are reduced in greater proportion than expected on the basis of the increased cellular water content. This parallels the finding in *Mytilus* (Potts, 1958; also Section IV), and presumably some of the reduction is due to excretion, polymerization or metabolism of a proportion of the amino acids.

It has been suggested, principally from a consideration of decapod crustaceans, that adaptation to fresh water evolved by two main stages: (*1*) a slight reduction of the salt level in the blood and active absorption of ions from the medium; and (*2*) the lowering of the blood concentration and the evolution of renal salt reabsorption (Beadle and Cragg, 1940). The river-crab *Potamon* would still be at the first stage and crayfishes at the second (Robertson, 1960a). From his calculations on the energetics of osmotic regulation in *Anodonta*, Potts (1954c) has pointed out that fresh-water lamellibranchs could never have maintained high blood concentrations in fresh water: the energy demand would be too great for animals as permeable as *Anodonta*. Thus the first step must have been toleration of a low blood concentration.

The successful acclimatization to fresh water of such marine molluscs as *Patella, Nucella, Cardium, Ostrea,* and *Mytilus* by gradual dilution of the sea water over a period of 5–8 months (Beudant, 1816) shows that the tissues of these gastropods and bivalves can function at very low salinities. Failure of these species to live in fresh water in nature must be due to other factors, among which may be lack of tolerance by the reproductive cells and larvae to a low salinity, as in *Mytilus californianus* (Section IV). Nothing is known of the tolerance of cephalopods to reduced salinity, and one can but speculate on their absence from brackish and fresh waters. Although they have large excretory organs capable of marked differential ionic excretion and presumably capable of evolving reabsorption of salts, their skin is usually naked and probably permeable to water to a considerable degree. Lacking a waterproof skin, these active, highly organized invertebrates simply may be unable to tolerate the considerable fall in the osmotic concentration of their blood and tissues which would result from migration to brackish and fresh waters. Their rather specialized feeding habits would not seem to be sufficient reason for their restriction to the sea.

VI. SUMMARY AND CONCLUSIONS

Marine molluscs are in osmotic equilibrium (or steady state) with sea water, and those which have been studied show ionic regulation to various degrees, despite permeability to water and salts. The mechanism of ionic regulation has been studied only in larger species such as cephalopods, and in these animals differential excretion of ions occurs, coupled with uptake of ions and water, probably chiefly through the gills. Little is known of this controlled uptake of fluid.

In brackish water few molluscs can maintain their body fluids hyperosmotic to the medium; most simply adjust osmotically, some bivalves resisting this temporarily by closure of the shell valves.

Fresh-water gastropods and bivalves maintain very low concentrations of ions. In these animals hyperosmotic regulation is effected by active uptake of ions, particularly sodium and chloride, from fresh water, thus replacing those lost by outward diffusion and excretion. Elimination of a hypo-osmotic urine reduces the amount of osmotic work required.

Terrestrial molluscs also have low blood concentrations which vary with their intake of food and physiological state (hibernation, estivation, etc.).

Muscles of *Mytilus* and *Sepia* have large concentrations of free amino acids and trimethylamine oxide (the latter in *Sepia* at least) contributing to the osmotic concentration of their cells. Generally, the content of potassium is higher and sodium and chloride lower in fast muscles.

Calculations of the minimum thermodynamic work performed in osmotic regulation give a value in *Anodonta* of about 1.2% of the total metabolic energy estimated from the oxygen consumption. This figure is a minimal value for total osmotic work, which may be greater if the actual energy expended by the osmoregulatory organs is above the thermodynamic minimum. When *Mytilus edulis* is in sea water, the energy requirements for the active ionic work in extruding sodium from the muscle cells may be half that calculated as available in the muscle.

REFERENCES

Allen, K. (1961). The effect of salinity on the amino acid concentration in *Rangia cuneata* (Pelecypoda). *Biol. Bull.* **121**, 419–424.

Amoore, J. E., Rodgers, K., and Young, J. Z. (1959). Sodium and potassium in the endolymph and perilymph of the statocyst and in the eye of *Octopus*. *J. Exptl. Biol.* **36**, 709–714.

Arvanitaki, A., and Cardot, H. (1932). Sur les variations de la concentration du milieu intérieur chez les mollusques terrestres. *J. physiol. et pathol. gén.* **30**, 577–592.

Beadle, L. C. (1957). Comparative physiology: osmotic and ionic regulation in aquatic animals. *Ann. Rev. Physiol.* **19**, 329–358.

Beadle, L. C., and Cragg, J. B. (1940). Studies on adaptation to salinity in *Gammarus* spp. I. Regulation of blood and tissues and the problem of adaptation to fresh water. *J. Exptl. Biol.* **17**, 153–163.

Berger, E., and Bethe, A. (1931). Die Durchlässigkeit der Körperoberflächen wirbelloser Tiere für Jodionen. *Pflügers Arch. ges. Physiol.* **228**, 769–789.

Bethe, A. (1929). Ionendurchlässigkeit der Körperoberfläche von wirbellosen Tieren des Meeres als Ursache der Giftigkeit von Seewasser abnormer Zusammensetzung. *Pflügers Arch. ges. Physiol.* **221**, 344–362.

Bethe, A. (1930). The permeability of the surface of marine animals. *J. Gen. Physiol.* **13**, 437–444.

Bethe, A. (1934). Die Salz- und Wasser-Permeabilität der Körperoberflächen verschiedener Seetiere in ihrem gegenseitigen Verhältnis. *Pflügers Arch. ges. Physiol.* **234**, 629–644.

Beudant, F. S. (1816). Mémoire sur la possibilité de faire vivre des mollusques fluviatiles dans les eaux salées, et des mollusques marins dans les eaux douces, considérée sous le rapport de la géologie. *J. phys. chim. et hist. nat.* **83**, 268–284.

Bielawski, J. (1961). The influences of the salinity of the medium on respiration in isolated gills of the clam *Dreissena polymorpha* (Pall.). *Comp. Biochem. and Physiol.* **3**, 250–260.

Bottazzi, F. (1908). Osmotischer Druck und elektrische Leitfähigkeit der Flüssigkeiten der einzelligen, pflanzlichen und tierischen Organismen. *Ergeb. Physiol.* **7**, 161–402.

Bouxin, H. (1931). Influence des variations rapides de la salinité sur la consommation d'oxygène chez *Mytilus edulis* var. *galloprovincialis* (Lmk.). *Bull. inst. océanogr.* No. 569, pp. 1–11.

Cole, W. H. (1940). The composition of fluids and sera of some marine animals and of the sea water in which they live. *J. Gen. Physiol.* **23**, 575–584.

Conklin, R. E., and Krogh, A. (1938). A note on the osmotic behaviour of *Eriocheir* in concentrated and *Mytilus* in dilute sea water. *Z. vergleich. Physiol.* **26**, 239–241.

Conway, E. J. (1957). Nature and significance of concentration relations of potassium and sodium ions in skeletal muscle. *Physiol. Revs.* **37**, 84–132.

Dakin, W. J. (1909). "Pecten," Liverpool Marine Biol. Comm. Mem. No. 17, 136 pp. Williams & Norgate, London.

Dakin, W. J., and Edmonds, E. (1931). The regulation of the salt contents of the blood of aquatic animals, and the problem of the permeability of the bounding membranes of aquatic invertebrates. *Australian J. Exptl. Biol. Med. Sci.* **8**, 169–187.

Deffner, G. G. J., and Hafter, R. E. (1960). Chemical investigation of the giant nerve fibers of the squid. IV. Acid-base balance in axoplasm. *Biochim. et Biophys. Acta* **42**, 200–205.

Denton, E. J., and Gilpin-Brown, J. B. (1959). Buoyancy of the cuttlefish. *Nature* **184**, Suppl. 17, 1330–1331.

Denton, E. J., Shaw, T. P., and Gilpin-Brown, J. B. (1958). Bathyscaphoid squid. *Nature* **182**, 1810–1811.

Denton, E. J., Gilpin-Brown, J. B., and Howarth, J. V. (1961). The osmotic mechanism of the cuttlebone. *J. Marine Biol. Assoc. U.K.* **41**, 351–363.

Drilhon, A., and Florence, G. (1942). Le métabolisme purique chez les Gastéropodes. Etude d'*Helix pomatia* L. et d'*Achatina achatina* Lameere. *Bull. soc. chim. biol.* **24**, 96–103.

Duchâteau, G., and Florkin, M. (1954). Cited in "Traité de Zoologie" (P.-P. Grassé, ed.), Vol. 12: Vertébrés, p. 1076. Masson, Paris.

Duval, M. (1930). Concentration moléculaire du sang de l'escargot. Ses facteurs, ses variations. Influence de l'état d'activité de l'animal. *Ann. Physiol. physicochim. biol.* **6**, 346–364.

Florkin, M. (1938). Contributions à l'étude de l'osmorégulation chez les invertébrés d'eau douce (I). *Arch. intern. physiol.* **47**, 113–124.

Florkin, M. (1943). Sur la composition inorganique du milieu intérieur des Invertébrés dulcicoles ou terrestres. *Bull. soc. roy. sci. Liège* No. 5, 301–304.

Florkin, M., and Duchâteau, G. (1948). Sur l'osmorégulation de l'anodonte (*Anodonta cygnea* L.). *Physiol. Comparata et Oecol.* **1**, 29–45.

Fox, D. L. (1941). Changes in the tissue chloride of the California muscle in response to heterosmotic environments. *Biol. Bull.* **80**, 111–129.

Freeman, R. F. H., and Rigler, F. H. (1957). The responses of *Scrobicularia plana* (Da Costa) to osmotic pressure changes. *J. Marine Biol. Assoc. U.K.* **36**, 553–567.

Garrey, W. E. (1905). The osmotic pressure of sea water and of the blood of marine animals. *Biol. Bull.* **8**, 257–270.

Hiscock, I. D. (1953a). Osmoregulation in Australian freshwater mussels (Lamellibranchiata). I. Water and chloride exchange in *Hyridella australis* (Lam.). *Australian J. Marine and Freshwater Research* **4**, 317–329.

Hiscock, I. D. (1953b). Osmoregulation in Australian freshwater mussels (Lamellibranchiata). II. Respiration and its relation to osmoregulation in *Hyridella australis* (Lam.). *Australian J. Marine and Freshwater Research* **4**, 330–342.

Hopkins, H. S. (1949). Metabolic reactions of clams' tissues to changes in salinity. I. Ciliary activity, narcotic and cyanide effects, and respiratory quotient. *Physiol. Zoöl.* **22**, 295–308.

Hubendick, B. (1948). Sur les variations de la taille du rein chez *Lymnaea limosa* (L.). *J. Conchyliol.* **88**, 5–10.

Huf, E. (1934). Über den Einfluss der Narkose auf den Wasser- und Mineralhaushalt bei Süsswassertieren. *Pflügers Arch. ges. Physiol.* **235**, 129–140.

Kamada, T. (1933). The vapour pressure of the blood of the edible snail. *J. Exptl. Biol.* **10**, 75–78.

Krogh, A. (1939). "Osmotic Regulation in Aquatic Animals," 242 pp. Cambridge Univ. Press, London and New York.

Lustig, B., Ernst, T., and Reuss, E. (1937). Die Zusammensetzung des Blutes von *Helix pomatia* bei Sommer- und Wintertieren. *Biochem. Z.* **290**, 95–98.

Maloeuf, N. S. R. (1937). Studies on the respiration (and osmoregulation) of animals. I. Aquatic animals without an oxygen transporter in their internal medium. *Z. vergleich. Physiol.* **25**, 1–28.

Martin, A. W. (1957). Recent advances in knowledge of invertebrate renal function. *In* "Recent Advances in Invertebrate Physiology" (B. T. Scheer, ed.), pp. 247–276. Univ. of Oregon Publ., Eugene, Oregon.

Martin, A. W., Harrison, F. M., Huston, M. J., and Stewart, D. M. (1958). The blood volumes of some representative molluscs. *J. Exptl. Biol.* **35**, 260–279.

Meyer, P., and Thibaudet, M.-A. (1937). Les modifications du milieu intérieur pendant l'hibernation et l'estivation des Hélices. *Compt. rend. soc. biol.* **124**, 185–187.

Michon, J., and Alaphilippe, F. (1958). Comparaison de quelques constantes biologiques de l'hémolymphe d'individus normaux de *Achatina marginata* (Gastéropode Pulmoné) et d'individus présentant une anomalie de croissance. *Compt. rend. soc. biol.* **152**, 1349–1352.

Neumann, D. (1960). Osmotische Resistenz und Osmoregulation der Flussdeckelschnecke *Theodoxus fluviatilis* L. *Biol. Zentr.* **79**, 585–605.

Obuchowicz, L. (1958). The influence of osmotic pressure of medium on oxygen consumption in the snail *Viviparus fasciatus* (O. F. Müll.) Streptoneura. *Bull. soc. amis sci. Poznań* **B14**, 367–370.

Picken, L. E. R. (1937). The mechanism of urine formation in invertebrates. II. The excretory mechanism in certain Mollusca. *J. Exptl. Biol.* **14**, 20–34.

Pieh, S. (1936). Über die Beziehungen zwischen Atmung, Osmoregulation und Hydratation der Gewebe bei euryhalinen Meeresevertebraten. *Zool. Jahrb., Abt. Allgem. Zool. u. Physiol. Tiere* **56**, 129–160.

Potts, W. T. W. (1952). Measurements of osmotic pressure in single cells. *Nature* **169**, 834.

Potts, W. T. W. (1954a). The inorganic composition of the blood of *Mytilus edulis* and *Anodonta cygnea*. *J. Exptl. Biol.* **31**, 376–385.

Potts, W. T. W. (1954b). The rate of urine formation in *Anodonta cygnea*. *J. Exptl. Biol.* **31**, 614–617.

Potts, W. T. W. (1954c). The energetics of osmotic regulation in brackish- and fresh-water animals. *J. Exptl. Biol.* **31**, 618–630.

Potts, W. T. W. (1958). The inorganic and amino acid composition of some lamellibranch muscles. *J. Exptl. Biol.* **35**, 749–764.

Potts, W. T. W. (1959). The sodium fluxes in the muscle fibres of a marine and a freshwater lamellibranch. *J. Exptl. Biol.* **36**, 676–689.

Potts, W. T. W. (1961). Personal communication.

Prosser, C. L., and Brown, F. A. (1961). "Comparative Animal Physiology," 2nd ed. Saunders, Philadelphia, Pennsylvania.

Robertson, J. D. (1941). The function and metabolism of calcium in the Invertebrata. *Biol. Revs. Cambridge Phil. Soc.* **16**, 106–133.

Robertson, J. D. (1949). Ionic regulation in some marine invertebrates. *J. Exptl. Biol.* **26**, 182–200.

Robertson, J. D. (1953). Further studies on ionic regulation in marine invertebrates. *J. Exptl. Biol.* **30**, 277–296.

Robertson, J. D. (1954). The chemical composition of the blood of some aquatic chordates, including members of the Tunicata, Cyclostomata and Osteichthyes. *J. Exptl. Biol.* **31**, 424–442.

Robertson, J. D. (1960a). Osmotic and ionic regulation. *In* "The Physiology of Crustacea" (T. H. Waterman, ed.), pp. 317–339. Academic Press, New York.

Robertson, J. D. (1960b). Ionic regulation in the crab *Carcinus maenas* (L.) in relation to the moulting cycle. *Comp. Biochem. and Physiol.* **1**, 183–212.

Robertson, J. D. (1961). Studies on the chemical composition of muscle tissue. II. The abdominal flexor muscles of the lobster *Nephrops norvegicus* (L.). *J. Exptl. Biol.* **38**, 707–728.

Robertson, J. D. (1963). In preparation.

Rotthauwe, H.-W. (1958). Untersuchungen zur Atmungsphysiologie und Osmoregulation bei *Mytilus edulis* mit einem kurzen Anhang über die Blutkonzentration von *Dreissena polymorpha* in Abhängigkeit vom Elektrolytgehalt des *Aussenmediums. Veröffentl. Inst. Meeresforsch. in Bremerhaven* **5**, 143–159.

Schlieper, C. (1957). Comparative study of *Asterias rubens* and *Mytilus edulis* from the North Sea (30 per 1,000 S) and the Western Baltic Sea (15 per 1,000 S). *Année biol.* **33**, 117–127.

Segal, E., and Dehnel, P. A. (1962). Osmotic behavior in an intertidal limpet, *Acmaea limatula. Biol. Bull.* **122**, 417–430.

Segerstråle, S. G. (1957). Baltic Sea. *In* "Treatise on Marine Ecology and Paleoecology" (J. W. Hedgpeth, ed.), Vol. 1: Ecology, pp. 751–800 (*Geol. Soc. Am. Mem.* **67**).

Shaw, J. (1958). Osmoregulation in the muscle fibres of *Carcinus maenas. J. Exptl. Biol.* **35**, 920–929.

Shaw, J. (1960). The mechanism of osmoregulation. *In* "Comparative Biochemistry" (M. Florkin and H. S. Mason, eds.), Vol. 2, pp. 471–518. Academic Press, New York.

Todd, M. E. (1962). Osmoregulatory studies on several invertebrates. Ph.D. Thesis, University of Glasgow.

van Weel, P. B. (1957). Observations on the osmoregulation in *Aplysia juliana* Pease (Aplysiidae, Mollusca). *Z. vergleich. Physiol.* **39**, 492–506.

Wells, G. P. (1944). The water relations of snails and slugs. III. Factors determining activity in *Helix pomatia* L. *J. Exptl. Biol.* **20**, 79–87.

Yazaki, M. (1929). On some physico-chemical properties of the pericardial fluid and of the blood of the Japanese oyster, *Ostrea circumpicta* Pils., with reference to the change of milieu extérieur. *Sci. Repts. Tôhoku Univ., Fourth Ser.* **4**, 285–314.

CHAPTER **10**

Muscle and Neuromuscular Physiology

G. Hoyle

DEPARTMENT OF BIOLOGY, UNIVERSITY OF OREGON, EUGENE, OREGON.

I. INTRODUCTION

The nervous control of molluscan muscles presents many fascinating problems which remain largely unsolved, although a great deal of attention has recently been paid to certain preparations with notable achievements. In no mollusc has the structural organization advanced beyond a relatively simple arrangement consisting largely of antagonistic sheets of muscle operating around a fluid-filled sac without an articulated skeleton. Only the muscles causing adduction of shell valves or retraction of byssus, foot, or radula are discrete units. The condition of the musculature is therefore primitive, analogous to that of the lower invertebrate phyla and in no way comparable with the arthropods or vertebrates. Nevertheless, it functions efficiently in a wide variety of activities, including swimming (in many different ways), crawling, burrowing, boring, etc., over an extremely wide range of speeds. In addition, the molluscs possess muscles capable of feats which seem prodigious by comparison with the muscles of other animals, including vertebrates, both in regard to tension development, which is the greatest known, duration of contractions, and also economy, for great tensions can be maintained for many hours with expenditure of very little energy.

A more subtle arrangement of the muscle fibers has been found in the arms of cuttlefish (Guerin, 1908), fins of the squid (Williams, 1910), and in the gastropod foot (Simroth, 1928), and there must surely be others. But in no case have the details of the functioning and the consequences of special arrangements of muscle fibers been worked out, Guerin's analysis of the cuttlefish arm being the nearest to a full description.

In studying the physiology of these varied muscles it cannot be overstressed that a detailed understanding of the nature of the muscle cells is a primary requirement, as is also the nature of their innervation. Elucidation of the many experimental problems must in most cases await further advance in these areas, for in no case is there satisfactory preliminary anatomical knowledge.

The problems resolve themselves into the ordinary ones of controlling the rate and extent of tension development to meet functional needs; the need to make a given muscle contract at widely different speeds; the continuous development of postural tone; the rapid relaxation of a muscle when necessary. Most of these activities have to be performed in molluscs by nonstriated muscles, a feature which in many ways adds to their interest. But by far the greatest interest is to be found in the fact that the molluscs have overcome a problem which does not seem to have been successfully tackled by any other phylum, namely, that of maintaining high tensions, such as are needed for closing the valves, for very prolonged periods without a high level of energy expenditure. It is not surprising, therefore, that interest in the physiology and biochemistry of molluscan muscles has centered largely around muscles showing these unique properties.

The relevant subject matter has already been reviewed by the author (Hoyle, 1957b) and certain aspects are very well dealt with in a recent article by Hanson and Lowy (1960).

II. HISTOLOGY OF MUSCLE

A. General Features

A great deal of histological work has been carried out on lamellibranch muscles and this is well reviewed by Bowden (1958). There is also extensive work on cephalopods and a certain amount on gastropods, but the more primitive molluscs have unfortunately received little attention. The majority of the musculature of all molluscs is composed of small, nonstriated, uninucleate cells. But a variety of striated fibers is also found, particularly in lamellibranch adductors. The variety of pattern is surprising in such obviously homologous and functionally similar muscles.

The general texture of the muscles also varies; most wholly smooth muscles which are also slowly-contracting are tough, opaque, and gray or creamy yellow. The differences are sometimes explained by the presence of a dense connective tissue framework, but they are due in some cases to the degree of regularity of ultrastructure and to internal linkages in the contractile material. The faster muscles are softer and may be quite translucent. All intermediates are also found, many of which have essentially weakly marked, usually oblique, apparent "striations." Pink adductors are found in *Teredo* and *Venus*, possibly due to the presence of hemoglobin (Fox, 1953).

The lamellibranch adductors are sometimes divided by a connective tissue sheet into two portions, one of which is composed of smooth muscle fibers (e.g., *Pecten, Ostrea, Modiolus*). But this division may be indistinct (*Mya, Mytilus, Pinna*) and in some (*Lima*) there is no division at all, the smooth and striated fibers being intermingled. The histological division is correlated with a functional one, the striated portion contracting very quickly and being referred to as the "fast" portion, while the nonstriated is much slower and is referred to as the "slow" portion. It is the slow portion which is principally responsible for the long-maintained, economical contractions which keep the valves closed on exposure, though it is doubtless assisted by periodical contractions of the fast portion in the animal.

Those adductors in which the fast portion is gray in appearance are also relatively slow (*Ostrea, Anodonta*), and in them the relatively fast fibers are obliquely or spirally, not transversely, banded. Similar striations also occur in the arm of *Octopus* and in its gizzard wall (Plenk, 1933). In the arms and fins of *Loligo*, the tentacles of *Sepia*, and the radular and tentacle retractor muscles of gastropods weakly transversely striated muscle fibers are to be found (Plenk, 1924; Merton, 1911). Many spiral bandings were also found by Plenk (1924) in various gastropod muscles, especially the retractor bulbi muscles. However, although the variety of these spirally and obliquely striated muscle fibers is so great, they have lost much of their interest since electron miscroscope studies by Hanson and Lowy (1959a, 1960) showed them to be smooth fibers with peripheral, twisted fibrils, rather than fibers with a unique form of cross banding. The muscle cells are all rather small. Normally the length does not exceed 1 mm, although in the adductors and byssal retractors they may well run from insertion to insertion and attain a length to 4 cm. The maximum diameter of the smooth muscle cells is only about 7 μ; nuclei are small and peripheral.

B. Ultrastructure

1. ORDINARY STRIATED MUSCLE FIBERS

The best known are fibers of the fast portion of species of *Pecten* and *Chlamys*. Under the light microscope, especially phase contrast, these fibers present an appearance identical with arthropod and vertebrate skeletal fibers. They are divided into sarcomeres by regularly spaced Z-bands and each sarcomere has I- and A-bands. Their ultrastructure has been examined electron microscopically by Kawaguti and Ikemoto (1958) and by Hanson and Lowy (1960). The I-band filaments are 50 Å thick, resembling the actin filaments of the rabbit psoas. The A-band filaments are thick in the center (*ca* 300 Å), tapering to 100 Å. These filaments are cross-linked to each other and it may confidently be expected that a sliding mechanism comparable to that proposed for the rabbit psoas (H. E. Huxley, 1957) operates also in these mollusc muscles. These muscles do not contain paramyosin (Schmitt *et al.*, 1947). Actomyosin can be extracted from them (Tonomura *et al.*, 1955) and also myosin (Rüegg, 1957), so the filaments may well be actin and myosin.

In some striated adductors, although the basic filament structure appears to be the same, the Z-bands are irregular and not too well marked, apparently consisting of a dense mass of small particles (*Promartellum* and *Spondylus*, Kawaguti and Ikemoto, 1959, 1960a).

2. ORDINARY SMOOTH MUSCLE FIBERS SHOWING VERY PROLONGED CONTRACTIONS AND PARAMYOSIN BANDING

The outstanding biochemical feature of the slowly-contracting smooth muscle fibers is the presence in many of them of a high-molecular-weight protein paramyosin. This is probably identical with the tropomyosin A, extracted in a different way, and present in annelids. Another tropomyosin, tropomyosin B, is present in vertebrate cardiac and skeletal muscle (Bailey, 1948; Hanson *et al.*, 1957). The protein was first recognized in electron microscope pictures by its regular axial periodicity of 145 Å (Hall *et al.*, 1945). In addition, actomyosin is also present, for example, in the smooth part of the *Pecten* adductor (Tonomura *et al.*, 1955), in the *Anodonta* foot (Dörr and Portzehl, 1954), and in the *Mytilus* anterior byssus retractor muscle (Kahn and Johnson, 1960).

The anterior byssus retractor muscle (a.b.r.m.) of *Mytilus* may be taken as the archetype of ordinary smooth molluscan muscle capable of prolonged contractions. It has received more attention than all other molluscan muscles together, a position which shows no sign of changing. It can exhibit extremely prolonged contractions (up to several hours) following a single stimulus, or relax quickly after a different stimulus. Constituent muscle fibers are stated to be as long as the muscle itself (3–4 cm) (Fletcher, 1937a; van Nieuwenhoven, 1947), but this point is not certain. A cross section of the muscle shows some thick, many thin fibers, and it is not certain whether the thick ones are contracted regions of an otherwise uniform set. A *Mytilus* (*crassitesta*) a.b.r.m. was first examined electron microscopically by Kawaguti and Ikemoto (1957a) but they failed to obtain a clear picture of its structure. More recently Hanson and Lowy (1959a, 1960), using water-glycerol-extracted a.b.r.m.'s of *Mytilus edulis*, obtained clear evidence of two kinds of filaments, thick (150–1000 Å) and thin (50 Å). The two kinds of filaments are cross-linked by bridges repeating at 100–200 Å intervals. The bridges belong to the thick filaments, for they remained in oyster muscles from which all the thin filaments were extracted by a fixative. The diameters of the thick filaments were measured in equivalent pairs of muscles fixed at different lengths. Although the short muscles were as little as ⅓ the length of their partners, the thick filaments showed no difference in diameter. Hence it is probable that they do not shorten during contraction. Also, the filaments must be discontinuous along the fiber. Furthermore, there is not a consistent difference in the number of filaments per unit area in long as compared with short muscles. This condition could only be arrived at by a sliding of the thick filaments over one another. The relative movement, if any, of the thin filaments could not be decided. There may be discontinuities in the thin filaments also.

These extremely important observations suggest an essential similarity in the basic mechanism of contraction in these muscles and in ordinary vertebrate skeletal muscle in which the sliding of cross-linked filaments over one another is thought to take place. They also illustrate a fundamental difference from vertebrate skeletal muscle, which may apply to smooth muscle in general; that is the ability of the thick filaments to slide as well, since they are not structurally tied down as they are in striated muscle. This could explain the greater extensibility and capacity for shortening of smooth muscle.

The thick filaments show a regular periodicity at 145 Å, which is characteristic of paramyosin (Hanson and Lowy, 1959a). From several smooth muscles, *Mytilus* a.b.r.m., white parts of *Ostrea*, *Crassostrea*, *Pinna*, and *Mercenaria*, mechanical disintegration releases paramyosin elements in the form of long, flat ribbons (Elliott *et al.*, 1957). Thus the thick filaments must contain, among other things, several paramyosin ribbons stacked together with their surfaces apposed. All muscles containing

fibers showing filaments with paramyosin banding are collectively referred to by Hanson and Lowy as "paramyosin smooth muscles." The
translucent part of the oyster adductor nevertheless provides an exception since although it contains paramyosin it has some of the elements
characteristic of striated muscles (Hanson and Lowy, 1961).

3. ORDINARY SMOOTH MUSCLE FIBERS NOT SHOWING PARAMYOSIN BANDING

These muscles do not show the very prolonged contractions characteristic of the presence of paramyosin. Electron microscopic examination
of three of them (*Helix* retractor pharynx and retractor penis, and
adductor of *Tamanovalva,* the unique, bivalve gastropod) showed only
thin filaments (Hanson and Lowy, 1957; Kawaguti and Ikemoto, 1956,
1960b), such as are also found in vertebrate smooth muscle (e.g., Mark,
1956).

4. INTERMEDIATE SMOOTH MUSCLE FIBERS

These are the spirally or obliquely "striated" fibers found particularly
in adductor muscles and the funnel retractor and mantle muscles of
squids. First, the spiral appearance is not a special form of division into
sarcomeres but is due merely to the presence of a layer of parallel-aligned
fibrils lying in the periphery of the fiber and twisted into a spiral (reviewed by Bowden, 1958, and Hanson and Lowy, 1960). The helix is
left-handed, and the angle with the fiber axis is a function of the length
of the fiber. The fibrils are evidently the contractile elements. Provided
the fiber cannot twist, and if the core around which the helix is wound
remains at constant volume, this is a satisfactory arrangement for shortening and developing tension. There is a considerable connective tissue
framework in these muscles, so the fibers are probably well anchored.

The fibrils of the squid mantle muscle and adductors of *Ostrea* and
Crassostrea have an ultrastructure similar to that of the a.b.r.m. fibrils, with
the thick filaments surrounded by thin filaments (Hanson and Lowy,
1960; Elliott, 1960). About 12 thin filaments surround each thick one
in the oyster muscle, and probably a larger number in the others. The
thick filaments, other than those of cephalopods, show the 145-Å periodicity characteristic of paramyosin. In a number of papers Kawaguti
and Ikemoto (1957b,c, 1958, 1959) report electron microscope studies on
similar muscles of other molluscs, and although their results are much
less clear than those of the London workers they report a comparable
situation. Nevertheless, there is a marked difference of opinion, in that
the Japanese workers claim that in some of the muscles they examined,
notably in the mantle of the cuttlefish *Sepia esculenta,* the two sets of
filaments are present in an orderly array, comparable to that of rabbit

psoas, but with rows of particles (J-particles) replacing Z-membranes. The thick filaments may then not be free to move over each other. The resolution of this difficulty probably lies in there being two kinds of obliquely "striated" muscle. One does not have regularly aligned filaments, the other does. It is proposed to call these latter muscles "pseudo-striated."

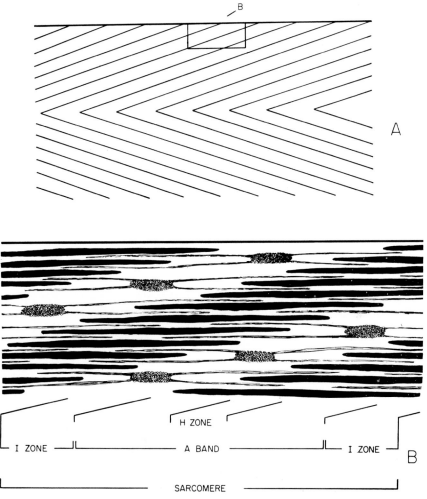

FIG. 1. A. Diagram of possible arrangement of "sarcomeres" in muscle fiber from translucent part of oyster adductor. B. Enlarged view of small portion of A (outlined) showing ultrastructure as revealed by electron micrographs. The place of Z-bands is taken by a regular row of "dense bodies" which in this muscle are staggered at an angle of about 12°. From these, thin filaments extend through an I-zone into a region where they overlap spindle-shaped thick filaments. They terminate short of the centers of the thick filaments leading to the formation of a lighter H-zone.

5. "Pseudo-Striated" Muscle Fibers

Kawaguti and Ikemoto's interpretation of the *Sepia* mantle muscle fibers is similar to that given in an account of the oyster adductor by

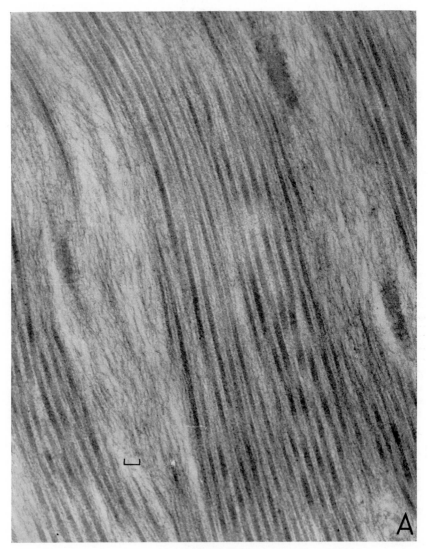

Fig. 2. A. Longitudinal section through muscle fiber from translucent part of oyster adductor muscle. Fiber was stretched slightly. The large, dark, oval areas are the "dense bodies." Light regions near them are sections through I-bands and contain only thin filaments. Thin filaments extend between thick filaments and are cross-linked to them by regularly spaced bridges. Scale represents 1000 Å. B. Transverse section through muscle fiber from translucent part of oyster adductor. Note

Hanson and Lowy (1961). They also found Kawaguti and Ikemoto's J-particles but referred to them as "dense bodies." These may well be present as filament anchors in many types of muscle.

The muscle fibers of the translucent part of the adductor of the oyster

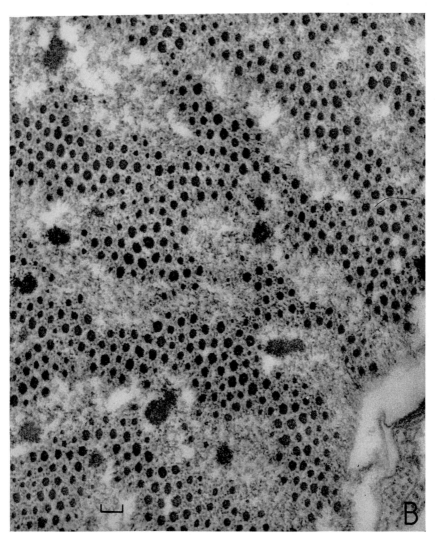

the following: dense bodies; light regions near them containing only thin filaments (= I-bands); apparent variable diameter of thick filaments resulting from their spindle shape; approximately 12 thin filaments surrounding each thick filament in overlap regions. Few or no thin filaments surrounding each thick filament in its thickest (central) part. Scale represents 1000 Å. Photomicrographs courtesy of Jean Hanson and J. Lowy.

Crassostrea angulata studied by Hanson and Lowy fall into the category "pseudo-striated." The over-all gross pattern is of a "double-oblique" striation. The authors do not commit themselves fully on the reasons for the appearance under the light microscope, but give sufficient data for postulating a probable pattern in each fiber comparable to that given in Fig. 1A. The fiber may be thought of as consisting of a series of deeply V-shaped sarcomeres, and its ultrastructure is illustrated in Fig. 1B (see also Fig. 2 for electron micrographs). The equivalent of Z-lines is composed, not of a continuous network of units, as in an ordinary Z-band, but of a number of staggered particles (dense bodies). Thin filaments, probably composed of actin threads, are attached to these particles and run parallel to the edge of the fiber.

On either side of the particles a zone containing only thin filaments is located, thereby forming an I-band. The thin filaments then run into a much denser zone composed of thick filaments staggered at the same angle. They do not extend as far as the centers of the thick filaments in the relaxed or extended state, and so an H-zone, slightly less dense than the overlap regions, is formed. The regularly aligned, thick filaments clearly form an A-band.

The mechanism of contraction in muscle fibers of this kind is evidently analogous to that of ordinary striated muscle fibers, occurring by the inward sliding of one set of filaments over another.

C. Functional Interpretation of Ultrastructure

Kawaguti and Ikemoto have variously interpreted the mechanism as a coiling of filaments, zig-zag bending, and latterly as sliding. It seems unlikely that there would be such diversity of mechanism. The interpretation given by Hanson and Lowy (1959a,b) is intended to be a universal one, applying to the contractile units of all these muscles (except perhaps the third category) and is based on the following points: (*1*) There are two kinds of filaments; (*2*) there are bridges between the filaments; (*3*) the filaments are not continuous along the length of the fiber; (*4*) the filament length is constant at different muscle lengths; (*5*) the relative positions of the two kinds of filament change as the muscle shortens; (*6*) at different muscle lengths the X-ray diffraction patterns are similar (results of Bear and Selby, 1956; Elliott, 1960). Points (*3*), (*4*), and (*5*) are not too well established for all the mollusc muscles they examined, although they appear very likely. The mechanism of contraction derived from these points is, by analogy, that proposed for rabbit psoas (A. F. Huxley and Niedergerke, 1954; H. E. Huxley and Hanson, 1954). The development of tension is probably due to the development of linkages between thick and thin filaments (cf. H. E. Huxley, 1957; A. F. Huxley, 1957). The extreme shortening found in the smooth and spirally banded muscles may be due to the further ability of the thick filaments to slide over one another, the thin filaments remaining between them.

A special relationship exists in muscles containing paramyosin in the thick filaments. The assumption is that the bridges between thick and thin filaments contain ordinary actin-myosin bonds. Subsequently additional bonds are made between these filaments and the paramyosin. This view is discussed later in the chapter. Electron microscopy following specific extraction methods indicates that paramyosin forms a core around which filaments of myosin are arranged (Kahn and Johnson, 1960).

III. INNERVATION

Our knowledge of the details of muscle innervation is still very slight and one can only hope that the impetus of comparative electron microscopy will promote a modern investigation. It is notoriously difficult to obtain good staining of the finer nerve branches, and only a few authors, e.g., Galeazzi (1888), Brück (1914), Röchling (1922), Rossi and Graziadei (1958), and Bowden (1958), have claimed to have seen any of the fine details. There is a great deal of branching, apparently by a large number of very fine motor axons. In the latter respect the molluscs stand in marked contrast to the arthropods and are allied with echinoderms. However, the nature of the neuromuscular junctions is not known well for any mollusc muscle, and it is not possible to guess from the histology whether or not the muscles receive multiterminal innervation, although this is likely on physiological grounds. Polyneuronal innervation is also to be inferred, for many muscle fibers must receive both excitor and inhibitor axons, and some receive "slow" and "fast" axons.

Brück (1914) found mulberry or ring-shaped structures in Golgi preparations of the fast part of the *Anodonta* adductor, which might have been motor end plates. His observations were strengthened by the finding of very similar endings on the same muscle by Bowden (1958) after using a quite different technique, namely the Koelle method for showing the presence of cholinesterase. The endings figured by Galeazzi (1888) in a *Mytilus* muscle are of the simplest kind, the axon coming to end in a filament along the muscle fiber. Filaments and also a simple claw were figured on *Helix* columella muscle by Röchling (1922). Deane and Twarog (1957) have reported a claw-like structure in methylene-blue-stained preparations of the a.b.r.m., but no details were defined. Sprenkel (1929) figured axons terminating in muscle cells in ring-shaped or pointed endings. He also claimed that endings may be intracellular. Two types of motor nerve ending were found in *Octopus* and *Sepiola* arms by Matoja and May (1956). Bowden and Lowy (1955) and Bowden (1958), while using the Koelle cholinesterase method on the *Mytilus* a.b.r.m., also found that staining occurred in certain structures which, they claimed, were probably nerve cell bodies, both uni- and multipolar. Similar bodies were also found in the posterior adductors of *Mytilus* and *Anodonta*. Since then, Deane and Twarog (1957) and Cambridge *et al.* (1959) have failed to find any in the a.b.r.m. and Abraham and Minker (1957) have failed to find them in the adductors. However, unipolar nerve cells have been found in *Octopus* arms (Rossi and Graziadei, 1956) and suckers (Rossi and Graziadei, 1958). Once again electron microscope studies are needed to resolve this problem, which is vitally concerned in the interpretation of function.

A double innervation of less discrete muscles than the a.b.r.m. and adductors, namely, in muscle fields, has been found for several muscles by physiological tests, but it is not known for any of them whether or not this should be attributed to a double innervation and responsiveness of individual muscle cells. Ramsay (1940) found two kinds of nerve fiber, one thick and lightly staining, the other thin but strongly staining, in the motor nerve supply to the buccal mass of *Helix*, which is dually responsive to electric shocks. He was not inclined to attach significance to the correlation. Inhibition has been observed at the muscular level in several preparations, and the inhibitory axons may be expected to run parallel with the excitatory. Röchling (1922), finding thick and thin fibers branching together in *Helix* columella muscle, called them excitatory and inhibitory, though without satisfactory evidence.

Numerous references are made in the earlier literature, especially of cephalopods, to peripheral motor nerve nets, e.g., by Guerin (1908), Mikhaïloff (1921), and Hofmann (1907). It is interesting to find that in the most recent study by Rossi and Graziadei (1958) on the innervation of the *Octopus* sucker, the final branches of motor nerves were found to form a closed anastomosing net. These authors say there are no free nerve endings; "the myoeffector apparatus forms neither a morphological nor a functional unit." Local reflex arcs supported by the histological findings of "sensorimotor" nerve cells have been suggested (e.g., Matoja and May, 1956) in *Sepiola* and *Octopus* arms.

IV. PHYSICAL PROPERTIES

A. *General Features*

It is fairly well established that the properties of the orthodox striated muscle of the fast adductor of *Pecten* and others like it are not greatly different from those of ordinary vertebrate skeletal muscles. It is in the various special properties of the many nonstriated muscles that the interest in molluscan muscle must surely be found.

Many molluscan smooth muscles are highly extensible, even a small load sufficing to cause extension to several times resting length (Jordan, 1918; Bozler, 1930). Although this led to the suggestion that there is little or no elastic material in parallel with the fibers (A. V. Hill, 1950), Abbott and Lowy (1956a) have shown that the *Helix* pharynx retractor, which is highly extensible, does in fact exert appreciable *resting tension* at appropriate lengths. Some of this might be due to the contractile components. Muscles of this kind (and there are many in molluscs) have a very much greater working range than ordinary vertebrate skeletal muscle. That is, they can develop active tension over a very wide range of lengths, down to 20% optimum length, at which the frog sartorius, for example, develops none.

Tension is produced in the muscle both by excitation (*active tension*) and by rapid stretch (*transient tension*). The study of all three forms of tension, and their decay rates, contributes to our understanding of the natural functioning of these muscles. Some values for mechanical features of representative mollusc muscles are given in Table I. Corresponding values for a frog muscle are also given. It should be mentioned that a great deal of work was done on these problems by Jordan and his school (for example, Jordan, 1938—a review) and more recently by Postma (1941a,b, 1942, 1943a,b, 1953). But many of their arguments are difficult to follow and the concepts developed cannot be fitted into the more orthodox views on the nature of muscle.

B. Stress Relaxation

This is the tension decay following quick stretch and it has been studied in the posterior adductors of *Mytilus*, and the ordinary striated part of the *Pecten* adductor by Abbott and Lowy (1957). They found that although the actual speeds are very different, in all three muscles tension decays rapidly at first, then more slowly; they were able to resolve the decay curve into two exponential components. Neither temperature nor the rate of stretch affected the curves significantly. The components in the muscle responsible for the relaxation can be replaced by a very simple model consisting of a spring obeying Hooke's law and a Newtonian viscosity element, parallel elastic elements being absent. It remains to be seen how this model may be interpreted in terms of the ultrastructure of the muscles.

C. Decay of Active Tension

Bozler (1941) claimed that the decay of isometric tension occurred in a manner similar to that following stretch and therefore the two were due to the same process. But in a recent analysis with more refined technique Abbott and Lowy (1958b), using partly the *Mytilus* a.b.r.m. and mainly the *Helix* pharynx retractor at lengths less than the longest

TABLE I

SOME MECHANICAL PROPERTIES OF MOLLUSC MUSCLES

Animal	Muscle	Temperature (°C)	Maximum speed of shortening (lengths/sec)	Tension (kg/cm²)	Breaking stress (kg/cm²) (relaxed)	Ratio twitch: tetanus	$\frac{a}{P_0}$	Time for relaxation to half (sec)	Time to relax to zero (sec)
Mytilus	Pedal retractor[a]	14	0.5–0.9	2–2.5		1:3	0.1		
	Anterior byssus retractor[a]	14	0.06–0.09	3.4–4.5	5	1:8	0.16	1–7000	3–15,000
	Posterior adductor[a]	14	0.09	0.5		1:14	0.2		
Helix	Pharynx retractor[a]	15	0.17	2.6	1–2	—	0.28		
Pinna	Adductor[b]	15	0.3	1.5		1:6	0.35	2	12
Rana	Sartorius (various sources)	0	2.0	2.2	2	1:1.4 1:5 (at 20°C)	0.25	0.05 (at 20°C)	0.2 (at 20°C)

KEY: a = Hill's force constant; P_0 = maximum isometric tension.

[a] Abbott and Lowy (1953).

[b] Abbott and Lowy (1956).

in the body, found significant differences, particularly since the decay of isometric tension was affected by temperature. These observations bring the molluscan smooth muscles into line with comparable results on vertebrate striated muscle (A. V. Hill, 1938), the difference being only of degree, not of kind. The length-tension and force-velocity relationships of various molluscan smooth muscles are not significantly different in principle from those of the more familiar vertebrate ordinary skeletal muscle (Abbott and Lowy, 1953, 1956a,b, 1957, 1958a,b).

In none of the mollusc muscles examined (*Pecten, Helix, Mytilus* and *Loligo* as sources) was latency relaxation found, but this may have been due to insensitivity of recording equipment. The speed of shortening of the a.b.r.m. is related to load during isotonic contraction, to the length, and to the isometric tension corresponding to a given length. The heat production is very much less than in ordinary vertebrate skeletal muscle during contraction maintained by repetitive electrical stimulation (Abbott and Lowy, 1955, 1958a).

V. NEUROMUSCULAR TRANSMISSION

A. Introduction

The study of the nervous control of muscles is greatly hampered by lack of knowledge of the fine details of innervation and also by the fact that the muscle cells (except the less-interesting, orthodox-striated ones of the *Pecten* adductor) are too small and surrounded by too tough connective tissue to permit penetration by conventional intracellular electrodes. Thus it is not known whether or to what extent any of the smooth muscle cells are directly electrically excitable, or if some are spontaneously active. A variety of excitatory processes has been found, but all by stimulating whole nerve trunks or even by stimulating ganglia, so the extent to which the differences can be attributed solely to neuromuscular processes is uncertain.

Inhibitory mechanisms have been found, also under conditions which do not permit conclusive establishment of the site of the inhibitory action. These include the classical work of Pavlov (1885) on *Anodonta*, that of Benson *et al.* (1942) on *Pecten*, Postma and Jordan (e.g., 1942) on *Helix*, and van Nieuwenhoven (1947) on the *Mytilus* a.b.r.m. Recent evidence, discussed later, points to a direct action within the muscle cells in some of these inhibitory processes, but other possibilities, namely, interruption of synaptic events, suppression of ganglion cell discharge, etc., have yet to be ruled out.

B. Nerve-Muscle Preparations

In the absence of knowledge regarding the full details of innervation it has not been possible to make a nerve-muscle preparation of any molluscan muscle and feel sure that no synaptic junctions in addition to the neuromuscular ones intervene. Nevertheless a number which may satisfy this requirement have been made and studied in a preliminary manner. These are as follows.

1. Squid Mantle/Giant Axon (Prosser and Young, 1937; Young, 1938)

In possibly the simplest of all the preparations, a single stimulus applied to a giant nerve fiber of the squid *Loligo* causes a large, fast twitch to occur in a large area of the circular muscle of the mantle. Successive stimuli lead to smooth tetanus at about 30 per sec. But there is only a very small (5–10%) increase in tension above the twitch tension even at resting length following isolation. The muscle is very readily fatigued by continued stimulation. Attempts to record from the muscle with intracellular electrodes have failed to find even resting membrane potentials. Nevertheless, external electrodes reveal potential changes during stimulation (Wilson, 1960) and these have a duration of about 10 msec. During repetitive stimulation they decline markedly in amplitude. Sereni and Young (1932) noted that the muscle becomes more opaque when stimulated to contract and this observation has been followed up by Abbott and Lowy (1956c), who studied the change in light transmission associated with a twitch. Preceding the first signs of tension rise there is a small decrease in opacity, but no latency relaxation. Thereafter the opacity increases greatly and then recovers at about the same rate as relaxation following the peak of twitch tension.

2. Squid Mantle/Small Axons (Young, 1938)

The same squid mantle circular muscle is also innervated by many small nerve fibers. When several of these are stimulated together, with a single shock, a small twitch is developed. Successive stimuli give facilitating as well as summating responses up to a frequency of about 100 per sec. The tetanus:twitch ratio is as high as 100:1 at resting length (Wilson, 1960). The rate of rise of tension slows markedly after an initially fast rise during prolonged stimulation. There is a very marked increase in response magnitude with increasing stimulus strength above threshold, indicating the presence of a large number of motor nerve fibers. The importance of these observations is that they show conclusively a physiological double innervation of the squid mantle muscle comparable in its mechanical effects to that of arthropod muscles (Hoyle, 1957a). The functional relationships of the responses are readily interpreted, the "slow" being used for respiratory movements and the "fast" for escape backward by "jet propulsion."

3. Octopus Mantle (Burian, 1908; Fröhlich, 1910)

No giant axons innervate the octopus mantle and it cannot propel itself backward with quite the same force as the squid. Nevertheless, two kinds of electrical and mechanical response have been found (Wilson, 1960). There is a large, all-or-nothing response having a low tetanus:twitch ratio and also a slower, facilitating response with a very high tetanus:twitch ratio. The electrical response associated with the former declines markedly on repetition while the latter grows in size (Fig. 3). Both are greatly

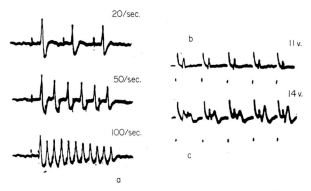

Fig. 3. External recordings of potentials from octopus mantle. (a and b) At threshold. An electrical response which fatigues rapidly with repetition. (c) Above threshold, an additional electrical response appears which, by contrast with the first component, shows marked facilitation. (From Wilson, 1960.)

affected by stimulus strength so that large numbers of motor nerve fibers are probably involved. The principal difference between the octopus and the squid lies in the large area, i.e., total number of muscle fibers, innervated by a giant axon of the squid compared with that supplied by the much smaller "fast" axon of the octopus. Physiologically the responses are similar. Unfortunately, without intracellular recording it will not be possible to resolve the question as to whether the dual neuromuscular mechanisms occur in the same, or different, muscle cells.

4. Snail Retractor Pharynx (Ramsay, 1940)

Bozler (1930) in studying this preparation stimulated the muscle mass directly rather than via the motor nerves, as Ramsay had done. However, the stimuli applied by Bozler were probably indirect. Since the magnitude of the mechanical response increases with increasing stimulus strength over a considerable range, there must be many motor nerve fibers. Very strong shocks nevertheless produce only small mechanical responses. With repetitive stimuli a very marked facilitation as well as summation occurs. Externally recorded electric potentials consist of a sharp spike followed by a slower and smaller potential wave. The height of the spike portion declines rapidly on repetition at frequencies above 10 per sec while the slower potentials continue to grow and also summate, setting up a pronounced negativity. Continued contraction is associated with the depolarization. The simplest interpretation of the results is in terms of a dual nerve supply, one set ("fast" axons) leading to the spike responses and relatively quick contraction, the other ("slow" axons) leading to the slower potential changes and slower contractions. It is remarkable that these rapidly decaying fast potentials should occur in octopus, squid, and snail alike.

Sato *et al.* (1960) have attempted to record from this muscle with intracellular leads. Unfortunately the penetration causes irreversible damage, but the authors did succeed in getting very good external recordings. By varying the stimulus strength they obtained two kinds of response, a nonpropagated, purely end-plate-potential type and a second, spike-like, and at least partially propagated response. The latter fatigued rapidly on repetition and is clearly identical with the spike responses of Bozler (1930) and Ramsay (1940). The local response did not fatigue and showed summation on repetition. The corresponding contractions are twitches and a slower contraction associated only with repetition. By analogy, these responses are comparable to those of the "fast" and "slow" nerve fibers of insects. They could occur in the same muscles cells, as they do in insects (Hoyle, 1957b) and the Japanese authors take this view.

5. Adductor of *Anodonta* (Pavlov, 1885)

This is probably the oldest preparation historically and it is unfortunate that it has not been studied recently, although a detailed study of its normal mode of action in the animal has been made by Barnes (1955). Pavlov excised the visceral ganglion and stimulated the cut end of the nerve. With weak faradic stimulation he found that the adductors, which were in a state of tonic contraction following the operation, became quickly relaxed. This demonstration of a relaxing action, suggesting some kind of an inhibitory mechanism, stimulated a great deal of interest in these muscles (cf. Biedermann, 1896). Barnes (1955) studied the behavior of the adductor in the intact animal in spontaneous and reflex action and showed that the slow portion has a slow rhythm of contraction, the fast a faster rhythm; both are under nervous control.

6. Anterior Byssus Retractor (A.B.R.M.) of *Mytilus* (Winton, 1937; Twarog, 1960a)

Winton introduced this muscle as an example of an isolated, parallel-fibered ("noninnervated") smooth muscle and it has usually been treated as if that is what it is. However, the presence of intramuscular nerves, and possibly ganglion cells as well, means that stimulation may well occur indirectly (see Fig. 4). Twarog (1960a) has studied the muscle responses

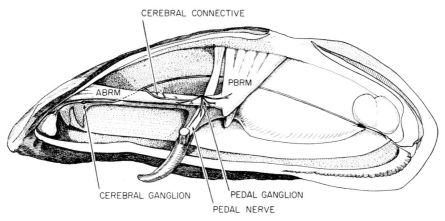

FIG. 4. Inside view of right half of a *Mytilus* to show the position and innervation of the anterior byssus retractor muscle (a.b.r.m.) and its innervation.

to stimuli applied to the motor nerve. If there are no or few neural synapses before the neuromuscular ones, this becomes a valid nerve-muscle preparation. According to Twarog's study, the excitatory innervation comes entirely from the cerebropedal connective between the pedal ganglion and the branching of the visceral connective, probably through the visceral nerves. All nerves to the pedal ganglion except the cerebrovisceral connective were cut and the ganglion freed. Its connective was then cut and the cut end of nerve drawn into a suction electrode. There is no doubt that some nerve cell bodies are included in this nerve trunk although what part they may play, if any, is unknown. The results of stimulating the nerve consisted always of a quick contraction and relaxation (phasic contraction) of the muscle. Action potentials were propagated outwards in both directions from the point of nerve entry at 25–50 cm per sec. This could represent propagation by the nerve elements. The muscle response was from 0.5–5.0 mV and 80–140 msec duration. The amplitude decreased progressively away from the center. It is not clear why.

In addition to these large potentials, many small potentials, all less than 1 mV, were also recorded, occurring spontaneously. These will be discussed later.

C. Semi-Nerve-Muscle Preparations

Stimulation of the muscle by directly applied electrodes often results in indirect or nerve-muscle stimulation owing to a lower threshold of intramuscular nerve elements or to electrical inexcitability of the muscle fibers. Also, during the elicitation of reflex actions much can be learned about neuromuscular processes. Preparations which fall into these categories include the following:

1. SLOW PART OF THE ADDUCTOR OF *Pecten* (Bayliss *et al.*, 1930)

The slow part of the adductor was isolated in the relaxed state and found to give very slow twitches which fused to give a powerful tetanus. The contractures which often accompanied isolation were caused to relax by weak, directly applied faradic stimulation. However, there was no increased viscosity in the contracture, in marked contrast to the results obtained on the a.b.r.m. (see Section VII, A).

Benson *et al.* (1942) found that a much faster relaxation occurs during natural reflex "inhibition." A band of nerve was identified which caused this fast relaxation when stimulated (visceral ganglion removed); since stimulation of another band caused contraction, excitatory and "inhibitory" events could be played against one another. Only small contractions could be completely suppressed but stronger ones were diminished and slowed down. The "inhibitory" effect outlasted an excitatory one of similar duration. The authors suggested that "inhibitory" nerves cause a substance to be released into the muscle which diffuses out only slowly. In this they anticipated recent views on "inhibitory" action. It is unfortunate that further studies have not been made on this preparation.

2. MANTLE RETRACTOR OF *Mya* (Pumphrey, 1938)

These muscles (right and left sides) are innervated by the anterior pallial nerves. When an anterior sensory area on the mantle is touched, an efferent discharge occurs in the pallial nerve. This was monitored electrically and potentials were recorded also from the muscle. The tension developed was monitored. The response obtained depended on the vigor of the stimulus; two distinct kinds were found. One was accompanied by small electric potentials and caused little tension change. Pumphrey suggested that its function might be to delay relaxation. Another response was accompanied by much larger potentials and gave larger contractions. In the mixed nerve trunk the conduction velocity of impulses resulting in the latter, larger responses was faster than the other. This clearly indicates a set of thicker "fast" nerve fibers contrasted with a "slow" thin set.

3. FOOT OF SNAIL (Postma and Jordan, 1942)

The isolated foot is a whole organ, clearly complex, probably having built-in neural reflex arcs and relays. Stimulation of the cut end of the pedal nerve after removal of the ganglion causes either a contraction or a relaxation according to stimulus strength, the relaxation coming first. This means that there are two sets of nerves, inhibitory and excitatory, although the inhibitory cannot suppress the latter, or at most only weakly.

VI. NERVOUS CONTROL IN THE INTACT ANIMAL

The problem of how the nervous system regulates muscular contraction in the intact animal was taken up by Lowy (1953, 1954) in regard to the adductor muscles of *Mytilus*, *Pecten*, and others. Pairs of platinum electrodes were inserted into the muscle in the intact animal and electrical activity was led off on an ink-writing oscillograph. Movements of the valves were also recorded at the same time. It was found in all the muscles examined that tension is accompanied by electrical activity of a very irregular kind, such as might be caused by discharges in a large number of units occurring asynchronously. Each phasic contraction or increase in tonus was accompanied by bursts of, or prolonged, electrical activity. Electrical activity ceased when the nerves were cut, during the elicitation of inhibitory reflexes, or by counteracting hinge-ligament tension. Spontaneous relaxation was accompanied by a decline or cessation of electrical activity, but sometimes a burst actually accompanied the onset of relaxation.

Apart from these bursts, which Lowy suggested might be associated with some form of β-inhibition (Marmont and Wiersma, 1938), the control of tension was due entirely to the number of excitor nerves thrown into action, as judged by the electric potentials. Lowy concluded that his results supported the view that all forms of contraction in these muscles are due to a form of tetanus.

VII. THE "CATCH-MECHANISM" HYPOTHESIS

A number of early observations on the slower molluscan adductor muscles (see Grützner, 1904; Marceau, 1909) suggested that these muscles possess a special mechanism not found in ordinary skeletal muscles. The ideas were crystallized by von Uexküll (1912), following experiments on the *Pecten* adductor, by the suggestion that a molecular ratchet mechanism, the *Sperrung* or "catch-mechanism" existed within the muscle fibers. Following excitation and contraction the catch was supposed to set itself automatically. Thus a state of tension would be maintained without the expenditure of energy. Ritchie (1928) and Bayliss (1928), however, then pointed out that these muscles are intrinsically very slow and that a very low frequency of motor excitation would keep them in a state of continuous contraction, probably with the expenditure of little (though definitely some) energy. The second point of view was called the "tetanus" hypothesis.

A. *The Anterior Byssus Retractor Muscle Preparation*

1. GENERAL FEATURES

The use of this muscle was introduced into physiology by Winton (1937), primarily as an example of a long-fibered smooth muscle which survives well in isolation and is very suitable for experiments. As an example of smooth muscle in general it was clearly a very unfortunate choice, for there is probably no more highly specialized and peculiar muscle in the whole animal kingdom. The idea that there are "representative generalized muscles" dies hard with pharmacologists, general and mammalian physiologists, and in particular some biophysicists, in spite of the abundant examples from comparative physiology of such diversity in muscle that no two are yet known to be exactly alike in significant detail. However, the *Mytilus* a.b.r.m. has since been studied to such an extent that papers on it greatly outnumber all other recent ones on mollusc muscle and it has featured in the general controversy over von Uexküll's "catch-mechanism" hypothesis.

Winton found that when stimulated by direct current, the muscle contracts but then relaxes only very slowly. Relaxation time is very variable, but takes at least a few minutes and may extend to several hours. When stimulated by alternating current, the rising phase (20–30 sec) is more or less the same, though sometimes reaching a greater height, but relaxation time is very different, taking as little as 30 sec and not more than a couple of minutes. The dc contraction was associated with greatly increased viscosity. A burst of ac interposed during dc contraction caused a brief additional contraction, but this was then followed by rapid relaxation, the state of high viscosity having been abolished by the alternating current (see Fig. 5). Fletcher (1937a) examined the muscle histologically and found no cell bodies in it; hence it looked very much as if the effects of direct and alternating current were due to direct actions on the contractile element. The muscle gave an electric response to cathodal stimulation (Fletcher, 1937a,b) and an associated local contraction. Brief pulses evoked responses similar to those due to ac (Fletcher, 1937c; Singh, 1938a,b). These authors, all in search of fundamental principles, did not enter into the catch-mechanism controversy. But zoologists did. It was evident that Winton's findings formed an apparent confirmation of the *Sperrung* hypothesis, dc being followed by a locking of the catch, which could very conveniently be unlocked by ac. van Nieuwenhoven (1947) found that weak faradic stimulation of the pedal ganglion effected

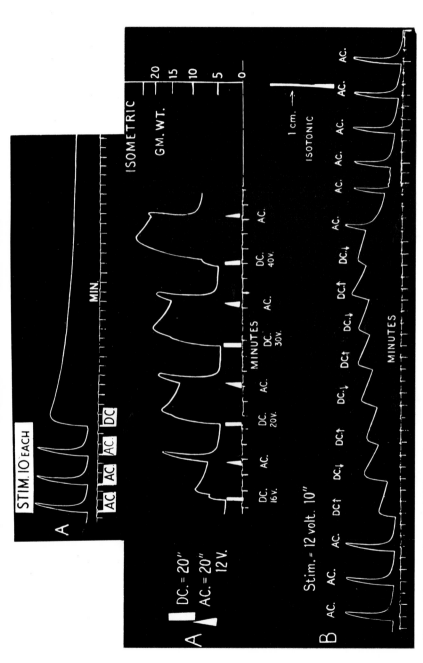

Fig. 5. The experiments of Winton (1937) on the anterior retractor of the byssus of *Mytilus edulis*. Upper (A). A period of stimulation by alternating current (ac) causes a contraction which is followed by relatively rapid relaxation. In contrast, stimulation by direct current (dc) leads to a contraction followed by only very slow relaxation. Middle (A). Interpolation of ac during slow relaxation phase following dc is followed by much faster relaxation rate. Lower (B). Reversal of current does not affect the dc response.

a relaxation of the tonically contracted muscle, thus giving evidence of efferent nerve fibers with the function of "releasing the catch."

It was next supported by Twarog (1954) following pharmacological studies. She made the important observation that the muscle is sensitive to acetylcholine ($10^{-6} M$) which depolarizes it and causes a contraction. The contraction, however, greatly outlasts the depolarization, and so she concluded that a "catch" has been set in the excitation process. An even more important finding was her discovery that 5-hydroxytryptamine (5-HT) in extremely low concentrations ($10^{-9} M$) causes the immediate relaxation of the tonically contracted muscle. She was able to show that this substance occurs naturally in the a.b.r.m. and so proposed that it was the normal "inhibitory transmitter substance." In the presence of 5-HT the muscle still gives powerful contractions to electric stimulation (Hoyle and Lowy, 1956) and may contract rhythmically, particularly in the presence of both acetylcholine and 5-HT (Twarog, 1960b); consequently, the action is a relaxing, not an inhibitory one, as will be discussed later (see Fig. 6).

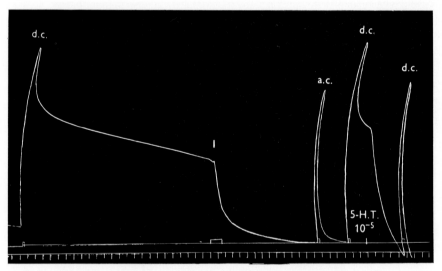

Fig. 6. Relaxation of tonic contraction of *Mytilus* a.b.r.m. by stimulation of inhibitory nerve (at 1) and also by 5-hydroxytryptamine (5-HT). Following the addition of 5-HT, a direct-current stimulus (dc) gives a contraction which is no longer followed by a slow relaxation rate. (From Hoyle and Lowy, 1956.)

Meanwhile, Lowy had been making his studies of electrical activity in the intact animals and later in denervated muscles and was reverting to the Ritchie-Bayliss view of contraction as being due to a form of tetanus (Lowy, 1955). In some instances isolated a.b.r.m.'s investigated by students in routine classroom experiments based on Winton's paper gave anomalous results. The most striking were a failure to obtain tonic contraction following dc stimulation, sometimes also anomalously combined with success following ac stimulation, and the appearance of contractions spontaneously. These observations suggested that the characteristic current stimuli are not necessarily specific but act indirectly, exciting mechanisms which can, under different circumstances, be stimulated in an anomalous manner, or fire spontaneously. They led to a reexamination of electrical events associated with contraction.

2. ELECTRICAL ACTIVITY IN THE A.B.R.M.

Although Fletcher (1937c) had found the a.b.r.m. electrically silent during the contraction, recordings made at high amplification did reveal small spike-like potential changes accompanying phasic contractions (Hoyle and Lowy, 1956). These potentials decreased in frequency and soon terminated following the application of acetylcholine or 5-HT. Recently their presence has been confirmed by Johnson and Twarog (1960) and observations on them extended by Twarog (1960a).

The potentials must originate within the isolated muscle, and the possible intramuscular ganglion cells were implicated as their source. On this basis Hoyle and Lowy proposed a tetanus mechanism for the contracture of the isolated a.b.r.m. following dc or acetylcholine. A stimulus causing the ganglion cells to discharge for a prolonged period would give rise to the tonic contraction. Stimuli causing the cells to discharge only briefly would give only a phasic response. The capacity for inducing quick relaxation of the tonically contracted muscle was attributed to the presence of inhibitory nerve fibers. These would probably act on the source of the spontaneous discharge and therefore have a truly inhibitory action.

There are a number of weaknesses in this hypothesis, engendered largely by ignorance of both histology and the nature of the small potentials. Recently there has been a tendency to return to a modified version of the catch-mechanism hypothesis. The several authors responsible have come to this conclusion independently, and to some extent from different points of argument. But although the weight of evidence is at present apparently in their favor, the matter can still not be regarded as finally settled.

3. RECENT THEORIES OF FUNCTIONING OF THE A.B.R.M.

Lowy and Millman (1958, 1959a,b) studied the mechanical properties of the a.b.r.m. in the conventional manner. In a phasic contraction of the muscle, *active state* (defined as the capacity for developing isometric tension following quick release) disappears long before the tension in the muscle has decayed to zero. The latter tension is called *passive tension*, and is not to be confused with the (additional) resting tension. Passive tension greatly reinforces the resting tension in resisting stretch. This means that a true increase in stiffness occurs following excitation. Nevertheless, the passive tension does decay gradually at a steady rate which can be resolved into three components with half-decay times of about 0.17, 2.2, and 45 seconds, respectively. The first two are similar to the corresponding values for other slow muscles but the latter is much longer. This highly significant component is eliminated if the inhibitory (relaxing) nerve is stimulated or if 5-HT is added. Thus, it may be due to the development of a special set of linkages, different from those found in ordinary muscles, which Lowy and Millman proposed be called "tonic linkages."

The rate of breakage of the tonic linkages is normally very slow, but it would be drastically increased by the natural inhibitory (i.e., relaxing or plasticizing) substance and 5-HT. Thus, inhibitory nerves are regarded as releasing a substance which has to diffuse into the muscle cells, there exerting a direct chemical action. The difference between phasic and tonic contractions is explained by the former being the result of stimulation of both excitor and inhibitor nerves together. Inhibitor nerves are unable to suppress the contraction, which is presumed to be based on the sliding of actin and myosin filaments, but prevent the tonic linkages from being formed, or rather break them as fast as they are formed, so that relaxation is rapid.

Lowy and Millman do not, however, accept the catch-mechanism hypothesis, for as they point out, the relaxation rate is still too fast to account for the very prolonged contractions obtained, unless intermittent stimulation continues. However, this seems unjust. The formation of tonic linkages, which they propose, is clearly a unique mechanism that satisfies almost exactly the requirements of the catch-mechanism hypothesis. They even invoke a specific chemical mechanism for breaking the linkages, i.e., unlocking the catch. Everything in the argument turns on the validity of their value for the third decay component. Since it is not known how to remove relaxing substance from the muscle to prevent possible discharge of inhibitory nerve cells within the preparation, they could easily have obtained a false, low value for this due to the presence of some background plasticizing action.

Similar experiments to those described in the brief reports by Lowy and Millman have been presented fully by Jewell (1959). He made extensive investigations on the mechanical properties and came to very similar conclusions. He supposes that two states can occur in the muscle after excitation, an "active" state and an additional "fused" state. These clearly correspond to Lowy and Millman's normal active state and the same plus tonic linkages. He also proposes that simultaneous inhibitory nerve stimulation is the only reason for the failure of ac stimulation normally to lead to a tonic contraction. He found an increase in heat production to be associated with the fused state.

Unfortunately, none of these authors has explained why ac stimulation or unit pulses should lead to simultaneous stimulation of both excitor and inhibitor nerves, while dc normally does not. However, this may depend on the conditions, for, as has been pointed out, dc may fail to give the tonic contraction while ac may sometimes give it. Thus many of the known anomalies of stimulation can be explained by this notion that phasic contractions are due to an excitation of discharge in both excitor and relaxing nerve elements while prolonged contractions are due to stimulation of excitor nerve elements only. Alternatively, dc may evoke contraction by direct action on the muscle fibers. Some of the anomalies could be due to dc exerting on some occasions a direct action, on others indirect, and sometimes both.

In an entirely new approach, Johnson et al. (1959) and Johnson and Szent-Györgyi (1959), working with glycerinated a.b.r.m. fibers, found that in a medium of low ionic strength the fibers are very stiff at a pH slightly below 6.5, while at a slightly higher pH they are relaxed. These changes parallel those occurring in a solution of paramyosin, for below pH 6.5 paramyosin crystallizes out. Johnson and Szent-Györgyi have constructed a hypothesis of tonic contraction based on a pH change following contraction causing paramyosin crystallization. This would be a true catch mechanism, i.e., one not requiring the expenditure of energy for its maintenance except insofar as work was required to keep the pH low. Unfortunately, it does not fit many of the facts; furthermore, the authors did not suggest how rapid pH change might be brought about or obliterated by 5-HT. Their ideas were supported by electron micrographs showing the paramyosin banding only in tonically contracted, not in relaxed, a.b.r.m. Hanson and Lowy (1959a,b) have refuted these findings because they claim to have obtained the same banding in relaxed muscle.

Takahashi (1957) demonstrated that inhibitory effects are propagated, presumably by nerve elements, thus confirming the general supposition that inhibition by ac stimulation is not due to a direct unlocking of the catch. Later (1960) he found that acetylcholine or KCl applied to the pedal ganglion caused inhibition of the tonic contraction evoked by applying the same stimulants to the muscle. Stimulation of the ganglion electrically caused a phasic contraction which was then terminated abruptly. He interprets this result in exactly the same way as Lowy, Millman, and Jewell did; namely, that phasic contractions are the result of the simultaneous stimulation of inhibitory and excitatory nerves.

Twarog (1960a) has recently studied the relationship between the

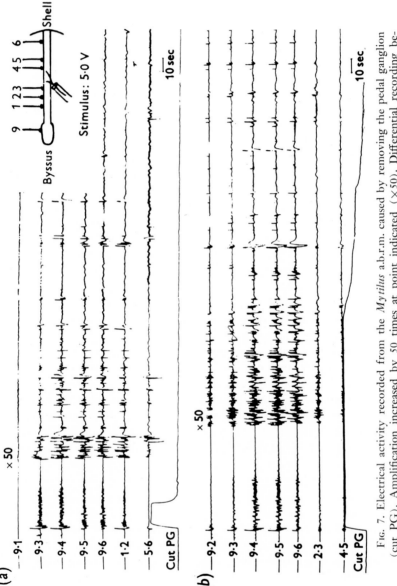

Fig. 7. Electrical activity recorded from the *Mytilus* a.b.r.m. caused by removing the pedal ganglion (cut PG). Amplification increased by 50 times at point indicated (×50). Differential recording between leads in positions indicated in insert. The lowest trace in each of the two records registers tension. (a) Brief contraction. (b) Prolonged contraction. Note the small electrical potential changes which accompany the contraction in (b). (From Twarog, 1960a).

small, spontaneously occurring potentials and tension, using multichannel recording. She found that these potentials propagate over appreciable distances, suggesting that they are not local in origin (see Fig. 7). Schmandt and Sleator (1955) had found a partial (i.e., decrementing) propagation of potentials evoked by electric stimulation. The spontaneous potentials are too prolonged to be nerve impulses; they are most likely local muscle potentials spreading electrotonically and initiated in and propagated by nerve elements. It seems doubtful that they could originate in the muscle fibers since they are always propagated in the same direction (outward). Their probable nervous origin is further suggested by the fact that they seldom appear in very small bundles of muscle fibers obtained by stripping, which are less likely to contain nerve elements.

Twarog also found that these small bundles nevertheless can be made to show tonic contractions which are relaxed by 5-HT. Of course it may not be surprising that the isolated bundle showed a tonic contraction in the absence of electrical activity. The same small bundle would also lack inhibitory nerve elements. When spontaneous potentials did occur they were often not readily correlated with tension; their significance is thus a mystery, although spontaneous excitatory potentials occurring at the same time as spontaneous inhibitory action would simply cancel. The whole field is rife with speculation and uncertainty and it is difficult to see how any significant advance can be made until intracellular recordings can be made, or until the motor nerve elements have been more selectively stimulated.

Cambridge et al. (1959) found that the response to pulses was blocked by a drug, propantheline, which is an acetylcholine-blocking agent. By contrast, the response to prolonged dc was not so blocked. On this basis they proposed that the former excitation occurs via motor nerve elements while the latter is a direct excitation (by depolarization) of the muscle fibers. Under the right conditions dc must also excite the nerve fibers, and in addition it will probably also cause some local contracture.

4. ACTION POTENTIAL OF THE A.B.R.M.

The so-called action potential of the a.b.r.m. is a relatively large (5 mV) electrical response to directly applied depolarization discovered by Fletcher (1937a) and further studied by Prosser et al. (1951b), Schmandt and Sleator (1955) and Twarog (1960a). It is graded in magnitude according to stimulus strength and declines in height with distance from the stimulating leads. There is little doubt that it is always indirect, i.e., neurally evoked and represents the summed responses of many muscle fibers to the excitation of many motor nerve fibers. On repetitive elicitation there is some degree of facilitation and also summation, even to complete fusion. This strongly suggests that the electrical responses are of purely junctional type; one would then expect only a limited, electrotonic spread along the muscle fibers themselves.

5. Other Features of the A.B.R.M.

An interesting effect of cooling has been found by Guttman (Guttman and Gross, 1956). When the a.b.r.m. is cooled rapidly it does not contract, but if it is first partially depolarized by adding KCl it contracts powerfully and this is associated with a marked fall in membrane potential. No mechanism has been proposed.

6. Summary of Views on the A.B.R.M.

The muscle may be regarded provisionally as having a normal but slow type of electric activation mechanism, probably depending on the elicitation of junctional potentials only at numerous synaptic sites. There is no evidence for a dual response mechanism such as has been described in other molluscan preparations. The a.b.r.m. does have a special mechanism which may be called a catch-mechanism, dependent on the presence of large quantities of paramyosin ribbons in the thick filaments. Following activation, a sliding filament mechanism causes shortening and tension development. Tension development may be due to development of linkages between actin and myosin-paramyosin, or to a change in state of part of the system involving the paramyosin. The state of tension declines following cessation of the stimulus at a rate which depends on the presence of a chemical agent, called a relaxing or plasticizing substance in the muscle, which may be released in the muscle naturally from inhibitory nerve endings.

A quick contraction and relaxation (phasic contraction) may occur when only a brief motor discharge occurs, or it may be that it can occur only when the inhibitory nerves are stimulated as well as the excitor so that a supply of the relaxing substance accumulates within the muscle. In the presence of relaxing substance, prolonged contraction can be maintained only by a repetitive stimulation, i.e., by a tetanic action. In the intact animal intermittent continued excitation is probably supplied by the nervous system.

Continued intermittent excitation may also occur in isolated preparations and be partly responsible for prolonged contractions. The final test of the notion that tonic contraction can be maintained without excitation depends on determination of the relaxation rate in the complete absence of the relaxing substance.

B. *Other Tonically Acting Muscles*

It may be fairly assumed that molluscan smooth muscles which contain large proportions of paramyosin probably function in a manner similar to the *Mytilus* a.b.r.m. However, they may have different effector control, principally in the form of a dual type of innervation, for which there is no evidence in the a.b.r.m. Von Uexküll (e.g., 1912), Jordan (e.g., 1938), Jordan and Postma (1941), Postma (1941a,b, 1942, 1943a,b), and others have always insisted that these muscles can be sent into a special stiff condition which is then rendered more or less plastic by the action of a relaxing nerve. They did not find peripheral inhibition in the form of complete blockage of motor excitation in any of the systems they investigated. This view is in accordance with the outline presented above for the functioning of the a.b.r.m. It will be convenient henceforth to refer to the action of the inhibitory nerve as a relaxing or plasticizing one, rather than the more customary inhibitory, since the latter implies excitation/contraction blocking while the former does not.

Very recently Rüegg has examined the proteins in the smooth part of the *Pecten* adductor. This contains tropomyosin A together with actin and myosin (Rüegg, 1961a). When the muscle is glycerinated and then treated with magnesium-ATP it has a high rigidity which may correspond to the tonic state. Rüegg (1961b) suggests that free ATP may act as a plasticizer, inducing changes in the muscle viscosity by affecting the interaction of molecules of tropomyosin.

C. Temperature Dependence

The relationship between temperature and tension was studied in an isolated adductor of *Pinna nobilis* by Reichel (1955). He found that contractions evoked by acetylcholine were greatly affected by temperature and had a positive coefficient. By contrast, the tension developed following dc was affected hardly at all. On this basis he says that the catch-mechanism is based on a different mechanism from that of contraction. What he means by this is not clear, and it is unfortunate that the many recent papers on the catch-mechanism hypothesis do not comment on Reichel's finding, apparently due to ignorance of his work. This matter should be cleared up, because Twarog and others clearly believe that acetylcholine causes an excitation which leads to catch-setting. Cambridge *et al.* (1959) claim that they found a difference between the acetylcholine contraction in the *Mytilus* a.b.r.m. and contraction due to dc. However, in view of the possibility of gross damage being done by passing strong direct current, it cannot be assumed without further careful tests that the peculiar effects these authors obtained were not due to "unnatural phenomena." Nevertheless, the dc contractions were relaxed by 5-HT. Thus it may be that the acetylcholine contraction is due to continued stimulation of the muscle, possibly via nerve elements but involving both excitor and relaxing nerve elements together. The failure to find viscosity changes in some maintained contractions (e.g., Bayliss *et al.*, 1930) might be explained in a similar manner. When relaxing substance is released at the same time as excitation occurs, the viscosity should not increase greatly.

D. General Control Mechanism of Paramyosin Muscles

In controlling a complex mass of musculature like the foot of a snail, in which all parts are continually under stress in various directions, either an increase in excitation or an increase in "plasticization" (= "inhibition") may be expected to lead to movement. For a contraction to be really effective, though, a decrease in viscosity must also occur. Alternating current stimuli lead to quicker and also greater extents of contraction in the a.b.r.m., presumably because the plasticizing nerve is stimulated at the same time as the excitor. Bush (1960) has recently shown that in Crustacea where a comparable effect is obtained owing to β-inhibition (the term plasticizing action is used by him to describe this function) the inhibitory axons usually fire at the same time as the excitors in reflexly evoked actions. In the Crustacea there is no evidence for an increased viscosity following excitation, but a background of motor activity at a low frequency, which is certainly often present, would have a similar action.

There may be simple rules regarding the extent to which excitor and plasticizer neurons fire together, or certain reflexes may involve them to different extents in a subtle fashion. It will be a long time before we know the answers to these problems.

VIII. PHARMACOLOGY

Many molluscan muscles are stimulated to contract by small concentrations of acetylcholine (see Prosser et al., 1951a), sometimes being potentiated by eserine, and so they are regarded as being cholinergic. The Mytilus a.b.r.m. has already been mentioned in this connection, and we may add the Octopus mantle, the Helix pharyngeal retractor, and Buccinum and Mya feet and siphons. However, the muscle most similar to vertebrate skeletal muscle in appearance and physiological features, the striated portion of the Pecten adductor, is not sensitive to acetylcholine (Bayliss et al., 1930).

The radular protractor of Busycon (R. B. Hill, 1958) and that of Buccinum (Fänge and Mattisson, 1958) are caused to contract by acetylcholine. Both are relaxed by 5-HT; when both drugs are present the muscles show strong rhythmic contractions analogous to those present in the normal functioning of this muscle in the animal. The remarkable relaxing action of minute quantities of 5-HT on the a.b.r.m. has already been mentioned. Botulinum toxin preparations have a relaxing action similar to that of 5-HT (Lowy, 1956). Sometimes rhythmic contractions are set up also in the a.b.r.m. by 5-HT (Hoyle and Lowy, 1956; Twarog, 1960b).

Other acetylcholine-like agents, for example, tetramethyl ammonium bromide (5×10^{-6}) and trimethyl (4-oxypentyl) ammonium chloride, cause depolarization and contracture of the a.b.r.m. (Twarog, 1959). Acetyl β-methylcholine has a similar action to acetylcholine but in higher concentrations; the duration of its effect is longer, suggesting that the *Mytilus* "cholinesterase" does not act on it efficiently (Twarog, 1954). Nicotine, in concentrations less than 10^{-4}, had a similar action. Acetylcholine action was blocked by various standard blocking agents such as atropine and decamethonium. The most effective blocking agents found by Cambridge *et al.* (1959) were also anticholinesterases, propantheline, and methantheline. Adrenaline, and to a lesser extent noradrenaline, also causes relaxation of the a.b.r.m. Unlike the situation in many mammalian preparations, however, lysergic acid diethylamide is not an antagonist of 5-HT but causes a similar, relaxing action (Hoyle and Lowy, 1956; Twarog, 1959). The action of acetylcholine is potentiated by eserine (Cambridge *et al.*, 1959).

Many anticholinesterases prevent the stimulating action of subsequent applications of acetylcholine, but once the contracture has developed these agents fail to cause relaxation. This is taken as providing good evidence that the contracture does not require continued excitation and therefore supports the catch-mechanism hypothesis.

The general conclusion is that acetylcholine or a very closely related substance is probably an excitatory transmitter substance in the a.b.r.m. and other lamellibranch smooth muscles, as well as in some gastropod and cephalopod muscles. The action of the inhibitory nerves does not give a true inhibition in the sense in which this phenomenon occurs in the central nervous system, but rather liberates a relaxing or plasticizing substance. The latter is destroyed only very slowly and diffuses into the muscle fibers where it has a direct action on the contractile mechanism, preventing certain kinds of bonds from forming or being maintained. The processes of activation and of contraction appear to be unaltered. There is very strong evidence that its identity is 5-HT. In those preparations for which a dual response mechanism has been demonstrated, it has not been determined whether acetylcholine affects either or both processes, although this seems an obvious experiment to make.

ACKNOWLEDGMENTS

I am greatly indebted to Dr. Jean Hanson and Dr. J. Lowy for their valuable comments on the manuscripts and for supplying the electron micrographs (Fig. 2).

346 G. HOYLE

References

Abbott, B. C., and Lowy, J. (1953). Mechanical properties of *Mytilus* muscle. *J. Physiol. (London)* **120**, 50p.

Abbott, B. C., and Lowy, J. (1955). Heat production in a smooth muscle. *J. Physiol. (London)* **130**, 25p.

Abbott, B. C., and Lowy, J. (1956a). Resting tension in snail muscle. *Nature* **178**, 147–148.

Abbott, B. C., and Lowy, J. (1956b). Mechanical properties of *Pinna* adductor muscle. *J. Marine Biol. Assoc. U.K.* **35**, 521–530.

Abbott, B. C., and Lowy, J. (1956c). A new muscle preparation for the study of optical changes during contraction. *Nature* **177**, 788.

Abbott, B. C., and Lowy, J. (1957). Stress relaxation in muscle. *Proc. Roy. Soc.* **B146**, 280–288.

Abbott, B. C., and Lowy, J. (1958a). Contraction in molluscan smooth muscle. *J. Physiol. (London)* **141**, 385–397.

Abbott, B. C., and Lowy, J. (1958b). Mechanical properties of *Helix* and *Mytilus* muscle. *J. Physiol. (London)* **141**, 398–407.

Abraham, A., and Minker, E. (1957). Innervation of the lamellibranch muscle. *Nature* **180**, 925–926.

Bailey, K. (1948). Tropomyosin: A new asymmetric protein component of the muscle fibres. *Biochem. J.* **43**, 271–279.

Barnes, G. E. (1955). The behaviour of *Anodonta cygnea* L., and its neurophysiological basis. *J. Exptl. Biol.* **32**, 158–175.

Bayliss, L. E. (1928). The energetics of plain muscle. *J. Physiol. (London)* **65**, 1.

Bayliss, L. E., Boyland, E., and Ritchie, A. D. (1930). The adductor mechanism of Pecten. *Proc. Roy. Soc.* **B106**, 363–376.

Bear, R. S., and Selby, C. C. (1956). The structure of paramyosin fibrils according to X-ray diffraction. *J. Biophys. Biochem. Cytol.* **2**, 55–70.

Benson, A. A., Hays, J. T., and Lewis, R. N. (1942). Inhibition in the slow muscle of the scallop, *Pecten circularis aequisulcatus* Carpenter. *Proc. Soc. Exptl. Biol. Med.* **49**, 289–291.

Biedermann, W. (1896). "Electrophysiology," 2 vols. Macmillan, New York.

Bowden, J. (1958). The structure and innervation of lamellibranch muscle. *Intern. Rev. Cytol.* **7**, 295–335.

Bowden, J., and Lowy, J. (1955). The lamellibranch muscle. Innervation. *Nature* **176**, 346.

Bozler, E. (1930). Untersuchungen zur Physiologie der Tonusmuskeln. *Z. vergleich. Physiol.* **12**, 579–602.

Bozler, E. (1941). The mechanical properties of resting smooth muscle. *J. Cellular Comp. Physiol.* **18**, 385–391.

Brück, A. (1914). Die Muskulatur von *Anodonta cellensis* Schröt. Ein Beitrag zur Anatomie und Histologie der Muskelfasern. *Z. wiss. Zool.* **110**, 481–619.

Burian, R. (1908). Methodische Bemerkungen über Nerven-Muskelpräparate von Octopoden. *Z. biol. Tech. u. Methodik* **1**, 136.

Bush, B. M. H. (1962). Peripheral reflex inhibition in the claw of the crab *Carcinus maenas* (L.). *J. Exptl. Biol.* **39**, 71–88.

Cambridge, G. W., Holgate, J. A., and Sharp, J. A. (1959). A pharmacological analysis of the contractile mechanism of *Mytilus* muscle. *J. Physiol. (London)* **148**, 451–464.

Deane, H. W., and Twarog, B. M. (1957). Histology of an invertebrate smooth muscle. *Anat. Record* **128**, 538–539.

Dörr, D., and Portzehl, H. (1954). Der Kontraktile Myosinfaden aus glatter Muskulatur. Z. *Naturforsch* **9b**, 550–555.

Elliott, G. F. (1960). The structure of certain smooth muscles which contain "paramyosin" elements. *Proc. 4th Intern. Congr. Electron Microscopy, Berlin, 1958* **2**, 328–330.

Elliott, G. F., Hanson, J., and Lowy, J. (1957). Paramyosin elements in lamellibranch muscle. *Nature* **180**, 1291.

Fänge, R. and Mattisson, A. (1958). Studies on the physiology of the radula-muscle of *Buccinum undatum. Acta. Zool. (Stockholm)* **39**, 53–64.

Fletcher, C. M. (1937a). Action potentials recorded from an unstriated muscle of simple structure. *J. Physiol. (London)* **90**, 233–253.

Fletcher, C. M. (1937b). Excitation of the action potential of a molluscan unstriated muscle. *J. Physiol. (London)* **90**, 415–428.

Fletcher, C. M. (1937c). The relation between the mechanical and electrical activity of a molluscan unstriated muscle. *J. Physiol. (London)* **91**, 172–185.

Fox, D. L. (1953). "Animal Biochromes and Structural Colours," 379pp. Cambridge Univ. Press, London and New York.

Fröhlich, F. W. (1910). Experimentelle Studien am Nervensystem der Mollusken. 5. Summation 'scheinbare Bahnung', Tonus und Hemmung am Nervensystem der Cephalopoden. Z. *allgem. Physiol.* **10**, 436–466.

Galeazzi, R. (1888). Sugli elementi nervosi dei muscoli di chiusura dei bivalvi. *Atti Accad. Sci. Torino* **23**, 556–561.

Grützner, P. (1904). Die glatten Muskeln. *Ergeb. Physiol.* **3**, 12–88.

Guerin, J. (1908). Contribution à l'étude des systèmes cutané, musculaire et nerveux des Céphalopodes. *Arch. zool. exptl. et gén.* **8**, 1–198.

Guttman, R., and Gross, M. M. (1956). Relationship between electrical and mechanical changes in muscle caused by cooling. *J. Cellular Comp. Physiol.* **48**, 421–433.

Hall, C. E., Jakus, M. A., and Schmitt, F. O. (1945). The structure of certain muscle fibrils as revealed by the use of electron stains. *J. Appl. Phys.* **16**, 459–465.

Hanson, J., and Lowy, J. (1957). Structure of smooth muscles. *Nature* **180**, 906–909.

Hanson, J., and Lowy, J. (1959a). Evidence for a sliding filament contractile mechanism in tonic smooth muscles of lamellibranch molluscs. *Nature* **184**, 286–287.

Hanson, J., and Lowy, J. (1959b). Structural features relating to the mechanism of tonic contraction in certain molluscan smooth muscles. *J. Physiol. (London)* **149**, 31P.

Hanson, J., and Lowy, J. (1960). Structure and function of the contractile apparatus in the muscles of invertebrate animals. *In* "Structure and Function of Muscle" (G. H. Bourne, ed.), Vol. 1, pp. 265–335. Academic Press, New York.

Hanson, J., and Lowy, J. (1961). The structure of the muscle fibres in the translucent part of the adductor of the oyster, *Crassostrea angulata. Proc. Roy. Soc.* **B154**, 173–196.

Hanson, J., Lowy, J., Huxley, H. E., Bailey, K., Kay, C. M., and Rüegg, J. C. (1957). Structure of molluscan tropomyosin. *Nature* **180**, 1134–1135.

Hill, A. V. (1938). The heat of shortening and the dynamic constants of muscle. *Proc. Roy. Soc.* **B126**, 136–195.

Hill, A. V. (1950). The series elastic component of muscle. *Proc. Roy. Soc.* **B137**, 273–280.

Hill, R. B. (1958). The effects of certain neurohumors and of other drugs on the ventricle and radula protractor of *Busycon canaliculatum* and on the ventricle of *Strombus gigas. Biol. Bull.* **115**, 471–482.

Hofmann, F. B. (1907). Gibt es in der Muskulatur der Mollusken periphere, kontinuierlich leitende Nervennetze bei Abwesenheit von Ganglienzellen? I. Untersuchungen an Cephalopoden. *Pflügers Arch. ges. Physiol.* **118**, 375–412.

Hoyle, G. (1957a). The nervous control of insect muscle. *In* "Recent Advances in Invertebrate Physiology" (B. T. Scheer, ed.), pp. 73–98. Univ. of Oregon Press, Eugene, Oregon.

Hoyle, G. (1957b). "Comparative Physiology of the Nervous Control of Muscular Contraction," 147pp. Cambridge Univ. Press, London and New York.

Hoyle, G., and Lowy, J. (1956). The paradox of *Mytilus* muscle: A new interpretation. *J. Exptl. Biol.* **33**, 295–310.

Huxley, A. F. (1957). Muscle structure and theories of contraction. *Progr. in Biophys. and Biophys. Chem.* **1**, 257–318.

Huxley, A. F., and Niedergerke, R. (1954). Structural changes in muscle during contraction. Interference microscopy of tiring muscle fibres. *Nature* **173**, 971–973.

Huxley, H. E. (1957). The double array of filaments in cross-striated muscle. *J. Biochem. Biophys. Cytol.* **3**, 631–648.

Huxley, H. E., and Hanson, J. (1954). Changes in the cross-striation of muscle during contraction and stretch and their structural interpretation. *Nature* **173**, 973–976.

Jewell, B. R. (1959). The nature of the phasic and the tonic responses of the anterior byssal retractor muscle of *Mytilus. J. Physiol. (London)* **149**, 154–177.

Johnson, W. H., and Szent-Györgyi, A. G. (1959). The molecular basis for the "catch" mechanism in molluscan muscle. *Biol. Bull.* **117**, p. 382.

Johnson, W. H., and Twarog, B. M. (1960). The basis for prolonged contraction in molluscan muscles. *J. Gen. Physiol.* **43**, 941–960.

Johnson, W. H., Kahn, J. S., and Szent-Györgyi, A. G. (1959). Paramyosin and contraction of "catch muscles." *Science* **130**, 160–161.

Jordan, H. J. (1918). Über die Physiologie der Muskulatur und des zentralen Nervensystems bei hohlorganartigen wirbellosen Tieren; insbesondere bei Schnecken. *Ergeb. Physiol.* **16**, 87–227.

Jordan, H. J. (1938). Die Physiologie des Tonus der Hohlmuskeln, vornehmlich der Bewegungsmuskulatur "hohlorganartiger" wirbelloser Tiere. *Ergeb. Physiol.* **40**, 437–533.

Jordan, H. J., and Postma, N. (1941). Über den Tonus des Schneckenfusses (*Helix pomatia* L.). III. Zwei antagonistische Zentren in den Pedalganglien. *Koninkl. Ned. Akad. Wetenschap., Proc.* **67**, 1169–1176.

Kahn, J. S., and Johnson, W. H. (1960). The localization of myosin and paramyosin in the myofilaments of the byssus retractor of *Mytilus edulis. Arch. Biochem. Biophys.* **86**, 138–143.

Kawaguti, S., and Ikemoto, M. (1956). Electron microscopy of smooth muscle fiber from a snail. *Biol. J. Okayama Univ.* **2**, 175–186.

Kawaguti, S., and Ikemoto, N. (1957a). Electron microscopy of the smooth muscle of a mussel, *Mytilus crassitesta* Lischke. *Biol. J. Okayama Univ.* **3**, 107–121.

Kawaguti, S., and Ikemoto, N. (1957b). Electron microscopy of the smooth muscle of a cuttlefish, *Sepia esculenta* Hoyle. *Biol. J. Okayama Univ.* **3**, 196–208.

Kawaguti, S., and Ikemoto, N. (1957c). Electron microscopy of the smooth muscle from the adductor of *Spanish oysters, Pinna attenuata* and *Atrina japonica. Biol. J. Okayama Univ.* **3**, 248–268.

Kawaguti, S., and Ikemoto, N. (1958). Electron microscopy on the adductor muscle of the scallop, *Pecten albicans. Biol. J. Okayama Univ.* **4**, 191–205.

Kawaguti, S., and Ikemoto, N. (1959). Electron microscopy of the adductor muscle of the thorn oyster, *Spondylus cruentus. Biol. J. Okayama Univ.* **5**, 73–87.

Kawaguti, S., and Ikemoto, N. (1960a). Electron microscopy on the adductor muscle of the file shell, *Promantellum hirasei*. *Biol. J. Okayama Univ.* **6**, 43–52.

Kawaguti, S., and Ikemoto, N. (1960b). Electron microscopic study on the adductor muscle of a bivalved gastropod, *Tamanovalva limax*. *Biol. J. Okayama Univ.* **6**, 61–70.

Lowy, J. (1953). Contraction and relaxation in the adductor muscles of *Mytilus edulis*. *J. Physiol. (London)* **120**, 129–140.

Lowy, J. (1954). Contraction and relaxation in the adductor muscles of *Pecten maximus*. *J. Physiol. (London)* **124**, 100–105.

Lowy, J. (1955). The lamellibranch muscle contractile mechanism. *Nature* **176**, 345.

Lowy, J. (1956). The action on *Mytilus* muscle of a heat-stable principle in partially purified type A botulinum toxin preparations. *J. Physiol. (London)* **132**, 672–676.

Lowy, J., and Millman, B. M. (1958). Tonic and phasic responses in the anterior byssus retractor mucle (ABRM) of *Mytilus*. *J. Physiol. (London)* **149**, 68.

Lowy, J., and Millman, B. M. (1959a). Contraction and relaxation in smooth muscles of lamellibranch molluscs. *Nature* **183**, 1730–1731.

Lowy, J., and Millman, B. M. (1959b). Tonic and phasic responses in the anterior byssus retractor muscle (ABRM) of *Mytilus*. *J. Physiol. (London)* **149**, 32.

Marceau, F. (1909). Morphologie, histologie et physiollogie comparées des muscles adducteurs des mollusques acéphales. *Arch. zool. exptl. et gén.* **2**, 296–469.

Mark, J. S. T. (1956). An electron microscope study of uterine smooth muscle. *Anat. Record* **125**, 473–485.

Marmont, G., and Wiersma, C. A. G. (1938). On the mechanism of inhibition and excitation of crayfish muscle. *J. Physiol. (London)* **93**, 173–193.

Matoja, R., and May, R. (1956). Comparaison de l'innervation brachiale des Céphalopodes *Octopus vulgaris* Lamark et *Sepiola rondelati* Leach. *Arch. zool. exptl. et gén.* **94**, Suppl. I, 1–59.

Merton, H. (1911). Quergestreifte Muskulatur und vesiculöses Gewebe bei Gastropoden. *Zool. Anz.* **37**, 561–573.

Miklhaïloff, S. (1921). Système nerveux cellulaire périphérique des Céphalopodes. *Bull. inst. oceanogr. Monaco* No. 402, 1–12.

Pavlov, J. (1885). Wie die Muschel ihre Schaale öffnet. *Pflügers Arch. ges. Physiol.* **37**, 6–31.

Plenk, H. (1924). Die Muskelfasern der Schnecken. Zugleich eine kritische Studie über die sogenannte Schrägstreifung. *Z. wiss. Zool.* **122**, 1–78.

Plenk, H. (1933). Zum Bau der Cephalopodenmuskelfasern. *Z. mikroskop. Anat. Forsch.* **33**, 605–624.

Postma, N. (1941a). Ueber den Tonus des Schneckenfusses (*Helix pomatia* L.) I. Der Tonus gemessen an der Pedalkonstanz. *Koninkl. Ned. Akad. Wetenschap., Proc.* **64**, 1151–1158.

Postma, N. (1941b). Über den Tonus des Schneckenfusses (*Helix pomatia* L.). II. Die Tonuslösung. *Koninkl. Ned. Akad. Wetenschap., Proc.* **64**, 1239–1247.

Postma, N. (1942). Über den Tonus des Schneckenfusses (*Helix pomatia* L.) *Koninkl. Ned. Akad. Wetenschap., Proc.* **65**, 758–765.

Postma, N. (1943a). Über den Tonus des Schneckenfusses (*Helix pomatia* L.). V. Elektrische Reizung der Pedalnerven hemmt nur dynamischen Tonus—Electrische prikkeling der Nn. pedales vemt slechts "jonge viscositeit." *Verslag Koninkl. Ned. Akad. Wetenschap.* **52**, 380–390.

Postma, N. (1943b). Über den Tonus des Schneckenfusses (*Helix pomatia* L.). VI. Tonus und Zerebralganglion-Tonus an Hersenuwknoop. *Verslag Koninkl. Ned. Akad. Wetenschap.* **52**, 228–239.

Postma, N. (1953). The lengthening reaction (Bingham curve) of smooth muscles of hollow organs is characteristic for some gastropods only and is due to lengthening and tension reflexes. *Proc. 14th Intern. Congr. Zool., Copenhagen, 1953*, pp. 310–311.

Postma, N., and Jordan, H. J. (1942). On the antagonistic influences playing a part in the regulation, by the pedal ganglia, of the foot muscle tone of the snail (*Helix pomatia* L.). *Acta Brevia Neerl.* **12**, 92–94.

Prosser, C. L., and Young, J. Z. (1937). Responses of muscles of the squid to repetitive stimulation of the giant nerve fibres. *Biol. Bull.* **73**, 237–241.

Prosser, C. L., Bishop, D. W., Brown, F. A., Jr., Jahn, T. L., and Wulff, V. J. (1951a). "Comparative Animal Physiology," 888pp. Saunders, Philadelphia, Pennsylvania (2nd ed., 1961).

Prosser, C. L., Curtis, H. J., and Travis, D. M. (1951b). Action potentials from some invertebrate non-striated muscles. *J. Cellular Comp. Physiol.* **38**, 299–319.

Pumphrey, R. J. (1938). The double-innervation of muscles in the clam (*Mya arenaria*). *J. Exptl. Biol.* **15**, 500–505.

Ramsay, J. A. (1940). A nerve-muscle preparation from the snail. *J. Exptl. Biol.* **17**, 96–115.

Reichel, H. (1955). Über die Temperaturabhängigkeit der Spannung im Zustand des Tonus und der Kontraktur im glatten Schliessmuskel von *Pinna nobilis*. *Publ. staz. zool. Napoli* **27**, 73–79.

Ritchie, A. D. (1928). "The Comparative Physiology of Muscular Tissue," 111pp. Cambridge Univ. Press, London and New York.

Röchling, E. (1922). Der Kolumellarmuskel von *Helix pom.* und seine Beziehung zur Schale. *Z. wiss. Zool.* **119**, 285–325.

Rossi, F., and Graziadei, P. (1956). Nouvelles contributions à la connaissance du système nerveux du tentacule des céphalopodes. II. Cordons ganglionnaires ou moelles périphériques du tentacule d'*Octopus. Acta. Anat.* **26**, 165–174.

Rossi, F., and Graziadei, P. (1958). Nouvelles contributions à la connaissance du système nerveux du tentacule des céphalopodes. IV. Le patrimoine nerveux de la ventouse de l'*Octopus Vulgaris. Acta Anat.* **34**, Suppl. 32, 1–79.

Rüegg, J. C. (1957). Die Reinigung der Myosin-ATP-ase eines glatten Muskels. *Helv. Physiol. et Pharmacol. Acta* **15**, 33–35.

Rüegg, J. C. (1961a). The proteins associated with contraction in lamellibranch 'catch' muscle. *Proc. Roy. Soc.* **B154**, 209–223.

Rüegg, J. C. (1961b). On the tropomyosin-paramyosin system in relation to the viscous tone of lamellibranch 'catch' muscle. *Proc. Roy. Soc.* **B154**, 224–249.

Sato, M., Tamasige, M., and Ozeki, M. (1960). Electrical activity of the retractor pharynx muscle of the snail. *Japan. J. Physiol.* **10**, 85–98.

Schmandt, W., and Sleator, W. (1955). Deviations from all-or-none behavior in a molluscan unstriated muscle: Decremental conduction and augmentation of action potentials. *J. Cellular Comp. Physiol.* **46**, 439–476.

Schmitt, F. O., Bear, R. S., Hall, C. E., and Jakus, M. A. (1947). Electron microscope and X-ray diffraction studies of muscle structure. *Ann. N.Y. Acad. Sci.* **47**, 799–812.

Sereni, E., and Young, J. Z. (1932). Nervous degeneration and regeneration in cephalopods. *Pubbl. staz. zool. Napoli* **12**, 173–208.

Simroth, H. (1928). *Gastropoda. In* Bronn's "Klassen und Ordnungen des Tierreichs," Vol. 3, Part 2. Akad. Verlagsges., Leipzig.

Singh, I. (1938a). Properties of tonic contractions produced by electrical stimulation of the anterior retractor of the byssus of *Mytilus edulis. J. Physiol. (London)* **94**, 1–12.

Singh, I. (1938b). The effects of calcium and some other factors on the excitability of the anterior retractor of the byssus of *Mytilus edulis*. *J. Physiol. (London)* **94**, 322–336.

Sprenkel, H. B. (1929). Nerve endings in the muscles of the arm of *Sepia officinalis*. *Koninkl. Ned. Akad. Wetenschap., Proc.* **32**, 151–155.

Takahashi, K. (1957). Propagation of relaxation in the tonically contracted anterior byssal retractor muscle of *Mytilus edulis*. *J. Fac. Sci. Univ. Tokyo, Sect. IV* **8**, 1–9.

Takahashi, K. (1960). Nervous control of contraction and relaxation in the anterior byssal retractor muscle of *Mytilus edulis*. *Annotationes Zool. Japon.* **33**, 67–84.

Tonomura, Y., Yagi, K., and Matsumiya, H. (1955). Contractile proteins from adductors of *Pecten*. Some enzymic and physicochemical properties. *Arch. Biochem. Biophys.* **59**, 76–89.

Twarog, B. M. (1954). Responses of a molluscan smooth muscle to acetylcholine and 5-hydroxytryptamine. *J. Cellular Comp. Physiol.* **44**, 141–164.

Twarog, B. M. (1959). The pharmacology of a molluscan smooth muscle. *Brit. J. Pharmacol.* **14**, 404–407.

Twarog, B. M. (1960a). Innervation and activity of a molluscan smooth muscle. *J. Physiol. (London)* **152**, 220–235.

Twarog, B. M. (1960b). Effects of acetylcholine and 5-hydroxytryptamine on the contraction of a molluscan smooth muscle. *J. Physiol. (London)* **152**, 236–242.

van Nieuwenhoven, S. J. (1947). An investigation into the structure and function of the anterior byssal retractor muscle of *Mytilus edulis* L. Ph.D. thesis, Utrecht.

von Uexküll, J. (1912). Studien über den Tonus. VI. Die Pilgermuschel. *Biol. Z.* **58**, 305–332.

Williams, L. W. (1910). "The Anatomy of the Common Squid, *Loligo pealii*," 87pp. Leiden.

Wilson, D. M. (1960). Nervous control of movement in cephalopods. *J. Exptl. Biol.* **37**, 57–72.

Winton, F. R. (1937). The changes in viscosity of an unstriated muscle (*Mytilus edulis*) during and after stimulation with alternating, interrupted and uninterrupted direct currents. *J. Physiol. (London)* **88**, 492–511.

Young, J. Z. (1938). The functioning of the giant nerve fibres of the squid. *J. Exptl. Biol.* **15**, 170–185.

CHAPTER 11

Special Effectors: Luminous Organs, Chromatophores, Pigments, and Poison Glands

J. A. C. NICOL

MARINE BIOLOGICAL LABORATORY, PLYMOUTH, ENGLAND

I. INTRODUCTION

The special effectors treated in this chapter are grouped for convenience, but it is also true that they are sometimes associated with one another and function synergistically in complex mechanisms. In this category are included chromatophores, pigment-secreting glands, luminous organs, poison and repugnatorial glands, and the cnidal sacs of æolid gastropods. These structures are chiefly, and in some instances exclusively, possessed by marine animals.

353

II. CHROMATOPHORES

Alterable chromatophores are found in most dibranchiate cephalopods and have been described in some pteropods.

A. Cephalopods

When pelagic and deep-sea cephalopods are considered, there are seen to be great variations in the chromatophore patterns of different species. Surface squids (e.g., *Stenoteuthis*) are richly colored by chromatophores, which are denser on the dorsal surface. *Calliteuthis*, from deep water, is reddish-brown; chromatophores are equally abundant on dorsal and ventral surfaces. Many of the deep-sea cranchiid squids, e.g., *Heterocranchia*, have only a few large brown chromatophores distributed over the surface, and sometimes aligned in transverse rows. The animal appears essentially colorless, except for an iridescent, glistening ink sac and visceral mass. In *Spirula*, the greater part of the mantle is devoid of pigment, but there are some colored areas, containing chromatophores, at the base of the fins and edge of the mantle. Squid from inshore waters (over the continental shelf and in the littoral zone) are well endowed with chromatophores, usually much more abundant on dorsal than on ventral surfaces.

Similarly, among octopods, there are deep-water species (e.g., *Cirroteuthis*) that have few or no chromatophores; these are transparent, gelatinous animals. Chromatophores are abundant in species of *Octopus* and *Eledone* from the neritic zone; again, they are much more densely distributed over the dorsal surface. *Vampyroteuthis* (Vampyromorpha) from deep waters is deep red-brown and black in color; presumably, this dark coloration is due to melanophores; deep-sea animals generally do not show color changes, but *Vampyroteuthis* may be an exception since the melanophores in preserved material sometimes show various degrees of contraction (Chun, 1910; Robson, 1925; Bruun, 1943; Pickford, 1946, 1949; Hardy, 1956).

Nautilus lacks chromatophores.

Chromatophores, in their expanded state, differ much in size. They are very small in *Sepia*, *Eledone* and *Octopus*, and especially large in *Sepiola*, *Ommastrephes*, and *Argonauta*, where they may be seen with the unaided eye (Fuchs, 1914; Parker, 1948).

1. STRUCTURE

Pigment cells in the skin of the cephalopods are of two kinds, chromatophores and iridocytes; only the former are alterable. Both lie in the dermis (Fig. 1).

Chromatophores are small flattened sacs, each a nucleated cell con-

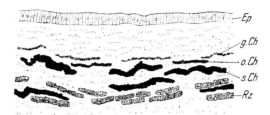

FIG. 1. Location of chromatophores and iridocytes in the skin of *Sepia officinalis* (vertical section). *Ep*, epidermis; *g.Ch*, yellow chromatophore; *o.Ch*, orange chromatophore; *s.Ch*, black chromatophore; *Rz*, iridocyte. (From Kühn and Heberdey, 1929.)

taining a bag of pigment and possessing an elastic bounding membrane (Fig. 2). From the equator of the disc there radiate contractile fibers:

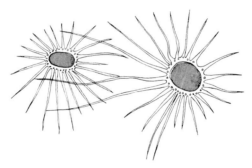

FIG. 2. Chromatophores in the skin of *Loligo vulgaris*. (Hofmann, 1907.)

these are smooth muscle cells, each with a nucleus at its base (Fig. 3). The muscular nature of the chromatophore fibers was finally demon-

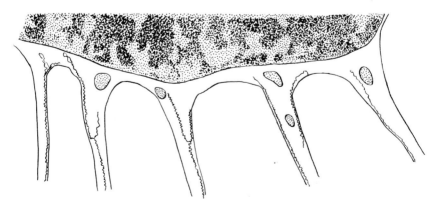

FIG. 3. Bases of radial muscle fibers and nerve endings on a chromatophore of *Loligo vulgaris*. (After Hofmann, 1907.)

strated by Steinach (1901). When the radial muscle fibers contract, they exert traction on the pigment cell and cause it to expand; when they relax, and cease pulling on the cell, the elastic membrane of the cell causes it to shrink. Expansion of the chromatophores causes the animal to darken or change color. When fully contracted, the chromatophores are reduced to mere points and have little influence on color or hue (Hofmann, 1907; Fuchs, 1914; Tompsett, 1939; Parker, 1948).

Iridocytes (= iridophores) are opaque reflecting cells lying beneath the chromatophores. They are flat, oval, and nucleated, and contain vertically disposed platelets of reflecting material arranged in convoluted chains. Those of *Sepia* show a chiefly greenish iridescence. This is a diffraction effect, produced by laminated guanine platelets (Parker, 1948).

2. Pigments

Chromatophores contain yellow, orange, red, red-brown, blue, violet-black or black pigments. (See Volume II, Chapter 4.) A squid, cuttlefish, or octopus may have an assemblage of differently colored chromatophores. Thus *Sepia* has yellow, orange, and black cells; *Stenoteuthis*, yellow, red, and blue cells. The color is due to pigments known as ommochromes, which belong to the class of phenoxazons. Ommochromes extracted from cuttlefish and octopods have broad absorption peaks in the visible range between about 425 and 525 mμ (oxidized, 450 mμ; reduced, 500–510 mμ) (Asano and Ito, 1955; Schwinck, 1956). Absorption spectra of single chromatophores in the skin of *Loligo* (fixed, reduced material) have maxima between 525 and 540 mμ (Fig. 4) (Bayer and Meyer-Arendt, 1959).

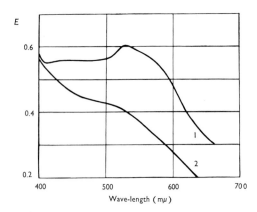

Fig. 4. Absorption spectra of a single pigment cell of *Loligo forbesi*, after reduction (curve 1) and oxidation (curve 2) for 24 hours. *E* is extinction (i.e., absorbance or optical density). (From Bayer and Meyer-Arendt, 1959.)

3. Physiology

Physiological work on chromatophores has been limited to those of easily procurable inshore species. Pelagic species also exhibit color changes, especially those which make vertical migrations and occur in surface waters, e.g., *Stenoteuthis* (Hardy, 1956). Bruun (1943) has recorded that the chromatophores of *Spirula*, a deep-water animal, contract when it is touched.

The various chromatophores, by virtue of their musculature, expand and contract very rapidly. Single contractions, produced by direct electrical stimulation, occur in 0.14–0.5 second in *Loligo* and in about 1 second in *Sepia*. With repetitive stimulation at short intervals the responses fuse, giving the appearance of clonus or tetanus; summation is nearly complete at a stimulation frequency of about 10 per second (Fig. 5). The response continues undiminished without fatigue for long

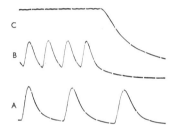

Fig. 5. Myograms from the chromatophores of *Sepia officinalis* (photoelectric recording). A. Single twitches, 45/min. B. Single twitches, partial summation, about 90/min, final relaxation. C. Nearly complete summation, 9.3 shocks/sec, final relaxation. Time marks, ⅓ sec. (Hill and Solandt, 1934.)

periods (30 minutes at a stimulation frequency of 30 per second). Strength-duration curves for the chromatophore response resemble those for fin nerve. In these preparations it is uncertain whether muscle fibers are being excited directly, or indirectly through the motor nerves (Bozler, 1931; Hill and Solandt, 1934).

The chromatophores are controlled by color centers in the brain, the lowermost of which lie in the subesophageal ganglia. The cell bodies of the nerve fibers innervating the chromatophore muscle fibers lie in the subesophageal ganglia, and the nerve fibers run, without interruption by synapses, directly to the chromatophore muscles. On reaching a radial muscle fiber, the motor fiber extends along its length and may branch near its termination (Fig. 3) (Hofmann, 1907; Boycott, 1953).

Fast chromatic changes are due to phasic contractions of radial muscle fibers, and are engendered by single or seriated motor impulses. This conclusion is derived from a comparison of normal responses with those produced by controlled electrical stimulation. When nervous excitation ceases the radial muscle fibers relax, the chromatophores shrink, and blanching occurs. This is the simplest explanation of the regulation of chromatic activity in cephalopods. Unfortunately, no investigation making use of electrical recording of nervous activity has been made to substantiate this conclusion (Parker, 1948).

Other kinds of tonic and autonomous activity remain to be explained. When a mantle nerve of a cephalopod is severed, the denervated area of skin blanches and ceases to exhibit the chromatic changes occurring elsewhere in the animal. In the course of a few days the denervated area becomes dark and remains in this condition until death ensues, when it blanches in common with the rest of the animal. The initial blanching would appear to be due to interruption of excitatory motor impulses, but contrary opinions must be noted. The persistent darkening which follows denervation is due to tonic contraction of radial muscle fibers or peripheral autotonus. According to one theory, peripheral autotonus is responsible for the normal contraction of the radial muscle fibers, producing chromatic darkening of the animal. Blanching is attributed to inhibition of peripheral tonus, and a category of inhibitory fibers in the mantle nerves is hypothesized for this function (Fuchs, 1914; ten Cate, 1928). In another explanation, by Fröhlich (1910), the late darkening of a denervated area is supposed to be the result of delayed excitation of the motor nerve following injury. Sereni (1930), however, has stated that the motor nerves have degenerated at this stage and no longer respond to stimulation, and he considered that the muscle fibers, deprived of their innervation, assume special properties.

In a third theory, by Bozler (1928, 1931), phasic and tonic contractions are produced by different parts of the muscle fiber. The muscle fibers are presumed to be doubly innervated, one kind of fiber regulating phasic, the other, tonic contraction.

Isolated pieces of skin also show peculiar changes. At first the skin blanches and then, after several hours, darkens. In some preparations the chromatophores begin to pulsate and waves of color change may pass over the skin. There are various explanations of these pulsations and the metachronism of the waves. Expansion of the chromatophores is usually attributed to heightening of peripheral autotonus. Pulsations and waves are believed to be governed by the refractory period of the muscle fibers, and by mutual and successive stimulation of one muscle fiber by another (ten Cate, 1928; Sereni, 1930).

The responses of cephalopod chromatophores to various salt solutions, drugs, and other chemicals have been investigated. In isolated skin, nicotine, choline, and acetylcholine cause expansion; tyramine increases excitability of the chromatophore muscles; serotonin (5-hydroxytryptamine) causes the chromatophores to contract. Drugs also act on the chromatic centers in the central nervous system, producing expansion or contraction of the chromatophores (Sereni, 1930; Kahr, 1959).

Hormonal control of chromatophores has been suggested. Sereni (1930) found that the octopus blanches when the posterior salivary glands are removed. When two octopuses are united in such a way that their circulatory systems become confluent, they both assume the same color; the result is more significant when the connection is made between individuals of different species which normally differ in coloration (Sereni, 1929). It has been suggested that hormones such as tyramine and serotonin, secreted by the posterior salivary glands, may affect the chromatic centers or act on the chromatophore muscles.

4. Function

Cephalopods differ greatly in their ability to change color. Chromatic alterations are simple in the common squid *Loligo vulgaris:* the animal is pallid white when swimming, and red-brown when disturbed, with a darker dorsal surface. *Stenoteuthis pteropus* shows color phases of silver-gray, orange, crimson, and purple (Boycott, 1953; Hardy, 1956).

Two kinds of chromatophores occur in *Octopus vulgaris:* yellow and reddish-brown. The octopus exhibits a considerable range of color phases and many kinds of striped and mottled patterns, described in detail by Cowdry (1911). Particular color phases accompany certain activities, e.g., swimming, feeding, etc.; others are evoked by certain stimuli; e.g., a mechanical blow, appearance of some swimming object, presence of another octopus, etc. To some extent the octopus changes hue and conforms with the brightness of the environment.

Equally complex are the color transformations of the cuttlefish *Sepia officinalis.* Some patterns noted by Holmes (1940) are: light mottled appearance when the animal is resting on sand; very dark upper body surface in a black environment; dark with a white square in a dark environment broken by a white object, etc. The chromatophores in *Sepia* are arranged in several layers (Fig. 1). In the outer there are yellow cells, in the middle, orange-red, and in the inner, brown cells. Below the chromatophores are the iridocytes. Contraction and expansion of these various chromatophores, acting in conjunction with the greenish iridescence of the underlying iridocytes, enable the cuttlefish to match the color of its surroundings to a limited extent (Kühn and Heberdey, 1929; Kühn, 1930, 1950; Holmes, 1940).

Color changes and behavior, and the influence of higher nervous centers on color response, are discussed in Volume II, Chapter 13.

B. Gastropods

Contractile chromatophores were described in various pteropods by Kölliker, Müller, and Gegenbaur over a century ago; few recent observations have been made upon them (see Fuchs, 1914 for early literature).

In *Cymbulia* (Thecosomata) there are a few red chromatophores on the wings. They pulsate, changing from large red spots to minute black points. When the animal is disturbed, the chromatophores expand at once, followed by contraction after a few seconds. These cells, as in cephalopods, are provided with radially arranged muscle fibers (Gegenbaur, 1855).

Gleba (= *Tiedemannia*) (Thecosomata) has two kinds of pigment cells in the parenchymatous tissue of the wings (Fig. 6). Cells of one type

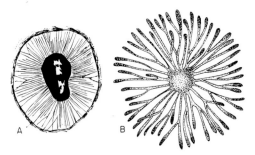

Fɪɢ. 6. Contractile pigment cells in *Gleba* (= *Tiedemannia*), a thecosomatous pteropod. A. Type 1, with attached contractile fibers. B. Type 2, stellate, with dispersible pigment. (After Gegenbaur, 1855.)

are lenticular, contain dark-brown pigment and are capable of contracting to minute black points and expanding again. Expansion is effected by the pull of radially arranged muscle fibers attached to the cell membrane. Speed of contraction is variable, from $\frac{1}{2}$ minute to $\frac{3}{4}$ hour or more. Cells of the second type are yellow and stellate, and the processes are branched and have swollen ends. The pigment may lie at one time in the cell body, at another in the processes, when the cell body appears colorless. Displacement of pigment is said to be due to some intracellular mechanism, and takes place very slowly. Some species of *Clione* (Gymnosomata) are also provided with chromatophores.

III. PIGMENT-SECRETING GLANDS

Many cephalopods discharge a black ink when disturbed, and some gastropods also discharge colored fluids.

A. Ink Gland of Cephalopods

An ink gland is present in many dibranchiate cephalopods. It is absent from *Nautilus* (Tetrabranchiata), *Vampyroteuthis* (Vampyromorpha), the bathypelagic octopods *Cirroteuthis* and *Opisthoteuthis*, and deep-water species of *Eledone* and *Octopus,* and is reduced in *Eledonella* (Bolitaenidae).

Girod (1882) made a detailed study of the ink apparatus of cephalopods. The ink gland lies in the dorsal wall of a large reservoir or vesicle situated in the ventral posterior wall of the visceral mass. The reservoir is connected by a long duct to the rectum, near the anus. Near its terminus the duct bears two circular sphincters enclosing a glandular ampulla. The gland contains a central colorless zone from which membranous trabeculae extend outward to the anterior and ventral parts. The trabeculae are covered with a glandular epithelium, consisting of cylindrical cells which have a basal nucleus, and a distal secretory zone containing black granules. These cells produce the black pigment or ink, which is released by breakdown of the distal zone. The ink escapes by an opening in the wall of the gland into the ink reservoir, where it is stored.

The supply of ink in the reservoir is maintained by continuous secretion in the gland. Ink is driven along the duct by peristalsis and enters the ampulla when the posterior sphincter relaxes. When discharge of ink takes place, the anterior sphincter relaxes and the ampulla contracts, thus driving ink into the rectum and from thence into the mantle cavity, from which it is expelled through the funnel.

The ink gland is innervated by a nerve of unknown function from the gastric ganglion. The ink sac is supplied by a branch of the visceral nerve which controls its contraction (Tompsett, 1939).

The secretion of the ink gland is a colorless fluid containing a suspension of dark-brown or black particles. The pigment, "sepia," is a typical melanin, possibly conjoined to protein (D. L. Fox, 1953; Asano and Ito, 1955).

When a cephalopod, such as a cuttlefish, is alarmed it darts backward, at the same time expelling ink from its funnel. Presumably, the ink contains some mucus carrier, for it does not diffuse readily, but persists for some time as a concentrated patch in the water. It is believed that the cloud of ink acts as a decoy to engage the attention of an enemy while the cuttlefish changes to a concealing color and shoots away (Hall, 1956).

B. *Purple Secretions of Gastropods*

1. PROSOBRANCHS

Purple secretions are produced by the hypobranchial glands of many prosobranch gastropods. Of these, the best known is the purple dye (purpurin, etc.) of the Muricacea—species of *Murex* and *Nucella* (or *Thais = Purpura*); a similar dye is secreted by *Mitra.* The dye is produced in the medial zone of the hypobranchial gland; in this region, the secretory epithelium bears colorless or yellow-green cells containing granular spherules. These are supposed to be the formative material of the purple chromogen. The secretion contains mucus, a photosensitive chromogen, and an odoriferous material. Under the influence of light the chromogen, initially colorless, becomes transformed into blue and red indigoid pigments. The malodorous substances are simpler mercaptans, believed to be associated with the production of chromogen.

Little is known about the physiology and biological significance of this purple secretion. It is produced when the snail is irritated or stimulated, and is said to be especially abundant during the reproductive season. It has been suggested that the odoriferous component in the secretion acts as a chemical attractant between the sexes (Lederer, 1940; D. L. Fox, 1953; Bouchilloux and Roche, 1954a,b, 1955; H. M. Fox and Vevers, 1960).

Molluscan pigments are treated in detail in Volume II, Chapter 4.

The pelagic snail *Ianthina* discharges a purple material from the hypobranchial gland when irritated, and also, periodically, when feeding upon *Velella*. This secretion may have a paralyzing effect upon the nematocysts of the latter. The chemical nature of the dye has still to be established (Wilson and Wilson, 1956). The littoral snail *Clathrus* also produces a purple dye.

2. Purple Gland of Sea Hares (Aplysiidae)

The sea hare *Aplysia* (Anaspidea) secretes an unstable red dye, aplysiopurpurin. This is produced in a purple gland in the mantle shelf. The organ consists of large unicellular glands opening by numerous ducts into the mantle cavity. The dye contains chromoproteins, the prosthetic groups of which are bilins, similar to urobilin. *Aplysia* purple bears only a superficial resemblance to the purple secretion of *Murex*. A great deal of mucus is secreted with the dye, which mixes slowly with sea water (Lederer, 1940; D. L. Fox, 1953; Christomanos, 1955; Winkler, 1959; H. M. Fox and Vevers, 1960).

Aplysia, when irritated discharges its purple dye after an interval of a few seconds. Supposedly the dye forms a screen, under cover of which the animal makes a retreat, but under what circumstances and from what enemies we are not told (Eales, 1921).

An opaline gland (poison gland, etc.), lying in the floor of the pallial cavity, discharges a milky acrid fluid into the latter space. The gland contains large unicellular vesicles resembling mucous cells. The output of the gland becomes mixed with the purple secretion and, in the Mediterranean *A. dipilans*, at least, has a nauseating fetid odor supposed to be protective (Eales, 1921).

The purple secretion emitted by *Akera* (Cephalaspidea) is possibly related to aplysiopurpurin. This mollusc has purple and opaline glands corresponding to those of *Aplysia* (Morton and Holme, 1955).

IV. LUMINOUS ORGANS

A. Introduction

In many ways the molluscs epitomize the entire gamut of animal luminescence. Fascinating as such diversity within the limits of a single phylum may be, it makes the task of condensing available information formidable. Three modes of luminescence are found among molluscs, viz., intracellular, extracellular, and bacterial. In the first two categories luminescence is intrinsic, i.e., it depends on the animal's own biochemical processes and it takes place within luminescent cells or photocytes (intracellular luminescence), or it results from the discharge of a luminous secretion (extracellular luminescence). The third category refers to animals that harbor symbiotic luminous bacteria. These three modes of luminescence are treated on a phyletic and a functional basis.

B. Intracellular Luminescence

1. GASTROPODS

Several littoral snails are luminous, but little is known about their habits and luminescent organs. *Tonna* shines when moving about, apparently spontaneously, whereas *Planaxis* emits light only when strongly stimulated. The luminous region of the latter animal occupies an elongated band in the dorsal mantle, and contains folds of luminescent tissue (Turner, 1948; Haneda, 1955, 1958).

The pelagic nudibranch *Phylliroe bucephala* emits flashes of light when mechanically stimulated. The light appears either as a weak diffuse glow over body and tentacles, or as a bright luminescence from many small points, especially in the posterior third of the body.

There is considerable diversity of opinion concerning the photocytes of *Phylliroe*. Panceri (1873) originally ascribed luminescence to large spherical cells containing a refractive yellow body, the Müller cells, and to peripheral ganglion cells. Basophile mucous cells and eosinophile glandular cells in the surface epithelium have also been linked with luminescence. Most workers have regarded the Müller cells as photocytes. Whether the light is truly intracellular, or whether a brief flash takes place at the moment when secretion is expelled, is still uncertain. There is little doubt that luminescence is under nervous control, but no unanimity exists about the innervation (Harvey, 1952).

A littoral nudibranch, *Kaloplocamus ramosum*, when irritated emits flashes of light from dendritic processes on head and trunk. The large luminous cells below the surface epithelium contain gross eosinophilic granules, and are innervated. This tissue appears to be of a different nature from that of *Plocamophorus*, which produces an extracellular secretion (Kato, 1949).

A terrestrial pulmonate *Diakia* has a small light organ in the anterior region of the foot, through the translucent tissues of which the light shines. The photocytes are large cells; bioluminescence is spontaneous and intermittent (Haneda, 1955).

2. Cephalopods

Spirula has a small bead-like light organ at the posterior extremity of the mantle; it shines continuously (Schmidt, 1922). In a circular swelling surrounding the organ Herfurth (1936) found large columnar epithelial cells containing abundant secretory granules.

Photophores occur in many pelagic squids, are sometimes very numerous, and are situated in the most diverse positions—on the arms and tentacles, head, eyeball, margin of the orbit, funnel, mantle, fins, and mantle cavity. Each species has its own particular pattern of light organs, and there is much diversity of structure; nevertheless, there are some family resemblances in the organization of photophores. Much information has been summarized and tabulated by Berry (1920).

Of simple structure are the subocular photophores of cranchiid squids (*Cranchia, Liocranchia, Leachia*). These range from simple epithelial folds to invaginated masses of photogenic cells that have lost contact with the surface epithelium. Hardly more complex are the tentacular organs of *Lycoteuthis*. These have a central mass of photocytes, a reflector or tapetum, and a pigment backing; the whole is surrounded by a connective tissue sheath (Chun, 1910).

In Chiroteuthids (*Mastigoteuthis, Chiroteuthis*), the ventral and integumentary photophores contain a small mass of photocytes lying in a capillary network. Bounding the organ is a fibrous reflector (or tapetum) and a layer of chromatophores; the interior is filled with some kind of gelatinous tissue (Chun, 1910).

The large arm photophores of enoploteuthids (*Watasenia, Abraliopsis*) have a large central mass of photogenic cells lying in a meshwork of blood vessels. A photophore is invested by a connective tissue mantle and a layer of chromatophores. Integumentary (or cutaneous) organs of enoploteuthids are complex, possessing photocytes, reflector, lens, and chromatophore sheath. The reflector consists of concentrically arranged, long fibrous cells. Lying over the photogenic tissue is a lens of fibrous or reticular connective tissue (*Watasenia, Abraliopsis, Enoploteuthis*).

Ocular light organs of enoploteuthids and chiroteuthids have another pattern, consisting of basal reflector, photogenic mass, and an external coronal apparatus. The latter is made up of long fibrous cells radiating fanwise from the photogenic tissue, and serving as a lens (*Enoploteuthis, Chiroteuthis*, etc.) (Chun, 1910; Grimpe and Hoffmann, 1921; Mortara, 1921; Kishitani, 1932).

Many other kinds of photophores, of equal or greater complexity, have been described and illustrated. In *Calliteuthis* (Histioteuthidae) the integumentary organ contains a single layer of elongated photocytes arranged in radial fashion (Fig. 7). A reflector of scale-like cells and a

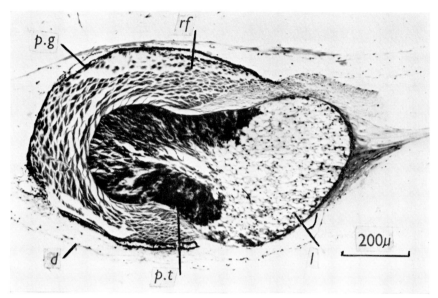

Fig. 7. Section through an integumentary photophore of *Calliteuthis reversa*. *d*, skin; *l*, lens; *p.g*, pigment backing; *p.t*, photogenic tissue; *rf*, reflector.

pigment layer surround the photogenic tissue. Externally is a lens, which extends as a core into the center of the photogenic layer. The photophore lies oblique to the surface, and above it is a concave mirror facing externally, from which light is directed to the exterior. The anal organs of *Lycoteuthis* and *Pyroteuthis* also possess complex arrangements of lenses, reflectors, and shutters (Chun, 1910; Mortara, 1921; Grimpe and Hoffmann, 1921).

Some features of squid photophores call for special comment. In many species they are situated largely or wholly on ventral surfaces, and the light is directed downward. Light emission is occasionally indirect: the arm photophores of *Chiroteuthis*, for example, are oriented away from the surface and the light must shine through the tissues of the arm to reach the exterior. Squid photophores are sometimes innervated (*Lycoteuthis, Calliteuthis, etc.*) Chromatophores which extend over the external surface of the light organs can act as a movable screen. It is curious that three kinds of light organs are situated on the ink sac of Decacera, viz., the bacterial and secretory light organs of sepiolids and *Loligo,* and the intracellular photophores of some oegopsids.

C. Extracellular Luminescence

1. GASTROPODS

Extracellular luminescence occurs in two groups of gastropods: Polyceridae (nudibranchs), and Ancylidae (pulmonates).

a. Polyceridae. In *Plocamophorus* luminous flashes are given off which are transmitted progressively along the body. Luminous regions are the dorsal crest, veil, dorsal processes, gills, and tail edges. Strong mechanical stimulation provokes the animal into swimming, and a cloud of luminous material is discharged (*P. ocellatus*). Luminescence is associated with tall columnar cells in the surface epithelium and in luminous sacs in the dorsolateral processes (Harvey, 1952).

b. Ancylidae. *Latia neritoides* has the distinction of being the only known luminous fresh-water animal, apart from aquatic glowworms. When disturbed, it emits a profuse luminous secretion from the mantle groove. The luminous tissue consists of large secretory cells on the head surface, anterior tentacles, lateral surfaces of the foot, inferior pallial lobe, and free surface of the mantle. Two cell types are present, both implicated in the luminous response (Bowden, 1950).

2. BIVALVES

Extracellular luminescence is encountered in two families of bivalves, viz., the Gastrochaenidae (*Gastrochaena*) and the Pholadidae (*Pholas* and *Barnea*). The luminescent glands lie in the siphons or mantle cavity into which the luminous material is secreted. In *Pholas dactylus*, the species which has received most attention, the luminescent tissue comprises a pair of cords extending along the inhalant siphon, two triangular patches at the base of the siphon, and a cord extending around the anterior and ventral edge of the mantle (Panceri, 1872). *Barnea candida* possesses two triangular organs at the base of the siphon (Okada, 1927b); *Gastrochaena grandis* has a luminescent stripe around the ventral pallial margin (Haneda, 1955).

The histology of the luminous organs of *P. dactylus* has been investigated repeatedly. Beneath is a layer of large mucous cells and, deeper still, a layer of photogenic cells (Fig. 8). The mucous and the photogenic cells discharge individually at the surface between the epithelial cells. Two types of granular cells have been distinguished in the photogenic layer. The secretory granules contain protein and polysaccharide as mucoprotein or glycoprotein (Bassot, 1959; Nicol, 1960).

3. CEPHALOPODS

Sepiolids with an extracellular luminous mechanism are *Heteroteuthis dispar* and *Sepiolina nipponensis*. The luminous gland is partially em-

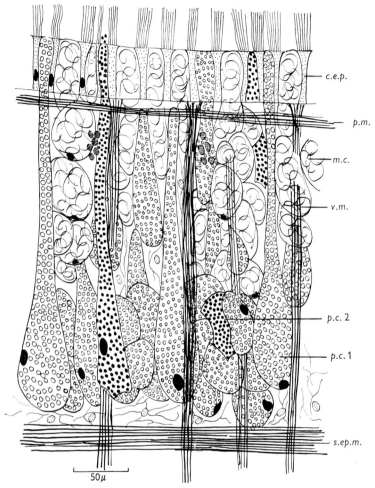

FIG. 8. Section through a light organ of *Pholas dactylus*. *c.e.p.*, ciliated epithelium; *p.m.*, subepithelial muscle; *m.c.*, mucous cell; *v.m.*, vertical muscle; *p.c.1* and *p.c.2*, photocytes types 1 and 2.

bedded in the ink sac and, when the animal is stimulated mechanically, a luminous secretion is released into the mantle cavity and is expelled through the funnel.

The gland opens into the mantle cavity by two pores or short ducts, each guarded by a muscular papilla. The interior is folded, partially dividing it into chambers or alveoli. The epithelium lining the interior is single layered and cuboidal, and the cavities contain granules or corpuscles. Bounding the light body is a connective tissue sheath containing spindle-shaped elements. The sheath behind the organ is regarded as a reflector, and between the light body and reflector is a thick mass of net-like cells. On the ventral surface there are muscle fibers, and two lenticular structures of a fibrous nature at the sides of the light organ have been termed lenses (Skowron, 1926; Okada, 1927a; Herfurth, 1936; Haneda, 1956). However, there seems to be general agreement that no light is emitted from the organ, and the significance of accessory structures—reflector and lens—is obscure.

D. Bacterial Light Organs

1. Sepiolidae

Light organs containing symbiotic luminous bacteria occur in the mantle cavity of some sepiolids, partially embedded in the ink sac (Fig. 9).

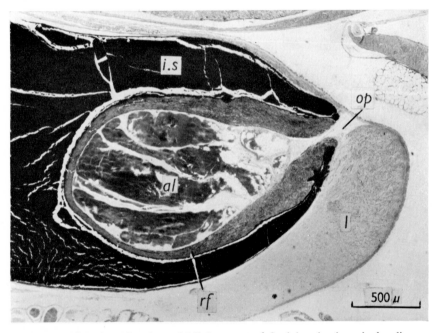

Fig. 9. Section through a bacterial light organ of *Sepiola atlantica*. *al*, alveoli containing luminous bacteria; *i.s*, ink sac; *l*, lens; *op*, opening or duct into light organ; *rf*, reflector.

They are paired—*Sepiola, Euprymna*—or fused to a single organ—*Rondeletia*. In *S. atlantica*, for example, the light-organs appear as ear-shaped masses, having an iridescent sheen when fresh. The lining is greatly folded and these folds of epithelium and connective tissue form septa which divide the lumen into compartments. The epithelium is simple and columnar. The lumen contains granular material in which rod-shaped bacteria have been recognized. Each light organ is bounded by a reflector layer containing platelets or scales oriented concentrically about the light sac. Lying below the light organ is a large lens which contains vacuolar connective tissue cells and fibers (Okada, 1927a; Kishitani, 1932; Herfurth, 1936; Buchner, 1953).

2. LOLIGINIDAE

Bacterial light organs, similar to those of sepiolids, have been described in Japanese specimens of *Loligo edulis*. There are two organs, partially embedded in the ink sac, one on either side of the rectum. Each consists of three parts, the luminous tissue, a reflector backing, and an external lens. The alveoli within contain luminous bacteria. The reflector is formed by the inner layer of the ink sac and consists of connective tissue containing rhomboid elements. A transparent gelatinous lens lies over the light organ, the lumen of which opens into the mantle cavity by a duct that penetrates the lens (Okada, 1927a; Kishitani, 1932).

Luminous bacteria have been isolated and cultured from the light organs of many of these squid, and from the accessory nidamental glands and the body surface. The bacteria have been named and their bacteriological properties and light emission described. The bacteria are rod or coccus forms, motionless or motile, and provided with a terminal cilium (Kishitani, 1932; Harvey, 1952).

E. Biochemistry of Luminescence

Pholas dactylus was one of the first animals in which the luciferin-luciferase reaction was demonstrated. Dried luminous organs of *Pholas* emit light when moistened. Two principles are resolved when an aqueous solution is treated as follows: (1) A sample is heated (100° dropping to 70°C), whereupon light emission stops; (2) a sample is allowed to stand at room temperature until luminescence fades away. On mixing samples (1) and (2) light appears. Sample (1) contains luminescent substrate or luciferin; sample (2), an enzyme, luciferase, which catalyzes the luminescent reaction. The luminescent reaction depends upon molecular oxygen (Harvey, 1952); ATP (adenosine triphosphate) is not involved (Haneda and Harvey, 1953). The luciferin-luciferase reaction has been demonstrated, additionally, in *Gastrochaena grandis*, a bivalve (Haneda, 1955), and in *Latia neritoides*, a pulmonate (Bowden, 1950).

Properties of crude *Pholas* luciferin were established by Dubois (1928), who showed that it is oxidized, with emission of light, in the presence of *Pholas* luciferase and molecular oxygen, and by a wide range of oxidizing agents. *Pholas* luciferase has properties of a protein and an enzyme (Harvey, 1952).

An indication of the nature of the *Pholas* luciferin-luciferase system is provided by Plesner (1959). A nonluminous enzyme extract was prepared by treating an aqueous solution of acetone-dried powder with an adsorbent and allowing to stand until light emission ceased. Enzyme-free extracts were obtained by heating an aqueous solution of acetone powder to 100°C. Enzyme extracts emitted light when mixed with boiled extract, or with FMN (flavin mononucleotide) + DPNH (diphosphopyridine nucleotide). FMN alone was not effective. These results suggest that the luminescent system of *Pholas* is akin to that of bacteria, in which light emission involves the oxidation of an aldehyde complex of $FMNH_2$ (reduced flavin mononucleotide) by bacterial luciferase (Strehler, 1955). In the bacterial system, *in vitro*, FMN is reduced to $FMNH_2$ by DPNH, and it seems that the same agencies are involved in the *Pholas* luminescent system. The participation of additional factors, such as a long-chain aldehyde and a coenzyme, is not excluded by the evidence available.

F. Physiology

Very little is known about the physiology and regulation of molluscan light organs.

1. Extracellular Luminescence

Light emission is continuous in *Spirula* (Schmidt, 1922), and intermittent in many oegopsid squid. Since the photophores of the latter are sometimes innervated, they may be subject to direct nervous control. Chromatophores, lying over the light organs, act as movable screens. The skin organs of *Watasenia* respond to electrical stimulation. The "fin" light organs of *Vampyroteuthis* are provided with a chromatophore screen and a movable lid (Pickford, 1946, 1949).

2. Intracellular Luminescence

Dubois (1928), who made an intensive study of *Pholas*, concluded that the light organs receive both excitatory and inhibitory fibers from a reflex center in the visceral ganglion. It is generally maintained, without convincing evidence, that the luminous secretions of gastropods and bivalves are expelled by muscular contraction.

The literature contains various observations on the effects of different salts, changes of pH, changes of temperature, etc., on luminescence (Harvey, 1952).

G. Color, Spectral Characteristics, and Intensity

Observations on the color and spectral characteristics of lights of molluscs are limited. In many instances the light is blue, e.g., in the prosobranch *Planaxis*, in the nudibranch *Plocamophorus*, in the lamel-

libranch *Pholas*, and in some oegopsid squid (blue or blue-white). The
light of sepioid squid containing luminous bacteria is also blue. The
luminous secretion of sepiolids is described as blue or green, and that of
the pulmonate *Latia* is green. In *Spirula* and some oegopsid squids the
photophores emit a yellow light. Indeed, in some species of squid there
are lights of several colors; thus, the brachial organs of *Watasenia scintil-
lans* emit blue light and the mantle (skin organs) yellow light. In *Thau-
matolampas diadema*, the lights of the various photophores are white,
"pearly" (pale blue-green?), and red, the last color being very rare in
the luminescence of marine animals (Schmidt, 1922; Kishitani, 1932;
Bowden, 1950; Harvey, 1952, 1955; Haneda, 1955).

A relative spectral emission curve (*a*) for the light of *Pholas dactylus*
is shown in Fig. 10. Emission extends from about 440 to 670 mμ, with a

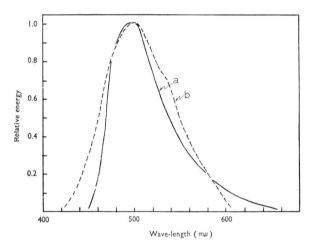

Fig. 10. Spectral emission curves for the luminous secretion of *Pholas dactylus*
(*a*) and for the light of a culture of luminous bacteria from sepioids (*b*) (Curve
a from Nicol, 1960; curve *b* from de Lerma, 1947.)

maximum at 490 mμ (Nicol, 1958). Half the energy emitted lies between
480 and 520 mμ. Cultures of luminous bacteria from *Sepia* and *Sepiola*
emit light in the range 420 to 610 mμ, with a peak at 500 mμ, as shown
in curve (*b*) of Fig. 10. Half the energy is found in the range 470 to
530 mμ (de Lerma, 1947).

The intensity of the luminescence of *P. dactylus* is given as 1/100
"bougie" (candle) (Dubois, 1928) and is almost certainly an overestimate.

H. *Ethological Considerations*

Although considerable advances are being made in the knowledge and
appreciation of the functional role of luminescence in the lives of marine

animals, relatively little information is as yet available for molluscs (Clarke and Denton, 1962).

1. LUMINESCENCE AND VISION

The blue lights of marine molluscs are of a spectral quality that matches the spectral sensitivity of the eyes of marine animals, notably the blue or blue-green photosensitive visual pigments of marine invertebrates and fishes. But beyond this generalization it is difficult to go because quantitative data are wanting and we do not know, in many instances, how the animals use their lights. The spectral emission curve and the spectral sensitivity curve of *Pholas* cover approximately the same range—around 440–640 mμ—but there is no correspondence of maxima and, indeed, no certainty that pholades employ photic signals for mutual stimulation (Nicol, 1958). The rhodopsin of a squid (species not specified) shows maximal absorption in the blue-green at 493 mμ (Hubbard and St. George, 1958). The lights of cephalopods are blue, yellow-green, yellow, and, in one instance, red. The behavioral significance, if any, of a red light is obscure since it is unlikely that deep-sea squid or, for that matter, other deep-sea animals, have color vision.

There is no information for luminous intensities and visual thresholds among molluscs.

2. BEHAVIOR

Since luminous mollusca are varied, live in many kinds of environments, and differ greatly in behavior, one might expect that luminescence would have different roles.

Squid that discharge a luminous secretion when irritated probably succeed in distracting temporarily the attention of potentially dangerous animals. There are no published accounts describing luminescence of sepiolids containing luminous bacteria; apparently, no one has seen the intact animal emit light, or has seen light coming from the light organ. The few positive references concern luminous material obtained by squeezing the organ or cutting it open. According to Haneda (1959), Hamabe (of Nikonkai-ku Fisheries Institution, Niigata City, Japan) has observed luminescence in a Japanese *Loligo*: in the mating season, when the male stimulates the female, her body becomes translucent and emits light. There is also a curious account of luminescence in *Sepia officinalis* (Girod, 1882). During the mating period, the females were observed to swim at the surface at night, emitting light, and males lurking on the bottom among the rocks would rush at them like luminous arrows. *Sepia officinalis* is not generally regarded as luminous and no luminous organ has been described.

Presumably, the highly developed and complex patterns of photophores of oegopsid squid, like those of fishes, are employed in signaling between the sexes, during schooling, vertical migration, etc.

V. POISON GLANDS

A. *Gastropods*

1. VENOM GLAND OF CONE SHELLS

A poison gland is present in most species of Conidae, Turridae, and Terebridae (suborder Toxiglossa). In these animals the radula is modified as a biting organ, permitting the injection of poison into the victim. Marginal teeth of the radula are elongate and spear-shaped; in the Conidae and Terebridae the lateral and median teeth have disappeared. The large poison gland opens into the pharynx by a long duct. It is not certain how the poison is introduced into the victim; possibly it is simply injected, by contraction of the muscular proboscis, into the wound produced by the stab of the radular teeth.

Cones and related forms are most active at night. They feed upon molluscs and possibly other animals that become available, since fish have been found in the gut. The poison is used primarily for paralyzing the prey before feeding; soft parts and juices of the victim are sucked through the long proboscis. The poison gland is used secondarily for defense. The bite of the cone is extremely painful, and there are recorded cases of death in man, resulting from the bite of species of *Conus*. The secretion has a curare-like action, blocking neuromuscular transmission. Several active principles are present, including protein, quaternary ammonium compounds, and possibly amines (Clench, 1946; Fish and Cobb, 1954; Kline, 1956; Kohn, 1958; Martoja, 1960; Kohn *et al.*, 1960).

2. HYPOBRANCHIAL GLAND OF WHELKS (RACHIGLOSSA)

The hypobranchial or purple gland of the Muricidae yields, in addition to chromogens, poisonous extracts which have curare-like properties and which produce paralysis of cold-blooded animals (crabs, fish, frogs). The glands are rich in choline esters having high acetylcholine equivalence. In various species of *Murex* and in *Thais lapillarus* (Muricidae), the principal active choline ester is murexine or urocanylcholine [β-(imidazolyl-(4)-acrylcholine)]. In *T. floridana* the active ester is β,β-dimethylacrylyl-choline (senecioyl choline); acrylylcholine occurs in the hypobranchial gland of *Buccinum* (Buccinidae), a nonpurple secreting whelk. Also, enteramine (= 5-hydroxytryptamine) occurs in the hypobranchial gland of *Murex* (Erspamer and Benati, 1953a,b; Vialli, 1954; Bouchilloux and Roche, 1954a,b, 1955; Keyl *et al.*, 1957; Courville *et al.*, 1958; Briggs, 1960; Whittaker, 1960).

Urocanylcholine, besides having certain properties in common with acetylcholine, is also an effective neuromuscular blocking agent. It has been suggested that the hypobranchial gland of *Murex* is a venom gland, and its secretion (murexine) is used to poison the prey upon which it feeds; that is, it is used to bring about relaxation of the closing muscles of mussels and other bivalves. This explanation is not in accordance with the generally accepted account of the feeding habits of these whelks, which gain access to the soft parts of their prey by boring a hole through the shell with the radula, and inserting the proboscis through the aperture. An external function for these choline esters has still to be established (Keyl *et al.*, 1957).

3. Salivary Gland of Whelks

The salivary glands of the whelk *Neptunea* (Buccinidae) contain a quaternary ammonium base, tetramine (tetramethyl-ammonium hydroxide), which is secreted as a salt. This is a toxic substance with curare-like properties, paralyzing motor-nerve endings. Injected into fish it causes convulsions, then death, and it has been responsible for cases of food poisoning in Japan when *Neptunea* has been eaten. The salivary secretion is probably employed by *Neptunea* for poisoning animals upon which it feeds (Asano and Ito, 1960; Fänge, 1960).

4. Repugnatorial Glands

Such glands are widely distributed among gastropods and, by secreting acid or bitter-tasting materials, they render the animal distasteful to potential predators. Acid glands occur in prosobranchs (*Lamellaria*, *Velutina*), in many opisthobranchs, and in a marine pulmonate (*Oncidium*). In the first two groups, acid is secreted from the general surface of the mantle, the foot, and from buccal acid glands, depending on the species. It is produced in ciliated epidermal cells or in large subepidermal "sacs." The secretion contains a mixture of HCl and H_2SO_4 (*Pleurobranchus*), of pH 1. Other opisthobranchs discharge bitter secretions from glands aggregated in dorsal papillae (Thompson and Slinn, 1959; Thompson, 1960a,b).

Oncidium produces an acid, bitter secretion, of pH 2.7, in large glands aggregated about the mantle edge. The discharge is expelled through the air with considerable force by contraction of ensheathing muscles when the animal is irritated. The reaction is a nervously controlled reflex (Arey, 1937; Arey and Barrick, 1942). *Trimusculus* may also possess such glands (Yonge, 1958).

B. Salivary Glands of Cephalopods

Cephalopods, with the exception of *Nautilus*, possess three sets of salivary glands which open into the buccal cavity, viz., the sublingual, the anterior salivary, and the posterior salivary glands. All consist of secretory tubules in a connective tissue matrix. Secretory cells of the several glands are similar; they are columnar, and the secretion, appearing as a globule in the distal region of the cell, is discharged into the lumen of the tubule (Tompsett, 1939; Halstead, 1959).

The function of the sublingual gland is unknown. The other salivary glands contain some toxin and cardioinhibitory and vasopressor substances. The toxin is secreted primarily from the posterior salivary glands; the anterior salivary glands are smaller and their secretions, seemingly, less important. The secretion of the octopus is especially virulent: it poisons crabs, crayfish, and frogs, the toxin or toxins affecting the central nervous system. Injected into the shore crab *Carcinus maenas*, the poison from *Octopus* produces paralysis of the limbs, succeeded by twitching, and death ensues after a few minutes. The posterior salivary glands of the octopus contain various indolic and phenolic amines—tyramine, 5-hydroxytryptamine, octopamine—acetylcholine, proteolytic enzymes, and a toxin, cephalotoxin, which may be a glycoprotein. The various amines have excitatory effects on the central nervous system of crustacea, but the cephalotoxin causes paralysis. These substances are secreted into the saliva, and tyramine and 5-hydroxytryptamine appear in the perfusate of stimulated posterior salivary glands. Since the last two compounds are secreted internally, a hormonal role has been suggested for them (Bacq and Ghiretti, 1951, 1953; Vialli, 1954; Courville et al., 1958; Ghiretti, 1960; Hartman et al., 1960; Schiff, 1962). The bite of an octopus causes pain and localized swelling in man, and has proved fatal on at least one occasion (Halstead, 1959).

An octopus, feeding on crabs, has two ways of dealing with its prey: either it breaks it open with its beak at once, or poisons it with the secretion of the posterior salivary glands, before devouring it. It seems that when an octopus seizes a crab, its arms, web, and mouth, together with the carapace of the crab, are arranged to form a watertight compartment, into which the saliva is discharged. The toxin is then absorbed by the crab. Alternatively, the octopus may open the crab with its beak, aided by the radula, and inject saliva into its prey. The saliva, containing digestive enzyme (protease) and poison, paralyzes the crab and liquefies the soft parts (Wilson, 1935; MacGinitie, 1938; MacGinitie and MacGinitie, 1949; Courville et al., 1958).

VI. CNIDAL SACS OF AEOLIDS

Many aeolid nudibranchs, e.g., *Coryphella*, *Facelina*, *Eolidina*, and *Aeolidia*, possess batteries of nematocysts, which they obtain from coelenterates on which they feed. The nematocysts are located in pockets or

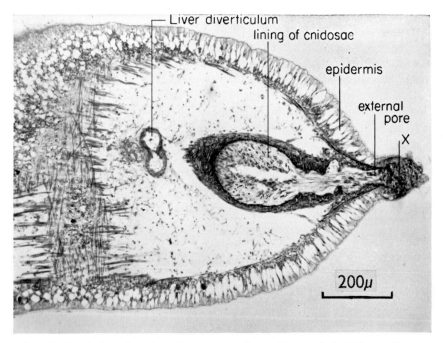

FIG. 11. Vertical section through a ceras and a cnidosac of *Aeolidia papillosa*. *x*, mucous plug, containing nematocysts, in the external pore of the cnidosac. Photograph by A. G. Best.

cnidal sacs in the tips of the dorsal papillae or cerata (Fig. 11). In aeolids the tubules of the digestive gland are situated in the cerata; each tubule connects basally with the stomach, and distally it leads into a cnidal sac. The cnidal sac can be regarded as a specialized portion of the liver tubule; a narrow canal between the liver tubule and the sac is guarded by a sphincter muscle, and a terminal orifice leads to the exterior. Within the lumen of the sac is an epithelial lining consisting of vacuolated, granular cells containing nematocysts.

The cnidae of aeolids are ingested with their food, the cnidoblast walls are dissolved, but the nematocysts themselves resist the action of the digestive juices of the sea slug. From the gut they pass into the liver tubules, and thence into the cnidal sacs; here they are ingested by the epithelial cells, and oriented so that their opercular ends face the lumen of the sac.

Most of the nematocysts are ingested undischarged; it is not known how the sea slug achieves this. Graham (1938), discussing this problem, suggests that the abundant mucus, secreted by the nudibranch, may have some deterrent action. The nematocysts, in the cells of the cnidal sac, have lost some part of their normal excitatory equipment, and they discharge when a ceras is squeezed or torn off as the result of some mechanical stimulus or action. The threads are shot out into the lumen and through the orifice of the sac.

Nematocysts confer some protection against certain predators. Fish, encountering a nudibranch for the first time, reject it; nudibranchs, placed among crabs, are left alone, but other molluscs are devoured (Naville, 1926; Graham, 1938; Kepner, 1943; Fischer, 1950).

REFERENCES

Arey, L. B. (1937). The physiology of the repugnatorial glands of *Onchidium*. *J. Exptl. Zool.* **77**, 251–286.

Arey, L. B., and Barrick, L. E. (1942). The structure of the repugnatorial glands of *Onchidium floridanum*. *J. Morphol.* **71**, 493–521.

Asano, M., and Ito, M. (1955). Biochemical studies on the *Octopus*. II. Pigments of the integument and ink sac of *Octopus*. *Tôhoku J. Agr. Research* **6**, 147–158.

Asano, M., and Ito, M. (1960). Salivary poison of a marine gastropod, *Neptunea arthritica* Bernardi, and the seasonal variation of its toxicity. *Ann. N.Y. Acad. Sci.* **90**, 674–688.

Bacq, Z. M., and Ghiretti, F. (1951). La sécretion externe et interne des glandes postérieures des Céphalopodes octopodes. *Bull. acad. roy. Belg., Classe sci.* **37**, 79–102.

Bacq, Z. M., and Ghiretti, F. (1953). Physiologie des glandes salivaires postérieures des Céphalopodes octopodes isolées et prefersées *in vitro*. *Publ. staz. zool. Napoli* **24**, 267–277.

Bassot, J.-M. (1959). Caractères histo-chimiques des organes photogènes du siphon chez *Pholas dactylus* (L.). *Compt. rend. acad. sci.* **249**, 1267–1269.

Bayer, M., and Meyer-Arendt, J. (1959). Redox absorption spectra from single pigment cells of squid. *Science* **129**, 644.

Berry, S. S. (1920). Light production in cephalopods, I, II. *Biol. Bull.* **38**, 141–195.

Bouchilloux, S., and Roche, J. (1954a). Sur le pourpre des *Murex* et ses précurseurs. *Compt. rend. soc. biol.* **148**, 1583–1587.

Bouchilloux, S., and Roche, J. (1954b). Sur les prochromogènes et les pigments purpuriques de *Murex trunculus* Linné. *Compt. rend. soc. biol.* **148**, 1732–1734.

Bouchilloux, S., and Roche, J. (1955). Contribution à l'étude biochimique de la pourpre des *Murex*. *Bull. inst. océanogr. Monaco* **52**, No. 1054, 23 pp.

Bowden, B. J. (1950). Some observations on a luminescent freshwater limpet from New Zealand. *Biol. Bull.* **99**, 373–380.

Boycott, B. B. (1953). The chromatophore system of cephalopods. *Proc. Linnean Soc. London* **164**, 235–240.

Bozler, E. (1928). Über die Tätigkeit der enizelnen glatten Muskelfaser bei der Kontraktion. II. Mitteilung: Die Chromatophorenmuskeln der Cephalopoden. *Z. vergleich. Physiol.* **7**, 379–406.

Bozler, E. (1931). Über die Tätigkeit der einzelnen glatten Muskelfaser bei der Kontraktion. 3. Mitteilung: Registrierung der Kontraktionen der chromatophoren Muskelzellen von Cephalopoden. *Z. vergleich. Physiol.* **13**, 762–772.

Briggs, M. H. (1960). The chemistry of animal venoms. *Sci. Progr.* **48**, 456–462.

Bruun, A. F. (1943). The biology of *Spirula spirula* (L.). *Dana Rept. Copenhagen* **4**, No. 24, 44 pp.

Buchner, P. (1953). "Endosymbiose der Tiere mit pflanzlichen Mikroorganismen," 771pp. Biirkhäuser, Stuttgart.

Christomanos, A. (1955). Nature of the pigment of *Aplysia depilans*. *Nature* **175**, 310.

Chun, C. (1910). Die Cephalopoden; Oegopsida. *Wiss. Ergeb. deut. Tiefsee-Exped.* (*Valdivia*) p. 18.

Clarke, G. L., and Denton, E. J. (1962). Light and animal life. *In* "The Sea" (M. N. Hill, ed.), Vol. 1, pp. 456–468. Wiley (Interscience), New York.

Clench, W. J. (1946). The poison cone shell. *Occasional Papers Mollusks (Harvard)* **1**, 49–80 (including a reprint of the paper by Clench and Kondo, 1943).

Clench, W. J., and Kondo, Y. (1943). The poison cone shell. *Am. J. Trop. Med.* **23**, 105–120.

Courville, D. A., Halstead, B. W., and Hessel, D. W. (1958). Marine biotoxins: isolation and properties. *Chem. Revs.* **58**, 235–248.

Cowdry, E. V. (1911). The colour changes of *Octopus vulgaris*. *Univ. Toronto Studies, Biol. Ser.* **10**, 53pp.

de Lerma, B. (1947). Ricerche spettrofotometriche sulla luce emissa da batteri fotogeni. Noto II. *Atti accad. nazl. Lincei, Rend., Classe sci. fis. mat. e nat.* [8] **2**, 78–82.

Dubois, R. (1928). Lumière (Production de la) ou biophotogénèse. *In* "Dictionnaire de Physiologie," (C. Richet, ed.), Vol. 10, pp. 277–394. Félix Alcan, Paris.

Eales, N. B. (1921). *Aplysia. Liverpool Marine Biol. Committee Memoir* **24**, 84pp. (Liverpool Univ. Press).

Erspamer V., and Benati, O. (1953a). Identification of murexine as β-[imidazolyl-(4)]-acryl-choline. *Science* **117**, 161–162.

Erspamer, V., and Benati, O. (1953b). Isolierung des Murexins aus Hypobranchial-drüsenextrakten von *Murex trunculus* und seine Identifizierung als β-[Imidazolyl-4 (5)]-acryl-choline. *Biochem. Z.* **324**, 66–73.

Fänge, R. (1960). The salivary gland of *Neptunea antiqua. Ann. N.Y. Acad. Sci.* **90**, 689–694.

Fischer, P.-H. (1950). "Vie et Moeurs des Mollusques," 312pp. Payot, Paris.

Fish, C. J., and Cobb, M. C. (1954). Noxious marine animals of the central and western Pacific Ocean. *U.S. Fish and Wildlife Serv. Research Rept.* No. 36, 45pp.

Fox, D. L. (1953). "Animal Biochromes and Structural Colours," 379pp. Cambridge Univ. Press, London and New York.

Fox, H. M., and Vevers, G. (1960). "The Nature of Animal Colours," 246pp. Sidgwick & Jackson, London.

Fröhlich, F. W. (1910). Experimentelle Studien am Nervensystem der Mollusken. 7. Über den peripheren Tonus der Cephalopodenchromatophoren und seine Hemmung. *Z. allgem. Physiol.* **11**, 99–106.

Fuchs, R. F. (1914). Der Farbenwechsel und die chromatische Hautfunktion der Tiere. *In* "Handbuch der vergleichenden Physiologie" (H. Winterstein ed.), Vol. 3, Part I, Section 2, pp. 1199–1285. Fischer, Jena.

Gegenbaur, C. (1855). "Untersuchungen über Pteropoden und Heteropoden," 228pp. Engelmann, Leipzig.

Ghiretti, F. (1960). Toxicity of *Octopus* saliva against Crustacea. *Ann. N.Y. Acad. Sci.* **90**, 726–741.

Girod, P. (1882). Recherches sur la poche du noir des Céphalopodes des côtes de France. *Arch. zool. exptl. et gén.* **10**, 1–100.

Graham, A. (1938). The structure and function of the alimentary canal of aeolid molluscs, with a discussion on their nematocysts. *Trans. Roy. Soc. Edinburgh* **59**, 267–307.

Grimpe, G., and Hoffmann, H. (1921). Über die Postembryonalentwicklung von Histioteuthis und über ihre sogennanten "Endorgane." *Arch. Naturgeschichte, Abt. A* **87**, No. 12, 179–219.

Hall, D. N. F. (1956). Ink ejection by Cephalopoda. *Nature* **177**, 663.

Halstead, B. W. (1959). "Dangerous Marine Animals," 146pp. Cornell Maritime Press, Cambridge, Maryland.

Haneda, Y. (1955). Luminous organisms of Japan and the Far East. *In* "The Luminescence of Biological Systems" (F. H. Johnson, ed.), pp. 335–385. Am. Assoc. Advance. Sci., Washington, D.C.

Haneda, Y. (1956). Squid producing an abundant luminous secretion found in Suruga Bay, Japan. *Sci. Rept. Yokosuka City Museum* No. 1, 27–32.

Haneda, Y. (1958). Studies on luminescence in marine snails. *Pacific Sci.* **12**, 152–156.

Haneda, Y. (1959). Personal communication.

Haneda, Y. and Harvey, E. N. (1953). Additional data on the adenosine triphosphate and the luciferin-luciferase reactions of various luminous organisms. *Arch. Biochem. Biophys.* **48**, 237–238.

Hardy, A. C. (1956). "The Open Sea. Its Natural History: the World of Plankton," 335pp. Collins, London.

Hartman, W. J., Clarke, W. G., Cyr, S. D., Jordon, A. L., and Leibhold, R. A. (1960). Pharmacologically active amines and their biogenesis in the octopus. *Ann. N.Y. Acad. Sci.* **90**, 637–666.

Harvey, E. N. (1952). "Bioluminescence," 649pp. Academic Press, New York.

Harvey, E. N. (1955). Survey of luminous organisms: problems and prospects. *In* "The Luminescence of Biological Systems" (F. H. Johnson, ed.), pp. 1–24. Am. Assoc. Advance. Sci., Washington, D.C.

Herfurth, A. H. (1936). Beiträge sur Kenntnis der Bakteriensymbiose der Cephalopoden. *Z. Morphol. Okol. Tiere* **31**, 561–607.

Hill, A. V., and Solandt, D. Y. (1934). Myograms from the chromatophores of *Sepia. J. Physiol. (London)* **83**, 13P–14P.

Hofmann, F. B. (1907). Histologische Untersuchungen über die Innervation der glatten und der ihr verwandten Muskulatur der Wirbeltiere und Mollusken. *Arch. mikroskop. Anat. u. Entwicklungsmech.* **70**, 361–413.

Holmes, W. (1940). The colour changes and colour patterns of *Sepia officinalis* L. *Proc. Zool. Soc. (London)* **A110**, 17–35.

Hubbard, R., and St. George, R. C. C. (1958). The rhodopsin system of the squid. *J. Gen. Physiol.* **41**, 501–528.

Kahr, H. (1959). Zur endokrinen Steuerung der Melanophoren-Reaktion bei *Octopus vulgaris. Z. vergleich. Physiol.* **41**, 435–448.

Kato, K. (1949). Luminous organ of *Kaloplocamus ramosum. Zool. Mag. (Tokyo)* **58**, 163–164. [In Japanese. Cited in Haneda (1955), p. 349.]

Kepner, W. A. (1943). The manipulation of the nematocysts of *Pennaria tearilla* by *Aeolis pilata. J. Morphol.* **73**, 297–311.

Keyl, M. J., Michaelson, I. A., and Whittaker, V. P. (1957). Physiologically active choline esters in certain marine gastropods and other invertebrates. *J. Physiol. (London)* **139**, 434–454.

Kishitani, T. (1932). Studien über Leuchtsymbiose von japanischen Sepien. *Folia Anat. Japon.* **10**, 315–418.

Kline, G. F. (1956). Notes on the stinging operation of *Conus. Nautilus* **69**, 76–78.

Kohn, A. J. (1958). Recent cases of human injury due to venomous marine snails of the genus *Conus. Hawaii Med. J.* **17**, 528–532.

Kohn, A. J., Saunders, P. R., and Wiener, S. (1960). Preliminary studies on the venom of the marine snail *Conus*. *Ann. N.Y. Acad. Sci.* **90**, 706–725.

Kühn, A. (1930). Über Farbensinn und Anpassung der Körperfarbe an die Umgebung bei Tintenfischen. *Nachr. Ges. Wiss. Göttingen, Jahresber. Geschäftsjahr, Math.-physik. Kl.* pp. 10–16.

Kühn, A. (1950). Über Farbenwechsel und Farbensinn von Cephalopoden. *Z. vergleich. Physiol.* **32**, 572–598.

Kühn, A., and Heberdey, R. F. (1929). Über die Anpassung von *Sepia officinalis* L. an Helligkeit und Farbton der Umgebung. *Verhandl. deut. zool. Ges.* **33**, *Zool. Anz. Suppl.* **4**, 231–237.

Lederer, E. (1940). Les pigments des Invertébrés (à l'exception des pigments respiratoires). *Biol. Revs. Cambridge Phil. Soc.* **15**, 273–306.

MacGinitie, G. E. (1938). Notes on the natural history of some marine animals. *Am. Midland Naturalist* **19**, 207–219.

MacGinitie, G. E., and MacGinitie, N. (1949). "Natural History of Marine Animals," 473pp. McGraw-Hill, New York.

Martoja, M. (1960). Données histologiques sur l'appareil venimeux de *Conus mediterraneus* Brug. *Ann. sci. nat. Zool. et biol. animale* [12] **2**, 513–523.

Mortara, S. (1921). Gli organi luminosi di *Pyroteuthis margaritifera* e le loro complicazioni morfologishe. *Mem. reale com. talassogr. ital.* **82**, 1–30.

Morton, J. E., and Holme, N. A. (1955). The occurrence at Plymouth of the opisthobranch *Akera bullata*, with notes on its habits and relationships. *J. Marine Biol. Assoc. U.K.* **34**, 101–112.

Naville, A. (1926). Notes sur les Éolidiens. *Rev. suisse zool.* **33**, 251–289.

Nicol, J. A. C. (1958). Spectral composition of the light of *Pholas dactylus* L. *J. Marine Biol. Assoc. U.K.* **37**, 43–47.

Nicol, J. A. C. (1960). Histology of the light organs of *Pholas dactylus*. *J. Marine Biol. Assoc. U.K.* **39**, 109–114.

Okada, Y. K. (1927a). Contribution à l'étude des Céphalopodes lumineux. (Notes préliminaires, II). *Bull. inst. océanogr. Monaco* No. 499, 15pp.

Okada, Y. K. (1927b). Luminescence chez les Mollusques lamellibranches. *Bull. soc. zool. France* **52**, 95–98.

Panceri, P. (1872). The luminous organs and the light of the Pholades. *Quart. J. Microscop. Sci.* **12**, 254–260.

Panceri, P. (1873). On the light emanating from the nerve cells of *Phyllirrhoe bucephala*. *Quart. J. Microscop. Sci.* **13**, 109–116.

Panizzi, L., and Nicolaus, R. (1952). Ricerche sulle melanine. I. Sulla melanine di Seppia. *Gazz. chim. ital.* **82**, 435–460.

Parker, G. H. (1948). "Animal Colour Changes and their Neurohumours. A Survey of Investigations 1910–1943," 377pp. Cambridge Univ. Press, London and New York.

Pickford, G. E. (1946). *Vampyroteuthis infernalis* Chun. An archaic dibranchiate cephalopod. *Dana Rept. Copenhagen* **5**, No. 29, 40pp.

Pickford, G. E. (1949). *Vampyroteuthis infernalis* Chun. An archaic dibranchiate cephalopod. II. External anatomy. *Dana Rept. Copenhagen* **6**, No. 32, 132pp.

Plesner, P. E. (1959). Light-emission mechanism of *Pholas dactylus*. *Pubbl. staz. zool. Napoli* **31**, Note tech., XLIV–XLVI.

Robson, G. C. (1925). The deep-sea Octopoda. *Proc. Zool. Soc.* (*London*) **1925**(2), 1323–1356.

Schiff, H. (1962). Wirkung des Cephalotoxins und anderer Pharmaka auf die glatte Muskulatur von *Octopus vulgaris* L. und auf das Zentralnervensystem von *Squilla mantis* L. *Pubbl. staz. zool. Napoli* **33**, 10–19.

Schmidt, J. (1922). Live specimens of *Spirula*. *Nature* **110**, 788–790.

Schwinck, I. (1956). Vergleich des Redox-Pigmentes aus Chromatophoren und Retina von *Sepia officinalis* mit Insektenpigmenten der Ommochromgruppe. *Verhandl. deut. zool. Ges.* **49**, *Zool. Anz. Suppl.* **19**, 71–75.

Sereni, E. (1929). Metodi per la circolazione crociata nei Cefalopodi. *Pubbl. staz. zool. Napoli* **9**, 293–315.

Sereni, E. (1930). The chromatophores of the cephalopods. *Biol. Bull.* **59**, 247–268.

Skowron, S. (1926). On the luminescence of some cephalopods. *Riv. biol. (Milan)* **8**, 236–240.

Steinach, E. (1901). Studien über die Hautfärbung und über den Farbenwechsel der Cephalopoden. *Pflügers Arch. ges. Physiol.* **87**, 1–37.

Strehler, B. L. (1955). Factors and biochemistry of bacterial luminescence. *In* "The Luminescence of Biological Systems", (F. H. Johnson, ed.), pp. 209–255. Am. Assoc. Advance. Sci., Washington, D.C.

ten Cate, J. (1928). Contribution à la question de l'innervation des chromatophores chez *Octopus vulgaris*. *Arch. néerl. sci., Sér. IIIC* **12**, 568–599.

Thompson, T. E. (1960a). Defensive acid-secretion in marine gastropods. *J. Marine Biol. Assoc. U.K.* **39**, 115–122.

Thompson, T. E. (1960b). Defensive adaptations in opisthobranchs. *J. Marine Biol. Assoc. U.K.* **39**, 123–134.

Thompson, T. E., and Slinn, D. J. (1959). On the biology of the opisthobranch *Pleurobranchus membranaceus*. *J. Marine Biol. Assoc. U.K.* **38**, 507–524.

Tompsett, D. H. (1939). *Sepia*. *Liverpool Marine Biol. Committee Memoir* No. **32**, 184pp. (Liverpool Univ. Press).

Turner, R. D. (1948). Cited in Harvey (1952), p. 253.

Vialli, M. (1954). Considerazioni morfologische e biologiche sulle localizzazioni di enteramina. Nota (1). *Rend. ist. lombardo sci., Pt. I* **87**, 61–85.

Whittaker, V. P. (1960). Pharmacologically active choline esters in marine gastropods. *Ann. N.Y. Acad. Sci.* **90**, 695–705.

Wilson, D. P. (1935). "Life of the Shore and Shallow Sea," 150pp. Ivor Nicholson & Watson, London.

Wilson, D. P., and Wilson, M. A. (1956). A contribution to the biology of *Ianthina janthina* (L.). *J. Marine Biol. Assoc. U.K.* **35**, 291–305.

Winkler, L. R. (1959). Intraspecific variation in the purple secretion of the California sea hare, *Aplysia californica* Cooper. *Pacific Sci.* **13**, 357–361.

Yonge, C. M. (1958). Observations in life on the pulmonate limpet *Trimusculus (Gadinia) reticulatus* (Sowerby). *Proc. Malacological Soc. (London)* **33**, 31–37.

Locomotion

J. E. Morton

DEPARTMENT OF ZOOLOGY, UNIVERSITY OF AUCKLAND, NEW ZEALAND

I. INTRODUCTION

A basic element in molluscan design is the foot, an organ with two main functions, the passive one of securing attachment to the substratum and the active one of movement upon or into the substratum, or of swifter propulsion through the water. There can be few principles of locomotion (including "flying" in certain squids) that have not been somewhere exploited by the molluscs, and the structure of the foot and body are as diverse as the modes of progression. Chitons and many gastropods retain the primitively wide sole, combining broad-footed stability with production of a continuous locomotor wave. The foot exhibits at one extreme the limpet form of a firm attachment disc, and at the other the form of an entrenching tool for thrusting into the substratum. Many gastropods may swim, adopting every device for water-borne movement, including the screw, the scull, rowing by oars, jet propulsion, and passive sailing. In bivalves and scaphopods the foot is used basically for providing an advance anchorage in the substratum upon which the body can be drawn down. Here surface progression is the adaptive exception, and many surface-dwelling bivalves are attached by the byssus. The cephalopods have brought pallial jet propulsion to a high pitch of speed and

---

* In collaboration with C. M. Yonge.

precision; creeping movement over the substratum is here a secondary adaptive development.

II. CHITONS AND GASTROPODS

A. *Locomotion by the Pedal Sole*

1. PEDAL MUSCULATURE

The muscles of the broadly expanded gastropod foot are shown schematically in Fig. 1. Elements to be noted are the sheet of longitudinal

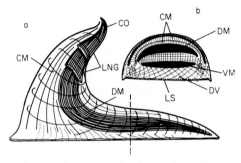

FIG. 1. Pedal musculature of a generalized prosobranch gastropod, based upon Weber's figure for *Nassarius*. (*a*) Sagittal section; (*b*) cross section at level of dashed line shown in (*a*). CO, columellar muscle; CM, circular muscle layers of the column; DM, dorsal (longitudinal) muscle band; DV, dorsoventral muscle slips to sole; LS, longitudinal muscles of the sole; LNG, superficial longitudinal muscles; VM, ventral (longitudinal) muscle.

muscles forming the sole which provide the rhythmic propulsive wave, and the muscles of the column and sides, continuous with the broad, spirally curved columellar muscle. From the columellar shell attachment, longitudinal muscles sweep downward into the expansible body of the foot. They are concentrated chiefly in the systems of dorsal and ventral pedal muscles that reach back to the metapodium, giving a strong rigidity to the whole organ. These antagonize with successive muscle layers, encircling the back and sides of the foot at various levels. In addition to its own longitudinal muscles, the sole has innumerable dorsoventral muscle slips proceeding ultimately from the longitudinal muscles of the column and inserted between the longitudinal elements. The foot owes its massive power of expansion to its permeation by a hemocoelic blood supply, extending into small turgid spaces among the muscles of the sole that can be locally acted on by the longitudinal and dorsoventral muscles and play the role of a diffuse fluid skeleton. The existence of the hemoskeleton is always to be kept in mind in a consideration of molluscan locomotion.

Shifting of blood can dramatically change the shape of the whole foot which, save for the cephalopods, forms a blood-filled muscular organ with a malleable rigidity.

The foot acts as a holdfast as well as a locomotor surface, relying generally upon the adhesive properties of its mucus rather than suction. *Helix* can completely attach in a few seconds to a sheet of glass, with a hole beneath the foot, but as it is pulled off air is sucked into the hole, showing that under high dislodgment tension the sole can be raised from the substratum to give the additional action of a sucker. In the long stationary *Patella* and *Crepidula*, moreover, the center of the sole is certainly lifted off the ground to give a sucker capable of withstanding a surprising load. In addition to an adhesive, mucus is also a lubricant: ciliary locomotion (Section II, A, 5) is possible even over a rough sandy surface on a continuous mucous sheet laid down by the foot.

2. The Direct Locomotor Wave

a. Kinematics. In Lissmann's (1945a) analysis of the gastropod pedal locomotor wave, *Helix* was taken as a convenient first example. Waves of longitudinal muscle contraction followed by relaxation pass along the foot from behind forward. The whole progressing sole displays at any one time a pattern of 8 to 10 dark, forwardly moving transverse bands. Any point on the sole is passed over by a phase of forward movement, indicated by a dark band, followed by a phase of rest. It is now well established that the dark bands represent longitudinally contracted furrows lifted off the ground and moving forward, while there are elongated areas which stay at rest (Parker, 1911; Olmsted, 1917). Lissmann showed experimentally that these bands are the site of both horizontal displace-

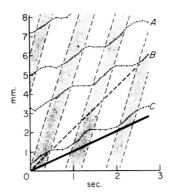

Fig. 2. Graphs from cinematograph data on forward movement of three marked points (*A*, *B*, and *C*) in anteroposterior direction on the foot of *Helix pomatia*. Full heavy line indicates the speed of the animal, the heavy dotted line the average speed of a point in forward motion. (From Lissmann, 1945a.)

ment and forward movement. Forward movement was detected by cine-
matographic records of the movement of parts of the foot which were
pigmented or marked by injected India ink. The graph in Fig. 2 shows
the discontinuous nature of the forward movement as correlated with the
passage of the dark band. Simultaneous vertical displacement, though small,
was recorded simultaneously with horizontal displacement. Through a

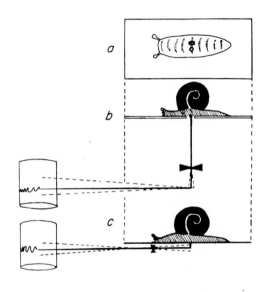

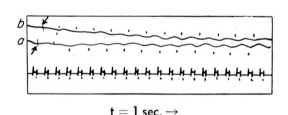

t = 1 sec. →

FIG. 3. *Helix pomatia.* Above: Simultaneous recording of (*b*) horizontal and (*c*)
vertical displacement of foot in locomotion. Below: tracing so obtained. The marks of
coincidence indicate the position of the dark waves. (From Lissmann, 1945a.)

2-mm hole in a glass plate was passed the rounded tip of a glass recording lever. The vertical displacement of the pedal surface thus recorded
was found to coincide with the visible passage of waves marked by tap-
ping a key. Horizontal movement was recorded by the foot sliding over
a recording lever passed through a longitudinal slit (see Fig. 3).

Locomotion was also studied by Lissmann in *Haliotis tuberculatas* and

Pomatias elegans. Pomatias is interesting in showing no passage of successive waves, but instead a bipedal locomotion, the right and left halves of the foot being demarcated in the mid-line. One half of the foot is raised, posterior end first, becomes smaller and then, after forward extension, is laid down. The other half is then lifted and brought forward again. This alternate bipedal locomotion resembles, as Gosse said expressively of the similarly moving *Turbinidae,* two human feet shuffling along in a sack. In *Haliotis* we see a condition in a sense intermediate between *Helix* and *Pomatias.* The foot is very active and shows agile turning movements. The locomotor wave is "ditaxic," or separate on its right and left halves, and the action of the two halves is alternate, showing at any one time two partial and one complete anteriorly moving dark areas. These represent areas of maximal longitudinal muscle contraction in active forward movement (see Fig. 4). Lissmann notes the parallel offered by this diago-

Fig. 4. *Haliotis tuberculatas.* Passage of darker areas on the right and left halves of the foot, redrawn from a film. The figures give the time interval in $\frac{1}{16}$ sec. The transverse lines mark distances of 1 cm. (From Lissmann, 1945a.)

nal coordination of three simultaneously moving areas separated by three areas of support, with the hexapod insect mode of locomotion and its obvious advantages with respect to turning and bilateral stability.

The difference in these three examples is one of wavelength relative to the total length of the foot, *Haliotis* and *Pomatias* making use also of a bilateral functional alternation. The length of a step is determined by the difference between the length of the part of the foot in the contracting phase and of that same part when fully relaxed.

On the nervous coordination of the propagation of locomotor waves, little light has been shed from either the physiological or microanatomical side. Lissmann (1945a) correlated the kinematics of locomotion with the forces set up by the moving foot.

b. Kinetics. In the simplest case, *Pomatias,* movement involves the existence of two antagonistic forces, one leading to elongation and the other to longitudinal contraction: longitudinal shortening cannot displace the anterior end forward, nor can elongation alone advance the posterior end of the foot. When a wave of contraction begins from the back of the

foot, this part is lifted off the ground and, by shortening of its longitudinal muscles, is drawn forward upon the anterior regions which, being
still relaxed, adhere firmly to the ground. The tension set up between
the adherent and nonadherent regions is due to the continuity of their
longitudinal musculature. As contraction passes forward, the area of the
adhering sole is reduced, both by detaching and by reduction of its
width. When the adherent region becomes insufficient to resist the force
of muscular contraction behind it, a backward slip of the anterior end
occurs and the whole half foot is eventually lifted off the ground. Relaxation of the lifted half now begins posteriorly and the posterior edge of
the foot is lowered. As soon as sufficient surface is in contact again
with the ground, adhesion is secured. The internal pressure or other force

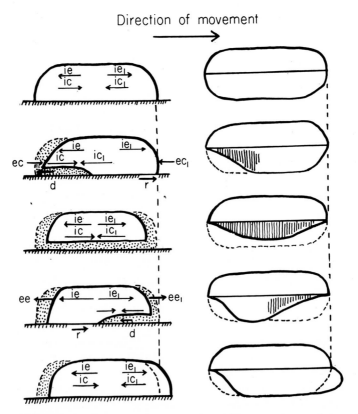

Direction of movement

Fig. 5. Left: Diagrammatic representation of the forces leading to locomotion in
Pomatias elegans. ie, ie_1, internal pressure; ic, ic_1, internal contraction; ec, ec_1, ee,
ee_1, external forces of contraction and expansion; d, dynamic friction; and r, static
reaction from the ground. The right half of the sole is shown. The left half is
indicated by the dotted area. Right: The corresponding state of the two halves of
the sole, viewed ventrally. (From Lissmann, 1945b.)

of elongation is increased while the force of longitudinal contraction decreases. The foot has regained its original length, but its position in relation to the ground has changed. The posteriorly directed component of
the force of extension is now resisted by the adhesion of the posterior
part of the foot; and the anterior part is pressed forward with the extending force sufficient to overcome any frictional resistance (Fig. 5).

In *Helix* each relaxed transverse furrow is bordered in front by an
area undergoing forward extension, while behind it is an area of active
contraction. This whole pattern continues to shift headward. Although a
single functional unit is the same in essentials as the whole half foot of
Pomatias, we must consider in *Helix* the whole foot acting in concert.
The forces of extension and of longitudinal contraction over the whole
foot must contribute equally to the movement forward of the entire animal or any part of it: thus, (*1*) an external force leading to elongation;
(*2*) an external force leading to longitudinal contraction; (*3*) a sliding
friction (drag) developed by parts of the foot going forward and acting
in a posterior direction; (*4*) a static reaction beneath the areas of fixation
acting in an anterior direction; and (*5*) possibly static tensions and
thrusts between successive areas of fixation. The external forces of dynamic friction and static reaction were measured as the snail crawled
across a movable bridge mounted upon a knife edge so as to record tensions or thrusts between the fixed platform and the bridge. Extending
forces widen the gap, contracting forces narrow it. The stages are illustrated in Fig. 6g. I. The gap widens as the force of extension acts against
a posterior surface of application (this represents sliding friction). II.
The gap narrows, by the forces that lead to longitudinal contraction and
the record is one of static reaction, the snail having established an anterior fixed point against which its posterior parts are protracted. When
the animal moves off the bridge to the fixed platform (III), a static reaction is recorded from the ground under the posterior point of purchase
(IV). Sliding friction is recorded from the posterior part of the body
moving forward. These four stages show the maxima of tension and
thrust. The magnitude of the forces decreases as the region of contraction
passes over the gap and the external resistance is thereupon decreased.

With the first widening of the gap, a typical tracing dips (Fig. 7); it
later rises above the base line, where it remains even after the whole
animal has passed, owing to the film of mucus still stretching across the
gap. The base line must thus be adjusted to allow for the tension of
mucus still remaining. Propulsion of the front end is so effected by the
regions of the foot lying further back, and the hind end is helped
forward by a pull from further forward. There is thus a continuous but
fluctuating thrust between the anterior and central regions and a continuous tension between the central and hind regions. Longitudinal contrac-

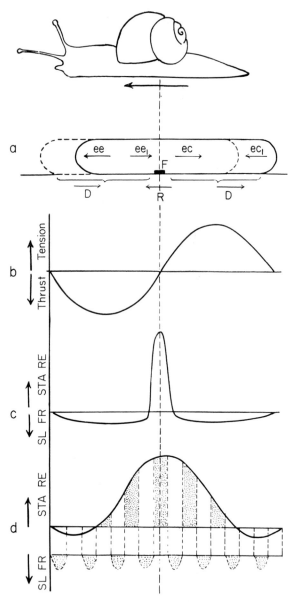

Fig. 6. Diagrams summarizing the kinetic effects in snail locomotion. (a) The mechanical effects of the foot are compared to those of a rubber balloon with its central region attached, its posterior end contracting and the anterior end relaxing. Movement will occur as shown by the dotted outline, giving a thrust/tension curve similar to that recorded by the snail. D, dynamic friction; F, area of fixation; R, static reaction; ec, ec_1, external force of contraction; ee, ee_1, external force of extension. (b) Thrust/tension curve. (c) Static reaction (STA RE)/sliding friction (SL FR) curve, as for a single fixed area. (d) Static reaction/sliding friction curve as resulting from the alternation of separate stationary expanded and moving contracted areas of the snail's foot.

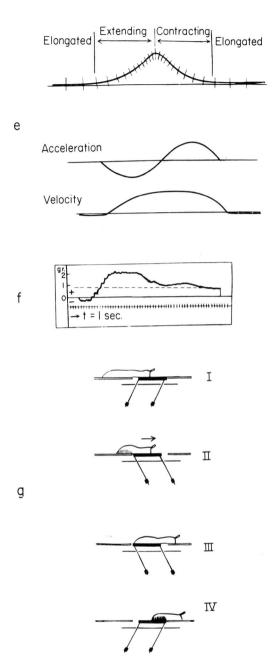

(e) Kinetics of an individual locomotory wave. (f) Tracings showing direction and magnitude of the forces (—, forward thrust; +, tractive force) recorded by *Helix aspersa* moving from a glass plate onto a recording bridge. Note the appreciable tension persisting after the snail has passed the gap, owing to the deposit of a mucous band upon the track. The dotted line shows the base line so adjusted. (g) Successive positions of the snail and the bridge. (From Lissmann, 1945b.)

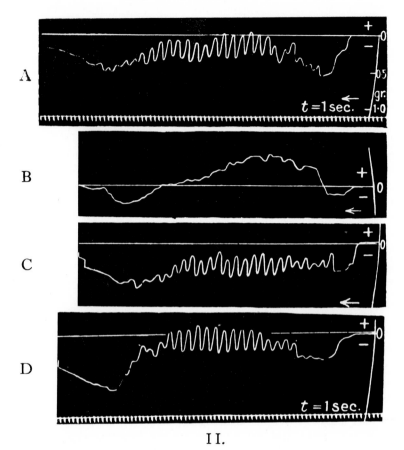

II.

FIG. 7. Tracings obtained from snails crossing a narrow glass strip. In *A*, *C*, and *D*, the width of the recording strip was 4 mm, in *B*, 7.5 mm. So long as the recording strip is no more than 4 mm wide it will be displaced in the direction of the snail's motion (−), the displacing force (sliding friction) being greatest during the passage of the dark waves. *B*, with a wider strip, gives a measure of static reaction (+). (From Lissmann, 1945b.)

tile waves coincide with these fluctuations, appearing superimposed on the thrust/tension curve.

Static reaction and dynamic friction were detected by further experiments replacing the bridge with narrow glass strips. The width of the forward gliding dark band is normally 1.5–4 mm. A movable glass strip of 4 mm or less mounted between two fixed platforms gives, when displaced, an entirely different tracing from a wider strip: when a dark wave at any point traverses the strip it is dragged forward to return to base line after the wave has passed. These displacements represent the sliding friction, measured in isolation. If the strip is made wider (5–8 mm), there will be no time at which it is not occupied in part by a relaxed area of fixation, and the tracing (Fig 7B) reveals the static reaction of the fixed parts. Lissmann has confirmed the accuracy of these experiments by showing that the magnitude of the static reaction is dependent in weight-dragging snails on the external resistance the snail has to overcome.

We may compare the locomotor mechanics of the snail with the different situation in the earthworm as revealed by the work of Gray and Lissmann (1938). In both it is "the turning points in muscular activity that form the most effective attachment points or anchors." The earthworm fixes at the regions of maximal longitudinal contraction by setal adhesion. The snail is fixed at the regions of maximal elongation by having a much wider attachment and greater stability upon the ground. Forward movement in a gastropod requires firm surface adhesion by a broad surface against the substratum, as distinct from the case of an earthworm sliding freely through a surrounding medium. In a snail, acceleration coincides with longitudinal contraction, the locomotor waves traveling from behind forward. In the earthworm, the wave moves posteriorly with forward movement at the phase of longitudinal extension. A snail can increase resistance to dislodgment merely by relaxing its longitudinal muscles; a worm must respond by active longitudinal contraction.

The kinetic and kinematic effects of locomotion as shown by the sole of the snail are summarized in Fig. 6, both for the foot as a whole and for an individual locomotor wave.

3. Other Locomotor Waves

In Lissmann's three examples, the locomotor wave passes forward. A comparative picture (Olmsted, 1917) shows many gastropod locomotor waves that pass posteriorly beginning at the front of the foot, and still produce forward locomotion. In either class, *direct* (or forward) and *retrograde* (or backward) waves, there are *monotaxic* waves with a single series running right across the foot and also *ditaxic* waves with separate though coordinated waves on the left and right halves of the sole.

Many pulmonates, eolids, and dorids, some aplysioids, and muscular-moving Naticidae typically show monotaxic direct waves. Monotaxic retrograde waves are characteristic of most chitons and are found also in *Dolabrifera*. Ditaxic direct waves of an alternate kind are found in *Pomatias*, with a single wave at one time, and in Trochidae with two or more waves. Tetrataxic direct waves, less adequately described, are known for some Littorinidae. In Neritidae an opposite ditaxic retrograde series originates at the front of the foot as a single wave, then divides to pass separately down right and left sides to unite again posteriorly. *Littorina rudis*, *L. littorea*, and *Tectarius* give examples of opposite ditaxic retrograde waves, while species of *Turbo* show variously both alternate and opposite retrograde waves.

A more unusual wave pattern is that of *Cypraea exanthema* (Olmsted, 1917), a monotaxic direct wave series beginning at the posterior end, then bending forward and lengthening to form lateral waves going from left to right across the foot, although the resultant movement is still forward. As the wave passes over any pigmented landmark, this can be seen to travel forward, although the wave is moving sideways. Instead of contractions taking place in sequence from behind forward, they must occur simultaneously on a given longitudinal strip for practically the whole length of the foot; the next series of fibers to contract being lateral to the previous ones, rather than in front, with the same effect as if single longitudinal fibers ran the whole length of the foot, each contracting in turn. A further mode of cypraeid locomotion involves periodical reversal of a pattern of diagonal direct waves, carrying the animal on an essentially straight forward path.

Some chitons and the fissurellid gastropods are able to move for limited distances backward. The elongate *Ischnochiton purpurascens* moves freely backward on a narrow (2 mm) foot, in negative phototactic response to bright light. Backward locomotion may be demonstrated in *Chiton tuberculatus*, where the posterior fourth of the foot (at least this much being needed for attachment) will adhere to the lower edge of a vertically held glass plate. The animal so attached crawls backward till it can turn round to resume forward locomotion. The wave carrying the chiton backwards is retrograde, in the same direction as its waves of forward locomotion, but it has a different appearance to the naked eye, being narrower and darker, and very deep, forming a furrow of up to 2 mm in depth. In a species of *Fissurella*, Olmsted (1917) demonstrated the same backward movement by the first few waves for 2 mm or more upon the glass plate before turning took place and forward motion continued. All such molluscs tested, except chitons and keyhole limpets, had a foot so large or freely flexible that rather than reverse they could bend over to attach the anterior part of the foot to the other side of the glass (see also Crozier, 1919).

Simroth's original hypothesis to explain the contractility and expansibility of the foot invoked an "extensile Muskulatur" whose active phase was one of stretching. The antagonism of the muscular systems with the hemoskeleton was first made clear by Jordan (1901) and Biedermann (1905). The pedal wave has nothing physiologically unique, and both longitudinal and dorsoventral fibers contract together against the elastic blood-filled spaces, collectively giving the foot such rigidity as it acquires when expanded. In a few gastropods, such as burrowing Naticidae and

Olividae, where the foot undergoes turgid hypertrophy, this is probably achieved by allocation of blood from the general hemocoele to the pedal spaces. In Naticidae (though never apparently in others) it was suggested that expansion of the foot may be governed by water intake into an elaborate series of aquiferous canals (Schiemenz, 1884). No worker has verified Schiemenz's canals and Morris (1950) showed that the foot of *Uber* could attain considerable expansion on a dry bench, though without disposing of the possibility of some water intake in the final stages of expansion.

No thorough kinetic analysis of a retrograde wave seems to have been made, but there would seem in principle no difficulty in constructing a model, to allow for the forward displacement of the sole with a contractile wave running backward. The dorsoventral muscles upon contraction merely raise successive segments of the foot from the ground, and such a wave could pass in either direction without any longitudinal displacement of the foot. The progressive element of movement is secured by contraction of the longitudinal muscles, the sequence and relative time of contraction at the back and front of the arch determining the direction traveled by the animal relative to that of the wave. Progression with a retrograde wave would begin with a lifting and protraction of the foot in front, with a repositioning of the front end under contraction, the contractile wave then proceeding backward. With a direct wave, lifting and protraction would begin by contraction at the posterior end, with a wave of contraction transmitted forward to eventuate in a stepwise protraction at the anterior end. In chitons and fissurellids going either way on a retrograde wave these conditions must be capable of reversal and a kinetic study would be especially instructive.

4. Righting and Leaping Movements

A locomotor role is not confined to the muscles of the sole. The column muscles, striking down into the foot from the columella, are of high importance, even in snails progressing by a sole wave, in restoring the normal carrying posture of the heavy shell and visceral mass as it tends to lag behind the advancing foot. Apart from retreat into the shell, the longitudinal column muscles of the foot—dorsal, ventral, and lateral— are most frequently used in the *righting reaction* employed when the shell has been overturned. This mode of heaving the shell forcibly over has been well discussed by Weber (1925) and Yonge (1937); we may illustrate it here for *Aporrhais pes-pelicani* (Fig. 8e). Its elements are first the great elongation and thrusting outward of the column, by the contraction of its circular musculature, and then—when the sole reaches and takes a hold upon the ground—the sharp contraction of the longitudinal muscles so as to turn the shell aperture downwards. In the super-

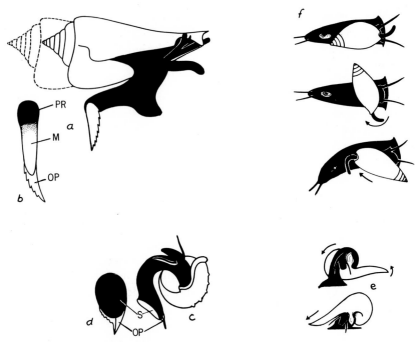

F<small>IG</small>. 8. The use of the column of the foot in gastropod locomotion. (*a*) *Strombus gibberulus*: right-side view showing the length of a single "leap." (*b*) The sole of the foot of *Strombus*, with the reduced plantar area in black. (*c*) *Struthiolaria papulosa*: viewed from the base of the shell to show the position of the foot and operculum in the "righting movement." (*d*) The sole of *Struthiolaria*. (*e*) *Aporrhais pes-pelicani*: the righting reaction. (*f*) *Nassarius reticulatus*: the swinging of the shell and body through 180° upon the foot, as in the shock reaction at the approach of a starfish. *M*, metapodium; *OP*, operculum; *PR*, propodium.

family Strombacea, even to some extent in the most primitive genus, *Aporrhais*, purchase upon the substratum is taken by an elongated and strengthened operculum, overlapping the back of the foot and projecting as a blade from the extended metapodium. In the Strombidae the sole is reduced and the propodium alone attaches to the ground; opercular progression is the normal locomotor action. The Strombidae leap not only in the water but in the air with the intermittent throwing of the heavy shell forward for half its length at each step. Leaping involves the forward protraction of the foot, the fixation of a curved opercular blade in the substratum, and then the vigorous contraction of the column muscles to advance the shell (Fig. 8a) (Parker, 1922). Some of the Xenophoridae—not closely related to Strombacea—also progress by leaps, using the purchase given by the embedded operculum.

    The great mobility of the shell and body upon the column of the foot is well exemplified by the shock reaction or escape behavior of such gastropods as *Nassarius* (see Weber, 1924) and trochids, which on stimulation, as by a starfish predator, can violently swing the shell through 180° in relation to the foot (Fig. 8f).

The locomotor use of the lateral and dorsal muscles of the foot, especially at the anterior end, is shown in the galloping locomotor wave of certain pulmonates and described by Carlson (1905) for *Helix dupeti-thouarsi* (Fig. 9a). The whole head and subjacent foot are first lifted and narrowed, then advanced forward a distance equal to half the animal's length. The anterior end so protracted is then brought down and fixed while the foot immediately behind is raised to form an arch. A series of such arches pass back along the body, freeing the hind end as they reach it. A similar gallop occurs in the pedal locomotion of *Aplysia californica* (Parker, 1917) (Fig. 9b). The sole here forms a ventral strip

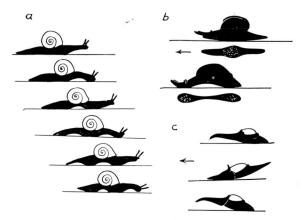

Fig. 9. (*a*) "Galloping" locomotor action of *Helix dupetithouarsi*. After Carlson. (*b*) The giant retrograde locomotor wave as used in the progression of *Aplysia californica* (lateral and ventral views). (After Parker, 1917.) (*c*) A comparable locomotor gallop in *Natica josephina*. (After Weber, 1925.)

that can contract to half its normal width. Retrograde waves pass back, each advancing the animal a quarter of its length. Parker held that these giant waves gave an opportunity to examine *in macro* the small waves of the *Helix* type. It is doubtful if this is so; the *Helix* wave is of a radically different type. In *Aplysia*, it is the anterior part of the pedal arch that moves forward, and the parts move not by longitudinal expansion but under contraction. The aplysiid sole indeed recalls that of the earthworm, being fixed at the transversely widest and longitudinally most shortened parts. The arch is the site of extension of the longitudinal muscles followed by their contraction up its anterior side. The wider attached part of the foot can resolve itself into many discrete holdfasts, each locally supplied with dorsoventral muscle strands and capable of holding separate objects no bigger than a sand grain. With *Aplysia*, crawling upon and loosely attached to discontinuous substrata, such as algae and rough gravel, the attachment problem is different from that of a prosobranch or larger pulmonate with a broadly expanded adhesive sole. The same progression over broken or irregular surfaces with discontinuous adhesion is provided by the transversely divided sole of some Ellobiidae, especially the expressively named *Pedipes*, progressing by first advancing the anterior lobe and then bringing the posterior part up behind. A discontinuous locomotor surface recalling the looping progression of a leech is found in the prosobranch *Truncatella*, related to *Pomatias*, and carrying further the tendency seen in that genus for the fixation of the flat proboscis disc in locomotion. *Pomatias* has no rhythmic coordination of the proboscis disc and the sole, but in the smaller *Truncatella* a well-marked rhythm exists. The sole forms a posterior rounded disc and the body then arches forward to the almost equal disc of the proboscis with the mouth at its center. The foot produces a single direct wave; its sole being advanced to be planted behind the proboscis. The three stages in locomotion are the arching forward of the proboscis by hydrostatic pressure to take a new attachment ahead; the throwing forward of the shell and body over this arch to advance the animal's center of gravity; and finally the bringing up of the foot to lie close behind the proboscis in its new position (Fig. 10).

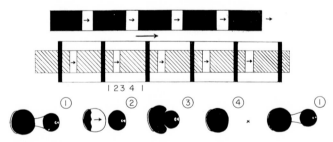

F<small>IG</small>. 10. *Truncatella subcylindrica*. Locomotor rhythm, involving the proboscis, foot, and protractor musculature of the body. Upper track: proboscis on ground (black), proboscis raised (white). Lower track: foot attached (shaded), foot moved forward (white); transverse bars, protraction of the body. Below: relative positions of proboscis and foot at stages indicated in track.

5. C<small>ILIARY</small> L<small>OCOMOTION</small>

Several prosobranchs show no rhythmic locomotor wave and move wholly or partly by the backward-beating cilia of the sole (Copeland, 1919). *Nassarius obsoletus* at rest on a glass plate shows the cilia quiescent. Ciliary beat ensues after touching the tentacle of one side with fish meat.

The narrow-footed *Alectrion trivittata* (foot 10 mm × 4 mm) creeps beneath the surface film by ciliary means. The nervous control of ciliary action is clearly shown by Copeland's experiments. Such muscular contractions as the foot displays are arhythmic and not extensive, usually merely a slight indenting of a section of the pedal margin. After magnesium sulfate anaesthesia, all muscular movements cease, but the ciliary beat goes on, removed from central control. Nerve impulses may arrive at the ciliated cells and the muscular elements at the same time, for the two may come into action together; or impulses may travel only to the muscles which transmit a stimulus to the overlying ciliated epithelium.

In the Naticidae, *Polinices duplicata* can use two types of locomotion, ciliary and muscular (Copeland, 1922). A large specimen, 36 gm in water, can move a centimeter in 5 seconds upon a ciliary surface of 132 square centimeters. Muscular locomotion, however, exerts more power and is used where considerable resistance has to be overcome, e.g., in the typical naticid habit of burrowing in sand. Direct pedal waves pass five in a series, and the speed is of the order of 1 cm in 3.5 sec. The pedal cilia are still active with the muscle waves, and muscular locomotion can pass into ciliary with a gradual reduction of rhythmic pedal movements till they entirely disappear. Activation of ciliary movement shows a wave-like spread as in *Alectrion*, cilia quiescent in a limited area suddenly becoming active, others remaining at rest. An intraepithelial peripheral propagation of impulses would, however, seem unlikely from the observation of sand particles on the sole in the righting movement, showing that cilia far apart come into action simultaneously. And on sheets of epithelium horizontally severed from the foot, ciliary action is halted although it continues in surrounding intact areas. Impulses activating the cilia must come from deeper subepithelial or nervous pathways.

6. Burrowing

In the numerous burrowing prosobranchs, such as Naticidae, Cassididae, Volutidae, Olividae, and some Nassariidae, submergence into a soft substratum is a continuation of normal surface movement, the propodium being inserted as a mobile, freely progressing wedge. Direct rhythmic contractions go on as in surface movement, and as these reach the propodium, it is extended and worked further into the sand. Burrowing, though not crawling, is prevented by the removal of the propodium (Fig. 11). A number of burrowing gastropods with a narrow unspecialized foot, such as *Terebra*, form an anchor by terminal distention of the foot, followed by retraction of the column to draw the animal downward as in many lamellibranchs.

Conus agassizi and *Marginella duplicata* (Olmsted, 1917) are also, among prosobranchs, credited with movement by cilia; the same is true

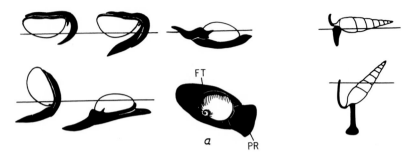

Fig. 11. Left: Burrowing action of the foot in *Natica*, with (*a*) the same animal viewed from the upper surface. *FT*, expanded posterior part of foot; *PR*, propodium. Right: *Terebra tristis*. Action of the foot in sand burrowing, showing the terminal dilation followed by downward retraction of the shell.

of the shelled opisthobranchs *Haminea antillarum* and *Bulla occidentalis*, and is probably widespread in fresh-water pulmonates, such as *Physa* and *Limnea*. Several genera, like *Philine* and *Scaphander*, actively burrow in the manner of Naticidae, having a broad, flat sole and a wedge-shaped body contour, built up by the great enlargement of the cephalic shield and well-adapted for sliding beneath the surface of the sand. In the pulmonates, burrowing is best exemplified in the specialized slug *Testacella*, which slides through the soil in the fashion of the earthworms, upon which it feeds. The shell is much reduced and pushed back with the mantle to the broader posterior end, the anterior parts being admirably tapered for burrowing progression by muscular waves involving the whole body wall.

B. Swimming in Gastropods

Among prosobranchs only the Heteropoda swim, the Ianthinidae being passive drifters. But in the opisthobranchs swimming of varying efficiency is widespread, with strikingly convergent adaptations turning up in numerous groups. The slug shape might be thought ill-suited to produce graceful swimmers, but a streamlined creeping form with elimination of the bulky visceral mass serves as a good preadaptation to pelagic life.

1. By Action of the Whole Body

A few opisthobranchs give over the whole body to produce a rhythmic, straight or spiral, backward, locomotor wave. Though this is not the most efficient of swimming modes, a few that practice it are permanently pelagic. This is the most efficient in the laterally compressed and translucent permanently pelagic Phyllirhoidae (*Phyllirhoe* and *Cephalopyge*), which have no foot, but a sharp ventral margin. These move by a backward undulation, giving the image of the "flowing leaf." Temporary pelagic life is possible for some of the larger and heavier-bodied Dendronotacea. The frondescent *Dendronotus* has two modes of progression, creeping and swimming. Creeping, less often employed, is accomplished by direct rhythmic waves along the narrow sole, and swimming is by a regular screw-like twisting of the body, beginning at the anterior end and passing posteriorly. A wave of twisting is begun by the downward and sideways bending of the head, passing back to the posterior end and disappearing as the head makes its next bend to the opposite side. The posterior part of the body makes an angle of 45° with the anterior, rotating at 45° with the vertical anterior part. With 45 sidestrokes a minute, a distance of 15 cm is covered in a few seconds. Essentially similar swimming has been described in *Lomanotus* (Garstang, 1890) and *Scyllaea*. Both *Melibe leonina*, with six pairs of dorsal, paddle-like outgrowths, and *Tethys leporina* swim by bending the large cowled anterior end from side to side at an angle of 45°. Movement is most rapid on relaxation from this bend, when the body is pulled forward by a complete sweep to the other side (Agersborg, 1922, 1923).

The large doridomorph, *Hexabranchus*, intermittently swims gracefully by the parallel undulating wave transmitted down both sides of the wide notal margin. These waves each take $3\frac{1}{2}$–4 sec and have a forward propulsive effect. A simultaneous slower action bends the body double to exclude water from beneath; an upward component is thus imparted to the movements, as by a jet principle (Fig. 12).

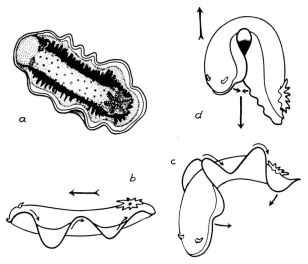

Fig. 12. *Hexabranchus marginalis.* (*a*) Animal viewed from the upper surface. (*b*), (*c*), and (*d*) The locomotor wave of the notal margin, and the flexion of the body in the sagittal plane.

2. BY PARAPODIA

The most accomplished opisthobranch swimming is by enlarged parapodial lobes of the foot. These are at their simplest in the aplysiomorphs
(Anaspidea), where they are in varying extent reflected upward over the
shell and mantle. *Akera*, although a primitive aplysiomorph, has the best-
developed parapodial swimming and it is strikingly paralleled by the
unrelated *Gasteropteron* among the bullomorphs. The parapodia are wide
and cloak-like, overlapping dorsally to ensheath the bulbous shell and
visceral mass. They can be raised and outstretched to form a heart-shaped
flange surrounding the body. The effector stroke causes the closure of this
skirt like the bell of a medusa, producing short spurts off the ground,
though the heavy body soon drops back and sustained swimming, except
in the breeding season, is not seen (Fig. 13b) (Morton and Holme, 1955).

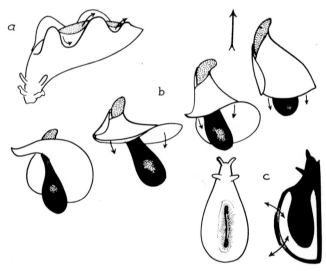

FIG. 13. Parapodial swimming in Anaspidea (Aplysiomorpha). (*a*) Parapodial wave
of *Aplysia punctata*. (*b*) Four stages (left to right) in the parapodial swimming of
Akera bullata. (From Morton and Holme, 1955.) (*c*) *Notarchus* sp., showing the
opening slit of the parapodial chamber (dorsal view) and (diagrammatic section) the
extent of this chamber around the body.

The Aplysiidae—as in the common *Aplysia* (Fig. 13a)—swim by smaller
parapodia with a rhythmic backward wave; or the parapodia may be
enlarged and semicircular moving dorsally and ventrally, with the animal
vertically suspended.

An effective modification of true parapodial swimming, with the development of jet propulsion, is found in the Dolabellinae and Notarchinae;
the parapodia are tightly drawn together at the top of the body to leave

a small funnel-shaped slit with a basal sphincter. The subparapodial space can suddenly expel a propulsive jet by which the animal darts off the ground (Fig. 13c) (Engel, 1933).

Two genera of primitively shelled sacoglossans are also semipelagic; *Oxynoe* with its elongate, tapered body and small, rounded rowing parapodia; and *Lobiger*, with prolonged, lateral, oar-like appendages of two or three pairs, whose use in life, whether in swimming or passive flotation, is not known with certainty.

Some pleurobranchoids have independently developed intermittent swimming. The thin parapodia stand out from the foot, and are very flat and thin, to form a wide extension of the sole. The two sides carry an asynchronous backward wave, alternating on right and left; up to 55–60 strokes a minute were observed by Thompson and Slinn (1959), the alternate beat providing a strong roll of 45° to either side. The parapodia moving down provide a lifting component and the trailing posterior margin a small amount of forward movement. The mantle also stands out widely from the body and the gill, and is lowermost in swimming, acting as a double keel to counteract the rolling and yawing resulting from the parapodial movements (Fig. 14).

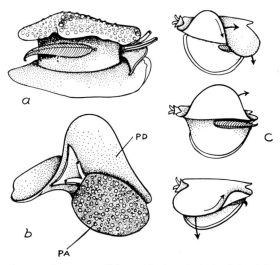

Fig. 14. *Oscanius membranaceus* (Notaspidea). (*a*) Animal in right side view. (*b*) The same in inverted swimming posture, showing the asynchronous wave of the parapodia. (*c*) Diagrams of the animal in successive swimming postures. *PA*, mantle; *PD*, parapodium. (After Thompson and Slinn, 1959.)

It is in the Pteropoda Thecosomata that we find the greatest development of the parapodia, to form—in the first family Limacinidae—long, narrowly attached "wings" for permanent swimming. The heavy body and spiral shell are, however, in *Limacina* still a handicap to easy maintenance of position which is achieved only by constant and vigorous action of the wings employed in unison as oars, with the sharp downward effector stroke carrying the animal upward, as it moves through a spiral course. A certain flotation is achieved by the wings when outspread and motionless, but when these are held together above the body, the pteropod drops as a dead weight. *Limacina* is permanently pelagic by virtue only of its almost continual swimming activity, its small size (never more than a millimeter or two), and the small ratio of its mass to the area of the very prolonged wings (Fig. 15a) (Morton, 1954).

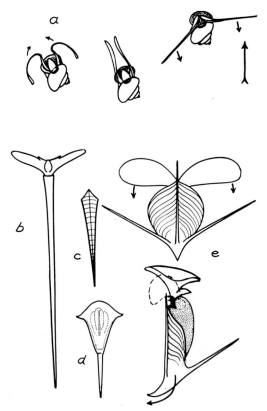

Fig. 15. Pteropoda Thecosomata. (*a*) *Limacina retroversa*. Parapodia in upward recovery stroke (with "feathering" of the oars) and downward effector stroke. (*b*) *Creseis*, showing shell form and extent of parapodia. (*c*) *Styliola*. (*d*) *Diacria*. (*e*) *Euclio pyramidata*, in ventral and right side view.

Further pelagic evolution in Thecosomata, with larger size, has required the emancipation of the body from its early gastropod shape; and in the family Cavoliniidae we find no trace of spiral organization,

but a calcified, nonspiral shell. Every detail of its design facilitates rowing, equilibration, and maintenance of vertical level with a minimum of
muscular work. First, in *Creseis* (Fig. 15b), the body is drawn out into a
tapered needle; upward movements encounter minimal resistance, but
with the greatest visceral weight at the apex the animal will still sink
rapidly when the rather small wings are not active. *Hyalocylix* has a
shorter, more conical shell; its evolution points the way to *Diacria* (Fig.
15d), where the shell is narrowly compressed with a broad upper and
lower aspect, its opening reduced to a slit in the wedge-shaped, expanded
end. Such a body can now be employed in swimming horizontally, and
in turning sideways, as well as rowing directly upward. Moreover, the
inflection of the pointed tip gives a corrective to the tendency to sink
when the wings are immobile, restoring the body to the horizontal position to present the maximum resisting surface to the water. In *Diacria*
and in *Euclio* (Fig. 15e) the mouth of the shell is prolonged laterally and
posteriorly into three spines forming a tripod that will retard sinking
and maintain posture. Finally, in *Cavolinia* we have a plumply inflated
test and heavier, yet still maneuverable, body. All cavoliniids, although the
fins are proportionally smaller and more rounded than in Limacinidae,
still progress by rowing, with the rapidly flicking upward effector stroke
and the slower recovery stroke. The site of the mantle cavity has changed
from the more normal upper position to lie as a wide space underneath
the visceral mass when placed horizontally. The heavy viscera are now
so placed that the center of gravity is at the structural center of the
body, with the wings above, making for the greatest adeptness in turning
and maneuverability.

Postural stability and ease of flotation are also achievements of the
much larger thecosomes, the Cymbuliidae. They reach 1 to 2 inches long,
being enclosed in a light cartilaginous vessel, the pseudoconcha. In *Cymbulia* this has a pointed prow and is open above like a slipper or narrow boat. The parapodia are rounded or triangular flaps, springing from
the foot at either side above the edge of the pseudoconcha. They beat
rapidly downward from a mid-dorsal position, serving as oars for upward
rowing and maintenance of posture. A forward component is also provided by the transmission of an anteroposterior undulating wave over the
wing surface (see Fig. 16a). The two advanced genera, *Gleba* and *Corolla*
(Fig. 16b), have much more of the habit of slow-moving medusae with
a great peripheral extension of the parapodial area. The pseudoconcha
is a shallow vessel like a bedpan, with the parapodia united above its
margins to form a circular or heart-shaped area, the animal progressing
with leisurely umbrella movements of the parapodia.

The more adeptly moving group of carnivorous pteropods, the order
Gymnosomata, have converted the parapodial wings into two-way scull-

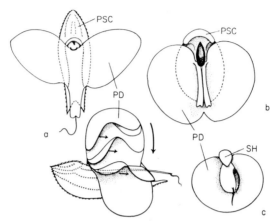

Fig. 16. (*a*) *Cymbulia peroni* in dorsal view with parapodia outspread and in lateral view with successive positions of the parapodia. (*b*) *Gleba neapolitana* in dorsal view with parapodia outspread. (*c*) *Gasteropteron rubrum* (Cephalaspidea) in similar view for comparison. *PD*, parapodia; *PSC*, pseudoconcha; *SH*, head shield.

ing organs. They are the fastest gastropod swimmers, of small size and shell-less, the body cylindrical or more often tapered behind, highly streamlined, and with no large excrescences save the pair of wings attached close together beneath the anterior third of the body. The wings are relatively smaller and more rounded than in the thecosomes, spreading out in the plane of movement, which is either horizontally forward or upward. They have an effective sculling stroke when moving either dorsally or ventrally. Each stroke gives a forward component, the dorsal beat having in addition a downward and the ventral an upward com-

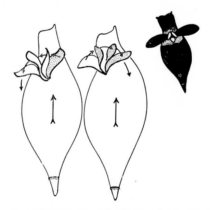

Fig. 17. *Clione limacina* (Gymnosomata). Upper right: the animal in ventral view. Below: lateral views. The action of the parapodia as a pair of locomotor "screws", showing ventral- and dorsalward strokes.

ponent. The tips of the wings thus describe a figure eight, and a pteropod such as *Clione* can attain considerable speed, and with the center of gravity at the middle, is freely maneuverable. The little sculls are kept in incessant action, without the spasmodic flicking beat shown by the thecosomes (Morton, 1958) (Fig. 17).

3. By a Median Fin

The permanently pelagic prosobranchs of the Heteropoda swim by sculling, but the foot has no paired parapodia. It forms instead a thin but muscular median fin, by the production of the mesopodium. The earliest family, the Atlantidae, are—like Limacinidae—small, spirally shelled snails, still with complete foot and operculum. The shell, however, is highly compressed, its edge prolonged into a sharp cut-water keel held upright in progression; the fin is undulated like a single sculling blade. In the two more specialized families, Carinariidae and Pterotracheidae, the median fin is the only remnant of the foot; the naked body is elongated and translucent with its jelly-like tissue spanned by muscle strips. The viscera lie in a small dorsal "nucleus," protected by a cap-like shell in *Carinaria* and absorbed into the body contour in *Pterotrachea*. The swimming position is normally upside down with the viscera hanging below, and the screw-like anteroposterior undulation of the foot continually proceeding above (see Fig. 18). In *Pterotrachea*, a vigorous anteroposterior spiral flexure runs down the body, assisting and facilitating rapid postural change.

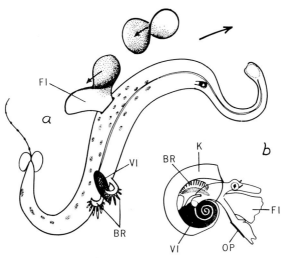

Fig. 18. Heteropoda. (*a*) *Pterotrachea coronata* in swimming position. (*b*) *Oxygyrus keraudreni*, Atlantidae, with the shell vertically held and swimming fin extended (after Yonge, 1942). *BR*, gill; *Fl*, median pedal fin; *K*, keel of shell; *OP*, operculum; *VI*, visceral mass.

III. BIVALVIA[1]

These molluscs early became basically specialized to penetrate soft substrata. Surface stability and adhesion are of secondary importance and
the majority of bivalves that do not burrow are byssally attached or
cemented (i.e., attached by the body or the mantle/shell). The basic requirement of the foot and shell is smooth passage through a soft and
all-enveloping medium. The foot has typically no sole but becomes compressed and blade-like, or cylindrical, thrusting ahead to achieve attachment; contraction of its retractor muscles draws the body down
upon it. The cycle of movements is one of terminal narrowing and
elongation, then usually distention with inflow of blood. A rhythmic
contractile wave then runs from the tip to the base of the fixed foot, with
ensuing downward movement of the animal.

A. Pedal Locomotion

1. MOVEMENTS AND MUSCULATURE

The fastest burrowers and the first to be studied in detail, the Solenacea (*Siliqua, Ensis, Solen,* etc.) (see Drew, 1907; Fraenkel, 1927), despite
the strong specialization of the razor shell and body form, tell us much
about the nature of bivalve locomotion in general. The foot is a firm,
laterally compressed, muscular plug directed forward through the gaping
anterior end of the shell. As burrowing begins, it is slowly protruded
with its pointed tip working as if to enter the substratum with a dorsal
thrust (referred to by Fraenkel as the *Keilform* phase). Further downward thrusts (*Hakenform*) result in penetration of the sand, till the foot
is fully extended, with the tip kept small and pointed well in advance of
the recumbent shell. At its greatest extension, the foot enters its *Schwellform* phase, the distal end dilating to a large bulb or anchor by a massive
inflow of blood and the musculature becoming very rigid. These initial
movements are called by Fraenkel the *Grabschritt*, and are followed at
once by a *Grabstufe*, a strong downward movement as the shell enters
the substratum by the forceful contraction of the retractor muscles. The
anchor remains swollen till the shell reaches it, and is then reduced in
size and the foot withdrawn or re-extended. During the *Grabstufe* pallial
water is ejected round the sides of the foot, and may serve to loosen
sand, as with the use of a water jet in the operation of sinking a pile. A
kymograph record is shown in Fig. 19 of the cycle of movements of
the foot with the shell held in a clamp.

The foot musculature has been investigated by Dawson, to whom
the authors are indebted for the details in Fig. 20, as well as for much

---

[1] In collaboration with C. M. Yonge.

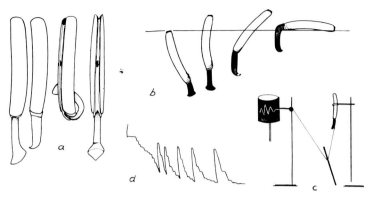

FIG. 19. *Ensis directus*. (*a*) The forms taken by the extended foot, showing also the ventrally closed mantle margins and the position of the "fourth" aperture. (After Drew, 1907.) From left: foot in *Schwellform*, in *Hakenform*, reflected beneath the shell as in preparation for leaping action, and in *Schwellform* (ventral view). (*b*) Burrowing movements of *Ensis ensis*. (After Fraenkel, 1927.) (*c*) Kymograph apparatus for recording extension and retraction of the foot, as used by Fraenkel. (*d*) Tracing showing successive phases of movement in *Ensis siliqua* (reading left to right). (After Fraenkel, 1927.)

other information. The body of the foot and its terminal shape are built up by the posterior retractors, inserted well back on the valves and comprising at either side an internal sheet (*PRI*) and an external one (*PRE*). The space between the internal sheets is filled with connective tissue invaded in some bivalves by the viscera and able to be charged with hemocoelic blood. It is crossed repeatedly by fine slips of transverse muscle (*TM*). The so-called anterior retractors (*ARI*, *ARE*) serve as

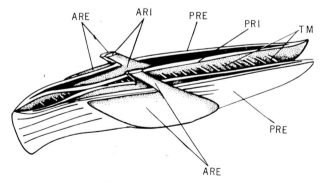

FIG. 20. *Ensis ensis*. Generalized scheme of the pedal musculature in horizontal sectional model viewed from the left side. *ARE*, external anterior retractor muscle; *ARI*, internal anterior retractor muscle; *PRE*, external posterior retractor muscle; *PRI*, internal posterior retractor muscle; *TM*, transverse muscles. (From a model prepared by E. W. Dawson.)

protractors, being respectively situated internally and externally to *PRE*. Protrusion of the foot (*Keilform*) is by contraction of *ARI* and probably *ARE*, as well as of *TM*, to compress and elongate the blood-filled space. The *Hakenform* shape comes about by differential contractions of *PRE*, and the *Schwellform* is achieved by contractions of *TM* and *ARE*, as well as by massive blood flow and relaxation of *PRI* and *PRE* distally. In many bivalves, protrusion and alteration of the shape of the foot must take place without significant volume change: the compressed foot of Cardiacea is, for example, a tongue-like organ, self-deformable by inter-antagonisms of its own muscles, rather than by entry of blood.

The muscular as against the hemal role is a matter of degree from group to group. Possible systems of expansible hollow organs run from the labile blood-filled tentacles of a gastropod (mechanically comparable with an echinoderm tube-foot) to the massively muscular foot of a bivalve. In most bivalves there must clearly exist circulatory paths for a blood shunt between the pallial vascular depots and the sinuses of the foot. The highest pressures in the foot of *Ensis* were recorded by Dawson at the *Grabstufe* retraction (25–50 cm water).

Ensis has also a surprising versatility above ground: it can both leap and swim. The extended foot may be looped back under the shell and then suddenly straightened, to heave the body several inches a number of times in succession (see Fig. 19a). In swimming, the foot is slowly thrust out, then rapidly withdrawn with a simultaneous shutting of the valves to expel water from the centrally closed mantle cavity at the anterior pedal gape. This motive power produces backward jerks, each carrying the shell up to one-and-a-half times its own length.

The *Ensis* picture of burrowing holds good in essentials for most of the more "normal" eulamellibranchs. In the Veneracea, Quayle (1949) has shown, for *Venerupis*, a burrowing sequence of this order: (*1*) The foot is put out in front and extends narrowly to the length of the shell; (*2*) an angled heel is formed ventrally and behind; (*3*) the heel expands to give, with the anterior extension, an anchor upon which (*4*) the shell is pulled down as in *Ensis* into the sand. In this movement, the shell goes forward and down, the foot remaining embedded as the more distal part of the anterior retractors contract to draw the body forward. Kymograph tracing yielded 18 such sequences (*Grabstufe*), the mean interval being 2 minutes. Down movement is shown by the rising of the pen; the nose of the shell then tilts up to allow the pen to drop. Like many burrowers, *Venerupis* can move horizontally, making long furrows at the surface with the shell upright as in digging, save that the initial dip of the nose is less marked (Fig. 21) (See also Ansell, 1962).

Surface versatility is shown also by the shallow-burrowing Cardiacea, with rounded shells heavily ridged, as if to give stability rather than deep

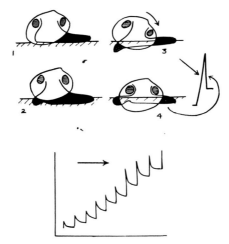

FIG. 21. *Venerupis pullastra*. Shape and posture of the foot in burrowing into sand. Below: kymograph tracing of burrowing movements (read left to right). (After Quayle, 1949.)

penetration. The cockle lies buried up to its posterior third, with digging movements as in *Venerupis* and horizontal crawling at the surface. The little *Cardium exiguum* can climb vertical surfaces by thrusting out and attaching its tongue-like foot. An impressive ability in Cardiacea, found also in Cyprinacea, Isocardiacea, and Trigoniacea, is the habit of leaping. The foot is a long, pointed tongue, tough and muscular and rounded in section. *Laevicardium crassum* and *Cardium echinatum* will use a leaping escape mechanism when touched by the tube-feet of a starfish predator. The foot is bent back under the shell and with startling suddenness re-covers to shoot the animal forwards some 15–20 cm (Fig. 22).

FIG. 22. Leaping movement of *Laevicardium crassum*.

Movement tends to be more specialized in the deposit-feeding Tel-linacea (Yonge, 1949), which typically burrow deeply and have separated siphons capable of great extension and withdrawal due to their charac-teristic intrinsic musculature (Chapman and Newell, 1956). The shell is usually light and, especially in the Tellinidae and Semelidae, wafer-thin,

and extremely compressed laterally. The foot extends into a broad triangular sheet which enters broadly into the sand. Anchorage is not by
terminal expansion, but by the wide surface of application of the inserted
foot, after which the streamlined shell is forcibly pulled down by the
pedal retractors. Asymmetrical retraction in some species of tellinids
produces the recumbent buried position lying on one (usually and perhaps always the left) valve (Holme, 1961), the animal being able to
move horizontally through the substratum. The more solid-shelled Donaci-
dae burrow in the same manner but even more rapidly. Species of
Donax are characteristic inhabitants of fully exposed sandy beaches
throughout the world. They can execute surface leaps as well as burrow
with great efficiency, and by these means certain species migrate up and
down the beach with the rising and falling tide (Stoll, 1938; Mori, 1938;
Jacobson, 1955).

2. Deep Burrowers

Apart from the Solenacea with their rapid up-and-down movements,
members of a number of other suspension-feeding eulamellibranchs have
taken to a purely passive deep-burrowing habit, gradually descending
deeper with advancing age. These animals live vertically embedded in
the substratum and make contact with the surface by way of long siphons
which, unlike those of the deposit-feeding Tellinacea, are united and
always protected by periostracum, i.e., incorporate the inner surface of
the outer lobe of the mantle margin (Yonge, 1957b). They cannot be fully
withdrawn. This is the case in *Mya* (Myacea), *Schizothaerus* and *Lutraria*
(Mactracea), *Panope* and *Panomya* (Saxicavacea), and *Zirphaea* (Adesmacea). In all, the foot becomes relatively smaller as the animal grows
larger and descends to greater depths; after a certain size, burrowing
is probably largely due to forcible expulsion of water anteriorly through
the small pedal gape. The shell is typically very convex and solidly constructed; it is never possible—or indeed necessary—for these suspension-
feeding burrowers to move about laterally as do the Tellinacea. Extrusion
of pseudofeces from the mantle cavity raises problems which are dealt
with in different ways by members of the same superfamily, e.g., *Schizothaerus* and *Lutraria* (Yonge, 1948).

3. Borers

The capacity for boring into hard substrata has evolved independently
in a number of superfamilies. It has come about in one of two ways, by
further evolution from either the habit of deep burrowing or of byssal
attachment, i.e., from the primitive infaunal or the secondary epifaunal
habit (Yonge, 1962). While the shell valves are always the actual instru-

ments of boring, the foot plays some part in the mechanism of boring in the first group and the byssus in the second.

The most obvious passage from deep burrowing in soft substratum to boring in rock is seen in *Platyodon* (Myacea) (Yonge, 1952). Here, as in the closely related *Mya*, the foot is very small and boring is entirely mechanical, the valves being probably forced apart by contraction of the

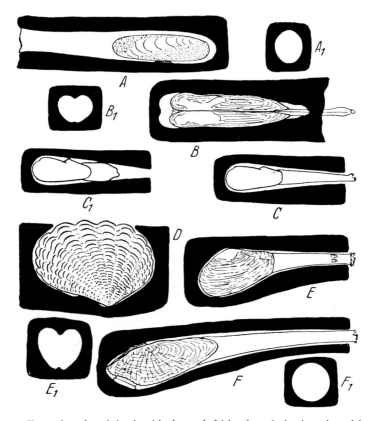

Fig. 23. Examples of rock-boring bivalves. *A*, *Lithophaga* in boring viewed laterally showing byssus threads, siphons withdrawn; *A₁*, cross section of boring, smooth owing to chemical action; *B*, *Botula* viewed from above within boring, siphons extruded, dorsal surface of valves eroded owing to abrasive action in boring; *B₁*, cross section of boring, ridges above and below in conformity with shape of shell; *C*, *Hiatella* (*Saxicava*) with siphons extended; *C₁*, with siphons withdrawn showing how these grip walls of boring (after Hunter, 1949); *D*, *Tridacna crocea*, in coral rock viewed laterally, boring downward with hinge and umbones undermost; *E*, *Platyodon* viewed laterally within boring, siphons with horny (periostracal) scales near tip; *E₁*, cross section of boring through region occupied by shell to shape of which boring conforms, i.e., mechanical action; *F*, *Pholas* viewed laterally within boring showing attachment by sucker-like foot; *F₁*, cross section of boring in region of shell, rounded owing to rotation of shell during boring. (From Yonge, 1951.)

closed siphons against the head of water in the mantle cavity [i.e., *not* by blood pressure in the mantle margins as originally postulated in Yonge (1952)]. The walls of the siphonal end of the boring are probably gripped by the contracted siphons; when they extend this region is widened by action of four periostracal "scales." The animal does not rotate in the boring (Fig. 23,E,E_1).

Although *Zirphaea* burrows into stiff clay, the bulk of the Adesmacea are borers, the Pholadidae (Purchon, 1955a) into rock and the Xylophaginidae (Purchon, 1941) and the Teredinidae [with the pholad, *Martesia* (Purchon, 1956)] into timber. In all, the foot is greatly modified, protruding forward through the rounded pedal gape to serve as an organ of attachment by gripping the anterior end of the boring (Fig. 23,F). The pedal retractors are attached to blade-like apophyses which extend ventrally from the mid-dorsal regions of the valves. The ligament is greatly reduced or lost and the valves rock horizontally on a single contact boss (two in *Xylophaga* and the Teredinidae), the adductors contracting alternately. The anterior adductor is carried dorsal to the hinge line by an upward reflection of the shell margin so that the articulating surface lies between the two adductors (Fig. 24,A). In all Adesmacea, owing to asymmetrical action of the adductors, the shell turns up to 90° alternately in each direction. Hence, a perfectly circular boring is cut in either rock or wood (Fig. 23,F_1) by means of appropriately disposed teeth or ridges on the surface of the valves. In the Xylophaginidae and Teredinidae rasping teeth are confined to the anterior half of the valves and the enlarged posterior adductor is alone concerned with abrasion. In the Teredinidae (shipworms), where the shell is reduced to a small but highly

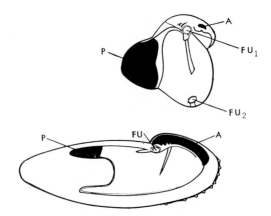

F‍ɪɢ. 24. Interior of left shell valve of *Barnea candida* (below) and *Teredo navalis* (above). Insertion areas of anterior (A) and posterior (P) adductor muscles; FU, fulcrum of contact between the valves in *Barnea*; FU_1 dorsal and FU_2 ventral fulcra in *Teredo*.

efficient cutting organ at the extreme anterior end, the rasping motion is repeated 8–12 times a minute (*Teredo navalis*). A 3-month-old *Teredo* may bore up to 19 mm a day.

All other borers probably assumed this habit after initial life as byssally attached "nestlers." This is most obviously true of *Hiatella* (Saxicavacea) where members of the same species may be either attached byssally in crevices or bore (Hunter, 1949). They do so by water pressure within the mantle cavity following withdrawal of the siphons (Fig. 23,C,C_1), i.e., as described above for *Platyodon*. A circular boring is cut, indicating that the animal rotates. Different species of *Petricola* (Veneracea) are varyingly adapted for boring, e.g., *P. carditoides* excavating no more than spherical borings (Yonge, 1958) but *P. pholadiformis*, with a more elongate shell, excavating deep burrows (Purchon, 1955b). The mode of burrowing is probably much the same as in *Hiatella* or *Platyodon*.

The boring species of the Tridacnidae (Cardiacea), notably *Tridacna crocea* (Yonge, 1936b), possess massive byssus and bore almost directly downward into the coral rock (Fig. 23,D) in which they are commonly found in the tropical Indo-Pacific. Boring is exclusively mechanical, the shell being pulled down against the rock and presumably rocked (on the fulcrum of the underlying byssal attachment) by the enlarged posterior pedal retractors. The remaining group of eulamellibranch borers is the Gastrochaenacea, all species of the genus *Rocellaria* (*Gastrochaena*) being highly specialized rock-borers (Purchon, 1954) with much superficial resemblance to the pholads including the anterior shell gape with the attaching, sucker-like foot. But there are no apophyses, while a small byssus is retained.

In the filibranch Bivalvia, an important section of the Mytilidae (Anisomyaria) bore. Descended from heteromyarians resembling *Mytilus* or *Modiola*, these borers have become secondarily elongate owing to greater development of the tangential component in shell growth (Yonge, 1955). The byssus is retained, and in species of *Botula* which bore mechanically into mudstone, it is by contraction of the posterior byssal retractor that the anterior end of the shell is forced against the head of the boring (Yonge, 1955). The powerful opening thrust of the ligament assists in boring, the valves being much eroded mid-dorsally (Fig. 23,B). The shell does not rotate in the boring (Fig. 23,B_1). The related and much better-known *Lithophaga* (the date mussel) bores invariably into limestone, being especially common in dead coral rock. There the byssus is reduced (Fig. 23,A) while the mantle margins emerge between the shell valves anteriorly (Fig. 25). Mucous glands in this region secrete what may be an acid mucus: certainly there is no abrasion of the shell valves as in *Botula*, although the shell valves must remove the calcareous paste produced by acid reaction. Hodgkin (1962) has demonstrated

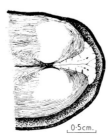

FIG. 25. *Lithophaga plumula*. Boring opened to show dorsal surface of shell with anterior mantle margins protruded against head of boring; arrows indicate direction of ciliary currents on these. (From Yonge, 1955.)

penetration of calcareous rock when purely abrasive action is impossible. Normally there is some rotation of the animal in the boring with formation of an oval-shaped boring (Fig. 23,A_1). Apparently with development of an acid reaction in enlarged mucous glands and the correlated reduction of the byssus, *Lithophaga* becomes confined to calcareous rocks (Yonge, 1951, 1955) which are themselves too hard for the purely mechanical boring of *Botula*.

4. PROTOBRANCH MOVEMENTS

In the protobranch Nuculidae and Nuculanidae, the pedal musculature operates essentially as in "normal" eulamellibranchs. *Nucula* or *Malletia* (Yonge, 1939) thrust the foot into the substratum by a protruding movement during which two side flaps, normally held together, open out by contraction of the *ARI* muscles (Fig. 20). A flat surface, with the appearance of a sole which it was formerly considered to represent, is formed by contractions of *TM*, *ARE*, and special protractor muscles. This constitutes an anchor upon which the shell is drawn down to the limited extent these animals burrow or else is pulled horizontally forward in a sandy furrow (e.g., *Nucula*) or just below the surface (*Malletia*). The movements of the extremely specialized *Solemya* were originally studied by Morse (1913), who observed its adeptness in both burrowing and swimming, and more recently by Yonge (1939) and Owen (1961). A deep burrower, it has a light, smooth, and elongate shell, the uncalcified margins of which tuck in when the valves contract. It burrows essentially as does *Nucula* but when exposed on the surface can swim, although this may be no more than the incidental consequence of sudden withdrawal of the foot with accompanying intucking of the shell causing violent expulsion of water from the posterior end. The animal then darts forward for 3 to 4 times the length of the shell and the process may be continued up to 40 times during half a minute before the animal again touches the bottom (Fig. 27d).

5. SURFACE PROGRESSION

Bivalves which have changed from the primitive infaunal to an epifaunal mode of life with accompanying byssal attachment (Yonge, 1962) can usually progress along a hard substratum. Thus the byssally attached *Mytilus* may thrust the narrow but turgid foot against the substratum so as to wrench off the byssus threads, and by applying the viscous surface of the foot to the substratum draw the shell forward in rhythmic extensile and retractile movements. The young *Tridacna crocea* before it starts to bore into rock has a similar habit (Yonge, 1936b). *Lasaea, Kellya*, and many of the small nestling Erycinacea can wander freely, the narrow foot attaching by the mucous trail; a byssus is secreted for intermittent fixation; in *Lasaea* steep surfaces are climbed with the secretion of a byssus safety line against the eventuality of dropping off the substratum (Morton, 1960) (Fig. 26). Some Erycinacea,

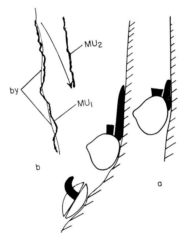

FIG. 26. *Lasaea rubra.* (*a*) The role of the foot in climbing locomotion on a hard surface. (*b*) Portion of the mucous trail (MU_1), showing also the secreted anchoring thread (*by*), attached to the substratum at intervals. The mucous trail is interrupted by the dislodgment of the animal followed by a new climbing trail (MU_2) as upward movement is resumed.

such as *Galeomma* and the commensal *Devonia*, have the foot flattened with the semblance of a nuculoid "sole," others moving upright on the sharp keel of the foot. Creeping is essentially of the cardiid or venerid sort, with a bivalve rhythm of extension and foreshortening, rather than a gastropod locomotor wave. Even in the specialized attached Anomiacea, the remarkable *Enigmonia*, a small lamellibranch "limpet" living on mangrove leaves, has redeveloped the use of its narrow protrusible foot for a similar stepwise locomotion (Yonge, 1957a).

B. *Swimming*

The Pectinidae and Limidae have evolved a nonpedal mode of swimming, short-sustained but of surprising efficiency as a derivative of the bivalve organization. Both are anisomyarian with a mantle cavity widely open and a single central (posterior) adductor with a large "fast" or phasic portion (see Chapter 10). The mantle has a well-developed inner ("velar") marginal fold. The basic adaptation is for the effective expulsion of sediment (or pseudofeces) from the mantle cavity, a matter of particular importance in a horizontally disposed bivalve. This is achieved by the periodic rapid closing of the valves which, with suitable direction of water expulsion, has served as a preadaptation to swimming (Yonge, 1936a). *Pecten, Amussium,* and some *Chlamys* species are freed from the byssal attachment primitive in the Pectinidae. The valves are rounded with equal or subequal auricles at either end of the hinge line. Both are convex in *Chlamys* and *Amussium;* in *Pecten* the upper (left) valve is flat. The foot is small and in the adult is concerned solely with cleansing the mantle cavity (as it is also in the cemented *Spondylus* and the permanently byssally attached anomiids). Scallops swim horizontally with left valve uppermost (von Buddenbrock, 1911; Yonge, 1936a), and can remain suspended in the water for an appreciable time between swimming movements. Water is expelled by clapping of the valves due to fast adductor contractions, the site of expulsion being controlled by the large inner muscular fold of the mantle margin. In so-called forward swimming, expulsion is from either side of the hinge (where pseudofeces collect) with the rest of the mantle closed by the inner mantle folds. The margin of the

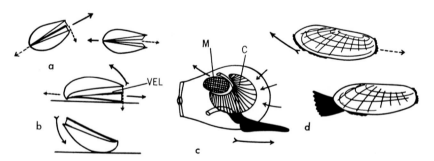

Fig. 27. Swimming in Bivalvia. (*a*) Movements of *Chlamys opercularis*, showing direction of water expulsion (broken arrows) and of movement (entire arrows). (*b*) *Pecten maximus* turning-over movement executed by directional water expulsion from beneath the velum. (After von Buddenbrock, 1911.) (*c*) *Lima hians*, diagram of arrangement of foot and pallial organs showing sites of water intake and expulsion and direction of both crawling and swimming. (From von Studnitz, 1930.) (*d*) *Solemya borealis*, swimming movement by withdrawal of the foot and siphonal expulsion of water. C, ctenidium; M, adductor muscle; VEL, velum.

upper fold overlaps that of the lower fold permitting some downward expulsion of water which imparts an upward position-maintaining component (see arrows in Fig. 27a). A more rapid "escape reaction" involves expulsion of water "ventrally" by withdrawal of the mantle margins in that region and their closure on either side of the hinge side which then progresses foremost (Fig. 27a).

In the Limidae (von Studnitz, 1930; Yonge, 1936a, 1953), swimming species (some are byssally attached) use the byssus only for nest formation. The foot is twisted completely round so that the animal crawls uniquely "backward," i.e., with the hinge hindmost. Here also the inner fold of the mantle margin is large and the inhalant current enters about the middle of the free margin, the exhalant current issuing posterodorsally (Fig. 27c) and also (not shown in Fig. 27) anterodorsally. When swimming, species such as *Lima hians* assume a vertical posture (unlike the Pectinidae) and, taking bites out of the water with the valves, expel this effectively on either side of the hinge line, as in the Pectinidae. These water jets drive the animal forward and slightly upward but it drops downward between each movement. Other movements including rowing with the tentacles are executed (Gilmour, 1963).

IV. SCAPHOPODA

The tusk shells lie buried obliquely in a sandy substratum, with the narrow posterior end emerging. They embed by means of the tongue-like, pointed foot, which is thrust into the sand in the bivalve manner. The anchoring action of the foot is made more efficient by the expansion

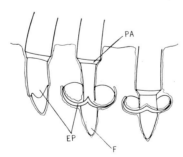

FIG. 28. *Dentalium entalis* (Scaphopoda). Action of the foot and epipodial skirt, forming an "anchor" in burrowing locomotion. *EP*, epipodium; *F*, foot; *PA*, mantle margin. (From Morton, 1959.)

of the epipodial membrane when the foot is elongated to its greatest extent; with foreshortening of the retractor muscles, the shell is then drawn down upon the fixed foot, the movement being repeated till burial is complete (Fig. 28) (Morton, 1959).

V. CEPHALOPODA

A. *Jet Propulsion*

The fast jet swimming of cephalopods is simple in principle and so fundamentally uniform as to need little discussion. All extinct Cephalopoda may (by definition) be credited with some means of buoyancy by gas-filled shell camerae and the possession of a funnel. There is much circumstantial evidence of a widespread, early swimming habit. In many ammonoids is found a hyponomic shell sinus attributed to the exit of a funnel; and at least one orthoconic nautiloid (*Orthonybyoceras;* see Flower, 1955) has provided us with traces of its swimming jet and ability to steer, with impressions alongside the fossil shells in Ordovician rocks.

Conditions in the shelled *Nautilus* indicate that the early jet mechanism cannot have worked with the lightning efficiency it has in the modern Coleoidea, where the pallial muscles are free from shell constraint and are themselves able to contract. The action of the circular muscles is mediated by a giant neuron system achieving both speed and synchrony of impulse passage. Expulsion of water in *Nautilus* is by contraction of the muscles of the incompletely fused funnel. The problems of buoyancy and maintenance of posture were already solved in the evolution of the older cephalopods; with the streamlining and attenuation and evolution of the fins in the modern coleoid naked body, the chief evolutionary preoccupation has been the attainment of speed. Locomotion may be not only "backward" with apex first, but head foremost by the backward reflection of the funnel (Russell and Steven, 1930), and great precision of steering is possible by lateral funnel deflections. The triangular fins of a squid form horizontal equilibrating keels that can be shut down in fast motion. In the fast Onychoteuthidae, the fins provide a broad horizontal tail vane, making an effective gliding surface upon which the animal is able to emerge torpedo-like from the water in escape from schooling carnivorous fish—the only essay in the animal kingdom into jet-flying. At another extreme, in the small, slower-moving *Sepiola*, the fins are small, rounded lappets laterally placed, by which the animal can embed itself in the sand, a truly fossorial cephalopod. The mechanism of buoyancy control in the Mollusca is discussed in Chapter 13.

B. *Web Swimming*

Accessory locomotor mechanisms are found in many Coleoidea, with partial loss of reliance on the funnel. None of the Octopodidae, for example, are strong funnel swimmers, the circlet of eight equal arms with a uniting web serving not only in food catching, but also for taking a light hold of the ground and pulling the animal forward in a swift scrambling, interspersed with frequent funnel spurts backward. The octopus is thus a benthic animal with a newly regained agility of arm as well as of funnel. The emphasis of the interarm web is a feature of most Octopoda, but reaches its greatest extent in three wholly unrelated groups, the deeper water Cirroteuthacea (a superfamily of the Octopoda), the Vampyromorpha, and the Histioteuthidae. In the two former the web is so ample that only the arm tips proceed beyond its edge. The bell-like animal moves chiefly by contractions of this web in a deep-bodied medusal fashion. In the cirroteuthacean *Opisthoteuthis*, the webbed body is flattened like an eight-pointed jellyfish; and in all these forms the funnel is reduced to small dimensions. In the decapod *Histioteuthis*, an ample arm web is similarly used.

REFERENCES

Agersborg, H. P. K. (1922). Notes on the locomotion of the nudibranchiate mollusk *Dendronotus giganteus* O'Donoghue. *Biol. Bull.* **42**, 257–265.

Agersborg, H. P. K. (1923). The morphology of *Melibe leonina*. *Quart. J. Microscop. Sci.* **67**, 507–592.

Ansell, A. D. (1962). Observations on burrowing in the Veneridae (Eulamellibranchia). *Biol. Bull. Woods Hole* **123**, 521–530.

Biedermann, W. (1905). Studien zur vergleichenden Physiologie der peristaltischen Bewegungen. II. Die locomotorischen Wellen der Schneckensohle. *Arch. ges. Physiol.* **107**, 1–56.

Carlson, A. J. (1905). Physiology of locomotion in gastropods. *Biol. Bull.* **8**, 85–92.

Chapman, G., and Newell, G. E. (1956). The role of the body fluid in the movement of soft-bodied invertebrates. II. The extension of the siphons of *Mya arenaria* L. and *Scrobicularia plana* (da Costa). *Proc. Roy. Soc.* **B145**, 564–580.

Copeland, M. (1919). Locomotion in two species of the gastropod genus *Alectrion*, with some observations on the behaviour of pedal cilia. *Biol. Bull.* **37**, 126–138.

Copeland, M. (1922). Ciliary and muscular locomotion in the gastropod *Polinices duplicata. Biol. Bull.* **42**, 132–142.

Crozier, W. J. (1919). On the use of the foot in some molluscs. *J. Exptl. zool.* **27**, 359–366.

Drew, G. A. (1907). The habits and movements of the razor clam, *Ensis directus* Con. *Biol. Bull.* **12**, 127–138.

Engel, H. (1933). *Aplysia saltator* Forbes. *Proc. Malacol. Soc. London* **20**, 321–322.

Flower, R. H. (1955). Trails and tentacular impressions of orthoconic cephalopods. *J. Palaeontol.* **29**, 857–867.

Fraenkel, G. (1927). Grabbewegung der Soleniden. *Z. vergleich. Physiol.* **6**, 167–220.

Garstang, W. (1890). A complete list of the opisthobranchiate Mollusca found at Plymouth. *J. Marine Biol. Assoc. U.K.* **1**, 399–457.

Gilmour, T. H. J. (1963). Studies on the Limidae. *Ph.D. Thesis, University of Glasgow*.

Gray, J. and Lissmann, H. W. (1938). An apparatus for measuring the propulsive forces of the locomotory muscles of the earthworm and other animals. *J. Exptl. Biol.* **15**:518–521.

Hodgkin, N. M. (1962). Limestone boring by the mytilid *Lithophaga. Veliger* **4**, 123–129.

Holme, N. A. (1961). Notes on the mode of life of the Tellinidae (Lamellibranchia). *J. Marine Biol. Assoc. U.K.* **41**, 699–703.

Hunter, W. R. (1949). The structure and behaviour of *Hiatella gallicana* (Lamarck) and *H. arctica* (L.) with special reference to the boring habit. *Proc. Roy. Soc. Edinburgh* **B72**, 271–289.

Jacobson, M. K. (1955). Observations on *Donax fossor* Say at Rockaway Beach, New York. *Nautilus* **68**, 73–77.

Jordan, H. (1901). Die Physiologie der Locomotion bei *Aplysia limacina*. *Z. Biol.* **41**, 196–238.

Lissmann, H. W. (1945a). The mechanism of locomotion in gastropod molluscs. I. Kinematics. *J. Exptl. Biol.* **21**, 58–69.

Lissmann, H. W. (1945b). The mechanism of locomotion in gastropod molluscs. II. Kinetics. *J. Exptl. Biol.* **22**, 37–50.

Mori, S. (1938). Characteristic tidal rhythmic migration of a mussel, *Donax semignosus* Dunker, and the experimental analysis of its behaviour at the flood tide. *Zool. Mag. (Japan)* **50**, 1–12.

Morris, M. (1950). Dilation of the foot in *Uber* (*Polinices*) *strangei* (Mollusca, Class Gastropoda). *Proc. Linnean Soc. N.S. Wales* **75**, 70–80.

Morse, E. S. (1913). Observations on living *Solenomya*. *Biol. Bull.* **25**, 261–281.

Morton, J. E. (1954). The biology of *Limacina retroversa*. *J. Marine Biol. Assoc. U.K.* **33**, 297–312.

Morton, J. E. (1958). Observations on the gymnosomatous pteropod *Clione limacina* (Phipps). *J. Marine Biol. Assoc. U.K.* **37**, 287–297.

Morton, J. E. (1959). The habits and feeding organs of *Dentalium entalis*. *J. Marine Biol. Assoc. U.K.* **38**, 225–238.

Morton, J. E. (1960). The responses and orientation of the bivalve *Lasaea rubra* Montagu. *J. Marine Biol. Assoc. U.K.* **39**, 5–26.

Morton, J. E., and Holme, N. A. (1955). The occurrence at Plymouth of the opisthobranch *Akera bullata* with notes on its habits and relationships. *J. Marine Biol. Assoc. U.K.* **34**, 101–112.

Olmsted, J. M. D. (1917). Notes on the locomotion of certain Bermudian molluscs. *J. Exptl. Zool.* **24**, 223–236.

Owen, G. (1961). A note on the habits and nutrition of *Solemya parkinsoni* (Protobranchia: Bivalvia). *Quart. J. Microscop. Sci.* **102**, 15–21.

Parker, G. H. (1911). The mechanism of locomotion in gastropods. *J. Morphol.* **22**, 155–170.

Parker, G. H. (1917). The pedal locomotion of the sea hare *Aplysia californica*. *J. Exptl. Zool.* **24**, 139–145.

Parker, G. H. (1922). The leaping of the stromb, *Strombus gigas*. *J. Exptl. Zool.* **36**, 205–9.

Purchon, R. D. (1941). On the biology and relationships of the lamellibranch *Xylophaga dorsalis* (Turton). *J. Marine Biol. Assoc. U.K.* **25**, 1–39.

Purchon, R. D. (1954). A note on the biology of the lamellibranch *Rocellaria* (*Gastrochaena*) *cuneiformis* Spengler. *Proc. Zool. Soc.* (London) **124**, 17–33.

Purchon, R. D. (1955a). The structure and function of the British Pholadidae (rock-boring Lamellibranchia). *Proc. Zool. Soc.* (*London*) **124**, 859–911.

Purchon, R. D. (1955b). The functional morphology of the rock-boring lamellibranch *Petricola pholadiformis* Lamarck. *J. Marine Biol. Assoc. U.K.* **34**, 257–278.

Purchon, R. D. (1956). A note on the biology of *Martesia striata* L. (Lamellibranchia). *Proc. Zool. Soc.* (*London*) **126**, 245–258.

Quayle, D. B. (1949). Movements in *Venerupis* (*Paphia*) *pullastra* Montagu. *Proc. Malacol. Soc. London* **28**, 31–37.

Russell, F. S., and Steven, G. A. (1930). The swimming of cuttlefish. *Nature* **126**, 893.

Schiemenz, P. (1884). Über die Wasseraufnahme bei Lamellibranchiaten und Gastropoden (einschliesslich der Pteropoden). *Mitt. zool. Sta. Neapel* **5**, III and IV, 509–543.

Stoll, E. (1938). Sur la mode de locomotion de quelques mollusques marins. *Trav. sta. biol. Roscoff* **16**, 3–33.

Thompson, T. E., and Slinn, D. J. (1959). On the biology of the opisthobranch *Pleurobranchus membranaceus*. *J. Marine Biol. Assoc. U.K.* **38**, 507–524.

von Buddenbrock, W. (1911). Untersuchungen über die Schwimmbewegung und die Statocysten der Gattung Pecten. *Sitzber. heidelb. Akad. Wiss.* **28**.

von Studnitz, G. (1930). Die Morphologie und Anatomie von *Lima inflata*, der Feilenmuschel, nebst biologischen Untersuchungen an *Lima hians* Gmel. *Zool. Jahrb. Abt. Anat. u. Ontog. Tiere* **53**, 199–316.

Weber, H. (1924). Ein Umdreh- und Fluchtreflex bei *Nassa mutabilis*. *Zool. Anz.* **60**, 261–269.

Weber, H. (1925). Über die Umdrehreflexe einiger Prosobranchier des Golfs von Neapel. Ein Beitrag zur Bewegungsphysiologie und Reflexbiologie der Gastropoden. *Z. vergleich. Physiol.* **3**, 389–474.

Yonge, C. M. (1936a). The evolution of the swimming habit in the Lamellibranchia. *Mem. Museum roy. Hist. nat. Belg.* (2) **III**, 77–100.

Yonge, C. M. (1936b). Mode of life, feeding, digestion and symbiosis with zooxanthellae in the Tridacnidae. *Sci. Repts. Great Barrier Reef Exped.* (*Brit. Museum Nat. Hist.*) **I**, 283–321.

Yonge, C. M. (1937). The biology of *Aporrhais pes-pelicani* (L.) and *A. serresiana* (Mich.). *J. Marine Biol. Assoc. U.K.* **21**, 687–703.

Yonge, C. M. (1939). The protobranchiate Mollusca: a functional interpretation of their structure and evolution. *Phil. Trans. Roy. Soc.* **B230**, 79–147.

Yonge, C. M. (1942). Ciliary currents in the mantle cavity of the Atlantidae. *Quart. J. Microscop. Sci.* **83**, 197–203.

Yonge, C. M. (1948). Cleansing mechanisms and the function of the fourth pallial aperture in *Spisula subtruncata* (da Costa) and *Lutraria lutraria* (L.). *J. Marine Biol. Assoc. U.K.* **27**, 585–596.

Yonge, C. M. (1949). On the structure and adaptations of the Tellinacea, deposit-feeding Lamellibranchia. *Phil. Trans. Roy. Soc.* **B234**, 29–76.

Yonge, C. M. (1951). Marine boring organisms. *Research* **4**, 162–167.

Yonge, C. M. (1952). Structure and adaptations for rock boring in *Platyodon cancellatus* (Conrad). *Univ. Calif.* (*Berkeley*) *Publs. Zoöl.* **55**, 401–407.

Yonge, C. M. (1953). The monomyarian condition in the Lamellibranchia. *Trans. Roy. Soc. Edinburgh* **62**, 443–478.

Yonge, C. M. (1955). Adaptation to rock boring in *Botula* and *Lithophaga* (Lamellibranchia, Mytilidae) with a discussion on the evolution of this habit. *Quart. J. Microscop. Sci.* **96**, 383–410.

Yonge, C. M. (1957a). *Enigmonia aenigmatica* Sowerby. A motile anomiid (saddle oyster), *Nature* **80**, 765–766.

Yonge, C. M. (1957b). Mantle fusion in the Lamellibranchia. *Pubbl. staz. zool. Napoli* **29**, 151–171.

Yonge, C. M. (1958). Observations on *Petricola carditoides* (Conrad). *Proc. Malacol. Soc. London* **33**, 25–31.

Yonge, C. M. (1962). On the primitive significance of the byssus in the Bivalvia and its effects in evolution. *J. Marine Biol. Assoc. U.K.* **42**, 113–125.

CHAPTER 13

The Buoyancy of Marine Molluscs

E. J. Denton

MARINE BIOLOGICAL LABORATORY, PLYMOUTH, ENGLAND

Animals which are denser than sea water, such as the common squid *Loligo*, have to work continuously if they are not to sink; it is, therefore, not surprising that many ingenious mechanisms have evolved which allow animals to bring their specific gravities very close to that of sea water. Some of the most interesting are found among the molluscs.

I. GELATINOUS ANIMALS

Very many gelatinous animals are found in the sea and a number of these have recently been studied by Denton and Shaw (1961), among them the heteropod *Pterotrachea coronata* and the thecosomatous ptero-pod *Cymbulia peroni*. Supernatant liquids, obtained by centrifuging these animals, were shown to have a lower specific gravity than sea water. These body fluids were isotonic with sea water but contained the common ions in different relative amounts. (See also Robertson, 1949.) Of these changes in composition by far the most important in giving lift was the partial exclusion of the sulfate ion.

Figure 1 shows the relation of buoyancy of gelatinous animals to sulfate. Agreement between observed and expected lifts was closer when the concentrations of other ions as well as sulfate were taken into account. *Pterotrachea* has a sulfate concentration of about 70% that of sea water and this can give a lift in sea water of only about 0.7 mg/ml of body fluid.

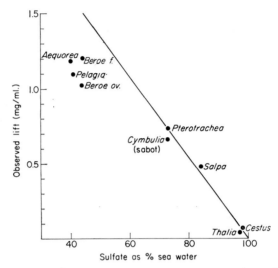

Fig. 1. Observed lift of body fluid in sea water plotted against sulfate concentration. The line shows the lift given for sea waters in which sulfate has been replaced isosmotically with chloride. (Calculated from data in the International Critical Tables, 1933.) The abscissa represents sulfate concentrations of body fluids, expressed as percentage of sulfate concentration of sea water. (After Denton and Shaw, 1961.)

This animal contains only a very small proportion of components denser than sea water and is not far from neutral buoyancy. For example, 100 ml of body fluid could balance the weight in sea water of 0.25 g of protein. The "design" of such animals is probably decided by their relatively ineffective buoyancy mechanism.

II. MOLLUSCS WHICH FLOAT ON THE SURFACE OF THE SEA

A. Ianthina janthina (L)

This snail can make itself a float by forming mucous-coated bubbles of air. The method of building the float has been described by several authors. A very clear, well-illustrated account is given by Wilson and Wilson (1956). If *Ianthina* is below the surface of the water, it can neither rise to the surface nor make a float, but if the propodium is able to break through the water surface, the snail can form a float of mucous-coated bubbles, sometimes at the rate of about one bubble a minute. The propodium is stretched upward and its upper part flattens out on the water surface film. The whole organ becomes spoon-shaped and then hood-shaped until a bubble of air is trapped. This bubble is attached to the base of the float and cemented in place. P. M. David (cited by Wilson and Wilson) has made the interesting observation that when *Ianthina* is found feeding on *Velella* it is usually without a float, the snail being buoyed up by the float of its prey. Its own float would clearly be in the way while the *Ianthina* is feeding.

B. *Peringia* (= *Hydrobia*) *ulva*

Newell (1962) gives an interesting account of the ecology of *Peringia ulva*. He shows that under natural conditions the animal floats on the surface film by means of a mucous raft which also acts as a food net. At mid-tide level the animals submerge to resurface again several hours later, launching themselves on the surface film of the water between ripple marks. Newell's experiments and observation do not support the earlier claim by Linke (1939) that the animals use trapped air to turn their shells into floats but agree with him that the animals keep afloat by secreting a mucous raft. It would be interesting to have a quantitative account of this mechanism.

III. THE CRANCHIIDAE

A very surprising buoyancy mechanism has been found by Denton *et al.* (1958) in oceanic squids of the family Cranchiidae. Three species of cranchid squids (*Verrilliteuthis hyperborea* Steenstrup, *Galiteuthis armata* Joubin, and *Helicocranchia pfefferi* Massy) were studied alive aboard R. V. "Sarsia." *Helicocranchia* was particularly common. Although this squid could swim using water jets from the siphon and two small fins at the stern it could also hang almost motionless without effort.

If the mantle of a freshly caught cranchid squid is opened by a cut along its ventral surface an enormous coelomic cavity filled with fluid can then be seen. This coelomic cavity, which bulges out, almost obliterating the mantle cavity, is covered by a transparent membrane through which such organs as the stomach, cecum, and reproductive gland can be seen (Fig. 2). When this membrane is punctured and the fluid from within the coelomic cavity drained away, the squid sinks. The buoyancy equilibrium of the intact animal is clearly dependent on the low densities of the coelomic fluid. This fluid, which amounted to about two-thirds of the squid's total volume, was noted as being transparent, colorless, and of bitter taste. It was then stored in a deep freeze and studied later in a land laboratory. From the volumes of coelomic fluid, the weights of the "drained" animals under sea water, and the density of that water, it was calculated that the densities of the coelomic fluids must have been close to 1.010 to give neutral buoyancy. Density bottle measurements showed that coelomic fluids from all the specimens of the three species studied had densities between 1.010 and 1.012. Such low densities could not be given simply by replacing the "heavier" ions of sea water by the

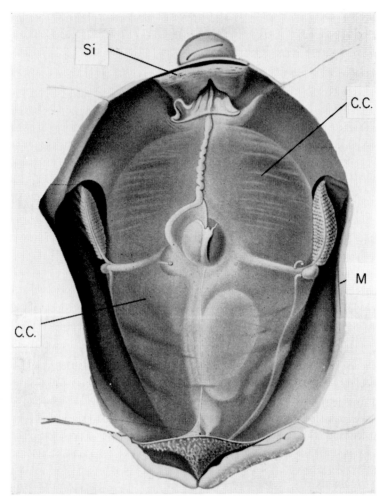

Fig. 2. *Cranchia scabra*. The mantle of the squid has been cut along the mid-ventral line and the large liquid-filled coelomic cavity can be seen. The head end of the animal is upwards. *M*, mantle; *C.C.*, coelomic cavity; *Si*, siphon. (After Chun, 1910.) Magnification × 3.

"lighter" ones, e.g., replacing calcium by sodium, and sulfate by chloride. It was therefore suspected that the coelomic fluids were hypotonic to sea water. Measurement of freezing points showed, however, that these fluids were almost isotonic with sea water. Of the common ions only ammonium can give a solution isotonic with sea water but of density close to 1.010. The coelomic fluids were shown to contain about 480 mM ammonium. The sodium concentration was 90 mM while chloride accounted for almost all the anion. The fluid was very acid, pH around 5, and perhaps this accounts for the retention of ammonia in the coelomic cavity. At this acidity ammonia would exist almost completely as ammonium, which, in contrast to molecular ammonia, does not pass easily through living tissues.

The buoyancy mechanism of the cranchid squid resembles the bathyscaphe of Professor Piccard. In the bathyscaphe a dense steel sphere is supported by a large flotation chamber filled with petrol (gasoline); in the cranchid squid the denser muscles are supported by a large flotation chamber full of ammonium chloride.

IV. CEPHALOPODS WITH GAS-FILLED BUOYANCY CHAMBERS

A. General

The Nautiloidea, Ammonoidea, and Belemnoidea, which dominated the Palaeozoic and Mesozoic Seas, probably owed their evolution and success to the development of a chambered, gas-filled shell. Only one genus, *Nautilus*, remains as living representative of this formerly enormous cephalopod fauna. The more recently evolved animals, *Spirula* and *Sepia*, have chambered shells which clearly are related to the fossil forms, and studies on them have therefore a paleontological, as well as a physiological, interest. Here we shall confine ourselves mainly to a description of the buoyancy mechanism of the shell (or bone) of *Sepia officinalis* (Denton and Gilpin-Brown, 1961a,b,c; Denton *et al.*, 1961). The relationships between the various cephalopod shells are discussed by Denton (1961).

B. Sepia

The cuttlebone consists of a number of thin chambers laid down one below the other at the rate of about one or two a week as the animal grows. The calcareous walls of these chambers are spaced at about 0.7-mm intervals and are held apart by numerous pillars. The whole cuttlebone accounts for about 9% of the total volume of the animal and contains gas spaces which give it a specific gravity of about 0.6 and so it approximately balances the weight in sea water of the rest of the animal. It has been shown that the cuttlefish can vary its specific gravity and that it does so by varying the proportions of liquid and gas which the cuttlebone contains.

The behavior of these cuttlefish is very much affected by light; in the daytime they bury themselves and at dusk they come out, swimming and hunting until dawn. Associated with these changes in behavior, there are changes in density. In the light, cuttlefish become more dense and in

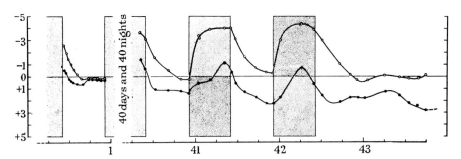

Fig. 3. The effect of light on the buoyancy of *Sepia officinalis*. Changes of weight in sea water of two specimens. The upper curve is for an animal weighing about 330 g and the lower for an animal weighing about 260 g. The ordinate shows the weight in grams of an animal in sea water (a negative weight means that the animal was less dense than sea water). The dark areas indicate times of darkness. (After Denton and Gilpin-Brown, 1961b.)

the dark they become less dense (Fig. 3). A cuttlefish kept in complete darkness for 2 days often becomes so buoyant that it cannot stay at the bottom of its tank and can only remain in mid-water with great difficulty. These changes in buoyancy are produced by changes in the density of the cuttlebone.

The cuttlefish uses its bone to change its buoyancy just as a submarine commander uses the buoyancy tanks of his craft. The cuttlebone contains both gas and liquid. When the cuttlefish is to become less dense, liquid is pumped out of the cuttlebone and the gas space is increased in volume; when the cuttlefish is to become denser, liquid is pumped into the cuttlebone and the volume of the gas space is decreased.

The gas within the cuttlebone is principally nitrogen and its average pressure is about $\frac{4}{5}$ of an atmosphere, no matter at what depth the cuttlefish is caught. There can therefore be no question of liquid being pumped out of the cuttlebone by gas pressure. When a new chamber is formed liquid is extracted actively, leaving behind a space which contains gas under very low pressure. Gas then slowly diffuses into this space until its partial pressure equals that in the surrounding tissues. This can be shown by a very simple experiment. A freshly dissected cuttlebone is placed under ink and scatched so as to open the posterior edges of its chambers. Ink will now rush into any partial vacuum within these chambers, the extent of the penetration of ink showing the degree of partial vacuum. Figure 4 shows a cuttlebone cut in half at the end of such an experiment. It can be seen that the newest chambers are almost completely filled with ink. This is because the animal has withdrawn liquid so recently from these chambers that very little gas has had time to diffuse into them; the pressure of gas within them is therefore still very low.

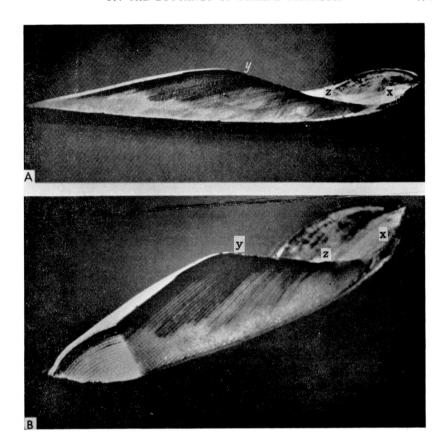

Fig. 4. A cuttlebone which has had its chambers punctured under sea water containing ink by a scratch along the siphuncular surface (x y). A. A longitudinal section. B. A section showing the same cuttlebone after cutting away its end to allow
the lateral penetration of ink to be seen. [The letter z represents the inflection on the
siphuncular surface marking the slow growth in the animal's first winter of life.
(Adam, 1940)]

Ink has been extensively drawn into the newest chambers which contained gas
under low pressure. In this figure the cuttlebone is shown ventral side upwards.
(After Denton and Gilpin-Brown, 1961c.)

It has also been shown that liquid is pumped in and out only through
the posterior ends of the chambers and we find here a specialized membrane which is thought to do the active pumping (Fig. 5). When an
animal has been kept in very shallow water the liquid inside the cuttlebone is isotonic with sea water while in animals just hauled up from the
sea bottom it is markedly hypotonic. This does not tell us how the liquid
pump works but it does suggest that equilibrium is maintained by balancing an osmotic force (between the blood and the cuttlebone liquid),
tending to extract liquid from the cuttlebone, against the hydrostatic

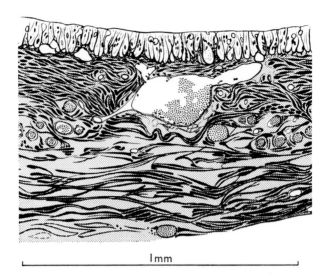

1 mm

FIG. 5. Structure of the siphuncular membrane. Transverse section through a part of the shell-sac lying against the siphuncular surface of the cuttlebone. The thin siphuncular membrane is uppermost and below this can be seen a large vein whose tributaries communicate with numerous spaces just below the membrane. Many of these smaller vessels contain fixed blood (heavy stipple). (Denton and Gilpin-Brown, 1961a.)

pressure of the sea which will be tending to push water into the cuttlebone. The calcareous structure must sustain the inevitable difference in pressure between the gas inside the chambers and the hydrostatic pressure of the sea. A diagrammatic summary of the functioning of this interesting organ is shown in Fig. 6.

The cuttlebone is a little more bulky than the swim bladder of a fish but it has the enormous merit of being a buoyancy device which is fairly independent of depth. If the cuttlefish changes depth a small exchange of salt or water between the blood and the cuttlebone liquid could re-establish equilibrium between the hydrostatic pressure of the sea and the osmotic difference which holds water out of the cuttlebone. The independence of the volume of the gas space of the cuttlebone to pressure is shown in Fig. 7 where the behavior of a cuttlebone in a living cuttlefish is compared with that of a swim bladder in a living fish.

C. Spirula and Nautilus

Spirula and Nautilus have an especial interest in that they are both thought to live very much deeper in the sea than does Sepia. If Spirula lives, as Bruun (1943) claims, down to 1750 m and uses a mechanism similar to that which is used by Sepia, i.e., the active extraction of liquid

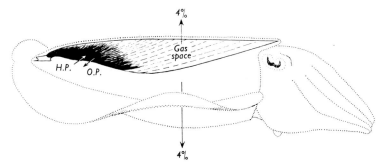

Fig. 6. Diagram summarizing knowledge of the cuttlebone. The cuttlebone here represented has a density of about 0.6. Liquid within the cuttlebone is marked black. It can be seen that the oldest and most posterior chambers are almost full of liquid. If they were filled with gas this would tend to tip the tail of the animal upwards. The newest 10 or so complete chambers, which lie centrally along the length of the animal, are completely filled with gas. These chambers can give buoyancy without disturbing the normal posture of the animal.

The hydrostatic pressure (H.P.) of the sea is balanced by an osmotic pressure difference (O.P.) between cuttlebone liquid and the blood. In sea water the cuttlebone gives a net lift of 4% of the animal's weight in air and thus balances the excess weight of the rest of the animal. Note that the black markings in this figure have quite a different meaning to those of Fig. 4. (After Denton and Gilpin-Brown, 1961c.)

from a newly formed chamber, leaving behind gas under a pressure very much less than atmospheric, then the liquid must be pumped out of a chamber against a hydrostatic pressure of about 175 atmospheres and cannot be extracted by a simple osmotic force.

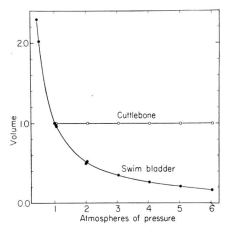

Fig. 7. The effect of pressure on the volume of the gas space of a cuttlebone in a living cuttlefish and on a swim bladder in a living fish (*Gadus pollachius*). The volumes of the gas spaces at one atmosphere pressure and room temperature are taken as unity. (After Denton *et al.*, 1961.)

REFERENCES

Adam, W., (1940). Résultats scièntifiques des croisières du navire École Belge 'Mercator.' IV. Cephalopoda. *Mém. musée hist. nat. Belg., Sér. 2* Fasc. 21, 82–171.

Bruun, A. F. (1943). The biology of *Spirula spirula* (L). *Dana Rept.* Copenhagen **24**, 1–46.

Chun, C. (1910). Die Cephalopoden; Oegopsida. *Wiss. Ergeb. deut. Tiefsee-Exped.* (*Valdivia*) p. 18.

Denton, E. J. (1961). The buoyancy of fish and cephalopods. *Progr. in Biophys. Biophys. Chem.* **11**, 177–234.

Denton, E. J., and Gilpin-Brown, J. B. (1961a). The buoyancy of the cuttlefish, *Sepia officinalis* (L.). *J. Marine Biol. Assoc. U.K.* **41**, 319–342.

Denton, E. J., and Gilpin-Brown, J. B. (1961b). The effect of light on the buoyancy of the cuttlefish. *J. Marine Biol. Assoc. U.K.* **41**, 343–350.

Denton, E. J., and Gilpin-Brown, J. B. (1961c). The distribution of gas and liquid within the cuttlebone. *J. Marine Biol. Assoc. U.K.* **41**, 365–381.

Denton, E. J., and Shaw, T. I. P. (1961). The buoyancy of gelatinous animals. *J. Physiol.* (*London*) **161**, 14–15.

Denton, E. J., Shaw, T. I., and Gilpin-Brown, J. B. (1958). Bathyscaphoid squid. *Nature* **182**, 1810–1811.

Denton, E. J., Gilpin-Brown, J. B., and Howarth, J. V. (1961). The osmotic mechanism of the cuttlebone. *J. Marine Biol. Assoc. U.K.* **41**, 351–364.

"International Critical Tables of Numerical Data" (1933). McGraw-Hill, New York.

Linke, O. (1939). Die Biota das Jadebusenwattes. *Helgoländ wiss. Meeresuntersuch.* **1**, 201–348.

Newell, R. (1962). Behavioural aspects of the ecology of *Peringia* (= *Hydrobia*) *ulvae* (Pennant) (Gasteropoda, Prosobranchia). *Proc. Zool. Soc.* (*London*) **138**, 49–75.

Robertson, J. D. (1949). Ionic regulation in some marine invertebrates. *J. Exptl. Biol.* **26**, 182–200.

Wilson. D. P., and Wilson, M. A. (1956). A contribution to the biology of *Ianthina janthina* (L.). *J. Marine Biol. Assoc. U.K.* **35**, 291–305.

Author Index

Numbers in italics indicate the pages on which the complete references are listed.

435

Subject Index

Numbers in bold-faced type indicate references to figures and tables.

Systematic Index

Numbers in bold-faced type indicate references to figures and tables. Each scientific name is followed by the name of the family to which the genus belongs, and frequently by names in successively higher taxa. Classification of species to class is accomplished by looking up alphabetically the last taxonomic name in a given entry and continuing in this way until class is reached. Page numbers apply specifically to the first taxonomic name in the entry.

461